Civil Disobedience
and Violence

Edited by

Jeffrie G. Murphy

The University of Arizona

Wadsworth Publishing Company, Inc. Belmont, California

Dedicated to my Mother and to the memory of my Father

Creon: . . . To transgress
Or twist the law to one's own pleasure, presume
To order where one should obey, is sinful,
And I will have none of it.
He whom the State appoints must be obeyed
To the smallest matter, be it right—or wrong. . . .

Antigone: . . . That order did not come from God. Justice,
That dwells with the gods below, knows no such law.
I did not think your edicts strong enough
To overrule the unwritten unalterable laws
Of God and heaven, you being only a man. . . .

Sophocles, *Antigone*

From Sophocles, *The Theban Plays,* translated by E. F. Watling,
Penguin Edition, London, 1947, pp. 144 and 138.

L. C. Cat. Card No.: 78–158119
ISBN: 0–534–0051–7

Printed in the United States of America

3 4 5 6 7 8 9 10—75 74

Contents

Introduction 1

On Disobeying the Law
Socrates 9

On the Duty of Civil Disobedience
Henry David Thoreau 19

Legal Obligation and the Duty of Fair Play
John Rawls 39

Social Protest and Civil Obedience
Sidney Hook 53

The Vietnam War and the Right of Resistance
Jeffrie G. Murphy 64

Civil Disobedience: Prerequisite for Democracy in Mass Society
Christian Bay 73

Non-violence
Mohandas K. Gandhi 93

A Fallacy on Law and Order: That Civil Disobedience Must Be Absolutely Nonviolent
Howard Zinn 103

On not Prosecuting Civil Disobedience
Ronald Dworkin   112

Law and Authority
Peter Kropotkin   131

Bibliography   146

Series Foreword

The Basic Problems in Philosophy Series is designed to meet the need of students and teachers of philosophy, mainly but not exclusively at the undergraduate level, for collections of essays devoted to some fairly specific philosophical problems.

In recent years there have been numerous paperback collections on a variety of philosophical topics. Those teachers who wish to refer their students to a set of essays on a specific philosophical problem have usually been frustrated, however, since most of these collections range over a wide set of issues and problems. The present series attempts to remedy this situation by presenting together, within each volume, key writings on a single philosophical issue.

Given the magnitude of the literature, there can be no thought of completeness. Rather, the materials included are those that, in the judgment of the editor, must be mastered first by the student who wishes to acquaint himself with relevant issues and their ramifications. To this end, historical as well as contemporary writings are included.

Each volume in the series contains an introduction by the editor to set the stage for the arguments contained in the essays and a bibliography to help the student who wishes to pursue the topic at a more advanced level.

A. I. Melden
S. Munsat

Basic Problems in Philosophy Series

A. I. Melden and Stanley Munsat
University of California, Irvine
General Editors

Human Rights
A. I. Melden

Introduction   The Second Treatise of Civil Government, Chapters 2 and 5, *John Locke*   Anarchical Fallacies, *Jeremy Bentham*   Natural Rights, *Margaret MacDonald*   Are There Any Natural Rights? *H. L. A. Hart*   Justice and Equality, *Gregory Vlastos*   Rights, Human Rights, and Racial Discrimination, *Richard Wasserstrom*   Persons and Punishment, *Herbert Morris*   Appendices   Bibliography

Guilt and Shame
Herbert Morris

Introduction   Stavrogin's Confession, *Fyodor Dostoyevsky*   Differentiation of German Guilt, *Karl Jaspers*   Origin of the Sense of Guilt, *Sigmund Freud*   Guilt and Guilt Feelings, *Martin Buber*   Real Guilt and Neurotic Guilt, *Herbert Fingarette*   "Guilt," "Bad Conscience," and the Like, *Friedrich Nietzsche*   The Sense of Justice, *John Rawls*   Shame, *Gerhart Piers and Milton B. Singer*   Autonomy v. Shame and Doubt, *Erik H. Erikson*   The Nature of Shame, *Helen Merrell Lynd*   Bibliography

The Analytic-Synthetic Distinction
Stanley Munsat

Introduction   First Truths, *Gottfried Wilhelm von Leibniz*   Necessary and Contingent Truths, *Gottfried Wilhelm von Leibniz*   Of Proposition, *Thomas Hobbes*   Introduction to the Critique of Pure Reason, *Immanuel Kant*, Kant, *Arthur Papp*   Of Demonstration, and Necessary Truths, *John Stuart Mill*   Views of Some Writers on the Nature of Arithmetical Propositions, *Gottlob Frege*   What Is an Empirical Science? *Bertrand Russell*   Two Dogmas of Empiricism, *Willard Van Orman Quine*   The Meaning of a Word, *John Austin*   In Defense of a Dogma, *H. P. Grice and P. F. Strawson*   Bibliography

Civil Disobedience and Violence
Jeffrie G. Murphy

Introduction   On Disobeying the Law, *Socrates*   On the Duty of Civil Disobedience, *Henry David Thoreau*   Legal Obligation and the Duty of Fair Play, *John Rawls*   Social Protest and Civil Obedience, *Sydney Hook*   The Vietnam War and the Right of Resistance, *Jeffrie G. Murphy*   Civil Disobedience: Prerequisite for Democracy in Mass Society, *Christian Bay*   Non-violence, *Mohandas K. Gandhi*   A Fallacy on Law and Order: That Civil Disobedience Must Be Absolutely Nonviolent, *Howard Zinn*   On Not Prosecuting Civil Disobedience, *Ronald Dworkin*   Law and Authority, *Peter Kropotkin*   Bibliography

Morality and the Law
Richard A. Wasserstrom

Introduction   On Liberty, *John Stuart Mill*   Morals and the Criminal Law, *Lord Patrick Devlin*   Immorality and Treason, *H. L. A. Hart* Lord Devlin and the Enforcement of Morals, *Ronald Dworkin*   Sins and Crimes, *A. R. Louch*   Morals Offenses and the Model Penal Code, *Louis B. Schwartz*   Paternalism, *Gerald Dworkin*   Four cases involving the enforcement of morality   Bibliography

War and Morality
Richard A. Wasserstrom

Introduction   The Moral Equivalent of War, *William James*   The Morality of Obliteration Bombing, *John C. Ford, S.J.*   War and Murder, *Elizabeth Anscombe*   Moral Judgment in Time of War, *Michael Walzer* Pacifism: A Philosophical Analysis, *Jan Narveson*   On the Morality of War: A Preliminary Inquiry, *Richard Wasserstrom*   Judgment and Opinion, The International Tribunal, Nuremberg, Germany   Superior Orders, Nuclear Warfare, and the Dictates of Conscience, *Guenter Lewy* Selected Bibliography

Jeffrie G. Murphy is an Associate Professor of Philosophy at the University of Arizona. He received a B.A. degree from Johns Hopkins University and a Ph.D. from the University of Rochester. During the academic year 1968–69 he was awarded a fellowship from the National Endowment for the Humanities for a year of study at the School of Law, University of California, Los Angeles. He has taught at the University of Minnesota, the University of Michigan, and the University of California, Los Angeles. He has published a book, *Kant: The Philosophy of Right* (1970), and several articles, including "Allegiance and Lawful Government" (*Ethics,* October, 1968) and "Criminal Punishment and Psychiatric Fallacies" (*Law and Society Review,* August, 1969). He is currently serving as chairman of the Arizona Civil Liberties Union Committee on Psychiatric Justice.

Introduction

Civil disobedience, unlike many other practical problems of importance, has received a great deal of attention from philosophers, legal scholars, and political theorists. Thus the selections that I have included in this collection represent but a small sample of the writings that are available on the topic. Their purpose is not to settle, once and for all, the difficult problems raised by the topic of civil disobedience. Rather the aim of the collection is much more modest: to acquaint the reader with the important issues and to provide him with some background and beginning tools for thinking these issues through for himself. For the most part, I have tried to select essays relevant to evaluating civil disobedience in the context of contemporary American democracy.

What is civil disobedience? This is itself a philosophical question, and it is one about which there has been much disagreement. Most, however, would agree that the following are at least *necessary* conditions for analyzing or defining "civil disobedience": An act *A* is properly called an act of civil disobedience only if (1) there is some law *L* according to which *A* is illegal, (2) *L* is believed by the agent to be immoral, unconstitutional, irreligious, or ideologically objectionable, and (3) this belief about *L* motivates or explains the performance of *A*.[1] It is of crucial importance here to distinguish the civil disobedient from the criminal disobedient and from the revolutionary. The revolutionary has a different *end* from that of the civil disobedient. The latter objects to particular laws or policies but has fidelity to the system as a whole. The former has

---

[1] Two qualifications need to be noted concerning this analysis. (1) The agent may have no objection to *L* per se but may violate *L* because he views it as symbolic for or instrumentally involved with some other law *L'* (or some general policy *P*) to which he does object. In my view, such a person (Thoreau for example) is also to be regarded as civilly disobedient. (2) The line between moral, constitutional, religious and ideological motives is not an easy one to draw. Also, more than one of these motives may be involved in explaining a particular case of civil disobedience. What is most important is that motives of this sort be distinguished from the typical criminal motive: self-interest. We do not think of a criminal act as a *public* act of *protest;* but these features *do* typically characterize acts of civil disobedience.

no such fidelity and wants to overthrow the system entirely.[2] The civil disobedient differs from the criminal primarily in terms of *motive*. The ordinary criminal may be viewed as acting primarily out of motives of self-interest—motives which render him morally blameworthy and socially dangerous. Though the civil disobedient violates penal statutes (and so in one clear sense *is* a criminal), he differs so markedly from the paradigm criminal (in terms of motives, moral blameworthiness, danger to society, etc.) that to classify him merely as "criminal" would be to blur some important distinctions and to miss some important moral problems—for example, the problem of how society ought to respond to him.

Now few would consider the conditions I have listed as controversial if they are regarded merely as necessary conditions for civil disobedience. Many, however, would argue that by themselves these conditions are not sufficient—that other conditions must be satisfied before we have a true case of civil disobedience. And here we enter dangerous conceptual territory. For it is unfortunately common for philosophers to build their own moral preferences into definitions, to try to solve substantive moral issues by stipulation. Thus civil disobedience may be defined in such a way that it is necessarily justified. Or it may be defined so as to logically require the acceptance of punishment or to logically require the use of nonviolent means. But such definitions may beg important questions of moral substance. Surely an act can properly be called an act of civil disobedience even if it is unjustified. And the question whether the civil disobedient must accept his punishment or the question whether he must avoid violence seem to me morally open questions. We make the matter appear too easy if we try to solve problems like these with definitions.[3]

---

[2] There can, of course, be borderline cases here. Some civil disobedients (pacifists and civil rights activists) have objected to large segments of law. And the question of exactly how much one must object to in order to be considered an objector to the system as a whole is not susceptible of an exact answer. Also some revolutionaries (such as Gandhi) may employ civil disobedience as a *tactic* and some (such as the Founding Fathers) may genuinely object only to a few laws. In spite of these difficulties, I think it is helpful to view those cases in which the end sought is *not* the total overthrow of the government as the paradigm of civil disobedience. The Founding Fathers, though their real objection was only to a few laws, were still revolutionaries because they believed that the only way to change these laws was by an overthrow of the existing government.

[3] It is extremely common for writers to confuse the problem of defining civil disobedience with the problem of justifying it, to regard civil disobedience as justified law violation. But this is a mistake. Acts of civil disobedience may be unjustified, and justified acts of law violation may not be acts of civil disobedience. Consider the following two cases: (1) Lester Maddox violating integration law and barring blacks from his restaurant and (2) an individual driving over the speed limit in order to get a critically

By way of illustration, let us briefly consider the connection between civil disobedience and the acceptance of punishment.[4] It has often been suggested that the civilly disobedient individual is *logically,* and not just morally, required to openly accept his punishment. To say that he is logically required is to say not merely that it is morally right for him to accept it, but that the term "civil disobedient" is not properly applied to him if he does not. Two reasons can be given in defense of this claim. First, it is conceptually important to distinguish the civil disobedient from the mere criminal. One way to do this is to argue that criminals flee their punishments whereas civil disobedients embrace theirs. Second, the civilly disobedient individual, unlike the revolutionary, respects the legal system as a whole but objects to particular laws. His disobedience testifies to his particular objection; his willingness to accept the legally prescribed punishment testifies to his general fidelity to the system as a whole.

I do not myself find either of these arguments convincing. It is plausible to maintain that what distinguishes the civil disobedient from the mere criminal is a motivational difference. Now willingness to accept punishment certainly provides *evidence* that one has a noncriminal motive, but it is surely possible that such a motive could be established on other grounds —such as past actions, statements, and religious upbringing. Thus I should argue that the connection between acceptance

---

injured child to the hospital. In the former, we have an act of civil disobedience (assuming Maddox's motives were in fact as he described them) which was in my view unjustified. In the latter, we have a justified act of law violation which (since no protest was involved) could hardly be called an act of civil disobedience. This confusion of definition with justification appears even in Gandhi's famous definition of civil disobedience as a "civil breach of unmoral statutory enactments" (*Non-Violent Resistance* [New York, 1964], p. 3). He could have improved his definition considerably by speaking, not of unmoral enactments, but of enactments *believed* by the agent to be unmoral. This would leave open the possibility for error on the part of the civil disobedient, and it is important to do this. Conscience, alas, is not an infallible guide to action. For the claim that civil disobedience logically requires the acceptance of punishment, see John Rawls, "The Justification of Civil Disobedience," in *Civil Disobedience: Theory and Practice,* ed. Hugo Adam Bedau (New York, 1969), p. 247. For the claim that civil disobedience logically requires nonviolence, see Hugo Adam Bedau, "On Civil Disobedience," *Journal of Philosophy,* Vol. LVIII, No. 21 (1961), pp. 656, 661. What is really at issue here is whether "civil disobedience" should be understood as a term of moral approbation. My view is that it facilitates moral debate to treat the term as morally neutral. Since the term has been bandied about so much in recent years, there is no standard meaning for it. Thus we must choose a meaning, and our criterion for choice should be whatever clarifies and facilitates debate on the topic. Morally loaded definitions do neither.

4 The logical relationship between civil disobedience and violence is discussed in this book in the essays by Christian Bay and Howard Zinn. Those who claim that civil disobedience logically requires nonviolence very often commit the following fallacy: believing that since civil disobedience and violence are logically distinct they are therefore logically incompatible.

of punishment and civil disobedience is a *contingent evidential* connection and not a logically necessary connection. Similarly with the problem of fidelity to the legal system. Acceptance of punishment provides evidence of fidelity, but it is logically possible that fidelity could be established in some other way. Indeed, one might be so loyal to the Constitution that he would not accept punishment under a statute which, in his judgment, violates the Constitution—even if the Supreme Court has upheld the statute's constitutional validity. The Court can make mistakes of interpretation, after all, and loyalty to the Constitution is not the same as loyalty to the Court.

Against the claim that civil disobedience logically requires the acceptance of punishment, it is also worth noting the following. The question "Should the civil disobedient accept his punishment?" seems to make perfectly good sense. Indeed, Plato devotes the whole dialogue *Crito* to reporting Socrates' answer to this question. If it were a logical truth or a truth of language that the civil disobedient accepts his punishment, however, it would be pointless to raise such a question. This would be like conducting an inquiry into the question "I wonder if there are any unmarried bachelors?" But the question of punishment for civil disobedience does not seem like this at all, and so in my judgment it is premature to close off moral discussion by regarding it as logically true that the civil disobedient accepts his punishment. If he must accept his punishment, I should want to regard this as a *moral* (and not a logical) "must"—a "must" that will have to be supported (as Socrates tries to support it) with moral argumentation. Obviously it is morally important that the civil disobedient demonstrate his sincerity and his fidelity, and accepting punishment is one good way to do this. Thus we might even say that the civil disobedient has a *prima facie* moral obligation to accept his punishment. But this leaves open the possibility that, in particular cases, strong moral reasons may weigh against such acceptance and that these reasons may override. Even considerations of self-interest may be relevant if the legally prescribed punishment is of a severity out of all reasonable proportion to the gravity of the offense. It is also worth considering whether an individual who believes that he is an important member of a protest movement, the goals of which he believes to be morally and politically important, might not reasonably choose to avoid punishment so as not thereby to weaken the movement. Civil disobedience, whether we like it or not, is in fact a way of mobilizing power for certain social goals. And thus civil disobedients will often and quite naturally consider, in making their decisions, the likely effect of their actions on their ability to mobilize power of the right sort.

To avoid begging any important questions, then, I propose that the conditions I have previously listed as necessary for civil disobedience be regarded (with the noted qualifications) as also jointly sufficient. (An act A is properly called an act of civil disobedience if and only if (1) there is some law L according to which A is illegal, (2) L is believed by the agent to be immoral, unconstitutional, irreligious or ideologically objectionable, and (3) this belief about L motivates or explains the performance of A.) This provides us with at least a provisional definition of civil disobedience as a background for the readings in this collection.[5]

The following essays, though some contain attempts at defining civil disobedience, are mainly concerned with problems of evaluation and justification. Following the classic statements by Socrates and Thoreau, the essay by John Rawls (using a sophisticated elaboration of the "social contract" argument put forth by Socrates) explores the general topic of the moral obligation to obey the law. This is the topic with which any discussion of civil disobedience has to begin; for if there is in general no obligation to obey the law, there is no special *problem* of civil disobedience. It is only because we typically believe that the burden of moral proof lies with the disobedient—that he (and not the law-abiding citizen) must justify his conduct—that we seek for theories of justification for civil disobedience.

Rawls' essay on the obligation to obey the law is followed by three essays on the justification for civil disobedience. Two essays are concerned with the circumstances in which individuals may be said to have a moral right to engage in civil disobedience. Sidney Hook, though a strong opponent of civil disobedience in contemporary America, believes that it is possible for circumstances to arise (as they have in the past) in which civil disobedience might be legitimate. He is concerned, however, to lay down careful rules governing the *form* that civil disobedience must take in order not to lose its legitimacy even in such circumstances. He argues, for example, that justified civil disobedience is always nonviolent. He also argues that one may rightfully engage in civil disobedience only if all

[5] It should be clear that it is simpleminded to characterize, as opponents of civil disobedience are often inclined to do, acts of civil disobedience as acts of "breaking laws one doesn't like." Of course a reasonable man would find it difficult to approve of an act so described; but, as the above analysis indicates, acts of civil disobedience are not to be so simply described.

legal channels for change are clearly closed. In my essay, I outline conditions under which one may claim a right to disobey the law, and I attempt to present a *prima facie* case that, with respect to draft resistance against the war in Vietnam, these conditions have been satisfied. I argue, among other things, that there is evidence that the legal channels Hook speaks of have been, for all practical purposes, closed. The next essay, by Christian Bay, is an attempt to set out conditions under which individuals may be said not merely to have a right to disobey, but to have good and perhaps sufficient moral-political reasons for disobeying—that is, conditions under which it is not merely morally *permissible* for them to break the law but under which they (at least *prima facie*) *ought* to break it. Bay develops his argument by stressing the importance of loyalty to the *values* and *ideals* that democracy is supposed to serve rather than loyalty to the mere forms of democracy.

These essays on justification are followed by two discussions of civil disobedience and violence.[6] (This topic is also explored at the end of Bay's article.) Against violent disobedience, Mohandas K. Gandhi suggests the following: that violence degrades and brutalizes the man who uses it and that no man, given that his beliefs are subject to error, should be so presumptuous as to inflict harm on others in furtherance of those beliefs. And to those who say that nonviolence does not work as a tactic, Gandhi asks the following questions. Has nonviolence ever been given an adequate test? Have we ever even seriously considered pouring into techniques of nonviolence the money and energy and patience that we now pour into techniques of destruction?

Howard Zinn, though himself suspicious of violence as a tactic, believes that it cannot be ruled out as *a priori* unjustified. Violence (as both Zinn and Bay stress) may be institutionalized in certain social and legal arrangements; so it may not always be possible to avoid its presence and damaging consequences. Thus (though we should be *very* cautious in making such a judgment) the use of violence against already violent institutions may, in the long run, reduce the amount of

---

[6] The proper analysis of the meaning of "violence" is philosophically controversial. The reader might consult Newton Garver's "What Violence Is" (*Nation*, June 24, 1968) and J. M. Cameron's "On Violence" (*New York Review of Books*, July 2, 1970). There is also an excellent study by Robert L. Holmes, "Violence and Nonviolence," which will appear in *Violence*, ed. Jerome Shaffer (New York, 1971). Holmes' essay was one of the winning essays in competition sponsored by the Council for Philosophical Studies on the topic "violence." The other winning essay, "Violence and the Rule of Law" by Bernard Harrison, will also appear in this volume.

violence in the world.[7] The advocate of political violence, then, is often concerned to argue that we are morally responsible for our omissions as well as for our commissions. If we claim to abhor violence, can we be satisfied merely with not doing any violence ourselves? If we really abhor it, might we not want to oppose (with some violence if necessary) those institutions which promote violence? If we do not effectively oppose such institutions, is it clear that (considering such omissions) we are free of moral responsibility for the remaining institutionalized violence? Is it clear that we are any less morally guilty than had we actually committed acts of violence? The reader must determine for himself the extent to which the Gandhian doctrine of nonviolence can be defended against these worries.

Following these discussions of civil disobedience and violence, the essay by Ronald Dworkin explores the question "How should government respond to the civilly disobedient individual?" This question is extremely important and yet has not drawn nearly the attention that it deserves. And, as Dworkin argues, it is a much more subtle and complex question than one might at first suppose—in part because the legal issues involved are subtle and complex.

The collection concludes with an essay by the anarchist Peter Kropotkin. All the previous writers (with the possible exception of Thoreau) appear to share the belief that in general all citizens have an obligation to obey the law, that any disobedience must be justified by overriding moral considerations. The underlying assumption here is that government, with its rule of law, provides essential benefits to its citizens and that, to retain these benefits, citizens must generally obey the law. In common with Marxist writers, Kropotkin argues that talk of a just rule of law, no matter how fine it sounds in theory, functions in actual societies as a rhetorical mask for exploitation and class privilege. He denies the assumption that the rule of law provides benefits sufficient to outweigh the oppression of its coercive power and thus denies that there is even in general any obligation to obey the law. Thus, if Kropotkin is right, there is no special problem of civil disobedience; for

[7] It is important to note that the question whether violence is effective is an empirical question and not a question of moral principle. Gandhi believes that using violence is not an effective way to reduce the amount of violence in the world, but he also typically appeals to moral principles which would condemn violence even if it were effective. For a philosophical attack on such principles, see Jan Narveson's "Pacifism: A Philosophical Analysis," *Ethics*, July 1965.

civil disobedience does not even *prima facie* stand in need of justification. It is rather *obedience* which needs to be justified![8]

It is hoped that the wide variety of opinions presented in these essays will stimulate the reader to further thought on the topics raised. We have all witnessed a great deal of political action in recent years, but very little in the way of political thought. And a rational man, whatever his own political ideology, must find this deeply troublesome. As action precedes thought, so does barbarism replace civilization.

I should like to express my thanks to Ronald Milo for valuable discussions on the topic of civil disobedience and to Charles Ares, Mitchell Axler, and Winton Woods for their helpful suggestions concerning the anthology. Marcella Brady and Kay Lane helped in the preparation of the manuscript, and my wife Nancy aided me in the correction of the proofs. I am very grateful to them all.

---

[8] I have not included an essay by a Communist writer because, being revolutionaries, Communists tend to think in terms broader than those of mere civil disobedience. If they talk about the problem at all, they tend to argue that civil disobedience is justified only in so far as it is an initial tactic in revolution. If it is not such a tactic, it is viewed as a bourgeois self-indulgence which (especially if coupled with a belief in nonviolence) provides a harmless safety valve for a system that ought to explode. See "Pacifism and Violence: A Study in Bourgeois Ethics" by Christopher Caudwell in his *Studies and Further Studies in a Dying Culture* (New York, 1938). John Locke, another revolutionary theorist, also made no place for civil disobedience in his theory.

Socrates

On Disobeying the Law

From *Apology*

. . . *Socrates.* . . . I have said enough in answer to the charge **9**
of Meletus:[1] any elaborate defence is unnecessary; but I know
only too well how many are the enmities which I have incurred,
and this is what will be my destruction if I am destroyed;—not
Meletus, nor yet Anytus, but the envy and detraction of the
world, which has been the death of many good men, and will
probably be the death of many more; there is no danger of my
being the last of them.

Some one will say: And are you not ashamed, Socrates, of a
course of life which is likely to bring you to an untimely end?
To him I may fairly answer: There you are mistaken: a man who
is good for anything ought not to calculate the chance of living
or dying; he ought only to consider whether in doing anything
he is doing right or wrong—acting the part of a good man or of
a bad. Whereas, upon your view, the heroes who fell at Troy
were not good for much, and the son of Thetis above all, who
altogether despised danger in comparison with disgrace; and

These selections (abridged) are from Benjamin Jowett's translations
(1892) of Plato's *Apology* and *Crito.* Scholars generally agree that these
dialogues, though written by Plato (approx. 428–348 B.C.), are primarily reports of the conversations of his teacher Socrates (approx. 470–399 B.C.)
on the topics of civil disobedience and the acceptance of punishment. In
Apology, Socrates, who has been charged with impiety and corrupting the
youth with his teaching of philosophy, presents his defense and, after conviction, his response to the sentence of death imposed by the court. He
argues that he is bound by a divine law that is higher than state law to publicly pursue the truth and that he would not desist from doing this even if
ordered to do so by the state. In *Crito,* Socrates presents his arguments
(one being the earliest known version of the social contract theory) in support of his view that he owes a duty of fidelity to the state. He argues that,
because of this duty, it would be wrong for him to escape his legal punishment even though he knows that his conviction was unjust. For an excellent
discussion of the ideas in these two dialogues, see A. D. Woozley's "Socrates on Disobeying the Law," forthcoming in *Socrates,* ed. Gregory Vlastos
(New York: Doubleday).

[1] [Meletus and Anytus are Socrates' accusers. Ed.]

when he was so eager to slay Hector, his goddess mother said to him, that if he avenged his companion, Patroclus, and slew Hector, he would die himself—'Fate,' she said, in these or the like words, 'waits for you next after Hector;' he, receiving this warning, utterly despised danger and death, and instead of fearing them, feared rather to live in dishonour, and not to avenge his friend. 'Let me die forthwith,' he replies, 'and be avenged of my enemy, rather than abide here by the beaked ships, a laughing-stock and a burden of the earth.' Had Achilles any thought of death and danger? For wherever a man's place is, whether the place which he has chosen or that in which he has been placed by a commander, there he ought to remain in the hour of danger; he should not think of death or of anything but of disgrace. And this, O men of Athens, is a true saying.

Strange, indeed, would be my conduct, O men of Athens, if I who, when I was ordered by the generals whom you chose to command me at Potidaea and Amphipolis and Delium, remained where they placed me, like any other man, facing death—if now, when, as I conceive and imagine, God orders me to fulfil the philosopher's mission of searching into myself and other men, I were to desert my post through fear of death, or any other fear; that would indeed be strange, and I might justly be arraigned in court for denying the existence of the gods, if I disobeyed the oracle because I was afraid of death, fancying that I was wise when I was not wise. For the fear of death is indeed the pretence of wisdom, and not real wisdom, being a pretence of knowing the unknown; and no one knows whether death, which men in their fear apprehend to be the greatest evil, may not be the greatest good. Is not this ignorance of a disgraceful sort, the ignorance which is the conceit that man knows what he does not know? And in this respect only I believe myself to differ from men in general, and may perhaps claim to be wiser than they are:—that whereas I know but little of the world below, I do not suppose that I know: but I do know that injustice and disobedience to a better, whether God or man, is evil and dishonourable, and I will never fear or avoid a possible good rather than a certain evil. And therefore if you let me go now, and are not convinced by Anytus, who said that since I had been prosecuted I must be put to death (or if not that I ought never to have been prosecuted at all); and that if I escape now, your sons will all be utterly ruined by listening to my words—if you say to me, Socrates, this time we will not mind Anytus, and you shall be let off, but upon one condition, that you are not to enquire and speculate in this way any more, and that if you are caught doing so again you shall die;—if this was the condition on which you let me go, I should reply: Men of Athens, I honour and love you; but I shall obey God rather than you, and while I have life and strength I shall never cease from the practice and teaching of philosophy, exhorting any one whom I meet and saying to him after my manner: You, my friend,—a citizen of the great and mighty and wise city of Athens,—are you not ashamed of heaping up the greatest amount of money and honour and reputation, and caring so little about wisdom and truth and the greatest improvement of the soul, which you never regard or heed at all? And if the person with whom I am arguing, says: Yes, but I do care; then I do not leave him or let him go at once; but I proceed to interrogate and examine and cross-examine him, and if I think that he has no virtue in him, but only says that he has, I reproach him with undervaluing the greater, and overvaluing the less. And I shall repeat the same words to every one whom I meet, young and old, citizen and alien, but especially to the citizens, inasmuch as they are my brethren. For know that this is the command of God; and I believe that no greater good has ever happened in the state than my service to the God. For I do nothing but go about persuading you all, old and young alike, not to take thought for your persons or your properties, but first and chiefly to care about the greatest improvement of the soul. I tell you that virtue is not given by money, but that from virtue comes money and every other good of man, public as well as private. This is my teaching, and if this is the doctrine which corrupts the youth, I am a mischievous person. But if any one says that this is not my teaching, he is speaking an untruth. Wherefore, O men of Athens, I say to you, do as Anytus bids or not as Anytus bids, and either acquit me or not; but whichever you do, understand that I shall never alter my ways, not even if I have to die many times. . . .

Some one may wonder why I go about in private giving advice and busying myself with the concerns of others, but do not venture to come forward in public and advise the state. I will tell you why. You have heard me speak at sundry times and in divers places of an oracle or sign which comes to me, and is the divinity which Meletus ridicules in the indictment. This sign, which is a kind of voice, first began to come to me when I was a child; it always forbids but never commands me to do anything which I am going to do. This is what deters me from being a politician. And rightly, as I think. For I am certain, O men of Athens, that if I had engaged in politics, I should have perished long ago, and done no good either to you or to myself. And do not be offended at my telling you the truth: for the truth is, that no man who goes to war with you or any other multitude, honestly striving against the many lawless and unrighteous deeds which are done in a state, will save his life; he who will fight for the right, if he would live even for a brief space, must have a private station and not a public one. . . .

Some one will say: Yes, Socrates, but cannot you hold your tongue, and then you may go into a foreign city, and no one will interfere with you? Now I have great difficulty in making you understand my answer to this. For if I tell you that to do as you say would be a disobedience to the God, and therefore that I cannot hold my tongue, you will not believe that I am serious; and if I say again that daily to discourse about virtue, and of those other things about which you hear me examining myself and others, is the greatest good of man, and that the unexamined life is not worth living, you are still less likely to believe me. Yet I say what is true, although a thing of which it is hard for me to persuade you. . . .

. . . The difficulty, my friends, is not to avoid death, but to avoid unrighteousness; for that runs faster than death. I am old and move slowly, and the slower runner has overtaken me, and my accusers are keen and quick, and the faster runner, who is unrighteousness, has overtaken them. And now I depart hence condemned by you to suffer the penalty of death,— they too go their ways condemned by the truth to suffer the penalty of villainy and wrong; and I must abide by my award— let them abide by theirs. I suppose that these things may be regarded as fated,—and I think that they are well. . . .

From *Crito*

. . . *Socrates.* From these premises[2] I proceed to argue the question whether I ought or ought not to try and escape without the consent of the Athenians: and if I am clearly right in escaping, then I will make the attempt; but if not, I will abstain. The other considerations which you mention, of money and loss of character and the duty of educating one's children, are,

[2] [In the earlier part of the dialogue, Crito has offered several arguments to persuade Socrates to escape from prison: escape would allow him to continue philosophizing in another country, would allow him to continue caring for his family, and would save his friends from the condemnation of public opinion as not having been resourceful enough to save their teacher. Socrates replies that he will be moved by neither passion nor appeals to public opinion but only by reason, that he will remain what he "always has been—a man who will accept no argument but that which on reflection I find to be the truest." These are the "premises" on which the following discussion must rest. Ed.]

I fear, only the doctrines of the multitude, who would be as ready to restore people to life, if they were able, as they are to put them to death—and with as little reason. But now, since the argument has thus far prevailed, the only question which remains to be considered is, whether we shall do rightly either in escaping or in suffering others to aid in our escape and paying them in money and thanks, or whether in reality we shall not do rightly; and if the latter, then death or any other calamity which may ensue on my remaining here must not be allowed to enter into the calculation.

Crito. I think that you are right, Socrates; how then shall we proceed?

Soc. Let us consider the matter together, and do you either refute me if you can, and I will be convinced; or else cease, my dear friend, from repeating to me that I ought to escape against the wishes of the Athenians: for I highly value your attempts to persuade me to do so, but I may not be persuaded against my own better judgment. And now please to consider my first position, and try how you can best answer me.

Cr. I will.

Soc. Are we to say that we are never intentionally to do wrong, or that in one way we ought and in another we ought not to do wrong, or is doing wrong always evil and dishonourable, as I was just now saying, and as has been already acknowledged by us? Are all our former admissions which were made within a few days to be thrown away? And have we, at our age, been earnestly discoursing with one another all our life long only to discover that we are no better than children? Or, in spite of the opinion of the many, and in spite of consequences whether better or worse, shall we insist on the truth of what was then said, that injustice is always an evil and dishonour to him who acts unjustly? Shall we say so or not?

Cr. Yes.

Soc. Then we must do no wrong?

Cr. Certainly not.

Soc. Nor when injured injure in return, as the many imagine; for we must injure no one at all?

Cr. Clearly not.

Soc. Again, Crito, may we do evil?

Cr. Surely not, Socrates.

Soc. And what of doing evil in return for evil, which is the morality of the many—is that just or not?

Cr. Not just.

Soc. For doing evil to another is the same as injuring him?

Cr. Very true.

Soc. Then we ought not to retaliate or render evil for evil to any one, whatever evil we may have suffered from him. But I would have you consider, Crito, whether you really mean what you are saying. For this opinion has never been held, and never will be held, by any considerable number of persons; and those who are agreed and those who are not agreed upon this point have no common ground, and can only despise one another when they see how widely they differ. Tell me, then, whether you agree with and assent to my first principle, that neither injury nor retaliation nor warding off evil by evil is ever right. And shall that be the premiss of our argument? Or do you decline and dissent from this? For so I have ever thought, and continue to think; but, if you are of another opinion, let me hear what you have to say. If, however, you remain of the same mind as formerly, I will proceed to the next step.

Cr. You may proceed, for I have not changed my mind.

Soc. Then I will go on to the next point, which may be put in the form of a question:—Ought a man to do what he admits to be right, or ought he to betray the right?

Cr. He ought to do what he thinks right.

Soc. But if this is true, what is the application? In leaving the prison against the will of the Athenians, do I wrong any? or rather do I not wrong those whom I ought least to wrong? Do I not desert the principles which were acknowledged by us to be just—what do you say?

Cr. I cannot tell, Socrates; for I do not know.

Soc. Then consider the matter in this way:—Imagine that I am about to play truant (you may call the proceeding by any name which you like), and the laws and the government come and interrogate me: 'Tell us, Socrates,' they say; 'what are you about? are you not going by an act of yours to overturn us— the laws, and the whole state, as far as in you lies? Do you imagine that a state can subsist and not be overthrown, in which the decisions of law have no power, but are set aside and trampled upon by individuals?' What will be our answer, Crito, to these and the like words? Any one, and especially a rhetorician, will have a good deal to say on behalf of the law which requires a sentence to be carried out. He will argue that this law should not be set aside; and shall we reply, 'Yes; but the state has injured us and given an unjust sentence.' Suppose I say that?

Cr. Very good, Socrates.

Soc. 'And was that our agreement with you?' the law would answer; 'or were you to abide by the sentence of the state?' And if I were to express my astonishment at their words, the

law would probably add: 'Answer, Socrates, instead of opening your eyes—you are in the habit of asking and answering
questions. Tell us,—What complaint have you to make against
us which justifies you in attempting to destroy us and the state?
In the first place did we not bring you into existence? Your
father married your mother by our aid and begat you. Say
whether you have any objection to urge against those of us
who regulate marriage?' None, I should reply. 'Or against those
of us who after birth regulate the nurture and education of children, in which you also were trained? Were not the laws, which
have the charge of education, right in commanding your father
to train you in music and gymnastic?' Right, I should reply.
'Well then, since you were brought into the world and nurtured
and educated by us, can you deny in the first place that you are
our child and slave, as your fathers were before you? And if
this is true you are not on equal terms with us; nor can you
think that you have a right to do to us what we are doing to you.
Would you have any right to strike or revile or do any other evil
to your father or your master, if you had one, because you have
been struck or reviled by him, or received some other evil at
his hands?—you would not say this? And because we think
right to destroy you, do you think that you have any right to
destroy us in return, and your country as far as in you lies?
Will you, O professor of true virtue, pretend that you are justified in this? Has a philosopher like you failed to discover that
our country is more to be valued and higher and holier far than
mother or father or any ancestor, and more to be regarded in
the eyes of the gods and of men of understanding? also to be
soothed, and gently and reverently entreated when angry, even
more than a father, and either to be persuaded, or if not persuaded, to be obeyed? And when we are punished by her,
whether with imprisonment or stripes, the punishment is to be
endured in silence; and if she leads us to wounds or death in
battle, thither we follow as is right; neither may any one yield
or retreat or leave his rank, but whether in battle or in a court
of law, or in any other place, he must do what his city and his
country order him; or he must change their view of what is just:
and if he may do no violence to his father or mother, much less
may he do violence to his country.' What answer shall we make
to this, Crito? Do the laws speak truly, or do they not?

    Cr. I think that they do.

    Soc. Then the laws will say, 'Consider, Socrates, if we are
speaking truly that in your present attempt you are going to do
us an injury. For, having brought you into the world, and nurtured and educated you, and given you and every other citizen

a share in every good which we had to give, we further proclaim to any Athenian by the liberty which we allow him, that if he does not like us when he has become of age and has seen the ways of the city, and made our acquaintance, he may go where he pleases and take his goods with him. None of us laws will forbid him or interfere with him. Any one who does not like us and the city, and who wants to emigrate to a colony or to any other city, may go where he likes, retaining his property. But he who has experience of the manner in which we order justice and administer the state, and still remains, has entered into an implied contract that he will do as we command him. And he who disobeys us is, as we maintain, thrice wrong; first, because in disobeying us he is disobeying his parents; secondly, because we are the authors of his education; thirdly, because he has made an agreement with us that he will duly obey our commands; and he neither obeys them nor convinces us that our commands are unjust; and we do not rudely impose them, but give him the alternative of obeying or convincing us; —that is what we offer, and he does neither.

'These are the sort of accusations to which, as we were saying, you, Socrates, will be exposed if you accomplish your intentions; you, above all other Athenians.' Suppose now I ask, why I rather than anybody else? they will justly retort upon me that I above all other men have acknowledged the agreement. 'There is clear proof,' they will say, 'Socrates, that we and the city were not displeasing to you. Of all Athenians you have been the most constant resident in the city, which, as you never leave, you may be supposed to love. For you never went out of the city either to see the games, except once when you went to the Isthmus, or to any other place unless when you were on military service; nor did you travel as other men do. Nor had you any curiosity to know other states or their laws: your affections did not go beyond us and our state; we were your special favourites, and you acquiesced in our government of you; and here in this city you begat your children, which is a proof of your satisfaction. Moreover, you might in the course of the trial, if you had liked, have fixed the penalty at banishment; the state which refuses to let you go now would have let you go then. But you pretended that you preferred death to exile, and that you were not unwilling to die. And now you have forgotten these fine sentiments, and pay no respect to us the laws, of whom you are the destroyer; and are doing what only a miserable slave would do, running away and turning your back upon the compacts and agreements which you made as a citizen. And first of all answer this very question: Are we right in saying that you agreed to be governed according to us in deed, and not in word only? Is that true or not?' How shall we answer, Crito? Must we not assent?

Cr. We cannot help it, Socrates.

Soc. Then will they not say: 'You, Socrates, are breaking the covenants and agreements which you made with us at your leisure, not in any haste or under any compulsion or deception, but after you have had seventy years to think of them, during which time you were at liberty to leave the city, if we were not to your mind, or if our covenants appeared to you to be unfair. You had your choice, and might have gone either to Lacedaemon or Crete, both which states are often praised by you for their good governments, or to some other Hellenic or foreign state. Whereas you, above all other Athenians, seemed to be so fond of the state, or, in other words, of us her laws (and who would care about a state which has no laws?), that you never stirred out of her; the halt, the blind, the maimed were not more stationary in her than you were. And now you run away and forsake your agreements. Not so, Socrates, if you will take our advice; do not make yourself ridiculous by escaping out of the city.

'For just consider, if you transgress and err in this sort of way, what good will you do either to yourself or to your friends? That your friends will be driven into exile and deprived of citizenship, or will lose their property, is tolerably certain; and you yourself, if you fly to one of the neighbouring cities, as, for example, Thebes or Megara, both of which are well governed, will come to them as an enemy, Socrates, and their government will be against you, and all patriotic citizens will cast an evil eye upon you as a subverter of the laws, and you will confirm in the minds of the judges the justice of their own condemnation of you. For he who is a corrupter of the laws is more than likely to be a corrupter of the young and foolish portion of mankind. Will you then flee from well-ordered cities and virtuous men? and is existence worth having on these terms? Or will you go to them without shame, and talk to them, Socrates? And what will you say to them? What you say here about virtue and justice and institutions and laws being the best things among men? Would that be decent of you? Surely not. But if you go away from well-governed states to Crito's friends in Thessaly, where there is great disorder and licence, they will be charmed to hear the tale of your escape from prison, set off with ludicrous particulars of the manner in which you were wrapped in a goatskin or some other disguise, and metamorphosed as the manner is of runaways; but will there be no one to remind you that in your old age you were not ashamed to violate the most sacred laws from a miserable desire of a little more life? Perhaps not, if you keep them in a good temper; but if they are out of temper you will hear many degrading things; you will live, but how?—as the flatterer of all men, and the servant of all men; and doing what?—eating and drinking in Thessaly, having gone abroad in order that you may get a dinner. And where will be your fine sentiments about justice and virtue? Say that you wish to live for the sake of your children—you want to bring them up and educate them—will you take them into Thessaly and deprive them of Athenian citizenship? Or are you under the impression that they will be better cared for and educated here if you are still alive, although absent from them; for your friends will take care of them? Do you fancy that if you are an inhabitant of Thessaly they will take care of them, and if you are an inhabitant of the other world that they will take care of them? Nay; but if they who call themselves friends are good for anything, they will—to be sure they will.

'Listen, then, Socrates, to us who have brought you up. Think not of life and children first, and of justice afterwards, but of justice first, that you may be justified before the princes of the world below. For neither will you nor any that belong to you be happier or holier or juster in this life, or happier in another, if you do as Crito bids. Now you depart in innocence, a sufferer and not a doer of evil; a victim, not of the laws but of men. But if you go forth, returning evil for evil, and injury for injury, breaking the covenants and agreements which you have made with us, and wronging those whom you ought least of all to wrong, that is to say, yourself, your friends, your country, and us, we shall be angry with you while you live, and our brethren, the laws in the world below, will receive you as an enemy; for they will know that you have done your best to destroy us. Listen, then, to us and not to Crito.'

This, dear Crito, is the voice which I seem to hear murmuring in my ears, like the sound of the flute in the ears of the mystic; that voice, I say, is humming in my ears, and prevents me from hearing any other. And I know that anything more which you may say will be vain. Yet speak, if you have anything to say.

Cr. I have nothing to say, Socrates.

Soc. Leave me then, Crito, to fulfil the will of God, and to follow whither he leads.

Henry David Thoreau

On the Duty of Civil Disobedience

I heartily accept the motto,—"That government is best which **19** governs least;" and I should like to see it acted up to more rapidly and systematically. Carried out, it finally amounts to this, which also I believe,—"That government is best which governs not at all," and when men are prepared for it, that will be the kind of government which they will have. Government is at best but an expedient; but most governments are usually, and all governments are sometimes, inexpedient. The objections which have been brought against a standing army, and they are many and weighty, and deserve to prevail, may also at last be brought against a standing government. The standing army is only an arm of the standing government. The government itself, which is only the mode which the people have chosen to execute their will, is equally liable to be abused and perverted before the people can act through it. Witness the present Mexican war, the work of comparatively a few individuals using the standing government as their tool; for, in the outset, the people would not have consented to this measure.

This American government,—what is it but a tradition, though a recent one, endeavoring to transmit itself unimpaired to posterity, but each instant losing some of its integrity? It has not the vitality and force of a single living man; for a single

The major part of this essay was delivered as a lecture in 1848 under the title "On the Relation of the Individual to the State" and was first published in 1849 under the title "Resistance to Civil Government." It has since been published under a variety of titles—the most common being "Civil Disobedience." Thoreau (1817–1862) is best known for his book *Walden,* a diary and commentary on a year spent in a hut at Walden Pond near Concord, Massachusetts. Like most writers in the American transcendentalist tradition (which includes his friend Ralph Waldo Emerson), Thoreau's thought is eloquent and polemical rather than analytic and systematic. The essay on civil disobedience was written specifically to defend his refusal to pay taxes in support of war and slavery (a refusal which cost him a night in jail) and generally to defend individual conscience against the claims of the state. Because of his actions and this essay, Thoreau has been an inspiration to all subsequent conscientious objectors and civil disobedients. Gandhi, for example, always acknowledged the influence of Thoreau on his own thought. The essay is published here in its entirety.

man can bend it to his will. It is a sort of wooden gun to the people themselves. But it is not the less necessary for this; for the people must have some complicated machinery or other, and hear its din, to satisfy that idea of government which they have. Governments show thus how successfully men can be imposed on, even impose on themselves, for their own advantage. It is excellent, we must all allow. Yet this government never of itself furthered any enterprise, but by the alacrity with which it got out of its way. *It* does not keep the country free. *It* does not settle the West. *It* does not educate. The character inherent in the American people has done all that has been accomplished; and it would have done somewhat more, if the government had not sometimes got in its way. For government is an expedient by which men would fain succeed in letting one another alone; and, as has been said, when it is most expedient, the governed are most let alone by it. Trade and commerce, if they were not made of India-rubber, would never manage to bounce over the obstacles which legislators are continually putting in their way; and, if one were to judge these men wholly by the effects of their actions and not partly by their intentions, they would deserve to be classed and punished with those mischievous persons who put obstructions on the railroads.

But, to speak practically and as a citizen, unlike those who call themselves no-government men, I ask for, not at once no government, but *at once* a better government. Let every man make known what kind of government would command his respect, and that will be one step toward obtaining it.

After all, the practical reason why, when the power is once in the hands of the people, a majority are permitted, and for a long period continue, to rule is not because they are most likely to be in the right, nor because this seems fairest to the minority, but because they are physically the strongest. But a government in which the majority rule in all cases cannot be based on justice, even as far as men understand it. Can there not be a government in which majorities do not virtually decide right and wrong, but conscience?—in which majorities decide only those questions to which the rule of expediency is applicable? Must the citizen ever for a moment, or in the least degree, resign his conscience to the legislator? Why has every man a conscience, then? I think that we should be men first, and subjects afterward. It is not desirable to cultivate a respect for the law, so much as for the right. The only obligation which I have a right to assume is to do at any time what I think right. It is truly enough said, that a corporation has no conscience; but a corporation of conscientious men is a corporation *with* a conscience. Law never made men a whit more just; and, by means of their respect for it, even the well-disposed are daily made the agents of injustice. A common and natural result of an undue respect for law is, that you may see a file of soldiers, colonel, captain, corporal, privates, powder-monkeys, and all, marching in admirable order over hill and dale to the wars, against their wills, ay, against their common sense and consciences, which makes it very steep marching indeed, and produces a palpitation of the heart. They have no doubt that it is a damnable business in which they are concerned; they are all peaceably inclined. Now, what are they? Men at all? or small movable forts and magazines, at the service of some unscrupulous man in power? Visit the Navy-Yard, and behold a marine, such a man as an American government can make, or such as it can make a man with its black arts,—a mere shadow and reminiscence of humanity, a man laid out alive and standing, and already, as one may say, buried under arms with funeral accompaniments, though it may be,—

Not a drum was heard, not a funeral note,
As his corse to the rampart we hurried;
Not a soldier discharged his farewell shot
O'er the grave where our hero we buried.

The mass of men serve the state thus, not as men mainly, but as machines, with their bodies. They are the standing army, and the militia, jailors, constables, posse comitatus, etc. In most cases there is no free exercise whatever of the judgment or of the moral sense; but they put themselves on a level with wood and earth and stones; and wooden men can perhaps be manufactured that will serve the purpose as well. Such command no more respect than men of straw or a lump of dirt. They have the same sort of worth only as horses and dogs. Yet such as these even are commonly esteemed good citizens. Others—as most legislators, politicians, lawyers, ministers, and office-holders—serve the state chiefly with their heads; and, as they rarely make any moral distinctions, they are as likely to serve the Devil, without *intending* it, as God. A very few, as heroes, patriots, martyrs, reformers in the great sense, and *men,* serve the state with their consciences also, and so necessarily resist it for the most part; and they are commonly treated as enemies by it. A wise man will only be useful as a man, and will not submit to be "clay," and "stop a hole to keep the wind away," but leave that office to his dust at least:—

I am too high-born to be propertied,
To be a secondary at control,
Or useful serving-man and instrument
To any sovereign state throughout the world.

He who gives himself entirely to his fellow-men appears to them useless and selfish; but he who gives himself partially to them is pronounced a benefactor and philanthropist.

How does it become a man to behave toward this American government to-day? I answer, that he cannot without disgrace be associated with it. I cannot for an instant recognize that political organization as *my* government which is the *slave's* government also.

All men recognize the right of revolution; that is, the right to refuse allegiance to, and to resist, the government, when its tyranny or its inefficiency are great and unendurable. But almost all say that such is not the case now. But such was the case, they think, in the Revolution of '75. If one were to tell me that this was a bad government because it taxed certain foreign commodities brought to its ports, it is most probable that I should not make an ado about it, for I can do without them. All machines have their friction; and possibly this does enough good to counterbalance the evil. At any rate, it is a great evil to make a stir about it. But when the friction comes to have its machine, and oppression and robbery are organized, I say, let us not have such a machine any longer. In other words, when a sixth of the population of a nation which has undertaken to be the refuge of liberty are slaves, and a whole country is unjustly overrun and conquered by a foreign army, and subjected to military law, I think that it is not too soon for honest men to rebel and revolutionize. What makes this duty the more urgent is the fact that the country so overrun is not our own, but ours is the invading army.

Paley,[1] a common authority with many on moral questions, in his chapter on the "Duty of Submission to Civil Government," resolves all civil obligation into expediency; and he proceeds to say, "that so long as the interest of the whole society requires it, that is, so long as the established government cannot be resisted or changed without public inconveniency, it is the will of God that the established government be obeyed, and no longer. . . . This principle being admitted, the justice

---

[1] [William Paley (1743–1805) had included a chapter entitled "Of the Duty of Civil Obedience, as Stated in the Christian Scriptures" in his *The Principles of Moral and Political Philosophy*, Ed.]

of every particular case of resistance is reduced to a computation of the quantity of the danger and grievance on the one
side, and of the probability and expense of redressing it on the
other." Of this, he says, every man shall judge for himself. But
Paley appears never to have contemplated those cases to
which the rule of expediency does not apply, in which a people, as well as an individual, must do justice, cost what it may.
If I have unjustly wrested a plank from a drowning man, I must
restore it to him though I drown myself. This, according to
Paley, would be inconvenient. But he that would save his life,
in such a case, shall lose it. This people must cease to hold
slaves, and to make war on Mexico, though it cost them their
existence as a people.

   In their practice, nations agree with Paley; but does any one
think that Massachusetts does exactly what is right at the
present crisis?

   A drab of state, a cloth-o'-silver slut,
   To have her train borne up, and her soul trail in the dirt.

Practically speaking, the opponents to a reform in Massachusetts are not a hundred thousand politicians at the South, but
a hundred thousand merchants and farmers here, who are more
interested in commerce and agriculture than they are in humanity, and are not prepared to do justice to the slave and to
Mexico, *cost what it may.* I quarrel not with far-off foes, but
with those who, near at home, coöperate with, and do the bid-
ding of, those far away, and without whom the latter would be
harmless. We are accustomed to say, that the mass of men are
unprepared; but improvement is slow, because the few are not
materially wiser or better than the many. It is not so important
that many should be as good as you, as that there be some absolute goodness somewhere; for that will leaven the whole
lump. There are thousands who are *in opinion* opposed to
slavery and to the war, who yet in effect do nothing to put an
end to them; who, esteeming themselves children of Washington and Franklin, sit down with their hands in their pockets, and
say that they know not what to do, and do nothing; who even
postpone the question of freedom to the question of free-trade,
and quietly read the prices-current along with the latest ad-
vices from Mexico, after dinner, and, it may be, fall asleep over
them both. What is the price-current of an honest man and
patriot to-day? They hesitate, and they regret, and sometimes
they petition; but they do nothing in earnest and with effect.
They will wait, well disposed, for others to remedy the evil, that

they may no longer have it to regret. At most, they give only a cheap vote, and a feeble countenance and Godspeed, to the right, as it goes by them. There are nine hundred and ninety-nine patrons of virtue to one virtuous man. But it is easier to deal with the real possessor of a thing than with the temporary guardian of it.

All voting is a sort of gaming, like checkers or backgammon, with a slight moral tinge to it, a playing with right and wrong, with moral questions; and betting naturally accompanies it. The character of the voters is not staked. I cast my vote, perchance, as I think right; but I am not vitally concerned that that right should prevail. I am willing to leave it to the majority. Its obligation, therefore, never exceeds that of expediency. Even voting *for the right* is *doing* nothing for it. It is only expressing to men feebly your desire that it should prevail. A wise man will not leave the right to the mercy of chance, nor wish it to prevail through the power of the majority. There is but little virtue in the action of masses of men. When the majority shall at length vote for the abolition of slavery, it will be because they are indifferent to slavery, or because there is but little slavery left to be abolished by their vote. *They* will then be the only slaves. Only *his* vote can hasten the abolition of slavery who asserts his own freedom by his vote.

I hear of a convention to be held at Baltimore, or elsewhere, for the selection of a candidate for the Presidency, made up chiefly of editors, and men who are politicians by profession; but I think, what is it to any independent, intelligent, and respectable man what decision they may come to? Shall we not have the advantage of his wisdom and honesty, nevertheless? Can we not count upon some independent votes? Are there not many individuals in the country who do not attend conventions? But no: I find that the respectable man, so called, has immediately drifted from his position, and despairs of his country, when his country has more reason to despair of him. He forthwith adopts one of the candidates thus selected as the only *available* one, thus proving that he is himself *available* for any purposes of the demagogue. His vote is of no more worth than that of any unprincipled foreigner or hireling native, who may have been bought. O for a man who is a *man,* and, as my neighbor says, has a bone in his back which you cannot pass your hand through! Our statistics are at fault: the population has been returned too large. How many *men* are there to a square thousand miles in this country? Hardly one. Does not America offer any inducement for men to settle here? The American has dwindled into an Odd Fellow,—one who may be known by the development of his organ of gregariousness, and a manifest lack of intellect and cheerful self-reliance; whose first and chief concern, on coming into the world, is to see that the Alms-houses are in good repair; and, before yet he has lawfully donned the virile garb, to collect a fund for the support of the widows and orphans that may be; who, in short, ventures to live only by the aid of the Mutual Insurance company, which has promised to bury him decently.

It is not a man's duty, as a matter of course, to devote himself to the eradication of any, even the most enormous wrong; he may still properly have other concerns to engage him; but it is his duty, at least, to wash his hands of it, and, if he gives it no thought longer, not to give it practically his support. If I devote myself to other pursuits and contemplations, I must first see, at least, that I do not pursue them sitting upon another man's shoulders. I must get off him first, that he may pursue his contemplations too. See what gross inconsistency is tolerated. I have heard some of my townsmen say, "I should like to have them order me out to help put down an insurrection of the slaves, or to march to Mexico;—see if I would go;" and yet these very men have each, directly by their allegiance, and so indirectly, at least, by their money, furnished a substitute. The soldier is applauded who refuses to serve in an unjust war by those who do not refuse to sustain the unjust government which makes the war; is applauded by those whose own act and authority he disregards and sets at naught; as if the state were penitent to that degree that it hired one to scourge it while it sinned, but not to that degree that it left off sinning for a moment. Thus, under the name of Order and Civil Government, we are all made at last to pay homage to and support our own meanness. After the first blush of sin comes its indifference; and from immoral it becomes, as it were, unmoral, and not quite unnecessary to that life which we have made.

The broadest and most prevalent error requires the most disinterested virtue to sustain it. The slight reproach to which the virtue of patriotism is commonly liable, the noble are most likely to incur. Those who, while they disapprove of the character and measures of a government, yield to it their allegiance and support are undoubtedly its most conscientious supporters, and so frequently the most serious obstacles to reform. Some are petitioning the state to dissolve the Union, to disregard the requisitions of the President. Why do they not dissolve it themselves,—the union between themselves and the state,—and refuse to pay their quota into its treasury? Do not they stand in the same relation to the state that the state does to the

Union? And have not the same reasons prevented the state from resisting the Union which have prevented them from resisting the state?

How can a man be satisfied to entertain an opinion merely, and enjoy *it*? Is there any enjoyment in it, if his opinion is that he is aggrieved? If you are cheated out of a single dollar by your neighbor, you do not rest satisfied with knowing that you are cheated, or with saying that you are cheated, or even with petitioning him to pay you your due; but you take effectual steps at once to obtain the full amount, and see that you are never cheated again. Action from principle, the perception and the performance of right, changes things and relations; it is essentially revolutionary, and does not consist wholly with anything which was. It not only divides states and churches, it divides families; ay, it divides the *individual,* separating the diabolical in him from the divine.

Unjust laws exist; shall we be content to obey them, or shall we endeavor to amend them, and obey them until we have succeeded, or shall we transgress them at once? Men generally, under such a government as this, think that they ought to wait until they have persuaded the majority to alter them. They think that, if they should resist, the remedy would be worse than the evil. But it is the fault of the government itself that the remedy *is* worse than the evil. *It* makes it worse. Why is it not more apt to anticipate and provide for reform? Why does it not cherish its wise minority? Why does it cry and resist before it is hurt? Why does it not encourage its citizens to be on the alert to point out its faults and *do* better than it would have them? Why does it always crucify Christ, and excommunicate Copernicus and Luther, and pronounce Washington and Franklin rebels?

One would think, that a deliberate and practical denial of its authority was the only offense never contemplated by government; else, why has it not assigned its definite, its suitable and proportionate penalty? If a man who has no property refuses but once to earn nine shillings for the state, he is put in prison for a period unlimited by any law that I know, and determined only by the discretion of those who placed him there; but if he should steal ninety times nine shillings from the state, he is soon permitted to go at large again.

If the injustice is part of the necessary friction of the machine of government, let it go, let it go: perchance it will wear smooth, —certainly the machine will wear out. If the injustice has a spring, or a pulley, or a rope, or a crank, exclusively for itself, then perhaps you may consider whether the remedy will not be worse than the evil; but if it is of such a nature that it requires you to be the agent of injustice to another, then, I say, break the law. Let your life be a counter friction to stop the machine. What I have to do is to see, at any rate, that I do not lend myself to the wrong which I condemn.

As for adopting the ways which the state has provided for remedying the evil, I know not of such ways. They take too much time, and a man's life will be gone. I have other affairs to attend to. I came into this world, not chiefly to make this a good place to live in, but to live in it, be it good or bad. A man has not everything to do, but something; and because he cannot do *everything,* it is not necessary that he should do *something* wrong. It is not my business to be petitioning the Governor or the Legislature any more than it is theirs to petition me; and if they should not hear my petition, what should I do then? But in this case the state has provided no way: its very Constitution is the evil. This may seem to be harsh and stubborn and unconciliatory; but it is to treat with the utmost kindness and consideration the only spirit that can appreciate or deserves it. So is all change for the better, like birth and death, which convulse the body.

I do not hesitate to say, that those who call themselves Abolitionists should at once effectually withdraw their support, both in person and property, from the government of Massachusetts and not wait till they constitute a majority of one, before they suffer the right to prevail through them. I think that it is enough if they have God on their side, without waiting for that other one. Moreover, any man more right than his neighbors constitutes a majority of one already.

I meet this American government, or its representative, the state government, directly, and face to face, once a year—no more—in the person of its tax-gatherer; this is the only mode in which a man situated as I am necessarily meets it; and it then says distinctly, Recognize me; and the simplest, most effectual, and, in the present posture of affairs, the indispensablest mode of treating with it on this head, of expressing your little satisfaction with and love for it, is to deny it then. My civil neighbor, the tax-gatherer, is the very man I have to deal with, —for it is, after all, with men and not with parchment that I quarrel,—and he has voluntarily chosen to be an agent of the government. How shall he ever know well what he is and does as an officer of the government, or as a man, until he is obliged to consider whether he shall treat me, his neighbor, for whom he has respect, as a neighbor and well-disposed man, or as a maniac and disturber of the peace, and see if he can get over this obstruction to his neighborliness without a ruder and more impetuous thought or speech corresponding with his action, I know this well, that if one thousand, if one hundred, if ten men whom I could name,—if ten *honest* men only,—ay, if *one honest* man, in this State of Massachusetts, *ceasing to hold slaves,* were actually to withdraw from this copartnership, and be locked up in the county jail therefor, it would be the abolition of slavery in America. For it matters not how small the beginning may seem to be: what is once well done is done forever. But we love better to talk about it: that we say is our mission. Reform keeps many scores of newspapers in its service, but not one man. If my esteemed neighbor, the State's ambassador, who will devote his days to the settlement of the question of human rights in the Council Chamber, instead of being threatened with the prisons of Carolina, were to sit down the prisoner of Massachusetts, that State which is so anxious to foist the sin of slavery upon her sister,—though at present she can discover only an act of inhospitality to be the ground of a quarrel with her,—the Legislature would not wholly waive the subject the following winter.

Under a government which imprisons any unjustly, the true place for a just man is also a prison. The proper place to-day, the only place which Massachusetts has provided for her freer and less desponding spirits, is in her prisons, to be put out and locked out of the State by her own act, as they have already put themselves out by their principles. It is there that the fugitive slave, and the Mexican prisoner on parole, and the Indian come to plead the wrongs of his race should find them; on that separate, but more free and honorable ground, where the State places those who are not *with* her, but *against* her,—the only house in a slave State in which a free man can abide with honor. If any think that their influence would be lost there, and their voices no longer afflict the ear of the State, that they would not be as an enemy within its walls, they do not know by how much truth is stronger than error, nor how much more eloquently and effectively he can combat injustice who has experienced a little in his own person. Cast your whole vote, not a strip of paper merely, but your whole influence. A minority is powerless while it conforms to the majority; it is not even a minority then; but it is irresistible when it clogs by its whole weight. If the alternative is to keep all just men in prison, or give up war and slavery, the State will not hesitate which to choose. If a thousand men were not to pay their tax-bills this year, that would not be a violent and bloody measure, as it would be to pay them, and enable the State to commit violence and shed innocent blood. This is, in fact, the definition of a peaceable revolution, if any such is possible. If the tax-gatherer, or any other public officer, asks me, as one has done, "But what shall I do?" my answer is, "If you really wish to do anything, resign your office." When the subject has refused allegiance, and the officer has resigned his office, then the revolution is accomplished. But even suppose blood should flow. Is there not a sort of blood shed when the conscience is wounded? Through this wound a man's real manhood and immortality flow out, and he bleeds to an everlasting death. I see this blood flowing now.

I have contemplated the imprisonment of the offender, rather than the seizure of his goods,—though both will serve the same purpose,—because they who assert the purest right, and consequently are most dangerous to a corrupt State, commonly have not spent much time in accumulating property. To such the State renders comparatively small service, and a slight tax is wont to appear exorbitant, particularly if they are obliged to earn it by special labor with their hands. If there were one who lived wholly without the use of money, the State itself would hesitate to demand it of him. But the rich man—not to make any invidious comparison—is always sold to the institution which makes him rich. Absolutely speaking, the more money, the less virtue; for money comes between a man and his objects, and obtains them for him; and it was certainly no great virtue to obtain it. It puts to rest many questions which he would otherwise be taxed to answer; while the only new question which it puts is the hard but superfluous one, how to spend it. Thus his moral ground is taken from under his feet. The opportunities of living are diminished in proportion as what are called the "means" are increased. The best thing a man can do for his culture when he is rich is to endeavor to carry out those schemes which he entertained when he was poor. Christ answered the Herodians according to their condition. "Show me the tribute-money," said he;—and one took a penny out of his pocket;—if you use money which has the image of Cæsar on it and which he has made current and valuable, that is, *if you are men of the State,* and gladly enjoy the advantages of Cæsar's government, then pay him back some of his own when he demands it: "Render therefore to Cæsar that which is Cæsar's, and to God those things which are God's,"—leaving them no wiser than before as to which was which; for they did not wish to know.

When I converse with the freest of my neighbors, I perceive that, whatever they may say about the magnitude and seriousness of the question, and their regard for the public tranquillity, the long and the short of the matter is, that they cannot spare the protection of the existing government, and they dread the consequences to their property and families of disobedience to it. For my own part, I should not like to think that I ever rely on the protection of the State. But, if I deny the authority of the State when it presents its tax-bill, it will soon take and waste all my property, and so harass me and my children without end. This is hard. This makes it impossible for a man to live honestly, and at the same time comfortably, in outward respects. It will not be worth the while to accumulate property; that would be sure to go again. You must hire or squat somewhere, and raise but a small crop, and eat that soon. You must live within yourself, and depend upon yourself always tucked up and ready for a start, and not have many affairs. A man may grow rich in Turkey even, if he will be in all respects a good subject of the Turkish government. Confucius said: "If a state is governed by the principles of reason, poverty and misery are subjects of shame; if a state is not governed by the principles of reason, riches and honors are the subjects of shame." No: until I want the protection of Massachusetts to be extended to me in some distant Southern port, where my liberty is endangered, or until I am bent solely on building up an estate at home by peaceful enterprise, I can afford to refuse allegiance to Massachusetts, and her right to my property and life. It costs me less in every sense to incur the penalty of disobedience to the State than it would to obey. I should feel as if I were worth less in that case.

Some years ago, the State met me in behalf of the Church, and commanded me to pay a certain sum toward the support of a clergyman whose preaching my father attended, but never I myself. "Pay," it said, "or be locked up in the jail." I declined to pay. But, unfortunately, another man saw fit to pay it. I did not see why the schoolmaster should be taxed to support the priest, and not the priest the schoolmaster; for I was not the State's schoolmaster, but I supported myself by voluntary subscription. I did not see why the lyceum should not present its tax-bill, and have the State to back its demand, as well as the Church. However, at the request of the selectmen, I condescended to make some such statement as this in writing:— "Know all men by these presents, that I, Henry Thoreau, do not wish to be regarded as a member of any incorporated society which I have not joined." This I gave to the town clerk; and he has it. The State, having thus learned that I did not wish to be regarded as a member of that church, has never made a like demand on me since; though it said that it must adhere to its original presumption that time. If I had known how to name them, I should then have signed off in detail from all the societies which I never signed on to; but I did not know where to find a complete list.

I have paid no poll-tax for six years. I was put into a jail once on this account, for one night; and, as I stood considering the walls of solid stone, two or three feet thick, the door of wood and iron, a foot thick, and the iron grating which strained the light, I could not help being struck with the foolishness of that institution which treated me as if I were mere flesh and blood and bones, to be locked up. I wondered that it should have concluded at length that this was the best use it could put me to, and had never thought to avail itself of my services in some way. I saw that, if there was a wall of stone between me and my townsmen, there was a still more difficult one to climb or break through before they could get to be as free as I was. I did not for a moment feel confined, and the walls seemed a great waste of stone and mortar. I felt as if I alone of all my townsmen had paid my tax. They plainly did not know how to treat me, but behaved like persons who are underbred. In every threat and in every compliment there was a blunder; for they thought that my chief desire was to stand the other side of that stone wall. I could not but smile to see how industriously they locked the door on my meditations, which followed them out again without let or hindrance, and *they* were really all that was dangerous. As they could not reach me, they had resolved to punish my body; just as boys, if they cannot come at some person against whom they have a spite, will abuse his dog. I saw that the State was half-witted, that it was timid as a lone woman with her silver spoons, and that it did not know its friends from its foes, and I lost all my remaining respect for it, and pitied it.

Thus the State never intentionally confronts a man's sense, intellectual or moral, but only his body, his senses. It is not armed with superior wit or honesty, but with superior physical strength. I was not born to be forced. I will breathe after my own fashion. Let us see who is the strongest. What force has a multitude? They only can force me who obey a higher law than I. They force me to become like themselves. I do not hear of *men* being *forced* to live this way or that by masses of men. What sort of life were that to live? When I meet a government which says to me, "Your money or your life," why should I be in haste to give it my money? It may be in a great strait, and not know what to do: I cannot help that. It must help itself; do as I do. It is not worth the while to snivel about it. I am not responsible for the successful working of the machinery of society. I am not the son of the engineer. I perceive that, when an acorn and a chestnut fall side by side, the one does not remain inert to make way for the other, but both obey their own laws, and spring and grow and flourish as best they can, till one, perchance, overshadows and destroys the other. If a plant cannot live according to its nature, it dies; and so a man.

The night in prison was novel and interesting enough. The prisoners in their shirt-sleeves were enjoying a chat and the evening air in the doorway, when I entered. But the jailer said, "Come, boys, it is time to lock up;" and so they dispersed, and I heard the sound of their steps returning into the hollow apartments. My room-mate was introduced to me by the jailer as "a first-rate fellow and a clever man." When the door was locked, he showed me where to hang my hat, and how he managed matters there. The rooms were white-washed once a month; and this one, at least, was the whitest, most simply furnished, and probably the neatest apartment in the town. He naturally wanted to know where I came from, and what brought me there; and, when I had told him, I asked him in my turn how he came there, presuming him to be an honest man, of course; and, as the world goes, I believe he was. "Why," said he, "they accuse me of burning a barn; but I never did it." As near as I could discover, he had probably gone to bed in a barn when drunk, and smoked his pipe there; and so a barn was burnt. He had the reputation of being a clever man, had been there some three months waiting for his trial to come on, and would have to wait as much longer; but he was quite domesticated and contented, since he got his board for nothing, and thought that he was well treated.

He occupied one window, and I the other; and I saw that if one stayed there long, his principal business would be to look out the window. I had soon read all the tracts that were left there, and examined where former prisoners had broken out, and where a grate had been sawed off, and heard the history of the various occupants of that room; for I found that even here there was a history and a gossip which never circulated beyond the walls of the jail. Probably this is the only house in the town where verses are composed, which are afterward printed in a circular form, but not published. I was shown quite a long list of verses which were composed by some young men who had been detected in an attempt to escape, who avenged themselves by singing them.

I pumped my fellow-prisoner as dry as I could, for fear I should never see him again; but at length he showed me which was my bed, and left me to blow out the lamp.

It was like traveling into a far country, such as I had never expected to behold, to lie there for one night. It seemed to me that I never had heard the town-clock strike before, nor the evening sounds of the village; for we slept with the windows open, which were inside the grating. It was to see my native village in the light of the Middle Ages, and our Concord was turned into a Rhine stream, and visions of knights and castles passed before me. They were the voices of old burghers that I heard in the streets. I was an involuntary spectator and auditor of whatever was done and said in the kitchen of the adjacent village-inn,—a wholly new and rare experience to me. It was a closer view of my native town. I was fairly inside of it. I never had seen its institutions before. This is one of its peculiar institutions; for it is a shire town. I began to comprehend what its inhabitants were about.

In the morning, our breakfasts were put through the hole in the door, in small oblong-square tin pans, made to fit, and holding a pint of chocolate, with brown bread, and an iron spoon. When they called for the vessels again, I was green enough to return what bread I had left; but my comrade seized it, and said that I should lay that up for lunch or dinner. Soon after he was let out to work at haying in a neighboring field, whither he went every day, and would not be back till noon; so he bade me good-day, saying that he doubted if he should see me again.

When I came out of prison,—for some one interfered, and paid that tax,—I did not perceive that great changes had taken place on the common, such as he observed who went in a youth and emerged a tottering and gray-headed man; and yet a change had to my eyes come over the scene,—the town, and State, and country,—greater than any that mere time could effect. I saw yet more distinctly the State in which I lived. I saw to what extent the people among whom I lived could be trusted as good neighbors and friends; that their friendship was for summer weather only; that they did not greatly propose to do right; that they were a distinct race from me by their prejudices and superstitions, as the Chinamen and Malays are; that in their sacrifices to humanity they ran no risks, not even to their property; that after all they were not so noble but they treated the thief as he had treated them, and hoped, by a certain outward observance and a few prayers, and by walking in a particular straight though useless path from time to time, to save their souls. This may be to judge my neighbors harshly; for I believe that many of them are not aware that they have such an institution as the jail in their village.

It was formerly the custom in our village, when a poor debtor came out of jail, for his acquaintances to salute him, looking through their fingers, which were crossed to represent the grating of a jail window, "How do ye do?" My neighbors did not thus salute me, but first looked at me, and then at one another, as if I had returned from a long journey. I was put into jail as I was going to the shoemaker's to get a shoe which was mended. When I was let out the next morning, I proceeded to finish my errand, and, having put on my mended shoe, joined a huckleberry party, who were impatient to put themselves under my conduct; and in half an hour,—for the horse was soon tackled,—was in the midst of a huckleberry field, on one of our highest hills, two miles off, and then the State was nowhere to be seen.

This is the whole history of "My Prisons."

I have never declined paying the highway tax, because I am as desirous of being a good neighbor as I am of being a bad subject; and as for supporting schools, I am doing my part to educate my fellow-countrymen now. It is for no particular item in the tax-bill that I refuse to pay it. I simply wish to refuse allegiance to the State, to withdraw and stand aloof from it effectually. I do not care to trace the course of my dollar, if I could, till it buys a man or musket to shoot with,—the dollar is innocent,—but I am concerned to trace the effects of my allegiance. In fact, I quietly declare war with the State, after my fashion, though I will still make what use and get what advantage of her I can, as is usual in such cases.

If others pay the tax which is demanded of me, from a sympathy with the State, they do but what they have already done in their own case, or rather they abet injustice to a greater extent than the State requires. If they pay the tax from a mistaken interest in the individual taxed, to save his property, or prevent his going to jail, it is because they have not considered wisely how far they let their private feelings interfere with the public good.

This, then, is my position at present. But one cannot be too much on his guard in such a case, lest his action be biased by obstinacy or an undue regard for the opinions of men. Let him see that he does only what belongs to himself and to the hour.

I think sometimes, Why, this people mean well, they are only ignorant; they would do better if they knew how: why give your neighbors this pain to treat you as they are not inclined to? But I think again, This is no reason why I should do as they do, or permit others to suffer much greater pain of a different kind. Again, I sometimes say to myself, When many millions of men, without heat, without ill will, without personal feeling of any kind, demand of you a few shillings only, without the possibility, such is their constitution, of retracting or altering their present demand, and without the possibility, on your side, of appeal to any other millions, why expose yourself to this overwhelming brute force? You do not resist cold and hunger, the winds and the waves, thus obstinately; you quietly submit to a thousand similar necessities. You do not put your head into the fire. But just in proportion as I regard this as not wholly a brute force, but partly a human force, and consider that I have relations to those millions as to so many millions of men, and not of mere brute or inanimate things, I see that appeal is possible, first and instantaneously, from them to the Maker of them, and, secondly, from them to themselves. But if I put my head deliberately into the fire, there is no appeal to fire or to the Maker of fire, and I have only myself to blame. If I could convince myself that I have any right to be satisfied with men as they are, and to treat them accordingly, and not according, in some respects, to my requisitions and expectations of what they and I ought to be, then, like a good Mussulman and fatalist, I should endeavor to be satisfied with things as they are, and say it is the will of God. And, above all, there is this difference between resisting this and a purely brute or natural force, that I can resist this with some effect; but I cannot expect, like Orpheus, to change the nature of the rocks and trees and beasts.

I do not wish to quarrel with any man or nation. I do not wish to split hairs, to make fine distinctions, or set myself up as better than my neighbors. I seek rather, I may say, even an excuse for conforming to the laws of the land. I am but too ready to conform to them. Indeed, I have reason to suspect myself on this head; and each year, as the tax-gatherer comes round, I find myself disposed to review the acts and position of the general and State governments, and the spirit of the people, to discover a pretext for conformity.

> We must affect our country as our parents,
> And if at any time we alienate
> Our love or industry from doing it honor,
> We must respect effects and teach the soul
> Matter of conscience and religion,
> And not desire of rule or benefit.

I believe that the State will soon be able to take all my work of this sort out of my hands, and then I shall be no better a patriot than my fellow-countrymen. Seen from a lower point of view,

the Constitution, with all its faults, is very good; the law and
the courts are very respectable; even this State and this American government are, in many respects, very admirable, and
rare things, to be thankful for, such as a great many have described them; but seen from a point of view a little higher, they
are what I have described them; seen from a higher still, and
the highest, who shall say what they are, or that they are worth
looking at or thinking of at all?

However, the government does not concern me much, and I
shall bestow the fewest possible thoughts on it. It is not many
moments that I live under a government, even in this world. If a
man is thought-free, fancy-free, imagination-free, that which *is
not* never for a long time appearing *to be* to him, unwise rulers
or reformers cannot fatally interrupt him.

I know that most men think differently from myself; but those
whose lives are by profession devoted to the study of these or
kindred subjects content me as little as any. Statesmen and
legislators, standing so completely within the institution, never
distinctly and nakedly behold it. They speak of moving society,
but have no resting-place without it. They may be men of a certain experience and discrimination, and have no doubt invented ingenious and even useful systems, for which we sincerely thank them; but all their wit and usefulness lie within
certain not very wide limits. They are wont to forget that the
world is not governed by policy and expediency. Webster never
goes behind government, and so cannot speak with authority
about it. His words are wisdom to those legislators who contemplate no essential reform in the existing government; but
for thinkers, and those who legislate for all time, he never once
glances at the subject. I know of those whose serene and wise
speculations on this theme would soon reveal the limits of his
mind's range and hospitality. Yet, compared with the cheap
professions of most reformers, and the still cheaper wisdom
and eloquence of politicians in general, his are almost the only
sensible and valuable words, and we thank Heaven for him.
Comparatively, he is always strong, original, and, above all,
practical. Still, his quality is not wisdom, but prudence. The
lawyer's truth is not Truth, but consistency or a consistent expediency. Trust is always in harmony with herself, and is not
concerned chiefly to reveal the justice that may consist with
wrong-doing. He well deserves to be called, as he has been
called, the Defender of the Constitution. There are really no
blows to be given by him but defensive ones. He is not a leader,
but a follower. His leaders are the men of '87. "I have never

made an effort," he says, "and never propose to make an effort; I have never countenanced an effort, and never mean to
countenance an effort, to disturb the arrangement as originally
made, by which the various States came into the Union." Still
thinking of the sanction which the Constitution gives to slavery,
he says, "Because it was a part of the original compact,—let
it stand." Notwithstanding his special acuteness and ability, he
is unable to take a fact out of its merely political relations, and
behold it as it lies absolutely to be disposed of by the intellect,
—what, for instance, it behooves a man to do here in America
to-day with regard to slavery,—but ventures, or is driven, to
make some such desperate answer as the following, while pro-
fessing to speak absolutely, and as a private man,—from which
what new and singular code of social duties might be inferred?
"The manner," says he, "in which the governments of those
States where slavery exists are to regulate it is for their own
consideration, under their responsibility to their constituents,
to the general laws of propriety, humanity, and justice, and to
God. Associations formed elsewere, springing from a feeling of
humanity, or other cause, have nothing whatever to do with it.
They have never received any encouragement from me, and
they never will."

They who know of no purer sources of truth, who have traced
up its stream no higher, stand, and wisely stand, by the Bible
and the Constitution, and drink at it there with reverence and
humility; but they who behold where it comes trickling into this
lake or that pool, gird up their loins once more, and continue
their pilgrimage toward its fountainhead.

No man with a genius for legislation has appeared in
America. They are rare in the history of the world. There are
orators, politicians, and eloquent men, by the thousand; but
the speaker has not yet opened his mouth to speak who is capable of settling the much-vexed questions of the day. We love
eloquence for its own sake, and not for any truth which it may
utter, or any heroism it may inspire. Our legislators have not
yet learned the comparative value of free-trade and of freedom,
of union, and of rectitude, to a nation. They have no genius or
talent for comparatively humble questions of taxation and finance, commerce and manufactures and agriculture. If we
were left solely to the wordy wit of legislators in Congress for
our guidance, uncorrected by the seasonable experience and
the effectual complaints of the people, America would not long
retain her rank among the nations. For eighteen hundred years,
though perchance I have no right to say it, the New Testament

has been written; yet where is the legislator who has wisdom
and practical talent enough to avail himself of the light which
it sheds on the science of legislation?

The authority of government, even such as I am willing to
submit to,—for I will cheerfully obey those who know and can
do better than I, and in many things even those who neither
know nor can do so well,—is still an impure one: to be strictly
just, it must have the sanction and consent of the governed. It
can have no pure right over my person and property but what I
concede to it. The progress from an absolute to a limited monarchy, from a limited monarchy to a democracy, is a progress
toward a true respect for the individual. Even the Chinese philosopher was wise enough to regard the individual as the basis
of the empire. Is a democracy, such as we know it, the last improvement possible in government? Is it not possible to take
a step further towards recognizing and organizing the rights
of man? There will never be a really free and enlightened State
until the State comes to recognize the individual as a higher
and independent power, from which all its own power and authority are derived, and treats him accordingly. I please myself
with imagining a State at last which can afford to be just to all
men, and to treat the individual with respect as a neighbor;
which even would not think it inconsistent with its own repose
if a few were to live aloof from it, not meddling with it, nor em-
braced by it, who fulfilled all the duties of neighbors and fellow-
men. A State which bore this kind of fruit, and suffered it to
drop off as fast as it ripened, would prepare the way for a still
more perfect and glorious State, which also I have imagined,
but not yet anywhere seen.

John Rawls

Legal Obligation and the Duty of Fair Play

1. The subject of law and morality suggests many different questions. In particular, it may consider the historical and sociological question as to the way and manner in which moral ideas influence and are influenced by the legal system; or it may involve the question whether moral concepts and principles enter into an adequate definition of law. Again, the topic of law and morality suggests the problem of the legal enforcement of morality and whether the fact that certain conduct is immoral by accepted precepts is sufficient to justify making that conduct a legal offense. Finally, there is the large subject of the study of the rational principles of moral criticism of legal institutions and the moral grounds of our acquiescence in them. I shall be concerned solely with a fragment of this last question: with the grounds for our moral obligation to obey the law, that is, to carry out our legal duties and to fulfill our legal obligations. My thesis is that the moral obligation to obey the law is a special case of the prima facie duty of fair play.

I shall assume, as requiring no argument, that there is, at least in a society such as ours, a moral obligation to obey the law, although it may, of course, be overridden in certain cases by other more stringent obligations. I shall assume also that this obligation must rest on some general moral principle; that is, it must depend on some principle of justice or upon some principle of social utility or the common good, and the like. Now, it may appear to be a truism, and let us suppose it is, that

Reprinted by permission of New York University Press from *Law and Philosophy* by Sidney Hook, © 1964 by New York University. John Rawls is a Professor of Philosophy at Harvard University and is the author of several extemely influential articles in moral and political philosophy: "Two Concepts of Rules," 1955; "Outline of a Decision Procedure for Ethics," 1957; "Justice as Fairness," 1958; "The Sense of Justice," 1963—all in *The Philosophical Review;* "Constitutional Liberty and the Concept of Justice," *Nomos VI: Justice,* ed. Carl J. Friedrich and John W. Chapman (New York, 1963); and "Distributive Justice," *Philosophy, Politics, and Society,* Third Series, ed. Peter Laslett and W. G. Runciman (Oxford, 1967). He has further explored the topics of obligation to obey the law and civil disobedience in his "The Justification of Civil Disobedience," *Civil Disobedience: Theory and Practice,* ed. Hugo Adam Bedau (New York, 1969).

a moral obligation rests on some moral principle. But I mean to exclude the possibility that the obligation to obey the law is based on a special principle of its own. After all, it is not, without further argument, absurd that there is a moral principle such that when we find ourselves subject to an existing system of rules satisfying the definition of a legal system, we have an obligation to obey the law; and such a principle might be final, and not in need of explanation, in the way in which the principles of justice or of promising and the like are final. I do not know of anyone who has said that there is a special principle of legal obligation in this sense. Given a rough agreement, say, on the possible principles as being those of justice, of social utility, and the like, the question has been on which of one or several is the obligation to obey the law founded, and which, if any, has a special importance. I want to give a special place to the principle defining the duty of fair play.

2. In speaking of one's obligation to obey the law, I am using the term "obligation" in its more limited sense, in which, together with the notion of a duty and of a responsibility, it has a connection with institutional rules. Duties and responsibilities are assigned to certain positions and offices, and obligations are normally the consequence of voluntary acts of persons, and while perhaps most of our obligations are assumed by ourselves, through the making of promises and the accepting of benefits, and so forth, others may put us under obligation to them (as when on some occasion they help us, for example, as children). I should not claim that the moral grounds for our obeying the law is derived from the duty of fair-play except insofar as one is referring to an obligation in this sense. It would be incorrect to say that our duty not to commit any of the legal offenses, specifying crimes of violence, is based on the duty of fair play, at least entirely. These crimes involve wrongs as such, and with such offenses, as with the vices of cruelty and greed, our doing them is wrong independently of there being a legal system the benefits of which we have voluntarily accepted.

I shall assume several special features about the nature of the legal order in regard to which a moral obligation arises. In addition to the generally strategic place of its system of rules, as defining and relating the fundamental institutions of society that regulate the pursuit of substantive interests, and to the monopoly of coercive powers, I shall suppose that the legal system in question satisfies the concept of the *rule of law* (or what one may think of as justice as regularity). By this I mean that its rules are public, that similar cases are treated similarly, that there are no bills of attainder, and the like. These are all features of a legal system insofar as it embodies without deviation the notion of a public system of rules addressed to rational beings for the organization of their conduct in the pursuit of their substantive interests. This concept imposes, by itself, no limits on the *content* of legal rules, but only on their regular administration. Finally, I shall assume that the legal order is that of a constitutional democracy: that is, I shall suppose that there is a constitution establishing a position of equal citizenship and securing freedom of the person, freedom of thought and liberty of conscience, and such political equality as in suffrage and the right to participate in the political process. Thus I am confining discussion to a legal system of a special kind, but there is no harm in this.

3. The moral grounds of legal obligation may be brought out by considering what at first seem to be two anomalous facts: first, that sometimes we have an obligation to obey what we think, and think correctly, is an unjust law; and second, that sometimes we have an obligation to obey a law even in a situation where more good (thought of as a sum of social advantages) would seem to result from not doing so. If the moral obligation to obey the law is founded on the principle of fair play, how can one become bound to obey an unjust law, and what is there about the principle that explains the grounds for forgoing the greater good?

It is, of course, a familiar situation in a constitutional democracy that a person finds himself morally obligated to obey an unjust law. This will be the case whenever a member of the minority, on some legislative proposal, opposes the majority view for reasons of justice. Perhaps the standard case is where the majority, or a coalition sufficient to constitute a majority, takes advantage of its strength and votes in its own interests. But this feature is not essential. A person belonging to the minority may be advantaged by the majority proposal and still oppose it as unjust, yet when it is enacted he will normally be bound by it.

Some have thought that there is ostensibly a paradox of a special kind when a citizen, who votes in accordance with his moral principles (conception of justice), accepts the majority decision when he is in the minority. Let us suppose the vote is between two bills, *A* and *B* each establishing an income tax procedure, rates of progression, or the like, which are contrary to one another. Suppose further that one thinks of the constitutional procedure for enacting legislation as a sort of machine that yields a result when the votes are fed into it—the result being that a certain bill is enacted. The question arises as to how a citizen can accept the machine's choice, which (assuming that *B* gets a majority of the votes) involves thinking that *B* ought to be enacted when, let us suppose, he is of the declared opinion that *A* ought to be enacted. For some the paradox seems to be that in a constitutional democracy a citizen is often put in a situation of believing that both *A* and *B* should be enacted when *A* and *B* are contraries: that *A* should be enacted because *A* is the best policy, and that *B* should be enacted because *B* has a majority—and moreover, and this is essential, that this conflict is different from the usual sort of conflict between prima facie duties.

There are a number of things that may be said about this supposed paradox, and there are several ways in which it may be resolved, each of which brings out an aspect of the situation. But I think the simplest thing to say is to deny straightaway that there is anything different in this situation than in any other situation where there is a conflict of prima facie principles. The essential of the matter seems to be as follows: (1) Should *A* or *B* be enacted and implemented, that is, administered? Since it is supposed that everyone accepts the outcome of the vote, within limits, it is appropriate to put the enactment and implementation together. (2) Is *A* or *B* the best policy? It is assumed that everyone votes according to his political opinion as to which is the best policy and that the decision as to how to vote is not based on personal interest. There is no special conflict in this situation: the citizen who knows that he will find himself in the minority believes that, taking into account only the relative merits of *A* and *B* as prospective statutes, and leaving aside how the vote will go, *A* should be enacted and implemented. Moreover, on his own principles he should vote for what he thinks is the best policy, and leave aside how the vote will go. On the other hand, given that a majority will vote for *B*, *B* should be enacted and implemented, and he may know that a majority will vote for *B*. These judgments are relative to different principles (different arguments). The first is based on the person's conception of the best social policy; the second is based on the principles on which he accepts the constitution. The real decision, then, is as follows: A person has to decide, in each case where he is in the minority, whether the nature of the statute is such that, given that it will get, or has got, a majority vote, he should oppose its being implemented, engage in civil disobedience, or take equivalent action. In this situation he simply has to balance his obligation to oppose an unjust statute against his obligation to abide by a just constitution. This is, of course, a difficult situation, but not one introducing any deep logical paradox. Normally, it is hoped that the obligation to the constitution is clearly the decisive one.

Although it is obvious, it may be worthwhile mentioning, since a relevant feature of voting will be brought out, that the result of a vote is that a rule of law is enacted, and although given the fact of its enactment, everyone agrees that it should be implemented, no one is required to believe that the statute enacted represents the best policy. It is consistent to say that another statute would have been better. The vote does not result in a statement to be believed: namely, that *B* is superior, on its merits, to *A*. To get this interpretation one would have to suppose that the principles of the constitution specify a device which gathers information as to what citizens think should be done and that the device is so constructed that it always produces from this information the morally correct opinion as to which is the best policy. If in accepting a constitution it was so interpreted, there would, indeed, be a serious paradox: for a citizen would be torn between believing, on his own principles, that *A* is the best policy, and believing at the same time that *B* is the best policy as established by the constitutional device, the principles of the design of which he accepts. This conflict could be made a normal one only if one supposed that a person who made his own judgment on the merits was always prepared to revise it given the opinion constructed by the machine. But it is not possible to determine the best policy in this way, nor is it possible for a person to give such an undertaking. What this misinterpretation of the constitutional procedure shows, I think, is that there is an important difference between voting and spending. The constitutional procedure is not, in an essential respect, the same as the market: Given the usual assumptions of perfect competition of price theory, the actions of private persons spending according to their interests will result in the best situation, as judged by the criterion of Pareto. But in a perfectly just constitutional procedure, people voting their political opinions on the merits of policies may or may not reflect the best policy. What this misinterpretation brings out, then, is that when citizens vote for policies on their merits, the constitutional procedure cannot be viewed as acting as the market does, even under ideal conditions. A constitutional procedure does not reconcile differences of opinion into an opinion to be taken as true—this can only be done by argument and reasoning—but rather it decides whose opinion is to determine legislative policy.

4. Now to turn to the main problem, that of understanding how a person can properly find himself in a position where, by his own principles, he must grant that, given a majority vote, *B* should be enacted and implemented even though *B* is unjust. There is, then, the question as to how it can be morally justifiable to acknowledge a constitutional procedure for making legislative enactments when it is certain (for all practical purposes) that laws will be passed that by one's own principles are unjust. It would be impossible for a person to undertake to change his mind whenever he found himself in the minority; it is not impossible, but entirely reasonable, for him to undertake to abide by the enactments made, whatever they are, provided that they are within certain limits. But what more exactly are the conditions of this undertaking?

First of all, it means, as previously suggested, that the constitutional procedure is misinterpreted as a procedure for making legal rules. It is a process of social decision that does not produce a statement to be believed (that *B* is the best policy) but a rule to be followed. Such a procedure, say involving some form of majority rule, is necessary because it is certain that there will be disagreement on what is the best policy. This will be true even if we assume, as I shall, that everyone has a similar sense of justice and everyone is able to agree on a certain constitutional procedure as just. There will be disagreement because they will not approach issues with the same stock of information, they will regard different moral features of situations as carrying different weights, and so on. The acceptance of a constitutional procedure is, then, a necessary political device to decide between conflicting legislative proposals. If one thinks of the constitution as a fundamental part of the scheme of social cooperation, then one can say that if the constitution is just, and if one has accepted the benefits of its working and intends to continue doing so, and if the rule enacted is within certain limits, then one has an obligation, based on the principle of fair play, to obey it when it comes one's turn. In accepting the benefits of a just constitution one becomes bound to it, and in particular one becomes bound to one of its fundamental rules: given a majority vote in behalf of a statute, it is to be enacted and properly implemented.

The principle of fair play may be defined as follows. Suppose there is a mutually beneficial and just scheme of social cooperation, and that the advantages it yields can only be obtained if everyone, or nearly everyone, cooperates. Suppose further that cooperation requires a certain sacrifice from each person, or at least involves a certain restriction of his liberty. Suppose finally that the benefits produced by cooperation are, up to a certain point, free: that is, the scheme of cooperation is unstable in the sense that if any one person knows that all (or nearly all) of the others will continue to do their part, he will still be able to share a gain from the scheme even if he does not do his part. Under these conditions a person who has accepted the benefits of the scheme is bound ᴐy a duty of fair play to do his part and not to take advantage of the free benefit by not cooperating. The reason one must abstain from this attempt is that the existence of the benefit is the result of everyone's effort, and prior to some understanding as to how it is to be shared, if it can be shared at all, it belongs in fairness to no one. (I return to this question below.)

Now I want to hold that the obligation to obey the law, as enacted by a constitutional procedure, even when the law seems unjust to us, is a case of the duty of fair play as defined. It is, moreover, an obligation in the more limited sense in that it depends upon our having accepted and our intention to continue accepting the benefits of a just scheme of cooperation that the constitution defines. In this sense it depends on our own voluntary acts. Again, it is an obligation owed to our fellow citizens generally: that is, to those who cooperate with us in the working of the constitution. It is not an obligation owed to public officials, although there may be such obligations. That it is an obligation owed by citizens to one another is shown by the fact that they are entitled to be indignant with one another for failure to comply. Further, an essential condition of the obligation is the justice of the constitution and the general system of law being roughly in accordance with it. Thus the obligation to obey (or not to resist) an unjust law depends strongly on there being a just constitution. Unless one obeys the law enacted under it, the proper equilibrium, or balance, between competing claims defined by the constitution will not be maintained. Finally, while it is true enough to say that the enactment by a majority binds the minority, so that one may be bound by the acts of others, there is no question of their binding them in conscience to certain beliefs as to what is the best policy, and it is a necessary condition of the acts of others binding us that the constitution is just, that we have accepted its benefits, and so forth.

5. Now a few remarks about the principles of a just constitution. Here I shall have to presuppose a number of things about the principles of justice. In particular, I shall assume that there are two principles of justice that properly apply to the fundamental structure of institutions of the social system and,

thus, to the constitution. The first of these principles requires that everyone have an equal right to the most extensive liberty compatible with a like liberty for all; the second is that inequalities are arbitrary unless it is reasonable to expect that they will work out for everyone's advantage and provided that the positions and offices to which they attach or from which they may be gained are open to all. I shall assume that these are the principles that can be derived by imposing the constraints of morality upon rational and mutually self-interested persons when they make conflicting claims on the basic form of their common institutions: that is, when questions of justice arise.

The principle relevant at this point is the first principle, that of equal liberty. I think it may be argued with some plausibility that it requires, where it is possible, the various equal liberties in a constitutional democracy. And once these liberties are established and constitutional procedures exist, one can view legislation as rules enacted that must be ostensibly compatible with both principles. Each citizen must decide as best he can whether a piece of legislation, say the income tax, violates either principle; and this judgment depends on a wide body of social facts. Even in a society of impartial and rational persons, one cannot expect agreement on these matters.

Now recall that the question is this: How is it possible that a person, in accordance with his own conception of justice, should find himself bound by the acts of another to obey an unjust law (not simply a law contrary to his interests)? Put another way: Why, when I am free and still without my chains, should I accept certain a priori conditions to which any social contract must conform, a priori conditions that rule out all constitutional procedures that would decide in accordance with my judgment of justice against everyone else? To explain this (Little has remarked),[1] we require two hypotheses: that among the very limited number of procedures that would stand any chance of being established, none would make my decision decisive in this way; and that all such procedures would determine social conditions that I judge to be better than anarchy. Granting the second hypothesis, I want to elaborate on this in the following way: the first step in the explanation is to

---

[1] The metaphor of being free and without one's chains is taken from I. M. D. Little's review of K. Arrow's book *Social Choice and Individual Values* (New York, 1951), which appeared in *Journal of Political Economy,* LX (1952). See p. 431. My argument follows his in all essential respects, the only addition being that I have introduced the concept of justice in accounting for what is, in effect, Arrow's non-dictatorship condition.

derive the principles of justice that are to apply to the basic form of the social system and, in particular, to the constitution. Once we have these principles, we see that no just constitutional procedure would make my judgment as to the best policy decisive (would make me a dictator in Arrow's sense).[2] It is not simply that, among the limited number of procedures actually possible as things are, no procedure would give me this authority. The point is that even if such were possible, given some extraordinary social circumstances, it would not be just. (Of course it is not possible for everyone to have this authority.) Once we see this, we see how it is possible that within the framework of a just constitutional procedure to which we are obligated, it may nevertheless happen that we are bound to obey what seems to us to be and is an unjust law. Moreover, the possibility is present even though everyone has the same sense of justice (that is, accepts the same principles of justice) and everyone regards the constitutional procedure itself as just. Even the most efficient constitution cannot prevent the enactment of unjust laws if, from the complexity of the social situation and like conditions, the majority decides to enact them. A just constitutional procedure cannot foreclose all injustice; this depends on those who carry out the procedure. A constitutional procedure is not like a market reconciling interests to an optimum result.

6. So far I have been discussing the first mentioned anomaly of legal obligation, namely, that though it is founded on justice, we may be required to obey an unjust law. I should now like to include the second anomaly: that we may have an obligation to obey the law even though more good (thought of as a sum of advantages) may be gained by not doing so. The thesis I wish to argue is that not only is our obligation to obey the law a special case of the principle of fair play, and so dependent upon the justice of the institutions to which we are obligated, but also the principles of justice are absolute with respect to the principle of utility (as the principle to maximize the net sum of advantages). By this I mean two things. First, unjust institutions cannot be justified by an appeal to the principle of utility. A greater balance of net advantages shared by some cannot justify the injustice suffered by others; and where unjust institutions are tolerable it is because a certain degree of injustice sometimes cannot be avoided, that social necessity requires it, that there would be greater injustice otherwise, and so on. Second, our obligation to obey the law, which is a

---

2 See Arrow, *opus cit. supra.*

48   Civil Disobedience and Violence

special case of the principle of fair play, cannot be overridden
by an appeal to utility, though it may be overridden by another
duty of justice. These are sweeping propositions and most
likely false, but I should like to examine them briefly.

I do not know how to establish these propositions. They are
not established by the sort of argument used above to show
that the two principles, previously mentioned, are the two principles of justice, that is, when the subject is the basic structure of the social system. What such an argument might show
is that, if certain natural conditions are taken as specifying the
concept of justice, then the two principles of justice are the
principles logically associated with the concept when the subject is the basic structure of the social system. The argument
might prove, if it is correct, that the principles of justice are
incompatible with the principle of utility. The argument might
establish that our intuitive notions of justice must sometimes
conflict with the principle of utility. But it leaves unsettled what
the more general notion of right requires when this conflict occurs. To prove that the concept of justice should have an absolute weight with respect to that of utility would require a
deeper argument based on an analysis of the concept of right,
at least insofar as it relates to the concepts of justice and
utility. I have no idea whether such an analysis is possible.
What I propose to do instead is to try out the thought that the
concept of justice does have an absolute weight, and to see
whether this suggestion, in view of our considered moral opinions, leads to conclusions that we cannot accept. It would seem
as if to attribute to justice an absolute weight is to interpret
the concept of right as requiring that a special place be given
to persons capable of a sense of justice and to the principle of
their working out together, from an initial position of equality,
the form of their common institutions. To the extent that this
idea is attractive, the concept of justice will tend to have an
absolute weight with respect to utility.

7. Now to consider the two anomalous cases. First: In the
situation where the obligation requires obedience to an unjust
law, it seems true to say that the obligation depends on the
principle of fair play and, thus, on justice. Suppose it is a matter of a person being required to pay an income tax of a kind
that he thinks is unjust, not simply by reference to his interests. He would not want to try to justify the tax on the ground
that the net gain to certain groups in society is such as to outweigh the injustice. The natural argument to make is to his obligation to a just constitution.

But in considering a particular issue, a citizen has to make two decisions: how he will vote (and I assume that he votes for what he thinks is the best policy, morally speaking), and, in case he should be in the minority, whether his obligation to support, or not obstruct, the implementation of the law enacted is not overridden by a stronger obligation that may lead to a number of courses including civil disobedience. Now in the sort of case imagined, suppose there is a real question as to whether the tax law should be obeyed. Suppose, for example, that it is framed in such a way that it seems deliberately calculated to undermine unjustly the position of certain social or religious groups. Whether the law should be obeyed or not depends, if one wants to emphasize the notion of justice, on such matters as (1) the justice of the constitution and the real opportunity it allows for reversal; (2) the depth of the injustice of the law enacted; (3) whether the enactment is actually a matter of calculated intent by the majority and warns of further such acts; and (4) whether the political sociology of the situation is such as to allow of hope that the law may be repealed. Certainly, if a social or religious group reasonably (not irrationally) and correctly supposes that a permanent majority, or majority coalition, has deliberately set out to undercut its basis and that there is no chance of successful constitutional resistance, then the obligation to obey that particular law (and perhaps other laws more generally) ceases. In such a case a minority may no longer be obligated by the duty of fair play. There may be other reasons, of course, at least for a time, for obeying the law. One might say that disobedience will not improve the justice of their situation or their descendants' situation; or that it will result in injury and harm to innocent persons (that is, members not belonging to the unjust majority). In this way, one might appeal to the balance of justice, if the principle of not causing injury to the innocent is a question of justice; but in any case, the appeal is not made to the greater net balance of advantages (irrespective of the moral position of those receiving them). The thesis I want to suggest then, is that in considering whether we are obligated to obey an unjust law, one is led into no absurdity if one simply throws out the principle of utility altogether, except insofar as it is included in the general principle requiring one to establish the most efficient just institutions.

Second: Now the other sort of anomaly arises when the law is just and we have a duty of fair play to follow it, but a greater net balance of advantages could be gained from not doing so. Again the income tax will serve to illustrate this familiar point: The social consequences of any one person (perhaps even many people) not paying his tax are unnoticeable, and let us suppose zero in value, but there is a noticeable private gain for the person himself, or for another to whom he chooses to give it (the institution of the income tax is subject to the first kind of instability). The duty of fair play binds us to pay our tax, nevertheless, since we have accepted, and intend to continue doing so, the benefits of the fiscal system to which the income tax belongs. Why is this reasonable and not a blind following of a rule, when a greater net sum of advantages is possible?—because the system of cooperation consistently followed by everyone else itself produces the advantages generally enjoyed and in the case of a practice such as the income tax there is no reason to given exemptions to anyone so that they might enjoy the possible benefit. (An analogous case is the moral obligation to vote and so to work the constitutional procedure from which one has benefited. This obligation cannot be overridden by the fact that our vote never makes a difference in the outcome of an election; it may be overridden, however, by a number of other considerations, such as a person being disenchanted with all parties, being excusably uninformed, and the like.)

There are cases, on the other hand, where a certain number of exemptions can be arranged for in a just or fair way; and if so, the practice, including the exemptions, is more efficient, and when possible it should be adopted (waiving problems of transition) in accordance with the principle of establishing the most efficient just practice. For example, in the familiar instance of the regulation to conserve water in a drought, it might be ascertained that there would be no harm in a certain extra use of water over and above the use for drinking. In this case some rotation scheme can be adopted that allots exemptions in a fair way, such as houses on opposite sides of the street being given exemptions on alternate days. The details are not significant here. The main idea is simply that if the greater sum of advantages can effectively and fairly be distributed amongst those whose cooperation makes these advantages possible, then this should be done. It would indeed be irrational to prefer a lesser to a more efficient just scheme of cooperation; but this fact is not to be confused with justifying an unjust scheme by its greater efficiency or excusing ourselves from a duty of fair play by an appeal to utility. If there is no reason to distribute the possible benefit, as in the case of the income tax, or in the case of voting, or if there is no way to do so that does not involve such problems as excessive costs, then the benefit should be foregone. One may disagree with this view, but it is not irrational, not a matter of rule worship: it is, rather, an appeal to the duty of fair play, which requires one to abstain from an advantage that cannot be distributed fairly to those whose efforts have made it possible. That those who make the efforts and undergo the restrictions of their liberty should share in the benefits produced is a consequence of the assumption of an initial position of equality, and it falls under the second principle. But the question of distributive justice is too involved to go into here. Moreover, it is unlikely that there is any substantial social benefit for the distribution of which some fair arrangement cannot be made.

8. To summarize, I have suggested that the following propositions may be true:

First, that our moral obligation to obey the law is a special case of the duty of fair play. This means that the legal order is construed as a system of social cooperation to which we become bound because: first, the scheme is just (that is, it satisfies the two principles of justice), and no just scheme can ensure against our ever being in the minority in a vote; and second, we have accepted, and intend to continue to accept, its benefits. If we failed to obey the law, to act on our duty of fair play, the equilibrium between conflicting claims, as defined by the concept of justice, would be upset. The duty of fair play is not, of course, intended to account for its being wrong for us to commit crimes of violence, but it is intended to account, in part, for the obligation to pay our income tax, to vote, and so on.

Second, I then suggested that the concept of justice has an absolute weight with respect to the principle of utility (not necessarily with respect to other moral concepts). By that I meant that the union of the two concepts of justice and utility must take the form of the principle of establishing the most efficient just institution. This means that an unjust institution or law cannot be justified by an appeal to a greater net sum of advantages, and that the duty of fair play cannot be analogously overridden. An unjust institution or law or the overriding of the duty of fair play can be justified only by a greater balance of justice. I know of no way to prove this proposition. It is not proved by the analytic argument to show that the principles of justice are indeed the principles of justice. But I think it may be shown that the principle to establish the most efficient just institutions does not lead to conclusions counter to our intuitive judgments and that it is not in any way irrational. It is, moreover, something of a theoretical simplification, in that one does not have to balance justice against utility. But this simplification is no doubt not a real one, since it is as difficult to ascertain the balance of justice as anything else.[3]

[3] [Not surprisingly, Rawls' argument has met challenge from utilitarians. The utilitarian will argue that, even if it would be bad for everyone to perform some act *A* (such as breaking the law), one may still be morally justified in performing *A* if he has reasonable grounds for believing that in fact not everyone will perform *A*. It would be bad for everyone to break the law, surely, but not everyone will. It is empirically false that, in most cases, an act of disobedience on the part of one man will lead to an "epidemic" of disobedience. And, according to the utilitarian, it is morally quite permissible to take this fact into account in justifying one's disobedient conduct. An action may be unfair; but the utilitarian, unlike Rawls, will argue that it is morally permissible on grounds of utility to perform unfair or unjust actions. For a development of the utilitarian position on this issue, see the following: Richard Brandt, "Utility and the Obligation to Obey the Law," *Law and Philosophy,* ed. Sidney Hook (New York, 1964); Richard Wasserstrom, "The Obligation to Obey the Law," *U.C.L.A. Law Review,* X (May 1963), reprinted in *Essays in Legal Philosophy,* ed. Robert S. Summers (Berkeley, 1968). On the general question of resolving conflicts between justice and utility, see Brian Barry, "Justice and the Common Good," *Analysis,* Vol. 21, 1960–61, reprinted in *Political Philosophy,* ed. Anthony Quinton (Oxford, 1967). Ed.]

Sidney Hook

Social Protest and
Civil Obedience

In times of moral crisis what has been accepted as common- **53**
place truth sometimes appears questionable and problematic.
We have all been nurtured in the humanistic belief that in a
democracy, citizens are free to disagree with a law but that
so long as it remains in force, they have a *prima facie* obligation to obey it. The belief is justified on the ground that this
procedure enables us to escape the twin evils of tyranny and
anarchy. Tyranny is avoided by virtue of the freedom and power
of dissent to win the uncoerced consent of the community.
Anarchy is avoided by reliance on due process, the recognition
that there is a right way to correct a wrong, and a wrong way to
secure a right. To the extent that anything is demonstrable in
human affairs, we have held that democracy as a political system is not viable if members systematically refused to obey
laws whose wisdom or morality they dispute.

Nonetheless, during the past decade of tension and turmoil
in American life there has developed a mass phenomenon of
civil disobedience even among those who profess devotion to
democratic ideals and institutions. This phenomenon has
assumed a character similar to a tidal wave which has not yet
reached its crest. It has swept from the field of race relations to
the campuses of some universities, subtly altering the connota-
tion of the term "academic." It is being systematically developed as an instrument of influencing foreign policy. It is leaving
its mark on popular culture. I am told it is not only a theme of
comic books but that children in our more sophisticated families
no longer resort to tantrums in defying parental discipline—
they go limp!

More seriously, in the wake of civil disobedience there has

This article first appeared in *The Humanist,* Fall 1967, and is reprinted by
permission. Sidney Hook is Professor of Philosophy at New York University,
a founder of the Congress for Cultural Freedom, and former President of
the American Philosophical Association (Eastern Division). His many publications include the following books: *The Paradoxes of Freedom, Religion
in a Free Society, Education for Modern Man,* and *Reason, Social Myths and
Democracy.*

occasionally developed *uncivil* disobedience, sometimes as a natural psychological development, and often because of the failure of law enforcement agencies especially in the South to respect and defend legitimate expressions of social protest. The line between civil and uncivil disobedience is not only an uncertain and wavering one in practice, it has become so in theory. A recent prophet of the philosophy of the absurd in recommending civil disobedience as a form of creative disorder in a democracy cited Shay's Rebellion as an illustration. This Rebellion was uncivil to the point of bloodshed. Indeed, some of the techniques of protesting American involvement in Vietnam have departed so far from traditional ways of civil disobedience as to make it likely that they are inspired by the same confusion between civil and uncivil disobedience.

All this has made focal the perennial problems of the nature and limits of the citizen's obligation to obey the law, of the relation between the authority of conscience and the authority of the state, of the rights and duties of a democratic moral man in an immoral democratic society. The classical writings on these questions have acquired a burning relevance to the political condition of man today. I propose briefly to clarify some of these problems.

To begin with I wish to stress the point that there is no problem concerning "social protest" as such in a democracy. Our Bill of Rights was adopted not only to make protest possible but to encourage it. The political logic, the very ethos of any democracy that professes to rest, no matter how indirectly, upon freely given consent *requires* that social protest be permitted—and not only permitted but *protected* from interference by those opposed to the protest, which means protected by agencies of law enforcement.

Not social protest but *illegal* social protest constitutes our problem. It raises the question: "When, if ever, is illegal protest justified in a democratic society?" It is of the first importance to bear in mind that we are raising the question as principled democrats and humanists in a democratic society. To urge that illegal social protests, motivated by exalted ideals are sanctified in a democratic society by precedents like the Boston Tea Party, is a lapse into political illiteracy. Such actions occurred in societies in which those affected by unjust laws had no power peacefully to change them.

Further, many actions dubbed civilly disobedient by local authorities, strictly speaking, are not such at all. An action launched in violation of a local law or ordinance, and undertaken to test it, on the ground that the law itself violates state or federal law, or launched in violation of a state law in the sincerely held belief that the state law outrages the Constitution, the supreme law of the land, is not civilly disobedient. In large measure the original sympathy with which the original sit-ins were received, especially the Freedom Rides, marches, and demonstrations that flouted local Southern laws, was due to the conviction that they were constitutionally justified, in accordance with the heritage of freedom, enshrined in the Amendments, and enjoyed in other regions of the country. Practically everything the marchers did was sanctioned by the phrase of the First Amendment which upholds "the right of the people peaceably to assemble and to petition the Government for a redress of grievances." Actions of this kind may be wise or unwise, timely or untimely, but they are not civilly disobedient.

They become civilly disobedient when they are in deliberate violation of laws that have been sustained by the highest legislative and judicial bodies of the nation, e.g., income tax laws, conscription laws, laws forbidding segregation in education, and discrimination in public accommodations and employment. Another class of examples consists of illegal social protest against local and state laws that clearly do not conflict with Federal Law.

Once we grasp the proper issue, the question is asked with deceptive clarity: "Are we under an obligation in a democratic community always to obey an unjust law?" To this question Abraham Lincoln is supposed to have made the classic answer in an eloquent address on "The Perpetuation of Our Political Institution," calling for absolute and religious obedience until the unjust law is repealed.

I said that this question is asked with deceptive clarity because Lincoln, judging by his other writings and the pragmatic cast of his basic philosophy, could never have subscribed to this absolutism or meant what he seemed literally to have said. Not only are we under no moral obligation *always* to obey unjust laws, we are under no moral obligation *always* to obey a just law. One can put it more strongly: sometimes it may be necessary in the interests of the greater good to violate a just or sensible law. A man who refused to violate a sensible traffic law if it were necessary to do so to avoid a probably fatal accident would be a moral idiot. There are other values in the world besides legality or even justice, and sometimes they may be of overriding concern and weight. Everyone can imagine some situation in which the violation of some existing law is the lesser moral evil, but this does not invalidate recognition of our obligation to obey just laws.

There is a difference between disobeying a law which one approves of in general but whose application in a specific case seems wrong, and disobeying a law in protest against the injustice of the law itself. In the latter case the disobedience is open and public; in the former, not. But if the grounds of disobedience in both cases are moral considerations, there is only a difference in degree between them. The rejection, therefore, of legal absolutism or the fetishism of legality—that one is never justified in violating any law in any circumstances—is a matter of common sense.

The implications drawn from this moral commonplace by some ritualistic liberals are clearly absurd. For they have substituted for the absolutism of law something very close to the absolutism of individual conscience. Properly rejecting the view that the law, no matter how unjust, must be obeyed in all circumstances, they have taken the view that the law is to be obeyed only when the individual deems it just or when it does not outrage his conscience. Fantastic comparisons are made between those who do not act on the dictates of their conscience and those who accepted and obeyed Hitler's laws. These comparisons completely disregard the systems of law involved, the presence of alternatives of action, the differences in the behavior commanded, in degrees of complicity of guilt, in the moral costs and personal consequences of compliance and other relevant matters.

It is commendable to recognize the primacy of morality to law but unless we recognize the centrality of intelligence to morality, we stumble with blind self-righteousness into moral disaster. Because, Kant to the contrary notwithstanding, it is not wrong sometimes to lie to save a human life; because it is not wrong sometimes to kill in defense to save many from being killed, it does not follow that the moral principles: "Do not lie!" "Do not kill!" are invalid. When more than one valid principle bears on a problem of moral experience, the very fact of their conflict means that not all of them can hold unqualifiedly. One of them must be denied. The point is that such negation or violation entails upon us the obligation of justifying it, and moral justification is a matter of reasons not of conscience. The burden of proof rests on the person violating the rules. Normally, we don't have to justify telling the truth. We do have to justify *not* telling the truth. Similarly, with respect to the moral obligation of a democrat who breaches his political obligation to obey the laws of a democratic community, the resort to conscience is not enough. There must always be reasonable justification.

This is all the more true because just as we can, if challenged, give powerful reasons for the moral principle of truthtelling, so we can offer logically coercive grounds for the obligation of a democrat to obey the laws of a democracy. The grounds are many and they can be amplified beyond the passing mention we give here. It is a matter of fairness, of social utility, of peace, or ordered progress, of redeeming an implicit commitment.

There is one point, however, which has a particular relevance to the claims of those who counterpose to legal absolutism the absolutism of conscience. There is the empirically observable tendency for public disobedience to law to spread from those who occupy high moral ground to those who dwell on low ground, with consequent growth of disorder and insecurity.

Conscience by itself is not the measure of high or low moral ground. This is the work of reason. Where it functions properly the democratic process permits this resort to reason. If the man of conscience loses in the court of reason, why should he assume that the decision or the law is mistaken rather than the deliverances of his conscience?

The voice of conscience may sound loud and clear. But it may conflict at times not only with the law but with another man's conscience. Every conscientious objector to a law knows that at least one man's conscience is wrong, *viz.,* the conscience of the man who asserts that *his* conscience tells him that he must not tolerate conscientious objectors. From this if he is reasonable he should conclude that when he hears the voice of conscience, he is hearing not the voice of God, but the voice of a finite, limited man in this time and in this place, and that conscience is neither a special nor an infallible organ of apprehending moral truth, that conscience without conscientiousness, conscience which does not cap the process of critical reflective morality, is likely to be prejudice masquerading as a First Principle or a Mandate from Heaven.

The mark of an enlightened democracy is, as far as is possible with its security, to respect the religious commitment of a citizen who believes, on grounds of conscience or any other ground, that his relation to God involves duties superior to those arising from any human relation. It, therefore, exempts him from his duty as a citizen to protect his country. However, the mark of the genuine conscientious objector in a democracy is to respect the democratic process. He does not use his exemption as a political weapon to coerce where he has failed to convince or persuade. Having failed to influence national policy by rational means within the law, in the political processes open to him in a free society, he cannot justifiably try to defeat that policy by resorting to obstructive techniques outside the law and still remain a democrat.

It is one thing on grounds of conscience or religion to plead exemption from the duty of serving one's country when drafted. It is quite another to adopt harassing techniques to prevent others from volunteering or responding to the call of duty. It is one thing to oppose American involvement in Vietnam by teach-ins, petitions, electoral activity. It is quite another to attempt to stop troop trains: to take possession of the premises of draft boards where policies are not made; to urge recruits to sabotage their assignments and feign illness to win discharge. The first class of actions falls within the sphere of legitimate social protest; the second class is implicitly insurrectionary since it is directed against the authority of a democratic government which it seeks to overthrow not by argument and discussion but by resistance—albeit passive resistance.

Nonetheless, since we have rejected legal absolutism we must face the possibility that in protest on ethical grounds individuals may refuse to obey some law which they regard as uncommonly immoral or uncommonly foolish. If they profess to be democrats, their behavior must scrupulously respect the following conditions:

First, it must be nonviolent—peaceful not only in form but in actuality. After all, the protesters are seeking to dramatize a great evil that the community allegedly has been unable to overcome because of complacency or moral weakness. Therefore, they must avoid the guilt of imposing hardship or harm on others who in the nature of the case can hardly be responsible for the situation under protest. Passive resistance should not be utilized merely as a safer or more effective strategy than active resistance of imposing their wills on others.

Secondly, resort to civil disobedience is never morally legitimate where other methods of remedying the evil complained of are available. Existing grievance procedures should be used. No grievance procedures were available to the southern Negroes. The Courts often shared the prejudices of the community and offered no relief, not even minimal protection. But such procedures *are* available in the areas of industry and education. For example, where charges against students are being heard such procedures may result in the dismissal of the charges not the students. Or the faculty on appeal may decide to suspend the rules rather than the students. To jump the gun to civil disobedience in bypassing these procedures is tell-tale evidence that those who are calling the shots are after other game than preserving the rights of students.

Thirdly, those who resort to civil disobedience are duty bound to accept the legal sanctions and punishments imposed by the laws. Attempts to evade and escape them not only involve a betrayal of the community, but erode the moral foundations of civil disobedience itself. Socrates' argument in the *Crito* is valid only on democratic premises. The rationale of the protesters is the hope that the pain and hurt and indignity they voluntarily accept will stir their fellow citizens to compassion, open their minds to second thoughts, and move them to undertake the necessary healing action. When, however, we observe the heroics of defiance being followed by the dialectics of legal evasion, we question the sincerity of the action.

Fourth, civil disobedience is unjustified if a major moral issue is not clearly at stake. Differences about negotiable details that can easily be settled with a little patience should not be fanned into a blaze of illegal opposition.

Fifth, where intelligent men of good will and character differ on large and complex moral issues, discussion and agitation are more appropriate than civilly disobedient action. Those who feel strongly about animal rights and regard the consumption of animal flesh as foods as morally evil would have a just cause for civil disobedience if *their* freedom to obtain other food was threatened. They would have no moral right to resort to similar action to prevent their fellow citizens from consuming meat. Similarly with fluoridation.

Sixth, where civil disobedience is undertaken, there must be some rhyme and reason in the time, place, and targets selected. If one is convinced, as I am not, that the Board of Education of New York City is remiss in its policy of desegregation, what is the point of dumping garbage on bridges to produce traffic jams that seriously discomfort commuters who have not the remotest connection with educational policies in New York? Such action can only obstruct the progress of desegregation in the communities of Long Island. Gandhi, who inspired the civil disobedience movement in the twentieth century, was a better tactician than many who invoke his name but ignore his teachings. When he organized his campaign of civil disobedience against the Salt Tax, he marched with his followers to the sea to make salt. He did not hold up food trains or tie up traffic.

Finally, there is such a thing as historical timing. Democrats who resort to civil disobedience must ask themselves whether the cumulative consequences of their action may in the existing climate of opinion undermine the peace and order on which the effective exercise of other human rights depend. This is a cost which one may be willing to pay but which must be taken into the reckoning.

These observations in the eyes of some defenders of the philosophy of civil disobedience are far from persuasive. They regard them as evading the political realities. The political realities, it is asserted, do not provide meaningful channels for the legitimate expression of dissent. The "Establishment" is too powerful or indifferent to be moved. Administrations are voted into office that are not bound by their election pledges. The right to form minority parties is hampered by unconstitutional voting laws. What does even "the right of the people to present petitions for the redress of grievances" amount to if it does not carry with it the right to have those petitions paid attention to, at least to have them read, if not acted upon?

No, the opposing argument runs on. Genuine progress does not come by enactment of laws, by appeals to the good will or conscience of one's fellow citizens, but only by obstructions which interfere with the functioning of the system itself, by actions whose nuisance value is so high that the Establishment finds it easier to be decent and yield to demands than to be obdurate and oppose them. The time comes, as one student leader of the civilly disobedient Berkeley students advised, "when it is necessary for you to throw your bodies upon the wheels and gears and levers and bring the machine to a grinding halt." When one objects that such obstruction, as a principle of political action, is almost sure to produce chaos, and that it is unnecessary and undesirable in a democracy, the retort is made: "Amen, if only this were a democracy, how glad we would be to stop!"

It is characteristic of those who argue this way to define the presence or absence of the democratic process by whether or not *they* get their political way, and not by the presence or absence of democratic institutional processes. The rules of the game exist to enable them to win and if they lose that's sufficient proof the game is rigged and dishonest. The sincerity with which the position is held is no evidence whatsoever of its coherence. The right to petition does not carry with it the right to be heard, if that means influence on those to whom it is addressed. What would they do if they received incompatible petitions from two different and hostile groups of petitioning citizens? The right of petition gives one a chance to persuade, and the persuasion must rest on the power of words, on the effective appeal to emotion, sympathy, reason, and logic. Petitions are weapons of criticism, and their failure does not justify appeal to other kinds of weapons.

It is quite true that some local election laws do hamper minority groups in the organization of political parties; but there is always the right of appeal to the Courts. Even if this fails there is a possibility of influencing other political parties. It is difficult but so long as one is free to publish and speak, it can be done. If a group is unsuccessful in moving a majority by the weapons of criticism, in a democracy it may resort to peaceful measures of obstruction, provided it is willing to accept punishment for its obstructionist behavior. But these objections are usually a preface to some form of elitism or moral snobbery which is incompatible with the very grounds given in defending the right of civil disobedience on the part of democrats in a democracy.

All of the seven considerations listed above are cautionary, not categorical. We have ruled out only two positions—blind obedience to any and all laws in a democracy, and unreflective violation of laws at the behest of individual consciences. Between these two obviously unacceptable extremes, there is a spectrum of views which shade into each other. Intelligent persons can differ on their application to specific situations. These differences will reflect different assessments of the historical mood of a culture, of the proper timing of protest and acquiescence, and of what the most desirable emphasis and direction of our teaching should be in order to extend "the blessing of liberty" as we preserve "domestic tranquility."

Without essaying the role of a prophet, here is my reading of the needs of the present. It seems to me that the Civil Rights Acts of 1964 and the Voting Acts of 1965 mark a watershed in the history of social and civil protest in the U.S. Upon their enforcement a great many things we hold dear depend, especially those causes in behalf of which in the last decade so many movements of social protest were launched. We must recall that it was the emasculation of the 15th Amendment in the South which kept the Southern Negro in a state of virtual peonage. The prospect of enforcement of the new civil rights legislation is a function of many factors—most notably the law-abiding behavior of the hitherto recalcitrant elements in the southern white communities. Their *uncivil,* violent disobedience has proved unavailing. We need not fear this so much as that they will adopt the strategies and techniques of the civil disobedience itself in their opposition to long-delayed and decent legislation to make the ideals of American democracy a greater reality.

On the other hand, I think the movement of civil disobedience, as distinct from legal protest, in regions of the country in which Negroes have made slow but substantial advances are not likely to make new gains commensurate with the risks. Those risks are that what is begun as civil disobedience will be perverted by extremists into uncivil disobedience, and alienate large numbers who have firmly supported the cause of freedom.

One of the unintended consequences of the two World Wars is that in many ways they strengthened the position of the Negroes and all other minorities in American political life. We do not need another, a third World War, to continue the process of liberation. We can do it in peace—without war and without civil war. The Civil Rights and Voting Acts of 1964 and 1965 are far in advance of the actual situation in the country where discrimination is so rife. Our present task is to bring home and reinforce popular consciousness of the fact that those who violate their provisions are violating the highest law of the land, and that their actions are outside the law. Therefore, our goal must *now* be to build up and strengthen a mood of respect for the law, for civil obedience to laws, even by those who deem them unwise or who opposed them in the past. Our hope is that those who abide by the law may learn not only to tolerate them but, in time, as their fruits develop, to accept them. To have the positive law on the side of right and justice is to have a powerful weapon that makes for voluntary compliance—but only if the *reasonableness* of the *prima facie* obligation to obey the law is recognized.

To one observer at least, that reasonableness is being more and more disregarded in this country. The current mood is one of growing indifference to and disregard of even the reasonable legalities. The headlines from New York to California tell the story. I am not referring to the crime rate which has made frightening strides, nor to the fact that some of our metropolitan centers have become dangerous jungles. I refer to a growing mood toward law generally, something comparable to the attitude toward the Volstead Act during the Prohibition era. The mood is more diffuse today. To be law-abiding in some circles is to be "a square."

In part, the community itself has been responsible for the emergence of this mood. This is especially true in those states which have failed to abolish the *unreasonable* legalities, particularly in the fields of marriage, divorce, birth control, sex behavior, therapeutic abortion, voluntary euthanasia, and other intrusions on the right of privacy. The failure to repeal foolish laws, which makes morally upright individuals legal offenders, tends to generate skepticism and indifference toward observing the reasonable legalities.

This mood must change if the promise of recent civil rights legislation is to be realized. Respect for law today can give momentum to the liberal upswing of the political and social pendulum in American life. In a democracy we cannot make an absolute of obedience to law or to anything else except "the moral obligation to be intelligent," but more than ever we must stress that dissent and opposition—the oxygen of free society —be combined with civic obedience, and that on moral grounds it express itself as legal dissent and legal opposition.

Jeffrie G. Murphy

The Vietnam War and the Right of Resistance

64 The contemporary American government generates a pervasive and substantial amount of moral agony among its citizens. And this is unfortunate. For one of the primary functions of a constitutional representative government is to provide a generally just and agreeable social decision procedure for political policy which will make moral confrontation between a citizen and his government rare. This leaves the citizen free to pursue his own limited aims—free to seek his own peace and happiness in the reasonable expectation that the rules under which he lives will resolve political matters, if not in the very best way, at least in a way that is neither highly unjust nor highly productive of human misery.

But this situation, though it is the ideal envisioned in democratic theory, is clearly nowhere near the reality which currently presents itself to us. Many reasonable and sensitive men find it increasingly difficult to continue recognizing a moral obligation to abide by the results of the decision procedures of the state; for the exercise of these procedures seems to them increasingly unjust, arbitrary, deceitful, and secret. Thus it is that they feel the moral necessity of subjecting every single act of our government to minute scrutiny. And such necessity compels them to ignore more and more those private satisfactions of the good life which democracy is supposed to secure for each citizen. For the pursuit of private goals, in the present context, strikes them as unjustifiably narrow and selfish. Such an attitude is reflected in the refusal of many students to go on with "business as usual" and in their decisions to abandon their studies and careers for direct political action.[1]

This essay was delivered at a teach-in at the University of Minnesota (1967) and to an undergraduate honors colloquium at the University of Michigan (1968). It is published here (with updating of references) for the first time. All rights reserved.

[1] For many students, such slogans are surely nothing but a rationalizing mask for indolence or even psychopathy. But for many others, they are just as surely an expression of conscience and moral sensitivity.

Such a state of affairs sets the stage for a more radical kind of resistance or civil disobedience than that found, for example, in the early Southern sit-ins led by Martin Luther King, Jr., and others. The disobedience practiced there typically involved a faith in the ultimate integrity of the legal system. A claim made by those in disobedience was that their actions were really legal, that they were of such a nature that—even if prohibited by local statute—they would ultimately be upheld as protected by our Constitution. Present-day radical resistance has no such faith. Those who, with Benjamin Spock and others, advocate or practice resistance to the operation of Selective Service may not be in the least dissuaded by any Supreme Court ruling that such resistance is not constitutionally protected. So much the worse, they may argue, for the Court and (for the present instance) the Constitution.[2]

It is hard to overestimate the gravity of this response to government, for it strikes at the roots of the very idea of law. It is surely a response to which a reasonable man will only slowly and regretfully come. But sometimes, as the history of Nazi Germany has surely taught us, it may have to come. My purpose here is to sketch one set of conditions (possibly satisfied, in my judgment, by our government's conduct of the Vietnam War) in which such a radical response may be claimed as a *moral* right.[3] No claim will be made that these are the only such conditions or that, having a right to resist, the citizen *ought* to exercise it. Whether one should resist the law obviously depends, among other things, upon the complex circumstances surrounding the particular case—for example, whether resistance is likely to advance one's aims, whether it will result in the harming of people, whether it will provoke repression, and

[2] There is, of course, an even more radical response which I shall not discuss here—namely, the response of the *revolutionary*. As I understand the intentions of people like Dr. Spock, they are not revolutionary. Many of those who advocate draft resistance do so, not because they find the American system of constitutional democracy evil in principle, but because they believe that the present government has not itself been loyal to the rules and ideals of that very system. Thus they desire to restore the system to health. The revolutionary, on the other hand, finds the very principles of the system corrupt and wants to overthrow them entirely. Revolutionary resistance raises interesting and important problems, but they are not problems of civil disobedience.

[3] The question of whether there might also be a legal or quasi-legal basis for such a right is discussed in Ronald Dworkin's "On Not Prosecuting Civil Disobedience," *New York Review of Books*, June 6, 1968. My interest will be in the person who resists Selective Service (refuses induction, for example) because he believes that the Vietnam War is illegal. Even if the war is illegal, it is not clear that this will entail the illegality of the draft laws (the laws actually resisted). Thus the draft resister, even if he bases his resistance in part on a belief that the war is illegal, will not necessarily be claiming a legal right to resist.

(so important but so often forgotten) whether it will harden or soften the hearts of men—whether it will advance or retard the cause of civilization and human decency.[4] My aim is simply to show that there are cases in which resistance, no matter how open to criticism on other grounds, cannot fairly be criticized as a violation of one's solemn moral obligation to obey the law of the land.

Pursuing certain implications of Enlightenment political theory (such as that of Locke and Kant), I want to suggest that a citizen is morally obligated to obey the law as such only if the government under which he lives satisfies what I shall call the obligation of reciprocity. A less technical name for this obligation is simply "fair play."[5] Law and government form a system of social benefits which is made possible only as a result of mutual forbearances. The benefits I enjoy are possible only because of the sacrifices (and obedience *is* a sacrifice) of others. Therefore it is an obligation of reciprocity (since it is only fair) that I bear the necessary burdens of obedience when my turn comes. I expect others to obey laws of which they do not approve, and so it is only fair that I be at least *prima facie* prepared to do likewise. Such reciprocity is required to make law and government possible; for if everyone acted solely on his own private judgment, there would be no sense to the notion of social rules or of the rule of law as a social decision procedure. When men start acting as judges with respect to their own controversies, the very concepts "judge" and "law" operate without sense. For if I propose to serve as my own judge and legislator, and thus to refuse allegiance to rules which conflict with my own private judgment, I am claiming a liberty for myself which could not (consistent with the maintenance of a just

---

[4] Michael Walzer has argued that some important considerations relevant to this question are the commitments that one has made to fellow members of secondary associations like political groups or religious sects. When these secondary associations have a "claim to primacy," then one's commitments can yield a *prima facie* obligation to disobey those rules of the state which are in conflict with the rules or ideals of the association. See his "The Obligation to Disobey," *Ethics*, April 1967. This may also be found in *Political Theory and Social Change*, edited by David Spitz (New York, 1967).

[5] I am here drawing on a theory elaborated by John Rawls in his "Legal Obligation and the Duty of Fair Play" in *Law and Philosophy*, edited by Sidney Hook (New York, 1964). See also my "Violence and the Rule of Law," *Ethics*, July 1970, and my "In Defense of Obligation," in *Nomos XII: Political and Legal Obligation*, edited by J. Roland Pennock and John W. Chapman (New York, 1970). The theory outlined is, of course, a version of the "social contract" theory found in the thought of such earlier philosophers as Hobbes, Locke, Kant, Rousseau, and Socrates (in Plato's *Crito*). Rawls has outlined a theory of civil disobedience in his "The Justification of Civil Disobedience," in *Civil Disobedience: Theory and Practice*, edited by Hugo Adam Bedau (New York, 1969).

rule of law) be extended to all other people. And this is a sign that I am proposing to act in an unfair or unjust way. To put the point very crudely, people who sincerely believe in the rule of law and in democracy must be prepared, on occasion, to *lose*. This does not mean that one must always, no matter what the circumstances, accept defeat. But it does mean that one has a *prima facie* obligation, based on reciprocity, to accept defeat—that is, the burden of moral proof lies on the man who proposes not to accept defeat. We are all inclined to talk about the sanctity of the law when *others* whose views we do not share (segregationists perhaps) seek to resist, and thus it is only fair that we find such appeals at least relevant (if not always decisive) when made against a cause like draft resistance of which we may approve.

Having outlined the obligation of reciprocity, I want now to insist on something that may be regarded as controversial—namely, that this obligation falls most heavily upon the *government itself*.[6] For if an individual citizen fails to obey the law, the damage he can do is minimal. We also have institutions to deal with him. Criminal punishment, after all, is an institution which functions to keep most citizens from unfairly suffering as a result of disobedience by others. But government is not in the position of the average citizen. Government holds a near monopoly on the force in a given society, and this makes it both highly dangerous and invulnerable. Thus its deviations from the rule of law present a threat to the integrity of society far beyond that posed by any individual citizen. Even more important, of course, is the fact that government—especially constitutional representative government—has the solemn trust of preserving the rule of law. It must call upon its citizens for

---

[6] Hobbes and Kant, for example denied this. (For Kant's views on legal obligation and resistance, see his "Concerning the Saying: That May be True in Theory but not in Practice," and for a discussion of his views see my *Kant: The Philosophy of Right* [London, 1970].) The legal positions of government officials and average citizens are, of course, different in certain important respects. Government officials and average citizens, though many of their legal obligations (not to drive over the speed limit, for example) overlap, also have nonoverlapping obligations. The President does not have a legal obligation to serve in the army, but he does have a legal obligation not to embark the nation on a war in violation of the Constitution. The average citizen, on the other hand, has a legal obligation to serve in the army but does not have a legal obligation to make war only in accord with the Constitution; for the citizen is not in a legal position to conduct war at all. The important point for our purposes, however, is that both government officials and the citizens have a common *moral* obligation—namely, to support the rule of law. This means, among other things, that both government officials and citizens, if they are indeed loyal to the principles of constitutional democracy, must recognize an obligation to pursue their own ends only in so far as doing so is consistent with their respective legal obligations.

obedience; and, if it is to be morally persuasive and not merely coercive in doing this, its own hands must be clean. Consider an analogy with a game: Deviations from rules by players make the game difficult, but this difficulty is in principle remediable. Deviations from the rules by the *umpire*, however, make the game impossible—make the game cease to operate as a system of rules at all.

Thus government, if it is to be justified in calling upon its citizens to honor an obligation to obey the law of the land, must be able to show that it has met its own obligations in that regard—that it has satisfied its own obligation of reciprocity or fair dealing. Government, after all, is not a good in itself. It is useful only insofar as it provides us with justice and the kind of security that living under a system of rules can make possible. When government deviates from those rules, its value is eroded. And with this erosion goes government's justification and its moral claim on our obedience.

What is the practical upshot of all this? I should like to suggest the following: When it can be demonstrated (and the burden of proof is on the citizen) that the government has violated its obligation of reciprocity by ignoring its own legal duties and limitations, then the government has no right to call upon the citizen to satisfy his own end of the social bargain. In such circumstances the citizen is *not* morally obligated to obey the law as such, and thus he may legitimately claim a right to resist. A believer in the rule of law and in democracy must be willing to accept defeat, yes, but only if the defeat is *just*—that is, only if it results from the fair use of fair procedures.

Now, as I have previously suggested, having a *right* to resist does not entail that one *ought* to resist. This depends upon a large number of other moral considerations—one being whether resistance will tend to restore or further deteriorate the rule of law.[7] Also, a right to resist does not make a citizen morally free to break any law he happens to feel like breaking. For even though a government may deal unfairly with its citizens in some areas, it may deal with them quite fairly in others. And surely there are sufficient moral reasons for obeying some rules (such as "Do not murder") regardless of the legal status of those rules, for some actions are wrong in themselves (*mala in se* and not just *mala prohibita*). Even when talk of resistance

---

[7] This will depend, in large measure, on the *manner* in which the resistance takes place. Simple refusal of induction (and consequent jail or exile), for example, will tend to threaten the rule of law to a much lesser extent than violent demonstrations and the repression they often provoke.

seems appropriate, in other words, reasonable men should still draw distinctions.

Having outlined a theoretical structure, I should now like to apply it to a concrete case—one of a current importance almost impossible to overestimate. The case is the Vietnam War and the right of resistance (draft resistance, for example) to that war. In my judgment the following claims (none of them unreasonable to believe) provide a *prima facie* case for a right to such resistance:[8]

1. *The war began as the private adventure of the President. It was not and never has been, as the Constitution requires, declared by Congress.*[9]

2. *The war is arguably in violation of treaties and the United Nations Charter—all of which are supposedly legally binding on our national action.*[10]

---

[8] I say *"prima facie* case" for the following reason: It is a matter of empirical and legal investigation, and not of philosophy, whether or not the following claims have indeed been established as facts. I (admittedly a nonexpert) tend to be persuaded by the evidence in their favor. If others are not persuaded, then we know where we disagree and how to develop our discussion. Thus the claims should at least serve to illustrate, even for a person who is unconvinced, what is relevant for applying the theory and how an application of that theory might look. For opposing views, see Sidney Hook, "Social Protest and Civil Obedience," *The Humanist,* Fall 1967; Abe Fortas, *Concerning Dissent and Civil Disobedience* (New York, 1968); and Judge Charles E. Wyzanski, Jr., "On Civil Disobedience," *Atlantic Monthly,* February, 1968. Fortas argues that the legal channels for redress of grievances are adequate, and Hook suggests that most people who complain that the channels are not adequate are simply angry at not having gotten their own way. I shall suggest that the evidence for this complaint is much stronger than Hook is willing to admit.

[9] Nicholas Katzenbach, former Assistant Secretary of State, once called the Gulf of Tonkin Resolution a "functional equivalent" of a declaration of war. In addition to wondering what this phrase might mean, it is important to note the following: There is evidence, much of it brought out in hearings conducted by Senator Fulbright, that the Johnson administration seduced Congress into passing this resolution by the presentation of misdescribed and even fabricated incidents of "attacks" on U.S. ships by the North Vietnamese. See Peter Dale Scott, "Tonkin Bay: Was There a Conspiracy?" *New York Review of Books,* July 29, 1970. Considering the length of the conflict and the number of casualties in Vietnam, it would be hard to deny that it really is properly called a "war" and that it is thus subject to Article I, section 8, of the Constitution, which was intended as an explicit restriction upon the power of the executive to initiate war on his own prerogative —such a power being then enjoyed by the British sovereign.

[10] This is argued in, among other places, the *Memorandum of Law of Lawyers' Committee on American Policy toward Vietnam,* read into the *Congressional Record* by Senator Morse on September 23, 1965. Defenders of the international legality of the war may, for example, cite the SEATO treaty as providing authorization for the war. The legal issues here are extremely complex, and this is the primary reason why so many concerned citizens desire a court ruling on the legality of the war. In the absence of such a ruling, what is the citizen to do except form his own reasoned individual judgment on the matter? For a review of the legal issues, see the following: Richard A. Falk, *The Six Legal Dimensions of the Vietnam War* (Princeton, 1968); Richard A. Falk, ed., *The Vietnam War and International Law* (Princeton, Vol. I [1968] and Vol. II [1969]); Roger H. Hull, *Law and Vietnam*

3. *The Selective Service, which is the major instrument supporting the war, has been used for the illegal purpose of punishing dissent. Even Justice Fortas, no friend of civil disobedients, once called its former director "a law unto himself."*
4. *The war was escalated contrary to all campaign pledges of President Johnson. Democracy demands the periodic review of officials and their policies. When these officials refuse to be candid about their policies, then the democratic process is made a sham. For no informed choice of consent is then possible.*

5. *The federal courts (including the Supreme Court) have refused to decide cases where citizens have challenged the legality of the war—typically by raising points 1 and 2 above. Thus a promised channel for the legal redress of grievances has, for all practical purposes, been closed.*[11]

6. *The war is an ideological war. That is, it does not appear to be a war in defense of those national benefits we should all perhaps be willing to maintain by our sacrifice. Rather it is more like a religious war—a war to stamp out the heresy of Communism. The Cold Warriors behind it are, of course, entitled to their religious beliefs. But are they entitled to sacrifice*

(New York, 1968); *In the Name of America: the conduct of the war in Vietnam by the armed forces of the United States as shown by published reports, compared with the laws of war binding on the United States Government and on its citizens,* Clergy and Laymen Concerned about Vietnam (New York, 1968); and Telford Taylor, *Nuremberg and Vietnam: An American Tragedy* (New York, 1970).

[11] Justice Fortas, in his *Concerning Dissent and Civil Disobedience* (New York, 1968), condemns radicals for not using legitimate channels for the redress of their grievances. And yet, while on the Supreme Court, he was one of the justices who refused to hear cases on the war. This makes his pleas for the use of "legitimate channels" sound rather hollow. (The important cases here are *Mitchell v. United States,* 369 F. 2d 323 (1966), cert. denied, 386 U.S. 972 (1967) and *Mora v. McNamara,* reported as *Luftig v. McNamara,* 252 F. Supp. 819 (D.D.C. 1966), aff'd 373 F. 2d 664 (D.C. Cir.), cert. denied sub nom., *Mora v. McNamara,* 389 U.S. 934 (1967)—Douglas dissenting in *Mitchell,* Douglas and Stewart dissenting in *Mora.*) In refusing to hear such cases, the Court typically relies on the "political question" doctrine—that is, that questions concerning the war are political in the sense that, rather than being purely legal or constitutional, they are properly to be decided by some other branch of government. This strikes many as a subterfuge which allows the Court to avoid its true responsibilities—particularly when the Court fails even to give a *reason* for refusing to hear the case. For a probing discussion of this problem, with application to civil disobedience, see Graham Hughes, "Civil Disobedience and the Political Question Doctrine," *New York University Law Review,* LXIII, No. 1 (March 1968), pp. 1–19. For a discussion of Hughes' article, see Stephen Wexler, "The 'Political Question' Doctrine: A Decision Not to Decide" and Kai Nielsen, "The 'Political Question' Doctrine," both in *Ethics,* October 1968. Hughes' paper was presented at the International Philosophy Year Conference at Brockport in 1968 and was sharply criticized by Justice Tom Clark. Clark's paper and a reprinting of Hughes' may be found in *Ethics and Social Justice,* edited by Howard E. Kiefer and Milton K. Munitz (Albany, 1970).

others for those beliefs? "Here is a cause I believe in; now you *go out and die for it" is not a very persuasive argument.*[12]

These claims, of course, are not new. Neither do they constitute all the important objections which can be made against the war. But the issues they raise constitute so great a threat to our constitutional democracy that they cannot be repeated too many times.[13] For these particular six points, in my judgment, provide evidence that our government in the present context has violated its obligation of reciprocity to the citizens. They provide evidence that the war has been instigated and conducted in violation of the law of the land, of the very principles which define our form of government. The government itself has perhaps been engaged in resistance to law.[14]

Now in my view, *if* these claims are indeed established as facts, the implication is clear: Those who oppose the war by resistance to Selective Service may not fairly be charged with violating their moral obligation to obey the law of the land. For a condition of that obligation has been violated by government and, in so doing, government has forfeited its moral right to call upon citizens for obedience in this area. It can and will

---

[12] This is relevant to the issue raised in point 1. There is some justification, in the modern world of nuclear missiles, for allowing the President to respond to attack without consulting Congress for a formal declaration of war. But it would be difficult to support a claim that the Vietnam War posed this kind of "crisis" problem.

[13] Even if these claims are false, it is a danger merely to have so many people *believe* that they are true. Government, to be respected, must not even give the *illusion* of arbitrariness and tyranny. A government can, of course, meticulously adhere to legal procedure and still enact policies that lie beyond the limit of moral tolerance—e.g. genocide. I should certainly want to say that, in such circumstances, it is right (even obligatory) for the citizen to resist. However, to argue this point would require another paper.

[14] Points 4 through 6 are more complex than the earlier three. For the claim made in the first three is that a reasonably clear legal obligation has been violated. The claim made by the latter three is that the government, though not violating a clear legal obligation, is acting so as to show lack of respect for the ideals of democracy and constitutional procedure. To use one of Kant's favorite metaphors, they show adherence to the letter but not to the spirit of the law. The President is not legally obligated to be honest in his statements of policy, and the court is not legally obligated to hear important constitutional cases. But surely presidential deceit and court inaction are not consistent with the ideals which constitutional democracy is supposed to maintain. And on the obligation to serve in wars, the following observation of Hobbes is instructive: "When the defence of the commonwealth, requireth at once the help of all that are able to bear arms, every one is obliged; because otherwise the institution of the commonwealth, which they have not the purpose, or courage to preserve, was in vain" (*Leviathan*, Part 2, Chapter 21). Is it really plausible to maintain that ideological wars, like the Vietnam War, can be fitted into this model of self-defense? A belief that the model does apply must lie behind the remarks of those who condemn as cowards and traitors all those who will not serve in Vietnam.

force them to obey (or face jail or exile), but it has forfeited its *moral* claim on them. And moral claims, in a democracy, are the most important kind.

It should be clear that I have not been concerned to advocate or recommend civil disobedience or draft resistance, for a *prima facie* case for a *right* to resist is a long way from a *conclusive* case for a *duty* to resist. What I am most concerned to advocate is government's responsibility for giving the same meticulous attention to its legal obligations that it demands of citizens.

In times when government appears to exceed its own legal limitations and flaunt the rule of law, decent people who truly believe in the rule of law may be classed as "criminals." But such a classification is terribly misleading when applied to many of the current draft resisters—particularly those who have been nonviolent. Perhaps they have merely believed and acted upon what they have always been taught and what ought to be true: that America is a government of laws and not of men.[15]

---

[15] It is not to be hoped that considerations such as these will have any practical influence during time of war. But when the war is over, and passions have calmed, we should surely be willing to face up to what has been at the very least the moral and legal *ambiguity* of the whole enterprise. So doing, we should seriously consider granting amnesty to those whose consciences have forced them into jail or exile—allowing them to re-enter the community with dignity. To require of a man that he invite the personal disintegration that may result from acting against his conscience is an evil that a decent government should always seek to avoid. It should require this, if at all, only when the necessity is clear. In circumstances of ambiguity, the benefit of the doubt should be resolved in favor of the individual and his conscience. Some radicals would do well to remember this point when they are tempted to self-righteous condemnation of all soldiers.

Christian Bay

Civil Disobedience: Prerequisite for Democracy in Mass Society

During a recent debate on the war in Vietnam an irate member of the audience demanded to know if I was in favor of civil disobedience. My reply was "Yes, on some occasions." He sat down in silence, with a broad grin. Nothing else that I said from then on was worth taking seriously, so far as he was concerned. I might as well have come out in favor of arson. And I am sure many in the audience felt as he did.

This widespread tendency to recoil from the very concept of disobedience, even passive and presumably nonviolent disobedience, in a society priding itself on its liberties, is a measure of the degree of stability, if not immunity to real social change, that has been achieved by the present socioeconomic and political system in the United States.

To the spiritual fathers of the American democracy, most notably John Locke and Thomas Jefferson, it seemed evident that any liberty-loving people should have the right to stage even a bloody revolution against a tyrannical government; by comparison, the remedy of nonviolent civil disobedience would seem a mild brew indeed.

Among the most forceful counter-norms, or norms tending to lead many of us to reject a priori the very thought of civil disobedience, is another Lockian principle: the sanctity of the

From Political Theory and Social Change, edited by David Spitz. Reprinted by Permission of the Publishers, Atherton Press, Inc. Copyright © 1967, Atherton Press, Inc., New York. All Rights Reserved. Christian Bay is Professor and Head of the Department of Political Science, University of Alberta (Edmonton). His writings in political theory include "Civil Disobedience" (International Encyclopedia of the Social Sciences, 1967) and The Structure of Freedom (New York, 1964, 1958).

rule of law. Spokesmen for our academic as well as our political and economic establishments are for obvious reasons far happier with this part of Locke's theory of civil government. Now, the classical writings of our democratic heritage, not unlike the Bible or the classical Marxist literature, can be used to prove the legitimacy of almost anything, and therefore, more critically viewed, of almost nothing. This point should be particularly poignant for those who have followed, during the last decades, developments in research and theory in the field of political behavior. For reasons of convenience and perhaps of habit as well, it has remained orthodox for our colleagues to proclaim their fealty to our democratic way of life (some, indeed, seem to feel that we are entitled to force other nations, too, to be guided by our example); and this fealty has remained unshaken, by and large, by the wealth of data that have come forth to demonstrate the wide and growing gulf between most of the classical ideals of democracy and what goes on in its name in today's mass societies.

Let us return to the part of our democratic heritage of particular concern here: the insistence on the sanctity of the rule of law. Now, a strong case for exalting the law (and indirectly, the lawyer) can be made from my own political ground of commitment to no system but to the sanctity of life, and the freedoms necessary for living,[1] *insofar as* laws (and lawyers) are to operate to protect all human lives, with priority for those most badly in need of protection. But to claim a corresponding sanctity for the laws that we have today, which, as in *every* state to a considerable extent, operate in the service of those who are privileged and influential in our socioeconomic order, seems to me to constitute an outright fraud at the expense of all the political innocents, unless one can claim for oneself, too, the innocence of not knowing any significant part of our modern behavioral literature.

At best a claim can be made that general obedience to the law is a lesser evil than general disobedience, which could well lead to much violence and conceivably even to a return to a Hobbesian state of nature. But this surely is a false issue, for no society has ever known either general obedience or general anarchy. Most of us have become trained, as generations of our ancestors have before us, to obey almost all laws almost by instinct, and certainly by habit if not by conviction. Others have become conditioned to breaking laws, frequently for reasons

[1] See below, section III. This position is developed at greater length in my *The Structure of Fredom* (New York, 1964, 1958).

of stunted growth on account of emotional as well as socio-economic deprivation.

Democracy has not yet been achieved, at least not in any real sense, as we shall see, in the modern world. If so, then the most familiar justifications demanding obedience to "democratically enacted" laws would seem to have no firm foundation. For the argument that every law represents the will of all, or the will of the majority, is empirically false; so is the argument that all laws aim at serving the common good. So is, as we have seen, the argument that disobedience to *any* law will promote anarchy.

Yet it obviously will not do, either, to assert that all laws can be ignored, or that any particular law can be obeyed or disobeyed as a matter of convenience. Nobody in his right mind will support all disobedience, however "civil," regardless of the issues involved. The question to be tackled, then, is not whether, but when and on what grounds civil disobedience can be justified.

My point of departure is essentially Locke's: Respect for the rule of law, or for the democratic processes that produce our laws, clearly must be contingent on and limited by standards for judging either the caliber of these processes or the purposes they promote; or, more precisely, by standards for judging how well these processes promote the purposes of politics. The *fundamental* purpose of politics, as I see it, is not to perpetuate a given political order but to protect human life and basic human rights. It cannot, if I may rub the point in, be the legitimizing purpose of politics or of government to perpetuate a political order that is democratic in name but in fact serves primarily to bolster privileges, not to equalize rights—as does ours and surely every other political order achieved till now.

The course of my argument in the remainder of this chapter will be as follows: first (II) comes a definition and a discussion of the concept of civil disobedience; next (III) a very brief statement of my own normative position, affirming the value of freedom and, only secondarily, of democracy as an aim; and then (IV) a discussion of the increasing chasm between current realities and the classical aims of democracy. I shall next (V) try to show how an expansion of the role of civil disobedience would, if anything could, turn the trend around, so that we might hope to move toward rather than away from democracy; and, finally (VI), I shall argue how essential civil disobedience is for the liberation of the individual as a political citizen—as a man and as a sharer of the burdens and benefits of politics. Since "real" democracy would require "real" citizens, this argument, too, will support the case for civil disobedience as a prerequisite for achieving something approximating democracy in modern societies.

II

"Civil disobedience" will here refer to any act or process of public defiance of a law or policy enforced by established governmental authorities, insofar as the action is premeditated, understood by the actor(s) to be illegal or of contested legality, carried out and persisted in for limited public ends, and by way of carefully chosen and limited means.

The notion of *disobedience* presupposes the concept of a norm to be disobeyed; typically a legal norm, but in any event a norm which is assumed by *some* people in power to be authoritative in the sense that transgressions would be expected to lead to punishment in one form or another. Disobedience can be active or passive; it can be a matter of doing what is prohibited or of failing to do what is required. But mere noncompliance is not enough; the action or nonaction must be openly insisted on if it is to qualify as civil disobedience, as the concept is interpreted here. For example, failure to vote in a country in which there is a legal obligation to vote does not in itself constitute civil disobedience; one would have to state in public that one does not intend to comply with the particular law; typically but not necessarily, one would publicly encourage others, too, to disobey.

The act of disobedience must be illegal, or at least be deemed illegal by powerful adversaries, and the actor must know this, if it is to be considered an act of civil disobedience.[2] Note the distinction between *conscientious objection* to military service and civil disobedience in countries that permit exemptions from otherwise obligatory service for reasons of conscience. The conscientious objector engages in civil disobedience only if he knowingly and explicitly objects to military service on grounds not recognized by the law, or in a country that makes no exceptions for reasons of conscience.

"Civil" is the more ambiguous of the two terms. At least five different meanings would appear plausible, and in this area it would seem reasonable to cast the net wide and consider each of the following meanings equally legitimate:

---

[2] See Harrop A. Freeman, "Civil Disobedience," in *Civil Disobedience,* Harrop A. Freeman *et al.* (Santa Barbara, 1966).

*1. The reference can be to a recognition of general obliga-
tions of citizenship and thus to the legitimacy of the existing
legal order as a whole; pains taken to limit defiance to a particular legal clause or policy, and/or to avoid violence, may
(but need not) be construed as an affirmation of general citizenship duties.*

*2. "Civil" can be taken to refer to the opposite of "military,"
in a broad sense. The customary stress on nonviolence may be
construed to signify either (a) a recognition of the state's claim
to monopoly with respect to legitimate use of physical violence,
or (b) a rejection of all physical violence as illegitimate or
morally wrong under all circumstances regardless of purpose.*

*3. "Civil" can refer to the opposite of "uncivil" or "uncivi-
lized"; acts of civil disobedience may seek to embody ideals of
citizenship or morality that will inspire adversaries and/or onlookers, hopefully, toward more civilized behavior, or behavior
more in harmony with the ideals that inspire a given campaign
of civil disobedience.*

*4. "Civil" can also be taken to refer to public as distinct
from private: as citizens we act in public. Acts of civil disobedience seek not only to affirm a principle in private, but to
call public attention to the view that a principle of moral importance is held to be violated by a law or a policy sanctioned
by public authorities.*

*5. "Civil" can suggest that the objective of obedience is to
institute changes in the political system, affecting not only one
individual's or group's liberties but the liberties of all citizens.
A religious sect persisting in outlawed practices of worship
(say, the Peyote cult among western American Indians, before
the U.S. Supreme Court came to its rescue) may insist only on
being left alone, or may at the same time consciously assert a
principle to the effect that other sects, too, should enjoy the
equivalent rights. Degrees of consciousness about the wider
implications of disobedient behavior are not well suited as
conceptual demarcation lines, however, and it would seem
most practical to include even very parochially motivated acts
of disobedience within the scope of the concept of civil disobedience.*

The ambiguities of the term "civil" are far from exhausted by
this brief list, but the five meanings presented are probably
among the more common. The chances are that most of those
who practice civil disobedience think of their behavior as "civil"
in a sense, whether articulated or not, which embraces more
than one of these associations, and perhaps others as well.

Returning now to the definition with which we began, let us note, first, that acts of civil disobedience may be illegal and legal at the same time, in cases of conflict of laws. For example, disobedience campaigns have been conducted against state segregation laws in the American South, in the belief that under the Federal Constitution such acts of disobedience will *eventually* be deemed legal in the Federal courts.

The ends of civil disobedience must be public and limited, it is suggested. The ostensible aim cannot, within the reference proposed, be a private or business advantage; it must have *some* reference to a conception of justice or the common good. (This is not to deny, of course, that individual motives for engaging in civil disobedience at times may be neurotic or narrowly self-seeking, consciously or subconsciously.) The proclaimed ends must be limited, too; they must fall short of seeking the complete abolition of the existing legal system; those who want a "nonviolent revolution" may engage in civil disobedience, but they, too, proclaim specific, limited ends each time. Also, according to the usage recommended here, the proclaimed aims must fall short of intending the physical or moral destruction of adversaries, even if at times a calculable risk of casualties may be tolerated. The ends of civil disobedience must be potentially acceptable to those in the *role* of adversaries even if to current adversaries they may be anathema on psychological grounds.

Above all, the proclaimed ends of civil disobedience, as the concept is understood here, must be formulated with a view to making them appear morally legitimate to onlookers and to the public. Educational objectives prompt most civil disobedience campaigns, and are never wholly absent. If a trade union violates the law to gain equality or justice, in some sense, for their members, we may speak of civil disobedience, but not if a key position in the economic system tempts a union to violate the law for the purpose of extorting unreasonable privileges in return for obeying the law. A civil disobedience campaign can aim at destroying privileges considered unjust, but not at abolishing the right to equal protection of an already underprivileged minority group.

The "carefully chosen and limited means" of civil disobedience are calculated to achieve maximum efficiency in promoting the ends and also maximum economy in seeking to reduce as much as possible the cost of the struggle in terms of suffering and deprivation. True, Gandhi at times stressed the value of bearing or even seeking suffering, but he always wanted to avoid inflicting suffering on his adversaries or on third parties.

"Civil disobedience" should be kept apart from "nonviolent action." The latter concept by definition rules out violent acts while the former does not as defined here.[3] Among some pacifist believers in civil disobedience it seems to be assumed that a complete commitment to nonviolence, even in the sense of avoiding the provocation of violence on the part of adversaries, is ethically superior to a more pragmatic attitude toward the possible use of violence. No such assumption is made here. "Carefully chosen and limited means" in the definition at the outset refers to choice of means rationally calculated to promote the limited ends. For many reasons it seems plausible that such rational calculation normally will suggest strenuous efforts toward either avoidance or reduction of violence. Civil disobedience activists and social scientists ought to be equally interested in research on the causation and consequences of violence and nonviolence under conditions of social conflict; the expansion of this type of knowledge would seem of crucial importance for achieving increasingly realistic calculations of the most effective and economic means toward the chosen ends of civil disobedience campaigns, and also toward determining when such campaigns are and when they are not likely to be successful.[4]

III

My normative position is essentially a simple one, even if it, like any other normative position, raises complex issues in application. Man and his world are, after all, almost infinitely complex.

The primary purpose of politics and of government, I hold, is to protect human life, and to expand the sphere of freedoms securely enjoyed by the individual—all individuals, mind you, on an equal basis. If all are equally entitled to grow and live in freedom, then those currently most deprived, in every unequal society, must have the highest priority claim on protection by the state.

A different way of stating the same fundamental commitment is to say that governmental coercion—and governments are by their nature coercive—can be justified only to the extent that

[3] An opposite view is adopted by Hugo A. Bedau, "On Civil Disobedience," *Journal of Philosophy*, LVIII (1961), 653–665; by Carl Cohen, "Essence and Ethics of Civil Disobedience," *The Nation*, CXCVIII (March 16, 1964), 257–262; and by Freeman, *op. cit.*

[4] My discussion in section II is adapted from my article, "Civil Disobedience," in the *International Encyclopedia of the Social Sciences* (1967).

it in fact serves to reduce coercion; and physical violence and oppressive economic deprivation prior to other, less debilitating restraints.

If I may anticipate for a moment my argument in the next section, no political order achieved so far, and that goes for our western ways of government, too, has been justifiable in these terms, if reasonably strictly construed. Demands on government arising from the lesser pains and frustrations suffered by influentials have generally taken precedence over demands arising, or demands that *should* arise, from the more debilitating indignities suffered by the poor and the inarticulate —whose very deprivation (with its cultural and psychological aspects) in fact prevents them, except in exceedingly rare revolutionary situations, almost unthinkable in the privilege-entrenched North American political order, from playing any political role at all.

According to the classical ideals, democracy should be a commonwealth of political equals, who are free to advance the common good and also their own good by constitutional means —that is, by legislation, brought about by processes designed to make sure that the laws express the well-deliberated desires *and* needs of the people. I feel committed to the aim of achieving democracy in this ideal sense because such a system would, to the extent that it could be brought about, be hospitable to respect for life and for human rights on the basis of equality. It would be easy to obey, presumably, the laws enacted in an ideal democracy. I shall argue, however, that this ideal cannot be realized, or even appreciably advanced, without a much expanded role for civil disobedience, given our present political order.

IV

Many leading political theorists would have us believe that western democracy as we know it in the United States and Britain today comes about as close to perfection as can any political order that fallible human beings can hope to attain. Some would have us dismiss as senseless "extremism" any radical questioning of the merits of our political *status quo,* and have even proclaimed an "end of ideology."

The classical ideals of democracy (excepting, most notably, the rule of law) have been all but abandoned by some of these theorists, or at any rate have been restructured so that their commitment to democracy has become a commitment to uphold what essentially amounts to the *status quo.*[5] Now, Bertrand Russell has remarked somewhere that the ruler of Hobbes's state would be far worse than Hobbes himself imagined if the citizens were to be as meek and submissive as Hobbes wanted. It is a fundamental part of my own thesis that every political order tends to become more tyrannical the more submissive its citizens are. Western democracies probably form no exception to this rule. In fact, as de Tocqueville saw, a peculiar hazard of democracies is that citizens are brought not only to comply with authority edicts but to regard them as binding morally as well, since they claim to represent the people's will.[6]

Democratic governments, like all others, seek to isolate and emasculate radical dissenters. If the domestic methods of democratic governments have been less extreme and less brutal than those of most dictator regimes, this probably reflects the usual stability of established democratic regimes, more so than any real appreciation of the value of dissent and dialogue about political fundamentals. True, the right to dissent is proclaimed as one of the many political virtues of our system, so that radical dissenters must be tolerated to a considerable extent, but there are many safeguards against permitting a fair hearing for their views. States and indeed all large organizations, as numerous studies from Michels'[7] on have shown, tend toward oligarchy and toward becoming instruments in the service of their respective oligarchies, at the expense of rank-and-file members.

The fact that the Anglo-Saxon democracies at most times have been able to dispense with the coarser methods of political repression, which in itself should be valued and indeed welcomed as a major achievement of our species, is at the same time a testimonial to the unlikelihood of any real changes taking place within the framework of established democracies. It is argued in our civics texts that the governing political parties in democracies tend to accept defeat at the polls gracefully because they know they may have a chance to come back to power again another time, if the rules of the democratic game are maintained. A fuller explanation of this willingness

---

[5] See, most notably, the last chapters in each of the following volumes: Bernard R. Berelson, Paul F. Lazarsfeld, and William N. McPhee, *Voting* (Chicago, 1954); Seymour Martin Lipset, *Political Man* (Garden City, 1960); and Gabriel A. Almond and Sidney Verba, *The Civic Culture* (Princeton, 1963).

[6] See Alexis de Tocqueville, *Democracy in America* (New York, 1954), Vintage Books ed., especially Vol. I, Chap. XV.

[7] Robert Michels, *Political Parties* (Glencoe, 1949, 1915).

to abide by election results surely should include, however, especially in the United States but in most other democracies as well, the fact that not much is really at stake in elections, generally speaking, for the major interests. The tradition of "negative government" prior to Franklin Roosevelt made the United States government unable, even if it had been willing, to reduce the amount of socioeconomic injustice; and even after Roosevelt, though a trend toward "positive government" has been growing, and perhaps culminating with the early years of Lyndon Johnson, the division of powers, the conservatism of the mass media, the enormity of the economic power of the privileged strata, and a host of other circumstances have made it virtually impossible to expect government to become an instrument, even in part, for the interests of the downtrodden, or for the enlargement of human rights at the expense of privileges.

True, there have been proclaimed programs of Square Deal, New Freedom, New Deal, Fair Deal, New Frontier, and more recently, the Great Society. In its affluence America has been able to keep most of its underprivileged from actual starvation and has increased the opportunities for gifted or energetic young people of all classes and races. This has been done perhaps in part with lofty motives but probably also in part to attract votes and also, especially in recent decades, out of concern for America's image abroad; surely also in part as a means to forestall or reduce the incidence of acts of desperation like race riots, industrial violence, and the like.

As Dahl has observed, democratic government, even an ideal democratic government, has no ready way of registering the intensity of feeling about public issues.[8] "One man, one vote" means equal weight for the concerned vote and the indifferent vote; for the intelligent and the foolish vote; for the vote in defense of elemental dignities of life and the vote in pursuit of added privileges for groups already favored. As David Truman has observed, however, in our democracy the potential existence of new groups and new coalitions does put some limits on what a government will do, even if elected by a wide margin.[9] But the trouble is, as most of our civic culture-championing pluralists fail to acknowledge, that the potential groups and coalitions a president or governor or mayor needs to worry about are rarely made up of the underprivileged—

---

[8] Robert A. Dahl, *A Preface to Democratic Theory* (Chicago, 1963), Phoenix Books ed., especially pp. 48–50, 90 ff., and 134–135.

[9] David B. Truman, *The Governmental Process* (New York, 1951), *passim.*

except, perhaps, if they are desperate to the point of being riot-prone, or intelligently led to the point of being prone to engage in civil disobedience. Normally, except in countries with strong political labor movements, the underprivileged have been made politically ineffective to the point of emasculation by their circumstances of life; coalitions of influentials and privileged are usually the only effective potential groups, and theirs are the interests that most executives prefer to appease rather than confront. As Murray Edelman puts it, in every conflict of interest between the many and the few, the many tend to be given symbolic gratification by way of democratic rhetoric and nice-sounding laws, while the few are given the tangible benefits, including a way of enforcing or not enforcing the laws that suit them.[10]

As Kolko and others have documented, the structure of economic wealth and power in this country has not been changed at all for the last half-century.[11] For all the slogans, Square Deal to Great Society, political influence remains in the hands of the economically strong while the poor remain inarticulate and largely without influence. Even the trade unions, though in the past they have served the economic interests of some categories of poor, are politically irrelevant today, having become guilds for the protection of their own shrinking number of members only, and uninterested in general issues of social justice, either domestically or internationally.

I am not out to castigate United States democracy as distinct from other democracies. My point is that the realities of western democracies keep stacking the cards in favor of the influentials and the privileged, who are therefore in a position to keep expanding their power and influence, while the underprivileged are becoming less and less able even to *think* and much less to act politically. The United States is merely the society in which this development has come the farthest, perhaps because the accumulation of private wealth has been and is larger than anywhere else. Ironically and significantly, the United States is also the modern nation most explicitly committed to the political principles of democracy, and has been for the longest time.

Democracy as we know it in the West has become, it would seem, an almost foolproof instrumentality to preserve the political and socioeconomic *status quo*. Orderly political change has become impracticable, I submit, except to the extent that

[10] Murray Edelman, *The Symbolic Uses of Politics* (Urbana, 1964).
[11] Gabriel Kolko, *Wealth and Power in America* (New York, 1962).

citizens free themselves from their prevailing belief that democracy has already been achieved, and that the laws enacted in their society therefore must be obeyed.

Under conditions of democratic pluralism, an uncritical submission to the rule of law means not only the shunning of violence but also, in effect, the abandonment of all intelligent effort to work effectively for changing the system. For it means agreeing in advance to live by rules in fact operating to forestall the development of democracy in any real sense. These are the rules by which the powerful have become more powerful, and the powerless more emasculated, while only the appearances of democracy have been maintained—an ever more challenging task, incidentally, but a task to which our media of communication and indoctrination so far have proved equal. Thus the discrepancies between our rose-colored perceptions of a government "by the people" and the stark realities of poverty and oppression have kept on growing.

Apparently, stability has kept growing, too. But for the human factors of alienation and desperation, this process might continue indefinitely. But social pathologies were bound to grow below the surface. Not only common crimes but also disorderly attacks against "the system" are likely to occur to an increasing extent. They will be destructive of lives and property but will fail to promote more democratic realities. They may well tempt the present and future American governments to engage in increasingly reckless violence abroad, as a means of seeking to recover national unity, to avoid the alternative of reducing the domestic socioeconomic injustice at the root of national disunity.

V

All organizational leaders are troubled by the fact that, as Philip Selznick has put it, human beings can be recalcitrant rather than pliant instruments in their designs.[12] This goes for statesmen and political leaders as well. Dictators may have to rely on secret police and recurrent terror to prevent revolutions and *coups d'état.* Democratic statesmen in some ways have an easier time of it, as we have seen, as they normally can rely on a broad consensus affirming not only a faith in democracy as an ideal but a belief that democracy has been achieved and that all democratically enacted laws must be obeyed, and that

[12] Philip Selznick, *TVA and the Grass Roots* (Berkeley, 1949), pp. 252–253.

whatever is done by democratically elected statesmen is legitimate. If Texas oilmen in effect are subsidized by all consumers of gasoline; if wars are fought to install aggressive satellite regimes on unwilling foreign nations; and so on: To the extent that people believe democracy has been achieved in their country they tend to become pliant rather than recalcitrant; they can be "managed."

Yet degrees of and extent of pliancy vary with issues and with events. Generally speaking, it is greater the less immediately the individual is affected by particular laws and policies—or rather, the less he is aware of being affected. A policy of supplying faraway foreign dictators with napalm and other achievements of American know-how for use against their rebellious compatriots is readily accepted as being in the national interest on the say-so of a president; it is only when sons and brothers and boy friends and husbands are sent off to kill and to risk their own lives far away that a policy may be questioned or even resisted.

On the other hand, these are precisely the situations in which strong feelings about the inherently superior righteousness of the "democratic cause" are most easily developed, and an intelligent dialogue made most difficult.[13] At such times public witness by way of disobedient acts may be the only way to convey to the average citizen even an *awareness* of the existence of strongly felt dissent. In times of hero-worship, resistance to jingo sentiments must perhaps be heroically bold in order to become visible, lest the average citizen either remain unaware of the existence of dissent or else confuse opposition to a war with cowardice.

Ironically, the most striking example of bold and also effective resistance to legislation in recent American history had little to do with heroism. I refer to our experiment with Prohibition during the twenties. Let me stress that this is not an example of civil disobedience as defined in this paper, for the Volstead Act was usually evaded in secret, even if Clarence Darrow is said to have referred to bootleggers as fighters for American liberties and to have predicted the erection of statues to Al Capone in many a public park.[14] My point is simply that

---

[13] "The first casualty in every shooting war is common sense, and the second is free and open discussion," wrote James Reston in The New York Times of February 12, 1965, five days after the beginning of the United States bombing of North Vietnam.

[14] See Harry Elmer Barnes, Prohibition Versus Civilization (New York, 1932), pp. 71–72.

our own recent history testifies to the power of popular defiance to change a law.[15] This result is more likely to come about, presumably, the more widespread and determined the defiance, civil or not, of a particular law.

But there is little prospect, alas, that laws and policies supported by far more powerful economic interests—say the Vietnam war, or the continuing inequities in our school systems—can be changed by way of disobedience, civil or not. It takes knowledge, independence of livelihood, and certain skills in interpersonal relations to engage in civil disobedience. True, something has been and more will perhaps be accomplished in race relations, a field in which some acts of disobedience against some southern state laws have become almost respectable elsewhere in the nation, under the impact of a growing concern for America's image abroad in its confrontation with communist nations. But issues of war and peace are beyond the reach of most people, as are even more the underlying issues of an economic system which depends on preparations for war and serves to bolster and expand privileges instead of rights.

Our only hope, as I see it, is in education—that is, education toward intellectual and political independence for the individual. We badly need an education that enables and encourages each young citizen to think for himself about the proper aims of government, or the state, and to judge by his own standards to what extent the government of his own nation pursues those aims. Only to that extent should it have his support. To the extent that his government pursues illegitimate aims, in his judgment, or employs means subversive of and menacing to the values a just government must uphold, civil disobedience may well be the right response if acts of protest within the framework of existing legislation would be ineffective or take too long a time.[16] Or it may be the wrong response. My point is that a man is not educated to the point of political responsibility unless he can and will make this decision for himself.

And the most elementary requirement of political education, thus conceived, is liberation from the prevailing pluralist demo-

---

[15] In fact, Mr. Darrow is quoted as claiming that this "nullification," as he calls it, is a traditional American way of changing the law, *ibid*. See also Clarence Darrow and Victor S. Yerros, *The Prohibition Mania* (New York, 1927).

[16] "What I have to do is see, at any rate, that I do not lend myself to the wrong which I condemn. As for adopting the ways which the state has provided for remedying the evil, I know not such ways. They take too much time, and a man's life will be gone." Henry David Thoreau, "Civil Disobedience," in his *Walden and Other Writings* (New York, 1950), Modern Library ed., pp. 644–645.

cratic myth, which claims a reverence for the Majesty of the Law—all laws!—on the ground that they have been democratically enacted. It is about time, I think, that political theorists, at least, free themselves from the stultifying grip of this myth, however convenient it may be as a rationalization for political inaction and, in my terms, political irresponsibility.

VI

In psychological terms, attention to the functions of political opinions for the individual provides an additional ground for arguing that the individual should strive to become sovereign in the choice of his fundamental political commitments.

We are aware today of the wide extent to which government policies as well as public opinion are the outcome of neurotic anxieties and fears, which are difficult to diagnose with exactitude and are more difficult still to cure. Modern psychologists and political scientists have established in a general way how political opinions are developed to meet personality needs, and how the individual's ability to cope with anxieties at various levels determines his capacity for rationality and a realistic long-term assessment of his own good as well as the common good.[17] Most people are neurotic and conformist as well as rational, in varying mixtures; enlightened, civilized policies are unlikely to emanate from democratic processes except to the extent that influential leaders become capable of farsighted rationality. Yet democratic competition for office and power almost invariably strengthens the neurotic aspects and lessens the rational aspects of political behavior; most electoral appeals, especially in times of crises when cool rationality is most needed, are directed to anxieties and paranoid sentiments rather than to reason or enlightened hopes.

The conscientious dissenter who cannot opt out of this system has no easy guide available for determining when to obey and when to disobey the law. There is no general solution to his dilemma, except to urge that he insist on protecting his own sanity and powers of reason, the autonomy of his own social conscience, and his own right to grow toward whatever moral stature or humanity he is capable of achieving. The criteria for concrete decisions to obey or disobey must depend

[17] See especially Daniel Katz, "The Functional Approach to the Study of Attitudes," *Public Opinion Quarterly*, XXIV (1960), 163–204; and M. Brewster Smith, Jerome S. Bruner and Robert W. White, *Opinions and Personality* (New York, 1964). In this section, too, several paragraphs are adapted from my forthcoming article for the *International Encyclopedia, op. cit.*

on the nature of each situation, anticipating by careful inquiry and reflection the consequences of either obeying or disobeying; but they must also depend on each moral dissenter's personality and beliefs, especially his beliefs concerning priorities among evils or among good causes.

This open-endedness of the modern dilemma of civil disobedience fits well with Albert Camus's theory of rebellion as an individual responsibility: While only an active and pressing social conscience can bring an individual to full life as a human being, his responsibility for action or inaction as a social being is strictly individual and lonesome. What is given, according to Camus, is only the immorality or inhumanity of a life of acquiescence in evil; he goes even further and argues that a commitment never to resist violence with violence amounts to such acquiescence, or "bourgeois nihilism." But he offers no guidelines for concrete political decisions.[18]

It is worth noting that legislation to legitimize certain grounds for conscientious objection to military service has tended to excuse only those who could prove they had no rational, politically articulate basis for objecting to becoming soldiers. In the United States as in other western democracies, only a religious basis for objection was recognized at the outset. To the extent that the courts or subsequent legislation have attempted to liberalize the rules, as has happened in the States and in other western nations, the tendency has been to lower the demand for evidence of church membership or religious orthodoxy of some kind, but to keep insisting that objection is no longer legitimate unless it remains apolitical, and condemns all past and future warfare indiscriminately.

For contrast, take Bertrand Russell's response when he was once chided on a British "Brain Trust" program over the BBC for having gone to jail for resisting World War I as a pacifist, while he had supported World War II, and now once again seemed prepared to object to the point of civil disobedience against preparations for a third world war. He said, "I want to pick my wars." This, in my view, is a simple but profound statement of responsible citizenship. What other human right can be more basic than the right to choose what cause, if any, to kill for and to die for?

Yet this, of course, is precisely the kind of human right that no government, dictatorial or democratic, wishes to grant. Legal recognition of politically motivated conscientious objection would hamper the pursuit of "tough" foreign policies in a way that religiously or pacifistically motivated objection

---

[18] Albert Camus, *The Rebel* (New York, 1958), especially Part V.

will not. Any government can limit the influence of saints; far
more dangerous to established privileges and policies are citizens who combine radical dissent with political know-how, or
saintly aims like social justice, freedom, or peace with flexible
tactics of protest inside and outside the law.

It seems to me that Camus's theory of rebellion has contributed at least two important thoughts toward a modern theory
of civil disobedience. One, which has been touched on already,
is his view that a rigid adherence to nonviolent means of protest in some situations may amount to acquiescence in continued violence and oppression. For him as for the orthodox
pacifists, violence is always the supreme evil; but to him it is
in part an empirical question whether violence in given situations can be overcome or reduced by entirely nonviolent
means (or, of course, by any combination of violent and non-
violent means). In my view and in Max Weber's terminology, he
argues that an ethics of a *priori* duty must be supplanted by
an ethics of responsibility, a responsibility for anticipating as
full a range of consequences of alternative means of action as
experience and research can establish, if there is time, before
deciding on a course of action, nonviolent or in part violent.

It is precisely because the consequences of revolutionary
activity are likely to be both violent and to a large extent un-
predictable (especially with respect to the extent and duration
of acts of violence) that Camus is so strongly in favor of rebellion, in his sense, as an alternative to revolution. His rebel
is the piecemeal revolutionary—the politically responsible citizen who is committed to fight violence and oppression by the
most *economic* means, i.e., he seeks to avoid the use of violence whenever possible, and above all to avoid the use of
remedies that could be worse than the present evil—worse in
terms of degrees and extent of violence suffered. With respect
to his aims, Camus's rebel is related to the revolutionary in that
he will be satisfied with nothing less than complete justice or a
complete end to oppression, but he is apt to be less confident
that this utopia can ever be fully realized. When it comes to his
choice of means, Camus's rebel is identical with the type of
responsible citizen extolled in these pages: the person who
honors not the Rule of Law so much as the Rule of Justice,
and who is prepared to support or commit civil disobedience
against oppressive government or legislation.

If Camus has helped draw the demarcation line and develop
the rationale for modern civil disobedience, as distinguished
from revolutionary activity,[19] he has also, as a second contri-

[19] To distinguish the two concepts is not to say that the same person or
movement cannot at the same time believe in civil disobedience and in

bution to a modern theory or civil disobedience, been the first to articulate the psychological necessity of being a rebel, or a citizen in principle prepared to commit civil disobedience against oppressive laws and policies, if one is to achieve one's full human stature. Rebellion, as a manifestation of revulsion against injustice, is to Camus an essential dimension of the free man's life; only men who remain too neurotic, too stymied to develop a consciousness of their own humanity, their own solidarity with all men, can remain indifferent and passive when confronted with victims or perpetrators of injustice. In a cruelly competitive society, perhaps most men remain stymied, or in Camus's sense less than fully human; yet at all times there have been rebels, believers in obedience to their own principles as a higher necessity than obedience to the powers that be, or the laws with which these powers guard their interests. I have argued in this chapter that only a good supply of such individuals can help us come closer to the achievement of democracy; Camus argues that only such qualities in a man can help him achieve his own individuality as well as his own humanity.

But in our time, with its unprecedented technology, capable of bureaucratizing acts of murder, and of dehumanizing men who may make decisions about life or death for millions of fellow human beings, the more effective education of an expanding supply of rebels may well be our civilization's last hope of survival. Without thousands of young men able and willing to disobey calls to contribute to moral monstrosities like, for example, American warfare in Vietnam, where is there hope that the bureaucratized, consensus-manufacturing forces of destruction of the modern superpowers—the Leviathans of our time—can be checked before our civilization becomes engulfed in a third world war?

In the name of democracy a new kind of servitude has developed in the West. Witness the hundreds of thousands of men who, educationally unequipped to judge for themselves, have been shipped to a far-off land to kill and perhaps die for what they cheerfully believe is the cause of democracy, or at any rate their own nation's best interests. And witness the many admonitions to dissenters against the war policy that they limit their protests to legal channels, again in the name of democracy, lest its rules of order be violated. Naturally, only

---

revolution. For example, one may have proximate or short-range aims to be served by civil disobedience and yet believe in eventual revolution; or one may believe in revolution as an ultimate resort if results of civil disobedience are too limited or too slow.

harmless, easily manageable forms of protest are desired; violence in contests for power at home is inveighed against with democratic moral fervor by the same leaders who look to violence as almost the only way to engage in contests for power abroad. Advocacy of force and violence at home is condemned, and so is advocacy *against* use of force and violence abroad, for both kinds of advocacy could menace the *status quo.*

Let me conclude by returning to the most fundamental argument of this essay: Governments exist for the purpose of establishing and defending human rights, with the most basic rights, like protection against violence and starvation, taking precedence over less basic rights. The common good, according to this view, hinges on the good of the least favored individuals, taking into account also the prospects for those not yet born.

This or any similar type of basis for political obligation directed to the ends of politics, which relegates not only democracy but also respect for the law in all its alleged majesty to the status of means, takes the vestiges of the role of subject out of the role of citizen. It substitutes an ethics of individual responsibility for the probable results of one's political behavior, including law-abiding as well as legally obligated behavior, for an ethics of duty to subordinate conscience, knowledge, and individual judgment to existing legal norms, government directives, or a majority vote.

The judgments at Nuremberg and the wide attention given to the Eichmann trial in Jerusalem have increased acceptance for the view that the autonomy of the individual conscience is a vital resource in our modern technological and bureaucratized civilization. The "essence of totalitarian government, and perhaps the nature of every bureaucracy," writes Hannah Arendt, "is to make functionaries and mere cogs in the administrative machinery out of men, and thus to dehumanize them."[20] "Each time we obey an order from higher up, without evaluating and judging it in moral terms, there is the Eichmann within ourselves bending his neck," writes a reviewer of Arendt's book, and further observes: "Eichmann was neither intellectually nor morally worse equipped than most people . . . his fault was that he did not feel personally responsible for what his government did. In this respect he is not unique."[21]

---

[20] *Eichmann in Jerusalem* (New York, 1963), p. 289.

[21] Jens Bjorneboe, "Eichmann i vaare hjerter" ("Eichmann in our hearts"), *Orientering,* Oslo (December 18, 1965).

The human race may never fully achieve democracy; no large nation is likely to come very close to this exacting ideal, although I believe it can be approximated in the foreseeable future in university communities and perhaps in some other local communities. What is important, if we value freedom for all on the basis of justice, is that we move toward rather than away from democracy. For this purpose our educational institutions must try to produce, I submit, men and women less like Eichmann, and more like his opposite, more like Camus's rebel. The rebel, or the believer in civil disobedience in the fight against oppression, is to this writer the model of the responsible citizen who wishes to promote democracy. What we don't need, in my view, and what we are now oversupplied with, is the cheerful, loyal, pliable, law-abiding, basically privatist type of citizen extolled not only in our high school civics texts but in our professional civic culture and end of ideology literature as well.

Mohandas K. Gandhi

Non-violence

My Task

426. In the past, non-co-operation has been deliberately expressed in violence to the evil-doer. I am endeavouring to show to my countrymen that violent non-co-operation only multiplies evil and that as evil can only be sustained by violence, withdrawal of support of evil requires complete abstention from violence. Non-violence implies voluntary submission to the penalty for non-co-operation with evil.—*YI, 23–3–22, 168.*

427. I am not a visionary. I claim to be a practical idealist. The religion of non-violence is not meant merely for the *rishis*[1] and saints. It is meant for the common people as well. Non-violence is the law of our species as violence is the law of the brute. The spirit lies dormant in the brute and he knows no law but that of physical might. The dignity of man requires obedience to a higher law—to the strength of the spirit.

I have therefore ventured to place before India the ancient law of self-sacrifice. For, *satyagraha*[2] and its off-shoots, non-co-operation and civil resistance, are nothing but new names for the law of suffering. The *rishis,* who discovered the law of

These passages are from *Selections from Gandhi,* Second Edition, edited by Professor Nirmal Kumar Bose, Navajivan Publishing House, 1957, pp. 149, 153–154, 156–157, 158–159, 163–167, and 170–172. They are reprinted here by permission of the Navajivan Trust, Copyright © 1957 the Navajivan Trust. The abbreviations at the ends of selections indicate their original sources: *YI-Young India* (1919–32); *Tagore-Young India* (1919–22), published in book form by Tagore and Company (1922); *H-*the *Harijan* (1933 onwards); *Nat.-Speeches and Writings of Mahatma Gandhi,* Fourth Edition, G. A. Natesan and Company; and *IHR-Hind Swaraj or Indian Home Rule,* 1944, Navajivan Publishing House. These brief selections can but give a hint of the richness of Gandhi's thought, and it is hoped that the reader will be stimulated to read more deeply into his writings. Mohandas K. Gandhi (1869–1948) needs little introduction. A truly outstanding religious and moral thinker, he was the leader in India's successful struggle for independence. His personal life was a testimony to the sincerity of his beliefs; and he was the most eloquent, articulate, and convincing spokesman for nonviolence that the world has known.

[1] [Holy Hindu sages, saints, or inspired poets. Ed.]

[2] [This has been variously rendered into English as love-force, truth-force, or soul-force. Ed.]

non-violence in the midst of violence, were greater geniuses than Newton. They were themselves greater warriors than Wellington. Having themselves known the use of arms, they realized their uselessness and taught a weary world that its salvation lay not through violence but through non-violence.—*YI*, 11–8–20, *Tagore, 712*. . . .

Moral Equivalent of War

439. Up to the year 1906, I simply relied on appeal to reason. I was a very industrious reformer. I was a good draftsman, as I always had a close grip of facts which in its turn was the necessary result of my meticulous regard for truth. But I found that reason failed to produce an impression when the critical moment arrived in South Africa. My people were excited; even a worm will and does sometimes turn—and there was talk of wreaking vengeance. I had then to choose between allying myself to violence or finding out some other method of meeting the crisis and stopping the rot and it came to me that we should refuse to obey legislation that was degrading and let them put us in jail if they liked. Thus came into being the moral equivalent of war. I was then a loyalist, because, I implicitly believed that the sum total of the activities of the British Empire was good for India and for humanity. Arriving in England soon after the outbreak of the war I plunged into it and later when I was forced to go to India as a result of the pleurisy that I had developed, I led a recruiting campaign at the risk of my life, and to the horror of some of my friends. The disillusionment came in 1919 after the passage of the Black Rowlatt Act and the refusal of the Government to give the simple elementary redress of proved wrongs that we had asked for. And so, in 1920, I became a rebel. Since then the conviction has been growing upon me, that things of fundamental importance to the people are not secured by reason alone but have to be purchased with their suffering. Suffering is the law of human beings; war is the law of the jungle. But suffering is infinitely more powerful than the law of the jungle for converting the opponent and opening his ears, which are otherwise shut, to the voice of reason. Nobody has probably drawn up more petitions or espoused more forlorn causes than I and I have come to this fundamental conclusion that if you want something really important to be done you must not merely satisfy the reason, you must move the heart also. The appeal of reason is more to the head but the penetration of the heart comes from suffering. It opens up the inner understanding in man. Suffering is the badge of the human race, not the sword.—*YI*, 5–11–31, 341.

The Essence of Non-violence

440. (1) Non-violence is the law of the human race and is infinitely greater than and superior to brute force.

(2) In the last resort it does not avail to those who do not possess a living faith in the God of Love.

(3) Non-violence affords the fullest protection to one's self-respect and sense of honour, but not always to possession of land or movable property, though its habitual practice does prove a better bulwark than the possession of armed men to defend them. Non-violence in the very nature of things is of no assistance in the defence of ill-gotten gains and immoral acts.

(4) Individuals and nations who would practise non-violence must be prepared to sacrifice (nations to the last man) their all except honour. It is therefore inconsistent with the possession of other people's countries, i. e. modern imperialism which is frankly based on force for its defence.

(5) Non-violence is a power which can be wielded equally by all—children, young men and women or grown up people, provided they have a living faith in the God of Love and have therefore equal love for all mankind. When non-violence is accepted as the law of life it must pervade the whole being and not be applied to isolated acts.

(6) It is a profound error to suppose that whilst the law is good enough for individuals it is not for masses of mankind. —*H*, 5–9–36, 236. . . .

Why Then not Kill Those Who Oppress Mankind?

446. No human being is so bad as to be beyond redemption, no human being is so perfect as to warrant his destroying him whom he wrongly considers to be wholly evil.—*YI*, 26–3–31, 49.

447. A *satyagrahi* must never forget the distinction between evil and the evil-doer. He must not harbour ill-will or bitterness against the latter. He may not even employ needlessly offensive language against the evil person, however unrelieved his evil might be. For it is an article of faith with every *satyagrahi* that there is no one so fallen in this world but can be converted by love. A *satyagrahi* will always try to overcome evil by good, anger by love, untruth by truth, *himsa* by *ahimsa*.[3] There is no other way of purging the world of evil.—*YI*, 8–8–29, 263.

---

[3] [*Himsa* is the causing of pain or death from anger or selfishness or with the intention to injure. To refrain from doing this is *ahimsa*. Ed.]

Absence of Hatred

448. I hold myself to be incapable of hating any being on earth. By a long course of prayerful discipline, I have ceased for over forty years to hate anybody. I know this is a big claim. Nevertheless, I make it in all humility. But I can and do hate evil wherever it exists. I hate the system of government that the British people have set up in India. I hate the ruthless exploitation of India even as I hate from the bottom of my heart the hideous system of untouchability for which millions of Hindus have made themselves responsible. But I do not hate the domineering Englishmen as I refuse to hate the domineering Hindus. I seek to reform them in all the loving ways that are open to me. My non-co-operation has its roots not in hatred, but in love. My personal religion peremptorily forbids me to hate anybody.—*YI*, 6–8–25, 272.

449. We can only win over the opponent by love, never by hate. Hate is the subtlest form of violence. We cannot be really non-violent and yet have hate in us.—*H*, 17–8–34, 212. . . .

Non-violent Resistance

457. My goal is friendship with the whole world and I can combine the greatest love with the greatest opposition to wrong.—*YI*, 10–3–20, *Tagore*, 139.

458. Non-violence is 'not a resignation from all real fighting against wickedness.' On the contrary, the non-violence of my conception is a more active and real fight against wickedness than retaliation whose very nature is to increase wickedness. I contemplate, a mental and therefore a moral opposition to immoralities. I seek entirely to blunt the edge of the tyrant's sword, not by putting up against it a sharper-edged weapon, but by disappointing his expectation that I would be offering physical resistance. The resistance of the soul that I should offer would elude him. It would at first dazzle him and at last compel recognition from him, which recognition would not humiliate him but would uplift him. It may be urged that this is an ideal state. And so it is.—*YI*, 8–10–25, 346. *cf.* 133, 386, 426, 551. . . .

Limitations of Violence

478. Hitherto I have given historical instances of bloodless non-co-operation. I will not insult the intelligence of the reader

by citing historical instances of non-co-operation combined with violence, but I am free to confess that there are on record as many successes as failures in violent non-co-operation.— *YI*, 4–8–20, *Tagore*, 320.

479. Revolutionary crime is intended to exert pressure. But it is the insane pressure of anger and ill-will. I contend that non-violent acts exert pressure far more effective than violent acts, for that pressure comes from goodwill and gentleness.— *YI*, 26–12–24, 420.

480. I do not blame the British. If we were weak in numbers as they are, we too would perhaps have resorted to the same methods as they are now employing. Terrorism and deception are weapons not of the strong but of the weak. The British are weak in numbers, we are weak in spite of our numbers. The result is that each is dragging the other down. It is common experience that Englishmen lose in character after residence in India and that Indians lose in courage and manliness by contact with Englishmen. This process of weakening is good neither for us two nations, nor for the world.—*YI*, 22–9–20, *Tagore*, 1092.

481. I object to violence because when it appears to do good, the good is only temporary; the evil it does is permanent. I do not believe that the killing of even every Englishman can do the slightest good to India. The millions will be just as badly off as they are today, if someone made it possible to kill off every Englishman tomorrow. The responsibility is more ours than that of the English for the present state of things. The English will be powerless to do evil if we will but be good. Hence my incessant emphasis on reform from within.—*YI*, 21–5–25, 178.

482. Good brought through force destroyed individuality. Only when the change was effected through the persuasive power of non-violent non-co-operation, i.e. love, could the foundation of individuality be preserved, and real, abiding progress be assured for the world.—*H*, 9–3–47, 58.

483. History teaches one that those who have, no doubt with honest motives, ousted the greedy by using brute force against them, have in their turn become a prey to the disease of the conquered.—*YI*, 6–5–26, 164.

To the Revolutionary

484. Those whom you seek to depose are better armed and infinitely better organized than you are. You may not care for your own lives, but you dare not disregard those of your coun-

trymen who have no desire to die a martyr's death.—*YI*, 25-12-24, 428.

485. From violence done to the foreign ruler, violence to our own people whom we may consider to be obstructing the country's progress is an easy natural step. Whatever may have been the result of violent activities in other countries and without reference to the philosophy of non-violence, it does not require much intellectual effort to see that if we resort to violence for ridding society of the many abuses which impede our progress, we shall add to our difficulties and postpone the day of freedom. The people unprepared for reform because unconvinced of their necessity will be maddened with rage over their coercion, and will seek the assistance of the foreigner in order to retaliate. Has not this been happening before our eyes for the past many years of which we have still painfully vivid recollections?—*YI*, 2-1-30, 4.

486. I hold that the world is sick of armed rebellions. I hold too that whatever may be true of other countries, a bloody revolution will not succeed in India. The masses will not respond. A movement in which masses have no active part can do no good to them. A successful bloody revolution can only mean further misery for the masses. For it would be still foreign rule for them. The non-violence I teach is active non-violence of the strongest. But the weakest can partake in it without becoming weaker. They can only be the stronger for having been in it. The masses are far bolder today than they ever were. A non-violent struggle necessarily involves construction on a mass scale. It cannot therefore lead to *tamas*[4] or darkness or inertia. It means a quickening of the national life. That movement is still going on silently, almost imperceptibly, but none the less surely.

I do not deny the revolutionary's heroism and sacrifice. But heroism and sacrifice in a bad cause are so much waste of splendid energy and hurt the good cause by drawing away attention from it by the glamour of the misused heroism and sacrifice in a bad cause.

I am not ashamed to stand erect before the heroic and self-sacrificing revolutionary because I am able to pit an equal measure of non-violent men's heroism and sacrifice untarnished by the blood of the innocent. Self-sacrifice of one innocent man is a million times more potent than the sacrifice of

---

[4] [The darkness, inertia, or dullness that constitutes one of the three primal qualities or elements of matter according to Sankhya philosophy. Ed.]

million men who die in the act of killing others. The willing
sacrifice of the innocent is the most powerful retort to insolent
tyranny that has yet been conceived by God or man.—*YI,*
12–2–25, 60.

Non-violence the Swifter Way

487. The spiritual weapon of self-purification, intangible as it
seems, is the most potent means of revolutionizing one's environment and loosening external shackles. It works subtly
and invisibly; it is an intense process though it might often
seem a weary and long-drawn process, it is the straightest way
to liberation, the surest and quickest and no effort can be too
great for it. What it requires is faith—an unshakable mountain-
like faith that flinches from nothing.

488. You need not be afraid that the method of non-violence
is a slow long-drawn out process. It is the swiftest the world
has seen, for it is the surest.—*YI,* 30–4–25, 153.

489. India's freedom is assured if she has patience. That
way will be found to be the shortest even though it may appear
to be the longest to our impatient nature. The way of peace in-
sures internal growth and stability.—*YI,* 20–5–26, 184.

Non-violence Also the Nobler Way

490. I am more concerned in preventing the brutalization of
human nature than in the prevention of the sufferings of my own
people. I know that people who voluntarily undergo a course
of suffering raise themselves and the whole of humanity; but
I also know that people who become brutalized in their desperate efforts to get victory over their opponents or to exploit
weaker nations or weaker men, not only drag down themselves
but mankind also. And it cannot be a matter of pleasure to me
or anyone else to see human nature dragged to the mire. If we
are all sons of the same God and partake of the same divine
essence, we must partake of the sin of every person whether
he belongs to us or to another race. You can understand how
repugnant it must be to invoke the beast in any human being,
how much more so in Englishmen, among whom I count numerous friends. I invite you all to give all the help that you can
in the endeavour that I am making.—*YI,* 29–10–31, 325.

491. The doctrine of violence has reference only to the doing of injury by one to another. Suffering injury in one's own
person is on the contrary of the essence of non-violence and
is the chosen substitute for violence to others. It is not because

I value life low that I can countenance with joy thousands voluntarily losing their lives for *satyagraha,* but because I know that it results in the long run in the least loss of life and what is more, it ennobles those who lose their lives and morally enriches the world for their sacrifice.—*YI,* 8–10–25, 345.

492. The method of passive resistance is the clearest and safest, because, if the cause is not true, it is the resisters, and they alone, who suffer.—*Nat.* 305.

493. Passive resistance is an all-sided sword; it can be used anyhow; it blesses him who uses it and him against whom it is used.—*IHR,* 48.

494. The beauty of *satyagraha,* of which non-co-operation is but a chapter, is that it is available to either side in a fight; that it has checks that automatically work for the vindication of truth and justice for that side, whichever it may be, that has truth and justice in preponderating measure. It is as powerful and faithful a weapon in the hand of the capitalist as in that of the labourer. It is as powerful in the hands of the government, as in that of the people, and will bring victory to the government, if people are misguided or unjust, at it will win the battle for the people if the government be in the wrong. Quick disorganization and defeat are bound to be the fate of bolstered up cases and artificial agitations, if the battle is fought with *satyagraha* weapons. Suppose the people are unfit to rule themselves, or are unwilling to sacrifice for a cause, then, no amount of noise will bring them victory in non-co-operation. —*YI,* 23–6–20, *Tagore,* 42. . . .

Can Aggression Be Stopped by Non-violence?

498. *Q.* How could a disarmed neutral country allow other nations to be destroyed? But for our army which was waiting ready at our frontier during the last war we should have been ruined.

A. At the risk of being considered a visionary or a fool I must answer this question in the only manner I know. It would be cowardly of a neutral country to allow an army to devastate a neighbouring country. But there are two ways in common between soldiers of war and soldiers of non-violence, and if I had been a citizen of Switzerland and a President of the Federal State what I would have done would be to refuse passage to the invading army by refusing all supplies. Secondly, by re-enacting a Thermopylae in Switzerland, you would have presented a living wall of men and women and children and invited the invaders to walk over your corpses. You may say that such a thing is beyond human experience and endurance. I say that it is not so. It was quite possible. Last year in Gujarat, women stood *lathi*[5] charges unflinchingly and in Peshawar thousands stood hails of bullets without resorting to violence. Imagine these men and women staying in front of an army requiring a safe passage to another country. The army would be brutal enough to walk over them, you might say. I would then say you will still have done your duty by allowing yourselves to be annihilated. An army that dares to pass over the corpses of innocent men and women would not be able to repeat that experiment. You may, if you wish, refuse to believe in such courage on the part of the masses of men and women; but then you would have to admit that non-violence is made of sterner stuff. It was never conceived as a weapon of the weak, but of the stoutest hearts.

Q. Is it open to a soldier to fire in the air and avoid violence?

A. A soldier who having enlisted himself flattered himself that he was avoiding violence by shooting in the air did no credit to his courage or to his creed of non-violence. In my scheme of things, such a man would be held guilty of untruth and cowardice both—cowardice in that in order to escape punishment he enlisted, and untruth in that he enlisted to serve as soldier and did not fire as expected. Such a thing discredits the cause of waging war against war. The war-resisters have to be like Caesar's wife—above suspicion. Their strength lies in absolute adherence to the morality of the question.—*YI,* 31–12–31, 427.

499. Indeed the weakest State can render itself immune from attack if it learns the art of non-violence. But a small State, no matter how powerfully armed it is, cannot exist in the midst of a powerful combination of well-armed States. It has to be absorbed by or be under the protection of one of the members of such a combination.—*H,* 7–10–39, 293.

500. Whatever Hitler may ultimately prove to be, we know what Hitlerism has come to mean. It means naked, ruthless force reduced to an exact science and worked with scientific precision. In its effect it becomes almost irresistible.

Hitlerism will never be defeated by counter-Hitlerism. It can only breed superior Hitlerism raised to n^{th} degree. What is going on before your eyes is the demonstration of the futility of violence as also of Hitlerism.

What will Hitler do with his victory? Can he digest so much

---

5 [A weapon used by police for riot control. Ed.]

power? Personally he will go as empty-handed as his not very remote predecessor Alexander. For the Germans he will have left not the pleasure of owning a mighty empire but the burden of sustaining its crushing weight. For they will not be able to hold all the conquered nations in perpetual subjection. And I doubt if the Germans of future generations will entertain unadulterated pride in the deeds fo which Hitlerism will be deemed responsible. They will honour Herr Hitler as a genius, as a brave man, a matchless organizer and much more. But I should hope that the Germans of the future will have learnt the art of discrimination even about their heroes. Anyway I think it will be allowed that all the blood that has been spilled by Hitler has added not a millionth part of an inch to the world's moral stature.

As against this imagine the state of Europe today if the Czechs, the Poles, the Norwegians, the French and the English had all said to Hitler: 'You need not make your scientific preparation for destruction. We will meet your violence with non-violence. You will therefore be able to destroy our non-violent army without tanks, battleships and airships.' It may be retorted that the only difference would be that Hitler would have got without fighting what he has gained after a bloody fight. Exactly. The history of Europe would then have been written differently. Possession might (but only might) have been taken under non-violent resistance, as it has been taken now after perpetration of untold barbarities. Under non-violence, only those would have been killed who had trained themselves to be killed, if need be, but without killing anyone and without bearing malice towards anybody. I dare say that in that case Europe would have added several inches to its moral stature. And in the end I expect it is moral worth that will count. All else is dross.—*H, 22-6-40, 172.*

Howard Zinn

A Fallacy on Law and Order: That Civil Disobedience Must Be Absolutely Nonviolent

Mr. Fortas reminds us that Gandhi, Martin Luther King, and Thoreau, did not believe in violence. He then says: "This is civil disobedience in a great tradition. It is peaceful, nonviolent disobedience of laws which are themselves unjust and which the protester challenges as invalid and unconstitutional." I deal elsewhere in this essay[1] with the other conditions he imposes; here I will concentrate on "peaceful, nonviolent . . ." If Fortas wants to define civil disobedience as having this limitation, this is his right. But others need not accept his definition, and indeed have not.

I would define civil disobedience more broadly, as "the deliberate violation of law for a vital social purpose." Unlike Fortas' definition, this would include violating laws which are immoral whether constitutional or not, and laws which themselves are not at issue as well as those that are. It would leave open the question of the *means* of disobedience, but with two

From *Disobedience and Democracy* by Howard Zinn. Copyright © 1968 by Howard Zinn. Reprinted by permission of Random House, Inc. Additional territory rights granted by Sterling Lord Agency. Zinn's book (subtitled *Nine Fallacies on Law and Order*) is structured as a reply to Abe Fortas' *Concerning Dissent and Civil Disobedience*. Fortas is primarily concerned to claim the following: (1) citizens have an obligation to obey laws even when they disapprove of them; (2) legal channels for the redress of grievances in America are sufficiently adequate to undercut present-day justifications for civil disobedience; and (3) under no circumstances is violence justified in civil disobedience. No selection from Fortas has been included here because other essays in the collection argue for these points: Rawls (1), Hook (1, 2, and 3), and Gandhi (3). Quotations from *Concerning Dissent and Civil Disobedience* by Abe Fortas © 1968 by Abe Fortas. Reprinted by arrangement with the New American Library, Inc., New York. Howard Zinn is Professor of Government at Boston University. His many publications include the following books: *SNCC, The New Abolitionists* (1964), *Vietnam: The Logic of Withdrawal* (1967), and *The Politics of History* (1970).

[1] [See pp. 8–26 and pp. 32–38 of *Disobedience and Democracy*. Ed.]

thoughts in mind: 1. that one of the moral principles guiding the advocate of civil disobedience is his belief that a nonviolent world is one of his ends, and that nonviolence is more desirable than violence as a means; 2. that in the inevitable tension accompanying the transition from a violent world to a nonviolent one, the choice of means will almost never be pure, and will involve such complexities that the simple distinction between violence and nonviolence does not suffice as a guide.

Such a broader definition has strong support among those who have theorized about civil disobedience, as well as those who have engaged in it. The political philosopher Christian Bay, commissioned to write the article on Civil Disobedience for the *International Encyclopedia of the Social Sciences,* has written: " 'Civil disobedience' should be kept apart from 'nonviolent action.' The latter concept by definition rules out violent acts while the former does not, as defined here." Bay does believe that "carefully chosen and limited means" should be part of the definition of civil disobedience but insists that the key to means is "increasingly realistic calculations of the most effective and economic means toward the chosen ends of civil disobedience campaigns."

Albert Camus spoke in *The Rebel* of the absurdities in which we are trapped, where the very acts with which we seek to do good cannot escape the imperfections of the world we are trying to change. And so the rebel's "only virtue will lie in never yielding to the impulse to allow himself to be engulfed in the shadows that surround him, and in obstinately dragging the chains of evil, with which he is bound, toward the light of good." In this situation, he recognizes that at certain times, for certain reasons, some departure from absolute nonviolence may be necessary. Camus says the rebel must somehow find his solutions along a spectrum of means between two impossible borders:

Absolute non-violence is the negative basis of slavery and its acts of violence; systematic violence positively destroys the living community and the existence we receive from it. To be fruitful, these two ideas must establish final limits.

The abolitionists in pre-Civil War America, although dominated by nonviolent spokesmen like Garrison, also included advocates of violent deeds. Before 1850, the use of violence was confined mostly to the victims of slavery themselves in various insurrections. After 1850, white abolitionists, beginning to think that perhaps slavery could not be dislodged by peaceful methods, looked more favorably on statements like that of Frederick Douglass, writing June 2, 1854, in *Frederick Douglass' Paper:* "Every slavehunter who meets a bloody death in his infernal business is an argument in favor of the manhood of our race."

Fortas points to Thoreau, accurately, as a believer in nonviolence. Yet, when John Brown carried out his attempt to seize arms and instigate a slave rebellion, Thoreau defended him, in "A Plea for Captain John Brown," delivered in Concord and Boston a month before the execution:

'Served him right'—'A dangerous man'—'He is undoubtedly insane.' So they proceed to live their sane, and wise, and altogether admirable lives. . . . It was Brown's peculiar doctrine that a man has a perfect right to interfere by force with the slaveholder, in order to rescue the slave. I agree with him. . . .

Emerson agreed too, speaking of John Brown in Salem; "All gentlemen, of course, are on his side."

Gandhi himself wrote at certain times (1919 and 1921) in *Young India:* "No rules can tell us how this disobedience may be done and by whom, when and where, nor can they tell us which laws foster untruth. It is only experience that can guide us. . . ." And: "I do believe that where there is only a choice between cowardice and violence I would advise violence." This is not to deny that Gandhi was preeminently a believer in nonviolence, but to emphasize that his belief was based on the specific conditions of India in his time, and his emphasis was on pragmatism—letting circumstances and results determine tactics.

Certainly Reinhold Niebuhr interprets Gandhi this way in *Moral Man and Immoral Society,* and while himself advocating nonviolence for the Negro (this was the 1930's) as a practical matter, says:

The differences between violent and non-violent methods of coercion and resistance are not so absolute that it would be possible to regard violence as a morally impossible instrument of social change. . . . The advantages of non-violent methods are very great but they must be pragmatically considered in the light of circumstances.

My point in all this is not at all to establish a case for violence. To me one of the cardinal principles in any moral code is the reduction and elimination of violence. The burden of proof in any argument about social tactics should rest on that person who wants to stray from nonviolence. What I have tried to show is that the problem of tactics in civil disobedience is far more complicated than Mr. Fortas leads us to believe with his easy and righteous dismissal of violence.

What is required is that a set of distinctions be made which will enable us to be more precise in evaluating the problem of violence and nonviolence in civil disobedience. If Mr. Fortas wants to say that civil disobedience must limit itself to nonviolent activity, then he is required to explain the moral principles which say why this should be so. This he does not do; he merely asserts his position.

One soon begins to see why he stays away from a careful discussion. When we attempt to put together a set of principles on violence from the scattered remarks in his essay, contradictions and simplifications appear.

For instance, we might conclude from Mr. Fortas' absolute insistence on nonviolence and civil disobedience that it requires no explanation because in his view nonviolence is an ultimate value, *the* supreme value, and therefore self-justifying. But if this were Mr. Fortas' belief, we would expect him to oppose violence in all forms, all the time. We know this is not his credo, because, as we shall see later in more detail, he defends the massive violence of a number of wars.

If some violence is acceptable and other violence is not, then we must have "a principle, a code, a theory" to give us the grounds, to tell us why it is sometimes justifiable in international relations (as by the United States in Korea and Vietnam, according to Mr. Fortas), and never justifiable by groups within a nation (let us say, to cite actions Mr. Fortas is against: burners of draft cards, or breakers of windows at the Pentagon). But Mr. Fortas gives us no such guide.

Let us try to find some principle on which he could possibly justify his absolute prohibition of violence in civil disobedience and his rather easy support of it in international affairs. Perhaps *the importance of the issue* at stake might be one test. There is good reason (as I pointed out earlier, citing Bay, Camus, Niebuhr, Douglass, Thoreau, Gandhi) for not being absolutist in adhering to nonviolence. There are other human values besides peace—so that it is possible to conceive of situations where a disturbance of the peace is justifiable if it results in some massive improvement of the human condition for large numbers of people.

Indeed, Mr. Fortas seems to invoke such a principle when he speaks of the Korean War:

It cost us over 150,000 casualties. [It cost the Koreans a million casualties.] It took us more than three years. But I think it is fairly universal opinion in the Western world that the war was a necessary action; that if we had not taken on the sad and heavy burden of repelling the invasion of South Korea, no one else would or could have done so; and that the consequences of our default would have been greatly to increase the peril to the non-Communist nations of the world—including ourselves.

But if Mr. Fortas justifies violence in Korea because he believes a vital issue was at stake, he cannot with any logical consistency rule out the possibility that for some aggrieved groups in the United States, *some* issues might be important enough to justify some degree of violence.

This brings us to another necessary element of any moral code on violence and nonviolence. Would not any reasonable code have to weigh the *degree* of violence used in any case against the *importance* of the issue at stake? Thus, a massive amount of violence for a small or dubious reason would be harder to justify than a small amount of violence for an important and a clear reason.

We can see now why Fortas might not want to discuss any test by which one could rationally, if roughly, decide when violence might be justified. That would show him supporting the enormous violence of the Korean war for rather hazy international objectives: Was the situation in Korea, North or South, any better because the war was fought? Was the situation in Asia as a whole improved? Did Korea "show" the Communists that they must not seek to unify divided nations by force? Yet we find him opposing any departure from nonviolence connected with removing an obvious, gross injustice, the plight of the black person in America.

One of the reasons Mr. Fortas can get away with his easy dismissal of violence in civil disobedience is that the term "violence," if undefined, can mean anything the reader conjures up in his mind, from breaking a window to dropping a bomb. If he got more specific, and set up a standard which took *degrees* of violence into account, wars might be much harder to justify than local acts of civil disobedience.

There is another point which he slides over—one which is very important, I believe, in drawing up a set of principles on violence and nonviolence in civil disobedience. That is the distinction between violence to people and violence to things; destruction of life, or destruction of property. Mr. Fortas lumps them together as if they were equally reprehensible. He says in his concluding section: "Violence must not be tolerated; damage to persons or property is intolerable." He does not differentiate, in this general prohibition. Yet, once Mr. Fortas has opened the door to *any* distinction on the problem of violence (which he does, once he allows the violence of war), he should not fail to discriminate between people and things. Surely that is one of the cardinal rules in any humanistic philosophy. A fixed devotion to property as something holy, when carried to its extreme, leads policemen to shoot to death black people who are taking *things* from stores.

At one point, Mr. Fortas mentions as intolerable "breaking windows in the Pentagon." Surely that is a mild form of violence compared to the violence a window-breaker might be protesting against—the decisions made in the Pentagon which result in thousands of American men returning to their families in coffins. Should property be so sacred that it must not be despoiled even where there is a need to protest mass murder? Or to express outrage at some great injustice? Should that act of violence in which several Baltimore clergymen burned some draft board records to protest killing in Vietnam be declared wrong, while the act of soldiers burning a peasant village (to see what this means, read Jonathan Schell's book, *The Village of Ben Suc*) is not?

Can we conceive that it might be necessary on certain occasions to depreciate, despoil, occupy or appropriate some piece of property to call attention to some grievous evil—as a wife might find it necessary on occasion to break a dish in anger to awaken her husband to the fact that her rights have been violated? In any case, isn't this distinction between property rights and human rights important in considering whether civil disobedience must always be nonviolent?

Fortas says: "An organized society cannot and will not long endure personal and property damage, whatever the reason, context, or occasion." If he can find a reason, context, occasion to justify 150,000 dead Americans and 1,000,000 dead Koreans, can he find no occasion for "property damage" as a protest by people desperately poor or viciously maltreated or facing arbitrary dispatch to an immoral war?

A carefully drawn moral code on violence in civil disobedience should also consider whether the disorder or violence is controlled or indiscriminate. Crowds rampaging through a city may or may not have a useful effect in changing a situation, but that is not civil disobedience, which involves the deliberate, organized use of power. Violence, no matter how important the cause, becomes unpardonable the more it becomes indiscriminate; hence war, even for "good" reasons, is very hard to justify in these days of high-level bombing and long-range artillery.

Violence might be justifiable as it approaches the focusing and control of surgery. Self-defense is by its nature focused, because it is counterviolence directed only at a perpetrator of violence. (Of course, it has been defined so loosely as to allow all sorts of aggressive actions.) Planned acts of violence in an enormously important cause (the Resistance against Hitler may be an example) could be justifiable. Revolutionary warfare, the more it is aimed carefully at either a foreign controlling power, or a local tyrannical elite, may be morally defensible.

All this is to suggest what criteria need to be kept in mind whenever civil disobedience, in situations of urgency where very vital issues are at stake, and other means have been exhausted, may move from mild actions, to disorder, to overt violence: it would have to be guarded, limited, aimed carefully at the source of injustice, and preferably directed against property rather than people.

There are two reasons for such criteria. One is the moral reason: that violence is in itself an evil, and so can only be justified in those circumstances where it is a last resort in eliminating a greater evil, or in self-defense. The other is the reason of effectiveness: The purpose of civil disobedience is to communicate to others, and indiscriminate violence turns people (rightly) away.

Another point seems so self-evident that Jefferson called it just that in the Declaration of Independence: the idea that all men are created equal. This means that violence to any man must be equated with violence to any other. I say it is self-evident, but we do not act as if it is. We do not react the same to the headline "200 Communists killed today" as we react to "200 Americans killed today." We don't react the same way to 5000 dying in an earthquake in Peru, as to five killed in an auto crash downtown. There are "in" people and "out" people in our normal equations, and they are *not* equal. This is important in considering rules for disorder in civil disobedience; to be aware of this guards against the "natural" reaction—that an egg thrown at one American by another becomes more outrageous than a bomb dropped on Vietnamese.

Likewise, there is a "here" and "there," with no equality between them. It helps explain why the President of the United States may express outrage at a disorderly act of civil disobedience at home, and say nothing about some large act of terror abroad. If it is happening to *them,* we consider the disorder more reasonable than if it is happening to us. At home, this is shown in the fact that the death of blacks is not as disturbing to white Americans as the death of whites, that *actual* destruction in the ghetto is much more tolerable than the *thought* of destruction in the suburbs. The disorder of civil disobedience, because it is directed at our own officials, or our own institutions, therefore is far less tolerated than a much greater disorder, directed at others. But we should insist on the principle that all victims are created equal.

There is an argument for excluding violence from civil disobedience which Justice Fortas does make: that it is impractical; it is not effective in achieving its ends. "But widespread violence—whether it is civil disobedience, or street riots, or guerrilla warfare—will, I am persuaded, lead to repression." He makes this argument specifically with regard to the Negro, saying: "The Negroes have gained much by the strength of their protests and the massiveness of their demonstrations. Even their riots—much as we dislike acknowledging it—produced some satisfaction of their demands. . . . But the reaction to repeated acts of violence may be repression instead of remedy."

By Fortas' own admission, he cannot clearly prove his case for the practicality of nonviolence by the Negro in the United States ("riots . . . produced some satisfaction," he says; and while the result "may" be repression, this is not certain). The evidence so far is that nonviolent tactics have only produced marginal benefits for America's 20 million black people. If there is uncertainty about the practicality of nonviolence in the one example Fortas does give—the race issue—how is he justified in making nonviolence an absolute condition for civil disobedience on *all* issues?

The historical evidence is far from supporting the idea that violence is not effective in producing change. True, there are many instances when violence is completely ineffective, and does result only in repression. But there are other instances when it does seem to bring results. Shays' armed uprising of 1786 had direct effect on tax reform in the Pennsylvania legislature, but more important, an influence on the Constitutional Convention which we cannot begin to measure. Violent labor struggles of the 1930's brought significant gains for labor. Not until Negro demonstrations resulted in violence did the national government begin to work seriously on civil rights legislation. No public statement on the race question has had as much impact as the Kerner Commission report, the direct result of outbreaks of violence in the ghettos.

Barrington Moore's elaborate study of modern social change (*Social Origins of Dictatorship and Democracy*) concludes that violence is an important factor in change. He points out that presumably "peaceful" transitions to modernism, as in England and the United States, really involved large amounts of violence. Certainly this country has not progressed purely on the basis of nonviolent constitutional development. We do not know what effect John Brown's violence had in that complex of events leading to the end of slavery, but it is certainly an open question. Independence, emancipation, labor unions— these basic elements in the development of American democracy all involved violent actions by aggrieved persons.

My point is not that violence is unquestionably an effective method of reforming a society; it seems to me we would have to be extremely careful in adapting historical experience to the conditions of the United States. Each situation in the world is unique and requires unique combinations of tactics. I insist only that the question is so open, so complex, that it would be foolish to rule out at the start, for all times and conditions, all of the vast range of possible tactics beyond strict nonviolence.

Mr. Fortas has given us grounds neither for the immorality, nor for the impracticality of violence in civil disobedience. What remains then to say which is so commonly conceded that it can be a basis for excluding violence absolutely as a form of civil disobedience? Only that it is illegal. We are back to our starting point—Fortas as a Legalist.

The argument of legality, however, is bound to get Mr. Fortas into difficulty—because he does support wars even when they involve violations of international law. He has been, it is known, a close adviser to President Johnson in the conduct of the Vietnam war, which has involved violating the U.N. Charter, the SEATO Treaty, the Kellogg-Briand Pact, and other treaties, all of which, by the U.S. Constitution, are "the highest law of the land." . . .[2]

However, there is no international body to punish the United States for its large act of civil disobedience. Is illegal violence then permissible when it is done by a great power, impervious to retaliation—and impermissible when done by vulnerable dissenters inside that nation? This would not be a moral code but an assertion of realpolitik—might makes right. If this (the legal argument) is behind Fortas' apparent inconsistency on violence, it has not carried us any closer to what he promised: "a principle, a code, a theory" to guide our actions.

[2] [See pp. 68–87 of *Disobedience and Democracy*. Ed.]

Ronald Dworkin

On not Prosecuting Civil Disobedience

112   How should the government deal with those who disobey the
draft laws out of conscience? Many people think the answer is
obvious: The government must prosecute the dissenters, and
if they are convicted it must punish them. Some people reach
this conclusion easily, because they hold the mindless view
that conscientious disobedience is the same as lawlessness.
They think that the dissenters are anarchists who must be punished before their corruption spreads. Many lawyers and in-
tellectuals come to the same conclusion, however, on what
looks like a more sophisticated argument. They recognize that
disobedience to law may be *morally* justified, but they insist
that it cannot be *legally* justified, and they think that it follows
from this truism that the law must be enforced. Erwin Griswold,
the Solicitor General of the United States, and the former Dean
of the Harvard Law School, appears to have adopted this view
in a recent statement. "[It] is of the essence of law," he said,
"that it is equally applied to all, that it binds all alike, irrespective of personal motive. For this reason, one who contemplates
civil disobedience out of moral conviction should not be surprised and must not be bitter if a criminal conviction ensues.
And he must accept the fact that organized society cannot endure on any other basis."

The New York Times applauded that statement. A thousand
faculty members of several universities had signed a *Times*
advertisement calling on the Justice Department to quash the
indictments of the Rev. William Sloane Coffin, Dr. Benjamin
Spock, Marcus Raskin, Mitchell Goodman, and Michael Ferber,
for conspiring to counsel various draft offenses. The *Times*
said that the request to quash the indictments "confused moral
rights with legal responsibilities."

Reprinted with permission from *The New York Review of Books*. Copyright
© 1968 The New York Review. Ronald Dworkin is Professor of Jurisprudence
in the University of Oxford and a Fellow of University College. He was
formerly Professor of Law and Master of Trumbull College at Yale. His
publications include "Lord Devlin and the Enforcement of Morals" (*Yale
Law Journal*, 76[1966], 986–1005) and "The Model of Rules" (*University of
Chicago Law Review*, 35[1967], 14–46).

But the argument that, because the government believes a man has committed a crime, it must prosecute him is much weaker than it seems. Society "cannot endure" if it tolerates all disobedience; it does not follow, however, nor is there evidence, that it will collapse if it tolerates some. In the United States prosecutors have discretion whether to enforce criminal laws in particular cases. A prosecutor may properly decide not to press charges if the lawbreaker is young, or inexperienced, or the sole support of a family, or is repentant, or turns state's evidence, or if the law is unpopular or unworkable or generally disobeyed, or if the courts are clogged with more important cases, or for dozens of other reasons. This discretion is not license—we expect prosecutors to have good reasons for exercising it—but there are, at least *prima facie,* some good reasons for not prosecuting those who disobey the draft laws out of conscience. One is the obvious reason that they act out of better motives than those who break the law out of greed or a desire to subvert government. If motive can count in distinguishing between thieves, then why not in distinguishing between draft offenders? Another is the practical reason that our society suffers a loss if it punishes a group that includes—as the group of draft dissenters does—some of its most loyal and law-respecting citizens. Jailing such men solidifies their alienation from society, and alienates many like them who are deterred by the threat. If practical consequences like these argued for not enforcing prohibition, why do they not argue for tolerating offenses of conscience?

Those who think that conscientious draft offenders should always be punished must show that these are not good reasons for exercising discretion, or they must find contrary reasons that outweigh them. What arguments might they produce? There are practical reasons for enforcing draft laws, and I shall consider some of these later. But Dean Griswold and those who agree with him seem to rely on a fundamental moral argument that it would be unfair, not merely impractical, to let the dissenters go unpunished. They think it would be unfair, I gather, because society could not function if everyone disobeyed laws he disapproved of or found disadvantageous. If the government tolerates those few who will not "play the game," it allows them to secure the benefits of everyone else's deference to law, without shouldering the burdens, such as the burden of the draft.

This argument is a serious one. It cannot be answered simply by saying that the dissenters would allow everyone else the privilege of disobeying a law he believed immoral. In fact, few draft dissenters would accept a changed society in which sincere segregationists were free to break civil rights laws they hated. The majority want no such change, in any event, because they think that society would be worse off for it; until they are shown this is wrong, they will expect their officials to punish anyone who assumes a privilege which they, for the general benefit, do not assume.

There is, however, a flaw in the argument. The reasoning contains a hidden assumption that makes it almost entirely irrelevant to the draft cases, and indeed to any serious case of civil disobedience in the United States. The argument assumes that the dissenters know that they are breaking a valid law, and that the privilege they assert is the privilege to do that. Of course, almost everyone who discusses civil disobedience recognizes that in America a law may be invalid because it is unconstitutional. But the critics handle this complexity by arguing on separate hypotheses: If the law is invalid, then no crime is committed, and society may not punish. If the law is valid, then a crime has been committed, and society must punish. This reasoning hides the crucial fact that the validity of the law may be doubtful. The officials and judges may believe that the law is valid, the dissenters may disagree, and both sides may have plausible arguments for their positions. If so, then the issues are different from what they would be if the law were clearly valid or clearly invalid, and the argument of fairness, designed for these alternatives, is irrelevant.

Doubtful law is by no means special or exotic in cases of civil disobedience. On the contrary. In the United States, at least, almost any law which a significant number of people would be tempted to disobey on moral grounds would be doubtful—if not clearly invalid—on constitutional grounds as well. The constitution makes our conventional political morality relevant to the question of validity; any statute that appears to compromise that morality raises constitutional questions, and if the compromise is serious, the constitutional doubts are serious also.

The connection between moral and legal issues is especially clear in the current draft cases. Dissent has largely been based on the following moral objections: (a) The United States is using immoral weapons and tactics in Vietnam. (b) The war has never been endorsed by deliberate, considered, and open vote of the peoples' representatives. (c) The United States has no interest at stake in Vietnam remotely strong enough to justify forcing a segment of its citizens to risk death there. (d) If an army is to be raised to fight that war, it is immoral to raise it by a draft that defers or exempts college students, and thus discriminates against the economically underprivileged. (e) The draft exempts those who object to all wars on religious grounds, but not those who object to particular wars on moral grounds; there is no relevant difference between these positions, and so the draft, by making the distinction, implies that the second group is less worthy of the nation's respect than the first. (f) The law that makes it a crime to counsel draft resistance stifles those who oppose the war, because it is morally impossible to argue that the war is profoundly immoral, without encouraging and assisting those who refuse to fight it.

Lawyers will recognize that these moral positions, if we accept them, provide the basis for the following constitutional arguments: (a) The constitution makes treaties part of the law of the land, and the United States is a party to international conventions and covenants that make illegal the acts of war the dissenters charge the nation with committing. (b) The constitution provides that Congress must declare war; the legal issue of whether our action in Vietnam is a "war" and whether the Tonkin Bay Resolution was a "declaration" is the heart of the moral issue of whether the government has made a deliberate and open decision. (c) Both the due process clause of the Fifth and Fourteenth Amendments and equal protection clause of the Fourteenth Amendment condemn special burdens placed on a selected class of citizens when the burden or the classification is not reasonable; the burden is unreasonable when it patently does not serve the public interest, or when it is vastly disproportionate to the interest served. If our military action in Vietnam is frivolous or perverse, as the dissenters claim, then the burden we place on men of draft age is unreasonable and unconstitutional. (d) In any event, the discrimination in favor of college students denies to the poor the equal protection of the law that is guaranteed by the constitution. (e) If there is no pertinent difference between religious objection to all wars and moral objection to some wars, then the classification the draft makes is arbitrary and unreasonable, and unconstitutional on that ground. The "establishment of religion" clause of the First Amendment forbids governmental pressure in favor of organized religion; if the draft's distinction coerces men in this direction, it is invalid on that count also. (f) The First Amendment also condemns invasions of freedom of speech. If the draft law's prohibition on counseling does inhibit expression of a range of views on the war, it abridges free speech.

The principal counterargument, supporting the view that the courts ought not to hold the draft unconstitutional, also involves moral issues. Under the so-called "political question" doctrine, the courts deny their own jurisdiction to pass on matters—such as foreign or military policy—whose resolution is best assigned to other branches of the government. The Boston court trying the Coffin, Spock case has already declared, on the basis of this doctrine, that it will not hear arguments about the legality of the war. But the Supreme Court has shown itself (in the reapportionment cases, for example) reluctant to refuse jurisdiction when it believed that the gravest issues of political morality were at stake and that no remedy was available through the political process. If the dissenters are right, and the war and the draft are state crimes of profound injustice to a group of citizens, then the argument that the courts must refuse jurisdiction is considerably weakened.

We cannot conclude from these arguments that the draft (or any part of it) is unconstitutional. If the Supreme Court is called upon to rule on the question, it will probably reject some of them, and refuse to consider the others on grounds that they are political. The majority of lawyers would probably agree with this result. But the arguments of unconstitutionality are at least plausible, and a reasonable and competent lawyer might well think that they present a stronger case, on balance, than the counterarguments. If he does, he will consider that the draft is not constitutional, and there will be no way of proving that he is wrong.

Therefore we cannot assume, in judging what to do with the draft dissenters, that they are asserting a privilege to disobey valid laws. We cannot decide that fairness demands their punishment until we try to answer the further question: What should a citizen do when the law is unclear, and when he thinks it allows what others think it does not? I do not mean to ask, of course, what it is *legally* proper for him to do, or what his *legal* rights are—that would be begging the question, because it depends upon whether he is right or they are right. I mean to ask what his proper course is as a citizen, what, in other words, we would consider to be "playing the game." That is a crucial question, because it cannot be unfair not to punish him if he is acting as, given his opinions, we think he should.[1]

There is no obvious answer on which most citizens would readily agree, and that is itself significant. If we examine our

---

[1] I do not mean to imply that the government should always punish a man who deliberately breaks a law he knows is valid. There may be reasons of fairness or practicality, like those I listed in the third paragraph, for not prosecuting such men. [See my "The Vietnam War and the Right of Resistance," above, for a discussion of this issue. Ed.] But cases like the draft cases present special arguments for tolerance; I want to concentrate on these arguments and therefore have isolated these cases.

legal institutions and practices, however, we shall discover some relevant underlying principles and policies. I shall set out three possible answers to the question, and then try to show which of these best fits our practices and expectations. The three possibilities I want to consider are these:

(1) If the law is doubtful, and it is therefore unclear whether it permits someone to do what he wants, he should assume the worst, and act on the assumption that it does not. He should obey the executive authorities who command him, even though he thinks they are wrong, while using the political process, if he can, to change the law.

(2) If the law is doubtful, he may follow his own judgment, that is, may do what he wants if he believes that the case that the law permits this is stronger than the case that it does not. But he may follow his own judgment only until an authoritative institution, like a court, decides the other way in a case involving him or someone else. Once an institutional decision has been reached, he must abide by that decision, even though he thinks that it was wrong. (There are, in theory, many subdivisions of this second possibility. We may say that the individual's choice is foreclosed by the contrary decision of any court, including the lowest court in the system if the case is not appealed. Or we may require a decision of some particular court or institution. I shall discuss this second possibility in its most liberal form, namely that the individual may properly follow his own judgment until a contrary decision of the highest court competent to pass on the issue, which, in the case of the draft, is the United States Supreme Court.)

(3) If the law is doubtful, he may follow his own judgment, even after a contrary decision by the highest competent court. Of course, he must take the contrary decision of any court into account in making his judgment of what the law requires. Otherwise the judgment would not be an honest or reasonable one, because the doctrine of precedent, which is an established part of our legal system, has the effect of allowing the decision of the courts to change *the law. Suppose, for example, that a taxpayer believes that he is not required to pay tax on certain forms of income. If the Supreme Court decides to the contrary, he should, taking into account the practice of according great weight to the decisions of the Supreme Court on tax matters, decide that the Court's decision has itself tipped the balance, and that the law now requires him to pay the tax.*

Someone might think that this qualification erases the difference between the third and the second models, but it does not.

The doctrine of precedent gives different weights to the decisions of different courts, and greatest weight to the decisions of the Supreme Court, but it does not make the decision of any court conclusive. Sometimes, even after a contrary Supreme Court decision, an individual may still reasonably believe that the law is on his side; such cases are rare, but they are most likely to occur in disputes over constitutional law when civil disobedience is involved. The Court has shown itself more likely to overrule its past decisions if these have limited important personal or political rights, and it is just these decisions that a dissenter might want to challenge.

We cannot assume, in other words, that the Constitution is always what the Supreme Court says it is. Oliver Wendell Holmes, for example, did not follow such a rule in his famous dissent in the *Gitlow* case. A few years before, in *Abrams,* he had lost his battle to persuade the court that the First Amendment protected an anarchist who had been urging general strikes against the government. A similar issue was presented in *Gitlow,* and Holmes once again dissented. "It is true," he said, "that in my opinion this criterion was departed from [in *Abrams*] but the convictions that I expressed in that case are too deep for it to be possible for me as yet to believe that it . . . settled the law." Holmes voted for acquitting Gitlow, on the ground that what Gitlow had done was no crime, even though the Supreme Court had recently held that it was.

Here then are three possible models for the behavior of dissenters who disagree with the executive authorities when the law is doubtful. Which of them best fits our legal and social practices?

I think it plain that we do not follow the first of these models, that is, that we do not expect citizens to assume the worst. If no court has decided the issue, and a man thinks, on balance, that the law is on his side, most of our lawyers and critics think it perfectly proper for him to follow his own judgment. Even when many disapprove of what he does—such as peddling pornography—they do not think he must desist just because the legality of his conduct is subject to doubt.

It is worth pausing a moment to consider what society would lose if it did follow the first model or, to put the matter the other way, what society gains when people follow their own judgment in cases like this. When the law is uncertain, in the sense that lawyers can reasonably disagree on what a court ought to decide, the reason usually is that different legal principles and policies have collided, and it is unclear how best to accommodate these conflicting principles and policies.

Our practice, in which different parties are encouraged to pursue their own understanding, provides a means of testing relevant hypotheses. If the question is whether a particular rule would have certain undesirable consequences, or whether these consequences would have limited or broad ramifications, then, before the issue is decided, it is useful to know what does in fact take place when some people proceed on that rule. (Much anti-trust and business regulation law has developed through this kind of testing.) If the question is whether and to what degree a particular solution would offend principles of justice or fair play deeply respected by the community, it is useful, again, to experiment by testing the community's response. The extent of community indifference to anti-contraception laws, for example, would never have become established had not some organizations deliberately flouted those laws.

If the first model were followed, we would lose the advantages of these tests. The law would suffer, particularly if this model were applied to constitutional issues. When the validity of a criminal statute is in doubt, the statute will almost always strike some people as being unfair or unjust, because it will infringe some principle of liberty or justice or fairness which they take to be built into the Constitution. If our practice were that whenever a law is doubtful on these grounds, one must act as if it were valid, then the chief vehicle we have for challenging the law on moral grounds would be lost, and over time the law we obeyed would certainly become less fair and just, and the liberty of our citizens would certainly be diminished.

We would lose almost as much if we used a variation of the first model, that a citizen must assume the worst unless he can anticipate that the courts will agree with his view of the law. If everyone deferred to his guess of what the courts would do, society and its law would be poorer. Our assumption in rejecting the first model was that the record a citizen makes in following his own judgment, together with the arguments he makes supporting that judgment when he has the opportunity, are helpful in creating the best judicial decision possible. This remains true even when, at the time the citizen acts, the odds are against his success in court. We must remember, too, that the value of the citizen's example is not exhausted once the decision has been made. Our practices require that the decision be criticized, by the legal profession and the law schools, and the record of dissent may be invaluable here.

Of course a man must consider what the courts will do when he decides whether it would be *prudent* to follow his own judgment. He may have to face jail, bankruptcy, or opprobrium if he does. But it is essential that we separate the calculation of prudence from the question of what, as a good citizen, he may properly do. We are investigating how society ought to treat him when its courts believe that he judged wrong; therefore we must ask what he is justified in doing when his judgment differs from others. We beg the question if we assume that what he may properly do depends on his guess as to how society will treat him.

We must also reject the second model, that if the law is unclear a citizen may properly follow his own judgment until the highest court has ruled that he is wrong. This fails to take into account the fact that any court, including the Supreme Court, may overrule itself. In 1940 the Court decided that a West Virginia law requiring students to salute the Flag was constitutional. In 1943 it reversed itself, and decided that such a statute was unconstitutional after all. What was the duty, as citizens, of those people who in 1941 and 1942 objected to saluting the Flag on grounds of conscience, and thought that the Court's 1940 decision was wrong? We can hardly say that their duty was to follow the first decision. They believed that saluting the Flag was unconscionable, and they believed, reasonably, that no valid law required them to do so. The Supreme Court later decided that in this they were right. The Court did not simply hold that after the second decision failing to salute would not be a crime; it held (as in a case like this it almost always would) that it was no crime after the first decision either.

Some will say that the flag-salute dissenters should have obeyed the Court's first decision, while they worked in the legislatures to have the law repealed, and tried in the courts to find some way to challenge the law again without actually violating it. That would be, perhaps, a plausible recommendation if conscience were not involved, because it would then be arguable that the gain in orderly procedure was worth the personal sacrifice of patience. But conscience was involved, and if the dissenters had obeyed the law while biding their time, they would have suffered the irreparable injury of having done what their conscience forbade them to do. It is one thing to say that an individual must sometimes violate his conscience when he knows that the law commands him to do it. It is quite another to say that he must violate his conscience even when he reasonably believes that the law does not require it, because it would inconvenience his fellow citizens if he took the most direct, and perhaps the only, method of attempting to show that he is right and they are wrong.

Since a court may overrule itself, the same reasons we listed for rejecting the first model count against the second as well. If we did not have the pressure of dissent, we would not have a dramatic statement of the degree to which a court decision against the dissenter is felt to be wrong, a demonstration that is surely pertinent to the question of whether it was right. We would increase the chance of being governed by rules that offend the principles we claim to serve.

These considerations force us, I think, from the second model, but some will want to substitute a variation of it. They will argue that once the Supreme Court has decided that a criminal law is valid, then citizens have a duty to abide by that decision until they have a reasonable belief, not merely that the decision is a bad law, but that the Supreme Court is likely to overrule it. Under this view the West Virginia dissenters who refused to salute the Flag in 1942 were acting properly, because they might reasonably have anticipated that the Court would change its mind. But if the Court were to hold the draft laws constitutional, it would be improper to continue to challenge these laws, because there would be no great likelihood that the Court would soon change its mind. This suggestion must also be rejected, however. For once we say that a citizen may properly follow his own judgment of the law, in spite of his judgment that the courts will probably find against him, there is no plausible reason why he should act differently because a contrary decision is already on the books.

Thus the third model, or something close to it, seems to be the fairest statement of a man's social duty in our community. A citizen's allegiance is to the law, not to any particular person's view of what the law is, and he does not behave unfairly so long as he proceeds on his own considered and reasonable view of what the law requires. Let me repeat (because it is crucial) that this is not the same as saying that an individual may disregard what the courts have said. The doctrine of precedent lies near the core of our legal system, and no one can make a reasonable effort to follow the law unless he grants the courts the general power to alter it by their decisions. But if the issue is one touching fundamental personal or political rights, and it is arguable that the Supreme Court has made a mistake, a man is within his social rights in refusing to accept that decision as conclusive.

One large question remains before we can apply these observations to the problems of draft resistance. I have been talking about the case of a man who believes that the law is not what other people think, or what the courts have held. This description may fit some of those who disobey the draft laws out of conscience, but it does not fit most of them. Most of the dissenters are not lawyers or political philosophers; they believe that the laws on the books are immoral, and inconsistent with their country's legal ideals, but they have not considered the question of whether they may be invalid as well. Of what relevance to their situation, then, is the proposition that one may properly follow one's own view of the law?

To answer this, I shall have to return to the point I made earlier. The Constitution, through the due process clause, the equal protection clause, the First Amendment, and the other provisions I mentioned, injects an extraordinary amount of our political morality into the issue of whether a law is valid. The statement that most draft dissenters are unaware that the law is invalid therefore needs qualification. They hold beliefs that, if true, strongly support the view that law is on their side; the fact that they have not reached that further conclusion can be traced, in at least most cases, to their lack of legal sophistication. If we believe that when the law is doubtful people who follow their own judgment of the law may be acting properly, it would seem wrong not to extend that view to those dissenters whose judgments come to the same thing. No part of the case that I made for the third model would entitle us to distinguish them from their more knowledgeable colleagues.

We can draw several tentative conclusions from the argument so far: When the law is uncertain, in the sense that a plausible case can be made on both sides, then a citizen who follows his own judgment is not behaving unfairly. Our practices permit and encourage him to follow his own judgment in such cases. For that reason, our government has a special responsibility to try to protect him, and soften his predicament, whenever it can do so without great damage to other policies. It does not follow that the government can guarantee him immunity—it cannot adopt the rule that it will prosecute no one who acts out of conscience, or convict no one who reasonably disagrees with the courts. That would paralyze the government's ability to carry out its policies; it would, moreover, throw away the most important benefit of following the third model. If the state never prosecuted, then the courts could not act on the experience and the arguments the dissent has generated. But it does follow that when the practical reasons for prosecuting are relatively weak in a particular case, or can be met in other ways, the path of fairness lies in tolerance. The popular view that the law is the law and must always be enforced refuses to distinguish the man who acts on his own judgment of a doubtful law, and thus behaves as our practices provide, from the common criminal. I know of no reason, short of moral blindness, for not drawing a distinction in principle between the two cases.

I anticipate a philosophical objection to these conclusions: that I am treating law as a "brooding omnipresence in the sky." I have spoken of people making judgments about what the law requires, even in cases in which the law is unclear and undemonstrable. I have spoken of cases in which a man might think that the law requires one thing, even though the Supreme Court has said that it requires another, and even when it was not likely that the Supreme Court would soon change its mind. I will therefore be charged with the view that there is always a "right answer" to a legal problem to be found in natural law or locked up in some transcendental strongbox.

The strongbox theory of law is, of course, nonsense. When I say that people hold views on the law when the law is doubtful, and that these views are not merely predictions of what the courts will hold, I intend no such metaphysics. I mean only to summarize as accurately as I can many of the practices that are part of our legal process.

Lawyers and judges make statements of legal right and duty, even when they know these are not demonstrable, and support them with arguments even when they know that these arguments will not appeal to everyone. They make these arguments to one another, in the professional journals, in the classroom, and in the courts. They respond to these arguments, when others make them, by judging them good or bad or mediocre. In so doing they assume that some arguments for a given doubtful position are better than others. They also assume that the case on one side of a doubtful proposition may be stronger than the case on the other, which is what I take a claim of law in a doubtful case to mean. They distinguish, without too much difficulty, these arguments from predictions of what the courts will decide.

These practices are poorly represented by the theory that judgments of law on doubtful issues are nonsense, or are merely predictions of what the courts will do. Those who hold such theories cannot deny the fact of these practices; perhaps these theorists mean that the practices are not sensible, because they are based on suppositions that do not hold, or for some other reason. But this makes their objection mysterious, because they never specify what they take the purposes underlying these practices to be; and unless these goals are specified, one cannot decide whether the practices are sensible. I understand these underlying purposes to be those I described earlier: the development and testing of the law through experimentation by citizens and through the adversary process.

Our legal system pursues these goals by inviting citizens to decide the strengths and weaknesses of legal arguments for themselves, or through their own counsel, and to act on these judgments, although that permission is qualified by the limited threat that they may suffer if the courts do not agree. Success in this strategy depends on whether there is sufficient agreement within the community on what counts as a good or bad argument, so that, although different people will reach different judgments, these differences will be neither so profound nor so frequent as to make the system unworkable, or dangerous for those who act by their own lights. I believe there is sufficient agreement on the criteria of the argument to avoid these traps, although one of the main tasks of legal philosophy is to exhibit and clarify these criteria. In any event, the practices I have described have not yet been shown to be misguided; they therefore must count in determining whether it is just and fair to be lenient to those who break what others think is the law.

I have said that the government has a special responsibility to those who act on a reasonable judgment that a law is invalid. It should make accommodation for them as far as possible, when this is consistent with other policies. It may be difficult to decide what the government ought to do, in the name of that responsibility, in particular cases. The decision will be a matter of balance, and flat rules will not help. Still, some principles can be set out.

I shall start with the prosecutor's decision whether to press charges. He must balance both his responsibility to be lenient and the risk that convictions will rend the society, against the damage to the law's policy that may follow if he leaves the dissenters alone. In making his calculation he must consider not only the extent to which others will be harmed, but also how the law evaluates that harm; and he must therefore make the following distinction. Every rule of law is supported, and presumably justified, by a set of policies it is supposed to advance and principles it is supposed to respect. Some rules (the laws prohibiting murder and theft, for example) are supported by the proposition that the individuals protected have a moral right to be free from the harm proscribed. Other rules (the more technical antitrust rules, for example) are not supported by any supposition of an underlying right; their support comes chiefly from the alleged utility of the economic and social policies they promote. These may be supplemented with moral principles (like the view that it is a harsh business practice to undercut a weak competitor's prices) but these fall short of recognizing a moral right against the harm in question.

The point of the distinction here is this: if a particular rule of law represents an official decision that individuals have a moral right to be free from some harm, then that is a powerful argument against tolerating violations that inflict those injuries. Laws protecting people from personal injury or the destruction of their property, for example, do represent that sort of decision, and this is a very strong argument against tolerating civil disobedience that involves violence.

It may be controversial, of course, whether a law does rest on the assumption of a moral right. The question is whether it is reasonable to suppose, from the background and administration of the law, that its authors recognized such a right. These are cases, in addition to rules against violence, where it is plain that they did; the civil rights laws are examples. Many sincere and ardent segregationists believe that the civil rights laws and decisions are unconstitutional, because they compromise principles of local government and of freedom of association. This is an arguable, though not a persuasive, view. But these laws and decisions clearly embody the view that Negroes, as individuals, have a right not to be segregated. They do not rest simply on the judgment that other national policies are best pursued by preventing racial segregation. If we take no action against the man who blocks the school house door, therefore, we violate the moral rights, confirmed by law, of the schoolgirl he blocks. The responsibility of leniency cannot go this far.

The schoolgirl's position is different, however, from that of the draftee, who may be called up sooner or given a more dangerous post if draft offenders are not punished. The draft laws, taken as a whole and with an eye to their administration, cannot be said to reflect the judgment that a man has a moral right to be drafted only after certain other men or groups have been called. The draft classifications, and the order-of-call within classifications, are arranged for social and administrative convenience. They also reflect considerations of fairness, like the proposition that a mother who has lost one of two sons in war ought not to be made to risk losing the other. But they presuppose no fixed rights. The draft boards are given considerable discretion in the classification process, and the army, of course, has almost complete discretion in assigning dangerous posts. If the prosecutor tolerates draft offenders, he makes small shifts in the law's calculations of fairness and utility.

These may cause disadvantage to others in the pool of draftees but that is a different matter from contradicting their moral rights.

This difference between segregation and the draft is not an accident of how the laws happen to have been written. It would run counter to a century of practice to suppose that citizens have moral rights with respect to the order in which they are called to serve; the lottery system of selection, for example, would be abhorrent under that supposition. If our history had been different, and if the community had recognized such a moral right, it seems fair to suppose that some of the draft dissenters, at least, would have modified their acts so as to try to respect these rights. So it is wrong to analyze draft cases in the same way as cases of violence or civil rights cases, as many critics do when considering whether tolerance is justified. I do not mean that fairness to others is irrelevant in draft cases; it must be taken into account, and balanced against fairness to dissenters and the long-term benefit to society. But it does not play the commanding role here that it does when rights are at stake.

Where, then, does the balance of fairness and utility lie in the case of those who counsel draft resistance? If these men had encouraged violence or otherwise trespassed on the rights of others, then there would be a strong case for prosecution. But in the absence of such actions, the balance of fairness and utility seems to me to lie the other way, and I therefore think that the decision to prosecute Coffin, Spock, Raskin, Goodman, and Ferber was wrong. It may be argued that if those who counsel draft resistance are free from prosecution, the number who resist induction will increase; but it will not, I think, increase much beyond the number of those who would resist in any event.

If I am wrong, and there is much greater resistance, then a sense of this residual discontent is of importance to policy makers, and it ought not to be hidden under a ban on speech. Conscience is deeply involved—it is hard to believe that many who counsel resistance do so on any other grounds. The case is strong that the laws making counseling a crime are unconstitutional; even those who do not find the case persuasive will admit that its arguments have substance. The harm to potential draftees, both those who may be persuaded to resist and those who may be called earlier because others have been persuaded, is remote and speculative.

The cases of men who refuse induction when drafted are more complicated. The crucial question is whether a failure to prosecute will lead to wholesale refusals to serve. It may not—there are social pressures, including the threat of career disadvantages, that would force many young Americans to serve if drafted, even if they knew they would not go to jail if they refused. If the number would not much increase, then the state should leave the dissenters alone, and I see no great harm in delaying any prosecution until the effect of that policy becomes clearer. If the number of those who refuse induction turns out to be large, this would argue for prosecution. But it would also make the problem academic, because if there were sufficient dissent to bring us to that pass, it would be most difficult to pursue the war in any event, except under a near-totalitarian regime.

There may seem to be a paradox in these conclusions. I argued earlier that when the law is unclear citizens have the right to follow their own judgment, partly on the grounds that this practice helps to shape issues for adjudication; now I propose a course that eliminates or postpones adjudication. But the contradiction is only apparent. It does not follow from the fact that our practice facilitates adjudication, and renders it more useful in developing the law, that a trial should follow whenever citizens do act by their own lights. The question arises in each case whether the issues are ripe for adjudication, and whether adjudication would settle these issues in a manner that would decrease the chance of, or remove the grounds for, further dissent.

In the draft cases, the answer to both these questions is negative: There is much ambivalence about the war just now, and uncertainty and ignorance about the scope of the moral issues involved in the draft. It is far from the best time for a court to pass on these issues, and tolerating dissent for a time is one way of allowing the debate to continue until it has produced something clearer. Moreover, it is plain that an adjudication of the constitutional issues now will not settle the law. Those who have doubts whether the draft is constitutional will have the same doubts even if the Supreme Court says that it is. This is one of these cases, touching fundamental rights, in which our practices of precedent will encourage these doubts. Certainly this will be so if, as seems likely, the Supreme Court appeals to the political question doctrine, and refuses to pass on the more serious constitutional issues.

Even if the prosecutor does not act, however, the underlying problem will be only temporarily relieved. So long as the law appears to make acts of dissent criminal, a man of conscience will face danger. What can Congress, which shares the responsibility of leniency, do to lessen this danger?

Congress can review the laws in question to see how much accommodation can be given the dissenters. Every program a legislature adopts is a mixture of policies and restraining principles. We accept loss of efficiency in crime detection and urban renewal, for example, so that we can respect the rights of accused criminals and compensate property owners for their damages. Congress may properly defer to its responsibility toward the dissenters by adjusting or compromising other policies. The relevant questions are these: What means can be found for allowing the greatest possible tolerance of conscientious dissent while minimizing its impact on policy? How strong is the government's responsibility for leniency in this case—how deeply is conscience involved, and how strong is the case that the law is invalid after all? How important is the policy in question—is interference with that policy too great a price to pay? These questions are no doubt too simple, but they suggest the heart of the choices that must be made.

For the same reasons that those who counsel resistance should not be prosecuted, I think that the law that makes this a crime should be repealed. The case is strong that this law abridges free speech. It certainly coerces conscience, and it probably serves no beneficial effect. If counseling would persuade only a few to resist who otherwise would not, the value of the restraint is small; if counseling would persuade many, that is an important political fact that should be known.

The issues are more complex, again, in the case of draft resistance itself. Those who believe that the war in Vietnam is itself a grotesque blunder will favor any change in the law that makes peace more likely. But if we take the position of those who think the war is necessary, then we must admit that a policy that continues the draft but wholly exempts dissenters would be unwise. Two less drastic alternatives might be considered, however: a volunteer army, and an expanded conscientious objector category that includes those who find this war immoral. There is much to be said against both proposals, but once the requirement of respect for dissent is recognized, the balance of principle may be tipped in their favor.

So the case for not prosecuting conscientious draft offenders, and for changing the laws in their favor, is a strong one. It would be unrealistic to expect this policy to prevail, however, for political pressures now oppose it. Relatively few of those who have refused induction have been indicted so far, but the pace of prosecution is quickening, and many more indictments are expected if the resistance many college seniors have pledged does in fact develop. The Coffin, Spock trial continues, although when the present steps toward peace negotiation were announced, many lawyers had hoped it would be dropped or delayed. There is no sign of any movement to amend the draft laws in the way I have suggested.

We must consider, therefore, what the courts can and should now do. A court might, of course, uphold the arguments that the draft laws are in some way unconstitutional, in general or as applied to the defendants in the case at hand. Or it may acquit the defendants because the facts necessary for conviction are not proved. I shall not argue the constitutional issues, or the facts of any particular case. I want instead to suggest that a court ought not to convict, at least in some circumstances, even if it sustains the statutes and finds the facts as charged. The Supreme Court has not ruled on the chief arguments that the present draft is unconstitutional, nor has it held that these arguments raise political questions that are not relevant to its jurisdiction. If the alleged violations take place before the Supreme Court has decided these issues, and the case reaches that Court, there are strong reasons why the Court should acquit even if it does then sustain the draft. It ought to acquit on the ground that before its decision the validity of the draft was doubtful, and it is unfair to punish men for disobeying a doubtful law.

There would be precedent for a decision along these lines. The Court has several times reversed criminal convictions, on due process grounds, because the law in question was too vague. (It has overturned convictions, for example, under laws that made it a crime to charge "unreasonable prices" or to be a member of a "gang.") Conviction under a vague criminal law offends the moral and political ideals of due process in two ways. First, it places a citizen in the unfair position of either acting at his peril or accepting a more stringent restriction on his life than the legislature may have authorized: As I argued earlier, it is not acceptable, as a model of social behavior, that in such cases he ought to assume the worst. Second, it gives power to the prosecutor and the courts to make criminal law, by opting for one or the other possible interpretations after the event. This would be a delegation of authority by the legislature that is inconsistent with our scheme of separation of powers.

Conviction under a criminal law whose terms are not vague, but whose constitutional validity is doubtful, offends due process in the first of these ways. It forces a citizen to assume the worst, or act at his peril. It offends due process in something like the second way as well. Most citizens would be deterred by a doubtful statute if they were to risk jail by violating it. Congress, and not the courts, would then be the effective voice in deciding the constitutionality of criminal enactments, and this also violates the separation of powers.

If acts of dissent continue to occur after the Supreme Court has ruled that the laws are valid, or that the political question doctrine applies, then acquittal on the grounds I have described is no longer appropriate. The Court's decision will not have finally settled the law, for the reasons given earlier, but the Court will have done all that can be done to settle it. The courts may still exercise their sentencing discretion, however, and impose minimal or suspended sentences as a mark of respect for the dissenters' position.

Some lawyers will be shocked by my general conclusion that we have a responsibility toward those who disobey the draft laws out of conscience, and that we may be required not to prosecute them, but rather to change our laws or adjust our sentencing procedures to accommodate them. The simple Draconian propositions, that crime must be punished, and that he who misjudges the law must take the consequences, have an extraordinary hold on the professional as well as the popular imagination. But the rule of law is more complex and more intelligent than that and it is important that it survive.

Postscript [1970]

The Nixon Administration, according to *The New York Times,* has sharply increased the number of prosecutions for draft offenses. The current rate of prosecution is well above the rate of prosecution when this article was written. The administration has not increased prosecutions in response to practical dangers of the sort I said might justify prosecution, for the draft call reductions and troop withdrawals it has announced would, if anything, reduce these dangers. On the contrary, it seems to have acted in the name of that maxim which I argued is too simple for an intelligent and fair legal policy, the maxim that the law is the law and must always be enforced.

Peter Kropotkin

Law and Authority

I

"When ignorance reigns in society and disorder in the minds
of men, laws are multiplied, legislation is expected to do everything, and each fresh law being a fresh miscalculation, men are
continually led to demand from it what can proceed only from
themselves, from their own education and their own morality."
It is no revolutionist who says this, not even a reformer. It is the
jurist, Dalloy, author of the collection of French law known as
Répertoire de la Législation. And yet, though these lines were
written by a man who was himself a maker and admirer of law,
they perfectly represent the abnormal condition of our society.

In existing States a fresh law is looked upon as a remedy
for evil. Instead of themselves altering what is bad, people
begin by demanding a *law* to alter it. If the road between two
villages is impassable, the peasant says:—"There should be
a law about parish roads." If a park-keeper takes advantage
of the want of spirit in those who follow him with servile observance and insults one of them, the insulted man says,
"There should be a law to enjoin more politeness upon park-
keepers." If there is stagnation in agriculture or commerce,
the husbandman, cattle-breeder, or corn speculator argues,
"It is protective legislation that we require." Down to the old
clothesman there is not one who does not demand a law to

"Law and Authority," written in English, was first published as a pamphlet from Freedom Press, London, in 1886. It has recently been reprinted
in the collection, *Kropotkin's Revolutionary Pamphlets,* edited by Roger
Baldwin, from Benjamin Blom, Inc., New York, 1968. It is reprinted here
(abridged) by permission of Benjamin Blom, Inc. Peter Kropotkin (1842–
1921) was born in Moscow, a Prince of the Russian nobility, and during his
childhood was a page of the Emperor. During his thirties, he became a
revolutionary anarchist. He was jailed in St. Petersburg, escaped after two
years, and made his way to England. Though a distinguished geographer,
his first concern was politics. He wrote extensive philosophical defenses of
anarchism and was also involved in political organization and activity. He
lived and visited in a variety of countries (including America). He returned
to Russia after the Revolution, but was gravely disturbed that the Soviet
Government was developing that very kind of "law and authority" which he
had always opposed.

protect his own little trade. If the employer lowers wages or increases the hours of labor, the politician in embryo exclaims, "We must have a law to put all that to rights." In short, a law everywhere and for everything! A law about fashions, a law about mad dogs, a law about virtue, a law to put a stop to all the vices and all the evils which result from human indolence and cowardice.

We are so perverted by an education which from infancy seeks to kill in us the spirit of revolt, and to develop that of submission to authority; we are so perverted by this existence under the ferrule of a law, which regulates every event in life —our birth, our education, our development, our love, our friendship—that, if this state of things continues, we shall lose all initiative, all habit of thinking for ourselves. Our society seems no longer able to understand that it is possible to exist otherwise than under the reign of law, elaborated by a representative government and administered by a handful of rulers. And even when it has gone so far as to emancipate itself from the thralldom, its first care has been to reconstitute it immediately. "The Year I of Liberty" has never lasted more than a day, for after proclaiming it men put themselves the very next morning under the yoke of law and authority.

Indeed, for some thousands of years, those who govern us have done nothing but ring the changes upon "Respect for law, obedience to authority." This is the moral atmosphere in which parents bring up their children, and school only serves to confirm the impression. Cleverly assorted scraps of spurious science are inculcated upon the children to prove necessity of law; obedience to the law is made a religion; moral goodness and the law of the masters are fused into one and the same divinity. The historical hero of the schoolroom is the man who obeys the law, and defends it against rebels.

Later when we enter upon public life, society and literature, impressing us day by day and hour by hour as the water-drop hollows the stone, continue to inculcate the same prejudice. Books of history, of political science, of social economy, are stuffed with this respect for law. Even the physical sciences have been pressed into the service by introducing artificial modes of expression, borrowed from theology and arbitrary power, into knowledge which is purely the result of observation. Thus our intelligence is successfully befogged, and always to maintain our respect for law. The same work is done by newspapers. They have not an article which does not preach respect for law, even where the third page proves every day the imbecility of that law, and shows how it is dragged through every variety of mud and filth by those charged with its administration. Servility before the law has become a virtue, and I doubt if there was ever even a revolutionist who did not begin in his youth as the defender of law against what are generally called "abuses," although these last are inevitable consequences of the law itself. . . .

To understand this [worship of law], we must transport ourselves in imagination into the eighteenth century. Our hearts must have ached at the story of the atrocities committed by the all-powerful nobles of that time upon the men and women of the people before we can understand what must have been the magic influence upon the peasant's mind of the words, "Equality before the law, obedience to the law without distinction of birth or fortune." He who until then had been treated more cruelly than a beast, he who had never had any rights, he who had never obtained justice against the most revolting actions on the part of a noble, unless in revenge he killed him and was hanged—he saw himself recognized by this maxim, at least in theory, at least with regard to his personal rights, as the equal of his lord. Whatever this law might be, it promised to affect lord and peasant alike; it proclaimed the equality of rich and poor before the judge. The promise was a lie, and to-day we know it; but at that period it was an advance, a homage to justice, as hypocrisy is a homage rendered to truth. This is the reason that when the saviors of the menaced middle class (the Robespierres and the Dantons) took their stand upon the writings of the Rousseaus and the Voltaires, and proclaimed "respect for law, the same for every man," the people accepted the compromise; for their revolutionary impetus had already spent its force in the contest with a foe whose ranks drew closer day by day; they bowed their neck beneath the yoke of law to save themselves from the arbitrary power of their lords.

The middle class has ever since continued to make the most of this maxim, which with another principle, that of representative government, sums up the whole philosophy of the bourgeois age, the nineteenth century. It has preached this doctrine in its schools, it has propagated it in its writings, it has moulded its art and science to the same purpose, it has thrust its beliefs into every hole and corner—like a pious Englishwoman, who slips tracts under the door—and it has done all this so successfully that today we behold the issue in the detestable fact that men who long for freedom begin the attempt to obtain it by entreating their masters to be kind enough to protect them by modifying the laws which these masters themselves have created!

But times and tempers are changed. Rebels are everywhere to be found who no longer wish to obey the law without knowing whence it comes, what are its uses, and whither arises the obligation to submit to it, and the reverence with which it is encompassed. The rebels of our day are criticizing the very foundations of society which have hitherto been held sacred, and first and foremost amongst them that fetish, law.

The critics analyze the sources of law, and find there either a god, product of the terrors of the savage, and stupid, paltry and malicious as the priests who vouch for its supernatural origin, or else, bloodshed, conquest by fire and sword. They study the characteristics of law, and instead of perpetual growth corresponding to that of the human race, they find its distinctive traits to be immobility, a tendency to crystallize what should be modified and developed day by day. They ask how law has been maintained, and in its service they see the atrocities of Byzantinism, the cruelties of the Inquisition, the tortures of the middle ages, living flesh torn by the lash of the executioner, chains, clubs, axes, the gloomy dungeons of prisons, agony, curses and tears. In our own days they see, as before, the axe, the cord, the rifle, the prison; on the one hand, the brutalized prisoner, reduced to the condition of a caged beast by the debasement of his whole moral being, and on the other, the judge, stripped of every feeling which does honor to human nature, living like a visionary in a world of legal fictions, revelling in the infliction of imprisonment and death, without even suspecting, in the cold malignity of his madness, the abyss of degradation into which he has himself fallen before the eyes of those whom he condemns.

They see a race of law-makers legislating without knowing what their laws are about; today voting a law on the sanitation of towns, without the faintest notion of hygiene, tomorrow making regulations for the armament of troops, without so much as understanding a gun; making laws about teaching and education without ever having given a lesson of any sort, or even an honest education to their own children; legislating at random in all directions, but never forgetting the penalties to be meted out to ragamuffins, the prison and the galleys, which are to be the portion of men a thousand times less immoral than these legislators themselves.

Finally, they see the jailer on the way to lose all human feeling, the detective trained as a blood-hound, the police spy despising himself; "informing," metamorphosed into a virtue; corruption, erected into a system; all the vices, all the evil qualities of mankind countenanced and cultivated to insure the triumph of law.

All this we see, and, therefore, instead of inanely repeating the old formula, "Respect the law," we say, "Despise law and all its attributes!" In place of the cowardly phrase, "Obey the law," our cry is "Revolt against all laws!"

Only compare the misdeeds accomplished in the name of each law with the good it has been able to effect, and weigh carefully both good and evil, and you will see if we are right.

II

Relatively speaking, law is a product of modern times. For ages and ages mankind lived without any written law, even that graved in symbols upon the entrance stones of a temple. During that period, human relations were simply regulated by customs, habits and usages, made sacred by constant repetition, and acquired by each person in childhood, exactly as he learned how to obtain his food by hunting, cattle-rearing or agriculture.

All human societies have passed through this primitive phase, and to this day a large proportion of mankind have no written law. Every tribe has its own manners and customs; customary law, as the jurists say. It has social habits, and that suffices to maintain cordial relations between the inhabitants of the village, the members of the tribe or community. . . .

Two distinctly marked currents of custom are revealed by analysis of the usages of primitive people.

As man does not live in a solitary state, habits and feelings develop within him which are useful for the preservation of society and the propagation of the race. Without social feelings and usages, life in common would have been absolutely impossible. It is not law which has established them; they are anterior to all law. Neither is it religion which has ordained them; they are anterior to all religions. They are found amongst all animals living in society. They are spontaneously developed by the very nature of things, like those habits in animals which men call instinct. They spring from a process of evolution, which is useful, and, indeed, necessary, to keep society together in the struggle it is forced to maintain for existence. Savages end by no longer eating one another because they find it in the long run more advantageous to devote themselves to some sort of cultivation than to enjoy the pleasure of feasting upon the flesh of an aged relative once a year. Many travelers have depicted the manners of absolutely independent tribes, where laws and chiefs are unknown, but where the members of the tribe have given up stabbing one another in every dispute, because the habit of living in society has ended by developing certain feelings of fraternity and oneness of interest, and they prefer appealing to a third person to settle their differences. The hospitality of primitive peoples, respect for human life, the sense of reciprocal obligation, compassion for the weak, courage, extending even to the sacrifice of self for others which is first learnt for the sake of children and friends, and later for that of members of the same community—all these qualities are developed in man anterior to all law, independently of all religion, as in the case of the social animals. Such feelings and practices are the inevitable results of social life. Without being, as say priests and metaphysicians, inherent in man, such qualities are the consequence of life in common.

But side by side with these customs, necessary to the life of societies and the preservation of the race, other desires, other passions, and therefore other habits and customs, are evolved in human association. The desire to dominate others and impose one's own will upon them; the desire to seize upon the products of the labor of a neighboring tribe; the desire to surround oneself with comforts without producing anything, while slaves provide their master with the means of procuring every sort of pleasure and luxury—these selfish, personal desires give rise to another current of habits and customs. The priest and the warrior, the charlatan who makes a profit out of superstition, and after freeing himself from the fear of the devil cultivates it in others; and the bully, who procures the invasion and pillage of his neighbors that he may return laden with booty and followed by slaves. These two, hand in hand, have succeeded in imposing upon primitive society customs advantageous to both of them, but tending to perpetuate their domination of the masses. Profiting by the indolence, the fears, the inertia of the crowd, and thanks to the continual repetition of the same acts, they have permanently established customs which have become a solid basis for their own domination.

For this purpose, they would have made use, in the first place, of that tendency to run in a groove, so highly developed in mankind. In children and all savages it attains striking proportions, and it may also be observed in animals. Man, when he is at all superstitious, is always afraid to introduce any sort of change into existing conditions; he generally venerates what is ancient. "Our fathers did so and so; they got on pretty well; they brought you up; they were not unhappy; do the same!" the old say to the young every time the latter wish to alter things. The unknown frightens them, they prefer to cling to the past even when that past represents poverty, oppression and slavery.

It may even be said that the more miserable a man is, the more he dreads every sort of change, lest it may make him more wretched still. Some ray of hope, a few scraps of comfort, must penetrate his gloomy abode before he can begin to desire better things, to criticize the old ways of living, and prepare to imperil them for the sake of bringing about a change. So long as he is not imbued with hope, so long as he is not freed from the tutelage of those who utilize his superstition and his fears, he prefers remaining in his former position. If the young desire any change, the old raise a cry of alarm against the innovators. Some savages would rather die than transgress the customs of their country because they have been told from childhood that the least infraction of established routine would bring ill-luck and ruin the whole tribe. Even in the present day, what numbers of politicians, economists, and would-be revolutionists act under the same impression, and cling to a vanishing past. How many care only to seek for precedents. How many fiery innovators are mere copyists of bygone revolutions.

The spirit of routine, originating in superstition, indolence, and cowardice, has in all times been the mainstay of oppression. In primitive human societies it was cleverly turned to account by priests and military chiefs. They perpetuated customs useful only to themselves, and succeeded in imposing them on the whole tribe. So long as this conservative spirit could be exploited so as to assure the chief in his encroachments upon individual liberty, so long as the only inequalities between men were the work of nature, and these were not increased a hundred-fold by the concentration of power and wealth, there was no need for law and the formidable paraphernalia of tribunals and ever-augmenting penalties to enforce it.

But as society became more and more divided into two hostile classes, one seeking to establish its domination, the other struggling to escape, the strife began. Now the conqueror was in a hurry to secure the results of his actions in a permanent form, he tried to place them beyond question, to make them holy and venerable by every means in his power. Law made its appearance under the sanction of the priest, and the warrior's club was placed at its service. Its office was to render immutable such customs as were to the advantage of the dominant minority. Military authority undertook to ensure obedience. This new function was a fresh guarantee to the power of the warrior; now he had not only mere brute force at his service; he was the defender of law.

If law, however, presented nothing but a collection of prescriptions serviceable to rulers, it would find some difficulty in insuring acceptance and obedience. Well, the legislators confounded in one code the two currents of custom of which we have just been speaking, the maxims which represent principles of morality and social union wrought out as a result of life in common, and the mandates which are meant to ensure external existence to inequality. Customs, absolutely essential to the very being of society, are, in the code, cleverly intermingled with usages imposed by the ruling caste, and both claim equal respect from the crowd. "Do not kill," says the code, and hastens to add, "And pay tithes to the priest." "Do not steal," says the code, and immediately after, "He who refuses to pay taxes, shall have his hand struck off."

Such was law; and it has maintained its two-fold character to this day. Its origin is the desire of the ruling class to give permanence to customs imposed by themselves for their own advantage. Its character is the skillful commingling of customs useful to society, customs which have no need of law to insure respect, with other customs useful only to rulers, injurious to the mass of the people, and maintained only by the fear of punishment.

Like individual capital, which was born of fraud and violence, and developed under the auspices of authority, law has no title to the respect of men. Born of violence and superstition, and established in the interests of consumer, priest and rich exploiter, it must be utterly destroyed on the day when the people desire to break their chains. . . .

III

. . . The great [French] Revolution began the demolition of this framework of law, bequeathed to us by feudalism and royalty. But after having demolished some portions of the ancient edifice, the Revolution delivered over the power of law-making to the bourgeoisie, who, in their turn, began to raise a fresh framework of laws intended to maintain and perpetuate middle-class domination among the masses. Their parliament makes laws right and left, and mountains of law accumulate with frightful rapidity. But what *are* all these laws at bottom?

The major portion have but one object—to protect private property, i. e., wealth acquired by the exploitations of man by man. Their aim is to open out to capital fresh fields for exploitation, and to sanction the new forms which that exploitation continually assumes, as capital swallows up another branch of human activity, railways, telegraphs, electric light, chemical industries, the expression of man's thought in literature and science, etc. The object of the rest of these laws is fundamentally the same. They exist to keep up the machinery of government which serves to secure to capital the exploitation and monopoly of the wealth produced. Magistrature, police, army, public instruction, finance, all serve one God—capital; all have but one object—to facilitate the exploitation of the worker by the capitalist. Analyze all the laws passed and you will find nothing but this.

The protection of the person, which is put forward as the true mission of law, occupies an imperceptible space among them, for, in existing society, assaults upon the person directly dictated by hatred and brutality tend to disappear. Nowadays, if anyone is murdered, it is generally for the sake of robbing him; rarely because of personal vengeance. But if this class of crimes and misdemeanors is continually diminishing, we certainly do not owe the change to legislation. It is due to the growth of humanitarianism in our societies, to our increasingly social habits rather than to the prescriptions of our laws. Repeal tomorrow every law dealing with the protection of the person, and tomorrow stop all proceedings for assault, and the number of attempts dictated by personal vengeance and by brutality would not be augmented by one single instance.

It will perhaps be objected that during the last fifty years, a good many liberal laws have been enacted. But, if these laws are analyzed, it will be discovered that this liberal legislation consists in the repeal of the laws bequeathed to us by the barbarism of preceding centuries. Every liberal law, every radical program, may be summed up in these words,—abolition of laws grown irksome to the middle-class itself, and return and extension to all citizens of liberties enjoyed by the townships of the twelfth century. The abolition of capital punishment, trial by jury for all "crimes" (there was a more liberal jury in the twelfth century), the election of magistrates, the right of bringing public officials to trial, the abolition of standing armies, free instruction, etc., everything that is pointed out as an invention of modern liberalism, is but a return to the freedom which existed before church and king had laid hands upon every manifestation of human life.

Thus the protection of exploitation directly by laws on property, and indirectly by the maintenance of the State is both the spirit and the substance of our modern codes, and the one function of our costly legislative machinery. But it is time we gave up being satisfied with mere phrases, and learned to appreciate their real significance. The law, which on its first appearance presented itself as a compendium of customs useful for the preservation of society, is now perceived to be nothing but an instrument for the maintenance of exploitation and the domination of the toiling masses by rich idlers. At the present day its civilizing mission is *nil;* it has but one object,—to bolster up exploitation.

This is what is told us by history as to the development of law. Is it in virtue of this history that we are called upon to respect it? Certainly not. It has no more title to respect than capital, the fruit of pillage. And the first duty of the revolution will be to make a bonfire of all existing laws as it will of all titles to property.

IV

The millions of laws which exist for the regulation of humanity appear upon investigation to be divided into three principal categories: protection of property, protection of persons, protection of government. And by analyzing each of these three categories, we arrive at the same logical and necessary conclusion: *the uselessness and hurtfulness of law.*

Socialists know what is meant by protection of property. Laws on property are not made to guarantee either to the individual or to society the enjoyment of the produce of their own labor. On the contrary, they are made to rob the producer of a part of what he has created, and to secure to certain other people that portion of the produce which they have stolen either from the producer or from society as a whole. When, for example, the law establishes Mr. So-and-So's right to a house, it is not establishing his right to a cottage he has built for himself, or to a house he has erected with the help of some of his friends. In that case no one would have disputed his right. On the contrary, the law is establishing his right to a house which is *not* the product of his labor; first of all because he has had it built for him by others to whom he has not paid the full value of their work, and next because that house represents a social value which he could not have produced for himself. The law is establishing his right to what belongs to everybody in general and to nobody in particular. The same house built in the midst of Siberia would not have the value it possesses in a large town, and, as we know, that value arises from the labor of something like fifty generations of men who have built the town, beautified it, supplied it with water and gas, fine promenades, colleges, theatres, shops, railways and roads leading in all directions. Thus, by recognizing the right of Mr. So-and-So to a particular house in Paris, London or Rouen, the law is unjustly appropriating to him a certain portion of the produce of the labor of mankind in general. And it is precisely becauṣe this appropriation and all other forms of property bearing the same character are a crying injustice, that a whole arsenal of laws and a whole army of soldiers, policemen and judges are needed to maintain it against the good sense and just feeling inherent in humanity.

Half our laws,—the civil code in each country,—serves no other purpose than to maintain this appropriation, this monopoly for the benefit of certain individuals against the whole of mankind. Three-fourths of the causes decided by the tribunals are nothing but quarrels between monopolists—two robbers disputing over their booty. And a great many of our criminal laws have the same object in view, their end being to keep the workman in a subordinate position towards his employer, and thus afford security for exploitation.

As for guaranteeing the product of his labor to the producer, there are no laws which even attempt such a thing. It is so simple and natural, so much a part of the manners and customs of mankind, that law has not given it so much as a thought. Open brigandage, sword in hand, is no feature of our age. Neither does one workman ever come and dispute the produce of his labor with another. If they have a misunderstanding they settle it by calling in a third person, without having recourse to law. The only person who exacts from another what that other has produced, is the proprietor, who comes in and deducts the lion's share. As for humanity in general, it everywhere respects the right of each to what he has created, without the interposition of any special laws.

As all the laws about property which make up thick volumes of codes and are the delight of our lawyers have no other object than to protect the unjust appropriation of human labor by certain monopolists, there is no reason for their existence, and, on the day of the revolution, social revolutionists are thoroughly determined to put an end to them. Indeed, a bonfire might be made with perfect justice of all laws bearing upon the so-called "rights of property," all title-deeds, all registers, in a word, of all that is in any way connected with an institution which will soon be looked upon as a blot in the history of humanity, as humiliating as the slavery and serfdom of past ages.

The remarks just made upon laws concerning property are

quite as applicable to the second category of laws; those for the maintenance of government, i. e., constitutional law.

It again is a complete arsenal of laws, decrees, ordinances, orders in council, and what not, all serving to protect the diverse forms of representative government, delegated or usurped, beneath which humanity is writhing. We know very well—anarchists have often enough pointed out in their perpetual criticism of the various forms of government—that the mission of all governments, monarchical, constitutional, or republican, is to protect and maintain by force the privileges of the classes in possession, the aristocracy, clergy and traders. A good third of our laws—and each country possesses some tens of thousands of them—the fundamental laws on taxes, excise duties, the organization of ministerial departments and their offices, of the army, the police, the church, etc., have no other end than to maintain, patch up, and develop the administrative machine. And this machine in its turn serves almost entirely to protect the privileges of the possessing classes. Analyze all these laws, observe them in action day by day, and you will discover that not one is worth preserving.

About such laws there can be no two opinions. Not only anarchists, but more or less revolutionary radicals also, are agreed that the only use to be made of laws concerning the organization of government is to fling them into the fire.

The third category of law still remains to be considered; that relating to the protection of the person and the detection and prevention of "crime." This is the most important because most prejudices attach to it; because, if law enjoys a certain amount of consideration, it is in consequence of the belief that this species of law is absolutely indispensable to the maintenance of security in our societies. These are laws developed from the nucleus of customs useful to human communities, which have been turned to account by rulers to sanctify their own domination. The authority of the chiefs of tribes, of rich families in towns, and of the king, depended upon their judicial functions, and even down to the present day, whenever the necessity of government is spoken of, its function as supreme judge is the thing implied. "Without a government men would tear one another to pieces," argues the village orator. "The ultimate end of all government is to secure twelve honest jurymen to every accused person," said Burke.

Well, in spite of all the prejudices existing on this subject, it is quite time that anarchists should boldly declare this category of laws as useless and injurious as the preceding ones.

First of all, as to so-called "crimes"—assaults upon persons

—it is well known that two-thirds, and often as many as three-fourths, of such "crimes" are instigated by the desire to obtain possession of someone's wealth. This immense class of so-called "crimes and misdemeanors" will disappear on the day on which private property ceases to exist. "But," it will be said, "there will always be brutes who will attempt the lives of their fellow citizens, who will lay their hands to a knife in every quarrel, and revenge the slightest offense by murder, if there are no laws to restrain and punishments to withhold them." This refrain is repeated every time the right of society *to punish* is called in question.

Yet there is one fact concerning this head which at the present time is thoroughly established; the severity of punishment does not diminish the amount of crime. Hang, and, if you like, quarter murderers, and the number of murders will not decrease by one. On the other hand, abolish the penalty of death, and there will not be one murder more; there will be fewer. Statistics prove it. But if the harvest is good, and bread cheap, and the weather fine, the number of murders immediately decreases. This again is proved by statistics. The amount of crime always augments and diminishes in proportion to the price of provisions and the state of the weather. Not that all murders are actuated by hunger. That is not the case. But when the harvest is good, and provisions are at an obtainable price, and when the sun shines, men, lighter-hearted and less miserable than usual, do not give way to gloomy passions, do not from trivial motives plunge a knife into the bosom of a fellow creature.

Moreover, it is also a well known fact that the fear of punishment has never stopped a single murderer. He who kills his neighbor from revenge or misery does not reason much about consequences; and there have been few murderers who were not firmly convinced that they should escape prosecution.

Without speaking of a society in which a man will receive a better education, in which the development of all his faculties, and the possibility of exercising them, will procure him so many enjoyments that he will not seek to poison them by remorse— even in our society, even with those sad products of misery whom we see today in the public houses of great cities—on the day when no punishment is inflicted upon murderers, the number of murders will not be augmented by a single case. And it is extremely probable that it will be, on the contrary, diminished by all those cases which are due at present to habitual criminals, who have been brutalized in prisons.

We are continually being told of the benefits conferred by law, and the beneficial effect of penalties, but have the speakers ever attempted to strike a balance between the benefits attributed to laws and penalties, and the degrading effect of these penalties upon humanity? Only calculate all the evil passions awakened in mankind by the atrocious punishments formerly inflicted in our streets! Man is the cruelest animal upon earth. And who has pampered and developed the cruel instincts unknown, even among monkeys, if it is not the king, the judge, and the priests, armed with law, who caused flesh to be torn off in strips, boiling pitch to be poured into wounds, limbs to be dislocated, bones to be crushed, men to be sawn asunder to maintain their authority? Only estimate the torrent of depravity let loose in human society by the "informing" which is countenanced by judges, and paid in hard cash by governments, under pretext of assisting in the discovery of "crime." Only go into the jails and study what man becomes when he is deprived of freedom and shut up with other depraved beings, steeped in the vice and corruption which oozes from the very walls of our existing prisons. Only remember that the more these prisons are reformed, the more detestable they become. Our model modern penitentiaries are a hundred-fold more abominable than the dungeons of the middle ages. Finally, consider what corruption, what depravity of mind is kept up among men by the idea of obedience, the very essence of law; of chastisement; of authority having the right to punish, to judge irrespective of our conscience and the esteem of our friends; of the necessity for executioners, jailers, and informers—in a word, by all the attributes of law and authority. Consider all this, and you will assuredly agree with us in saying that a law inflicting penalties is an abomination which should cease to exist.

Peoples without political organization, and therefore less depraved than ourselves, have perfectly understood that the man who is called "criminal" is simply unfortunate; that the remedy is not to flog him, to chain him up, or to kill him on the scaffold or in prison, but to help him by the most brotherly care, by treatment based on equality, by the usages of life among honest men. In the next revolution we hope that this cry will go forth:

"Burn the guillotines; demolish the prisons; drive away the judges, policemen and informers—the impurest race upon the face of the earth; treat as a brother the man who has been led by passion to do ill to his fellow; above all, take from the ignoble products of middle-class idleness the possibility of displaying their vices in attractive colors; and be sure that but few crimes will mar our society."

The main supports of crime are idleness, law and authority; laws about property, laws about government, laws about penalties and misdemeanors; and authority, which takes upon itself to manufacture these laws and to apply them.

No more laws! No more judges! Liberty, equality, and practical human sympathy are the only effectual barriers we can oppose to the anti-social instincts of certain among us.

Bibliography

Legal Cases

146 In order to get an idea of how the American legal system responds to civil disobedience and related issues, the reader should consult the judicial opinions in the following recent representative cases:

Edwards v. South Carolina, 372 U.S. 229 (1963)

Cox. v. Louisiana, 379 U.S. 536 (1964)

Williams v. Wallace, 240 F. Supp. 100 (M.D. Ala. 1965)

Adderley v. Florida, 385 U.S. 39 (1966)

Walker v. City of Birmingham, 388 U.S. 307 (1967)

United States v. O'Brien, 391 U.S. 367 (1968)

Shuttlesworth v. City of Birmingham, 394 U.S. 147 (1969)

Gutknecht v. United States, 396 U.S. 295 (1970)

Gillette v. United States and *Negre v. Larsen et al.,* decided on March 8, 1971.

Further relevant cases will be found cited in the texts and notes of the above.

Just before this volume went to press, the Supreme Court decided (March 8, 1971) in *Gillette v. United States* that objection to a particular war, even if conscientious, does not constitute a sufficient ground for exemption from the obligation to serve in the armed forces. Only pacifism may so exempt. The opinions in this case would merit the reader's careful examination.

Books and Articles

Acton, H. B. "Political Justification," *Contemporary British Philosophy* (H. D. Lewis, ed.). London: Macmillan, 1956.

Allen, Francis. "Civil Disobedience and the Legal Order," *University of Cincinnati Law Review* (Winter 1967).

Arendt, Hannah. *On Violence.* New York: Harcourt Brace Jovanovich, 1970.

Bay, Christian. "Civil Disobedience," *International Encyclopedia of the Social Sciences.* New York: Macmillan, 1968.

Bayne, D. C. *Conscience, Obligation and the Law.* Chicago: Loyola University Press, 1966.

Bedau, Hugo Adam. "On Civil Disobedience," *Journal of Philosophy* (October 12, 1961).

———— (ed.). *Civil Disobedience: Theory and Practice.* New York: Pegasus, 1969.

Bennett, John C. "The Place of Civil Disobedience," *Christianity and Crisis* (December 25, 1967).

Black, Charles L., Jr. "The Problem of the Compatibility of Civil Disobedience with American Institutions of Government," *Texas Law Review,* Vol. 43 (1965).

Blackstone, W. T. "Civil Disobedience: Is It Justified?" *Georgia Law Review,* Vol. 3 (1969).

Brown, Stuart M., Jr. "Civil Disobedience," *Journal of Philosophy,* Vol. 58 (1961).

Brownell, Herbert. "Civil Disobedience—A Lawyer's Challenge," *American Criminal Law Quarterly* (Fall 1964).

Cameron, J. M. "On Violence," *New York Review of Books* (July 2, 1970).

Campbell, A. H. "Obligation and Obedience to Law," *Proceedings of the British Academy,* Vol. 51 (1965).

Camus, Albert. *The Rebel.* New York: Vintage, 1958.

Carnes, John R. "Why Should I Obey the Law?" *Ethics* (October 1960).

Caudwell, Christopher. "Pacifism and Violence: A Study in Bourgeois Ethics," *Studies and Further Studies in a Dying Culture.* New York: Dodd, Mead, 1938.

Chomsky, Noam, William Earle, and John R. Silber. "Philosophers and Public Policy: A Symposium," *Ethics* (October 1968).

Clark, Tom C. "Philosophy, Law, and Civil Disobedience," *Ethics and Social Justice* (Howard E. Kiefer and Milton K. Munitz, eds.). New York: New York University Press, 1968. This is a reply to Hughes' "Civil Disobedience and the Political Question Doctrine."

Cohen, Carl. "Essence and Ethics of Civil Disobedience," *The Nation* (March 16, 1964).

————. *Civil Disobedience.* New York: Columbia University Press, 1971.

Cohen, Marshall. "Civil Disobedience in a Constitutional Democracy," *Massachusetts Review* (Spring 1969).

Conant, Ralph W. "Rioting, Insurrection and Civil Disobedience," *The American Scholar* (Summer 1968).

Cox, Archibald, et al. *Civil Rights, the Constitution, and the Courts.* Cambridge, Mass.: Harvard University Press, 1967.

Dellinger, David. *Revolutionary Nonviolence.* New York: Doubleday, 1971.

Dickinson, John. "A Working Theory of Sovereignty," *Political Science Quarterly* (1928).

Douglas, William O. *Points of Rebellion.* New York: Vintage, 1969.

Dworkin, Ronald. "A Theory of Civil Disobedience," *Ethics and Social Justice* (Howard E. Kiefer and Milton K. Munitz, eds.). New York: New York University Press, 1968.

Fortas, Abe. *Concerning Dissent and Civil Disobedience.* New York: Signet (NAL), 1968.

Freeman, Harrop A., et al. *Civil Disobedience.* Santa Barbara: Center for the Study of Democratic Institutions, 1966.

Gandhi, Mohandas K. *Non-violent Resistance.* New York: Schocken Books, 1964.

Garver, Newton. "What Violence Is," *The Nation* (June 24, 1968).

Green, Thomas Hill. *Lectures on the Principles of Political Obligation.* London (1921).

Griswold, Erwin N. "Dissent—1968," *Tulane Law Review* (June 1968).

Grodzins, Morton. *The Loyal and the Disloyal: Social Boundaries of Patriotism and Treason.* Chicago: University of Chicago Press, 1956.

Hall, Robert T. "Legal Toleration of Civil Disobedience," *Ethics* (January 1971).

Harrison, Bernard. "Violence and the Rule of Law," *Violence* (Jerome Shaffer, ed.). New York: McKay, 1971.

Holmes, Robert L. "Violence and Nonviolence," *Violence* (Jerome Shaffer, ed.). New York: McKay, 1971.

Hook, Sidney (ed.). *Law and Philosophy.* New York: New York University Press, 1964. This volume contains several replies to the article "Legal Obligation and the Duty of Fair Play" by John Rawls.

Hughes, Graham. "Civil Disobedience and the Political Question Doctrine," *New York University Law Review* (March 1968).

Kant, Immanuel. "Concerning the Common Saying: This May Be True in Theory but Does Not Apply in Practice," *The Philosophy of Kant* (Carl J. Friedrich, ed.-trans.). New York: Random House, 1949.

———. *The Metaphysical Elements of Justice* (John Ladd, trans.). Indianapolis: Bobbs-Merrill, 1965, esp. pp. 84–89, 133–137.

Keeton, Morris. "The Morality of Civil Disobedience," *Texas Law Review* (March 1965).

Kelsen, Hans. "Why Should the Law Be Obeyed?" *What Is Justice?* Berkeley: University of California Press, 1957.

King, Martin Luther, Jr. "Letter from Birmingham City Jail," *Liberation* (June 1963).

———. "Love, Law and Civil Disobedience," *New South,* Vol. 16 (1961).

Laski, Harold. *The Dangers of Obedience.* New York: Harper & Row, 1930.

Lewis, H. D. "Obedience to Conscience," *Mind,* Vol. 54 (1945).

Lewy, Guenter. "Resistance to Tyranny," *Western Political Quarterly* (September 1960).

———. "Superior Orders, Nuclear Warfare, and the Dictates of Conscience," *American Political Science Review* (March 1961).

Liebman, Morris I. "Civil Disobedience—A Threat to Our Law Society," *American Criminal Law Quarterly* (Fall 1964).

Locke, John. *Two Treatises of Government* (Peter Laslett, ed.). Cambridge: Cambridge University Press, 1960. Though not himself elaborating a theory of civil disobedience, Locke sets out ideals and principles that are very often appealed to in justifications of civil disobedience.

Lynd, Staughton (ed.). *Non-violence in America.* Indianapolis: Bobbs-Merrill, 1966.

MacFarlane, Leslie J. "Justifying Political Disobedience," *Ethics* (October 1968).

McWilliams, Wilson Carey. "Civil Disobedience and Contemporary Constitutionalism: The American Case," *Comparative Politics* (January 1969).

Marcuse, Herbert. "The Problem of Violence and the Radical Opposition," *Five Lectures.* Boston: Beacon Press, 1970.

Martin, Rex. "Civil Disobedience," *Ethics* (January 1970).

Miller, William R. *Nonviolence: A Christian Interpretation.* New York: Association Press, 1966.

The Monist, Vol. 54, No. 4 (October 1970) is entirely devoted to the topics of legal obligation and civil disobedience.

Murphy, Jeffrie G. "Violence and the Rule of Law," *Ethics* (July 1970). This is a reply to Robert Paul Wolff's "On Violence."

Naess, Arne. *Gandhi and the Nuclear Age.* Totowa: Bedminster Press, 1964.

Narveson, Jan. "Pacifism: A Philosophical Analysis," *Ethics* (July 1965).

Neumann, Franz L. "On the Limits of Justifiable Disobedience," *Conflict of Loyalties* (R. M. MacIver, ed.). New York: Institute for Religious and Social Studies, 1952.

Nieburg, H. L. "The Ethics of Resistance to Tyranny," *American Political Review* (December 1962).

Ofstad, H. "The Ethics of Resistance to Tyranny," *Inquiry* (Autumn 1961).

Pennock, J. Roland, and John W. Chapman (eds.). *Nomos XII: Political and Legal Obligation.* New York: Atherton Press, 1970.

Pitkin, Hannah. "Obligation and Consent," *American Political Science Review* (1965).

Power, Paul F. "On Civil Disobedience in Recent American Democratic Thought," *American Political Science Review* (March 1970).

Prosch, Harry. "Toward an Ethics of Civil Disobedience," *Ethics* (April 1967).

Rawls, John. "The Justification of Civil Disobedience," *Civil Disobedience: Theory and Practice* (Hugo Adam Bedau, ed.). New York: Pegasus, 1969.

Riehm, John W. "Civil Disobedience—A Definition," *American Criminal Law Quarterly* (Fall 1964).

Rostow, Eugene V. "No Right to Civil Disobedience," *Trial* (June–July 1970).

Rucker, Darnell. "The Moral Grounds of Civil Disobedience," *Ethics* (January 1966).

Russell, Bertrand. "Civil Disobedience," *New Statesman* (February 17, 1961).

Sibley, Mulford Q. "On Political Obligation and Civil Disobedience," *Journal of the Minnesota Academy of Science* (1965).

———— (ed.). *The Quiet Battle: Writings on the Theory and Practice of Non-violent Resistance.* New York: Doubleday, 1963.

————. *The Obligation to Disobey.* New York: Council on Religion and International Affairs, 1970.

Sorel, Georges. *Reflections on Violence.* New York: Macmillan, 1950.

Spitz, David. "Democracy and the Problem of Civil Disobedience," *Essays in the Liberal Idea of Freedom.* Tucson: University of Arizona Press, 1964.

Spock, Benjamin. "Vietnam and Civil Disobedience," *The Humanist* (January–February 1968).

Sturzo, Luigi. "The Right to Rebel," *Dublin Review* (1937).

Van den Haag, Ernest. "Government, Conscience, and Disobedience," *Sidney Hook and the Contemporary World* (Paul Kurtz, ed.). New York: John Day Co., 1968.

Van Dusen, Lewis H., Jr. "Civil Disobedience: Destroyer of Democracy," *American Bar Association Journal* (February 1969).

Walzer, Michael. "The Obligation to Disobey," *Ethics* (April 1967). Also in *Political Theory and Social Change* (David Spitz, ed.). New York: Atherton Press, 1967.

————. "Corporate Authority and Civil Disobedience," *Dissent* (September–October 1969).

————. *Obligations: Essays on Disobedience, War, and Citizenship.* Cambridge, Mass.: Harvard University Press, 1970.

Wasserstrom, Richard A. "Disobeying the Law," *Journal of Philosophy* (October 12, 1961).

————. "The Obligation to Obey the Law," *U.C.L.A. Law Review* (1963). Also in *Essays in Legal Philosophy* (Robert S. Summers, ed.). Berkeley: University of California Press, 1968.

Whittaker, Charles E., and William Sloane Coffin, Jr. *Law, Order and Civil Disobedience.* Washington, 1967.

Wofford, Harris, Jr. "Non-violence and the Law," *Journal of Religious Thought,* 1957.

Wolff, Robert Paul. "On Violence," *Journal of Philosophy* (October 2, 1969).

Woozley, A. D. "Socrates on Disobeying the Law," *Socrates* (Gregory Vlastos, ed.). New York: Doubleday, 1971.

Zahn, Gordon. *War, Conscience and Dissent.* New York: Hawthorn, 1967.

Pushing Gravity

New perspectives on Le Sage's theory of gravitation

Edited by Matthew R. Edwards

Apeiron
Montreal

Published by C. Roy Keys Inc.
4405, rue St-Dominique
Montreal, Quebec H2W 2B2 Canada
http://redshift.vif.com

First Published 2002

National Library of Canada Cataloguing in Publication Data

Main entry under title:

Pushing gravity : new perspectives on Le Sage's theory of
gravitation

ISBN 0-9683689-7-2

1. Le Sage, Georges-Louis, 1724-1803. 2. Gravitation.
I. Edwards, Matthew R.

QC178.P88 2002   531.14   C2002-900273-7

Cover design by Amanda Lawrence and Peter McArthur. The front cover
image is adapted from an original drawing by Georges-Louis Le Sage,
which appears in the article by James Evans. The drawing is reproduced
here with the permission of the Royal Society (©Royal Society).

Back cover graphic by Tom Sykes, representing electromagnetic Le Sage
models.

Table of Contents

Preface i

Halton Arp
    Foreword: The Observational Impetus
    for Le Sage Gravity 1

James Evans
    Gravity in the Century of Light:
    Sources, Construction and Reception of Le Sage's
    Theory of Gravitation 9

Frans van Lunteren
    Nicolas Fatio de Duillier on the Mechanical Cause
    of Universal Gravitation 41

E.J. Aiton
    Newton's Aether-Stream Hypothesis and the
    Inverse Square Law of Gravitation...................................... 61

Matthew R. Edwards
    Le Sage's Theory of Gravity: the Revival by Kelvin
    and Some Later Developments... 65

V.V. Radzievskii and I.I. Kagalnikova
    The Nature of Gravitation.. 79

Tom Van Flandern
    Gravity 93

Victor J. Slabinski
    Force, Heat and Drag in a Graviton Model 123

John Kierein
    Gravitation as a Compton Effect Redshift of Long
    Wavelength Background Radiation.................................... 129

Matthew R. Edwards
    Induction of Gravitation in Moving Bodies...................... 137

Toivo Jaakkola
    Action-at-a-Distance and Local Action in
    Gravitation 155

K.E. Veselov
Chance Coincidences or Natural Phenomena...................... 169

Barry Mingst and Paul Stowe
Deriving Newton's Gravitational Law
from a Le Sage Mechanism 183

Paul Stowe
Dynamic Effects in Le Sage Models 195

Nedelia Popescu-Adamut
The Electro-Thermodynamic Theory of Gravitation.......... 201

Roberto de Andrade Martins
Majorana's Experiments on Gravitational
Absorption 219

Roberto de Andrade Martins
Gravitational Absorption According to the
Hypotheses of Le Sage and Majorana 239

C.S. Unnikrishnan and G.T. Gillies
Constraints on Gravitational Shielding.............................. 259

H.-H. v. Borzeszkowski and H.-J. Treder
Non-Relativistic Effects in Gravitation 267

H.-J. Treder
Gravitational Ether and Riemann's
Theory of Gravity 279

Martin Kokus
Alternate Theories of Gravity and Geology in
Earthquake Prediction... 285

Vincent Buonomano
Co-operative Phenomena as a Physical Paradigm
for Relativity, Gravitation and Quantum Mechanics.......... 303

G.D. Hathaway
A Brief Survey of Gravity Control Experiments................ 311

Preface

To many readers of physics, the history of theories of gravitation may be summed up approximately as follows. After a chaotic period featuring vortex ether models and the like, gravity was at last put on a firm scientific footing by Newton. In the following centuries Newton's theory saw success after success, until a few unexplained anomalies, such as the advance of the perihelion of Mercury, paved the way for Einstein's General Relativity. The latter theory has remained without serious challenge to the present day. In this grand progression, few will likely have heard of a simple mechanical theory of gravitation, which from Newton's time has come down through the centuries almost unchanged. Its principal early expression was given by Georges-Louis Le Sage of Geneva in the mid-eighteenth century.

Le Sage's theory of gravitation has a unique place in science. For over three centuries it has periodically attracted some of the greatest physicists of the day, including Newton, who expressed interest in Fatio's earlier version of the theory, and later Kelvin, who attempted to modernize the theory in the late 1800's. At the same time, the theory has drawn just as many notable critics, including Euler, Maxwell and Poincaré. Despite frequent and spirited obituaries, Le Sage's theory in various guises has always survived to challenge the prevailing wisdom of the day. Now, at the start of this new century, it appears that the theory may be on the rise again.

The reasons for the present resurgence of Le Sage-type models of gravitation are their simplicity and depth—features desirable in any physical theory. Whereas Newton's theory and (later) Einstein's relativity were essentially mathematical descriptions of the motions of bodies in gravitation, Le Sage's theory attempts to arrive at the very cause of gravity. The basic idea runs like this. Space is filled with minute particles or waves of some description which strike bodies from all sides. A tiny fraction of the incident waves or particles is absorbed in this process. A single body will not move under this influence, but where two bodies are present each will be progressively urged into the shadow of the other. If any theory of gravity can be said to satisfy Occam's Razor, it is surely Le Sage's. Its simplicity and clarity guarantee that it will be conjured up again and again by those who seek to understand gravity's mechanism, as opposed to merely its rules.

Other reasons also exist for the recent upsurge of interest. Over the last half century, it has become increasingly common to view space once more as endowed with energy-dense fields, known variously as the zero-point fields, the quantum vacuum and many other names. Since the existence of such fields is the central postulate of Le Sage-type theories, the status of such theories has correspondingly risen. In addition, parallel veins of research in geophysics and cosmology also seem to point to in the direction of Le Sage. As Halton Arp discusses in his foreword, the geophysical link is to the theory of earth expansion (as opposed to conventional plate tectonics), while the cosmological link is to alternative cosmologies (rather than the Standard Model).

The first papers in the book explore the impressive three hundred-year history of Le Sage's theory. In the opening paper Evans discusses Le Sage's own contribution and the discouraging reception that Le Sage received from the scientists of his day, such as Euler and Laplace. Le Sage was in fact fighting a trend in the eighteenth century away from mechanical models of gravitation. The setting for his theory was actually much more favourable in the previous century, when another Genevan, Nicolas Fatio de Duillier, burst upon the scene with a very similar theory. Fatio's role is discussed by van Lunteren in his paper. Newton's own views on gravitation, which at times were very close to Le Sage's and Fatio's, are discussed in the reprinted paper by Aiton. The paper by Edwards discusses the attempt by Kelvin and others to revive Le Sage's theory in the late 1800's, when the theory was shown to be compatible with the kinetic theory of gases. This paper also has an overview of some twentieth century developments in the theory.

The modern wave of Le Sage-type theories is represented in the next group of papers. (While in later centuries it became common for authors to use "Lesage" or "LeSage", in this book we shall adopt the original spelling.) In these papers there will be seen to be many points of agreement, but also many differences. Some of the models, such as those of Van Flandern, Slabinski and Mingst and Stowe, are corpuscular models in the direct tradition of Le Sage. Others, such as those of Kierein, Edwards and Popescu-Adamut, explore electromagnetic analogues of Le Sage's theory. Historically, there have been countless names given to the Le Sage corpuscles or waves. In some of the papers the authors have adopted the term 'graviton' to refer to these entities.

The paper by Radzievskii and Kagalnikova provides a good overview of Le Sage's theory as well as a detailed mathematical description of a modern Le Sage theory. In their model, the gravitational force is propagated by material particles travelling at c. This paper was originally published in 1960 and later translated in a U.S. government technical report, of which the present paper is a slightly corrected version. Dr. Radzievskii, although reported to be ill at this time, nonetheless expressed his strong support for this project.

In his paper, Van Flandern develops Le Sage's theory from a modern standpoint and explores its relations to such problems as the existence of gravitational shielding, the advance of the perihelion of Mercury and heating effects. As did Le Sage, he argues that the absence of observed gravitational aberration is explicable with the gravitons having superluminal velocities.

A potentially major advance in Le Sage-type theories is given in the paper by Slabinski. In the past, these theories have generally supposed that the gravitons incident on bodies are either totally scattered or totally absorbed. In the former case, no gravitational force results, while in the latter an excessive heating of bodies is expected. Slabinski shows that, provided some small fraction of the gravitons is absorbed, the scattered gravitons can indeed generate a significant force.

In his paper, Kierein suggests that the Le Sage medium is in the form of very long wavelength radiation, as had earlier been proposed by Charles Brush. Such radiation penetrates matter easily and, in Kierein's model, a portion of the radiation traversing bodies is converted to mass through a Compton effect mechanism. The absorption of radiation leads to gravitation, while the mass increase is linked to earth expansion.

The paper by Edwards proposes that the absorption of gravitons by bodies in a Le Sage mechanism is proportional to the bodies' velocities as measured in the preferred reference frame defined by the gravitons (essentially the same frame as the cosmic background radiation). Graviton absorption increases the mass and rest energy of the bodies, which therefore lose velocity in the preferred frame. Overall there is conservation of energy (and thus no heating effect) since the rest energy gained by the bodies equals the kinetic energy lost.

The paper by Toivo Jaakkola is adapted from a longer paper that was originally published posthumously in the memorial issue of *Apeiron* dedicated to him. It presents Jaakkola's Le Sage-type model and many observations and conclusions about Le Sage theories in general. The paper by Veselov, reprinted from *Geophysical Journal*, presents a novel type of Le Sage mechanism, which Veselov links to earth expansion and various astrophysical phenomena.

In their paper, Mingst and Stowe present a corpuscular Le Sage model. Dynamical aspects of this and other Le Sage models are discussed in the companion paper by Stowe. In her paper, Popescu-Adamut reviews and updates the "electrothermodynamical theory of gravitation" proposed in the 1980's by her father, Iosif Adamut.

The next several papers consider the question of gravitational shielding, with special reference to the work of Quirino Majorana. Unlike Le Sage, Majorana proposed that matter itself emits an energy flux of some kind which produces gravitational effects on other bodies. Just as in Le Sage's theory, however, this flux would be attenuated in passing through other bodies. Majorana performed a famous set of experiments which appeared to demonstrate such a shielding effect. This work is discussed in Martins' first paper. In his second paper, Martins examines the links between Majorana's theory and Le Sage's. Whereas Majorana had thought it possible to distinguish experimentally between his own theory and Le Sage's, Martins proves that this supposition is false, *i.e.*, that the predictions of both theories in shielding experiments are precisely the same. This finding is in keeping with the notion that the theories of Le Sage and Majorana may actually be two sides of the same coin. In some Le Sage-type theories, the Le Sage flux upon interacting with matter is converted into a secondary flux, which itself does not transmit the gravitational force. Mathematically, such models can be made to resemble Majorana-type models if the primary fluxes are disregarded and the secondary fluxes are modelled as transmitting momentum in the negative sense.

Majorana's experiments were never repeated, however, and other confirmation of the existence of gravitational shielding has been very hard to come by. Some of the attempts to find such shielding are reviewed in the paper by Unnikrishnan and Gillies. While evidence for shielding at the present time appears limited, it can only be stated that the question remains open both theoretically and experimentally. For instance, there is the exciting possibility that the Zürich apparatus for measuring G, discussed by these authors, could also be used to directly repeat the experiments of Majorana.

In their paper von Borzeszkowski and Treder discuss possible non-relativistic effects in gravitation, such as absorption of gravity, but within the context of relativistic theories of gravitation. One such theory, originally proposed by Riemann, is examined in the following paper by Treder.

In his paper, Kokus examines the many unusual patterns in earthquakes and other seismic events and discusses the role of alternate theories of gravitation in accounting for them. He argues that many of the patterns can be accounted for in expanding earth or pulsating earth models. Buonomano, in his paper, discusses the possible roles of a Le Sage-type medium in quantum physics. The book concludes with a historical discussion by Hathaway of attempts to manipulate gravitation.

Collectively, the papers in this book show that the remarkable saga of Le Sage's theory of gravitation may be entering a new and exciting phase. In the new century, it may even pass that Le Sage's theory comes into prominence once more. If it does, it would not be entirely surprising. It is, after all, the simplest theory of gravitation.

Matthew Edwards

Acknowledgements

In preparation of this book, I received invaluable assistance from many quarters. Important suggestions on potential contributors and assistance in contacting them came from Craig Fraser, André K.T. Assis, Andreas Kleinert, John Kierein, Tom Van Flandern, Roy Keys, Henry Aujard, Ieronim Mihailă and Victor Kuligin. At the University of Toronto Library, Jeff Heeney, Sophia Kaszuba, Elaine Granatstein, Andrew Sorcik and Roy Pearson provided bibliographic, technical and other assistance. Peter McArthur proofread the many papers and provided valuable technical assistance. I also thank Dennis McCarthy and Robert Villahermosa for their help. The Bibliothèque publique et universitaire, Ville de Genève, and the Library of the Royal Society, London, generously allowed reproduction of figures.

Throughout the project I benefited immensely from countless discussions with the contributors, especially John Kierein, Tom Van Flandern, James Evans and Roberto de Andrade Martins. Most of all I thank Roy Keys for his assistance throughout the project and my wife Teresa Edwards and daughter Oriane Edwards for their enthusiastic support.

The Observational Impetus
for Le Sage Gravity

Halton Arp[*]

For many years I never questioned the obvious fact that masses attracted each other (inversely as the square of their separation, to complete the mantra). The 'attraction' was so blatant that it required no thought. But then observations of galaxies and quasars forced me to accept the fact that extragalactic redshifts were primarily intrinsic and not the result of recessional velocity in an expanding universe.

How did this lead to my abandoning pulling gravity and investigating pushing gravity? It is interesting how the crumbling of one fundamental assumption can have reverberations throughout the whole underpinning of one's science. In this case it was the necessity to find a mechanism which would explain intrinsic redshifts that eventually turned out to shake other fundamental assumptions. The search was motivated by a desire to have the discordant observations believed. (Unfortunately, when I asked Feynman about the Hoyle-Narlikar variable mass theory, he told me "We do not need a new theory because our present one explains everything.") Nevertheless, the ball had started rolling downhill so to speak and in 1991, with Narlikar's help, I outlined in Apeiron the way in which particle masses growing with time would account for the array of accumulated extragalactic paradoxes. Later Narlikar and Arp (1993) published in the Astrophysical Journal Narlikar's original 1977 solution of the basic dynamical equations along with the Apeiron applications to the quasar/galaxy observations.

We hoped, of course, to gain validation of the new theory by showing that it was a legitimate product of the accepted, one might even say worshipped, general relativistic field equations. All we gained in fact was an audience which totally ignored this new, more rigorous solution. Nevertheless, seeing it in print started the wheels slowly turning in my head.

The first insight came when I realized that the Friedmann solution of 1922 was based on the assumption that the masses of elementary particles were always and forever constant, m = const. He had made an approximation in a differential equation and then solved it. This is an error in mathematical procedure. What Narlikar had done was solve the equations for $m = f(x,t)$. This is a

---

[*] Max-Planck Institut für Astrophysik, 85741 Garching, Germany

Pushing Gravity: new perspectives on Le Sage's theory of gravitation
edited by Matthew R. Edwards (Montreal: Apeiron 2002)

more general solution, what Tom Phipps calls a covering theory. Then if it is decided from observations that m can be set constant (*e.g.*, locally) the solution can be used for this special case. What the Friedmann and following Big Bang evangelists did was succumb to the typical conceit of humans that the whole of the universe was just like themselves.

But Narlikar had overwhelmed me with the beauty of the variable mass solution by showing how the local dynamics could be recovered by the simple conformal transformation from t time (universal) to what we called τ time (our galaxy time). The advertisement here was that our solution inherited all the physics triumphs much heralded in general relativity, but also accounted for the non-local phenomena like quasar and extragalactic redshifts. Of course, to date, this still has made no impression on academic science.

In addition, I eventually realized that an important part of the variable mass solution was that it took place in perfectly flat, Euclidean space. This pointed directly at the revelation that the Riemannian, geometric terms on the left hand side of the famous $G_{\mu\nu} = T_{\mu\nu}$ equation were zero. If $G_{\mu\nu} = 0$, then the curved space-time had nothing to do with real cosmic physics.

Two thoughts then presented themselves:

1)   The $G_{\mu\nu}$ terms in the conventional solution usually represent forbiddingly complicated terms. But their existence appears to be required only for the purpose of compensating for the variable m in the $T_{\mu\nu}$ side of the equation, which was assumed constant in the Big Bang solution. These geometric terms, as is well known, are used to adjust parameters such as H_0, q_0, *etc.*, when the redshift–apparent magnitude relation is interpreted in an expanding universe. (In the variable mass solution H_0 equals only ⅔ the inverse age of our galaxy and is equal to around 50 km/sec/Mpc, with no adjustable parameters.)

2)   If there are no geometric space curvature terms in the variable mass solution, and this is a more valid solution, is there ever a legitimate use for these terms? For some time I entertained the idea that near high mass concentrations one might need them. But now I see work by Montanus and Gill which indicated physics with proper time and local time can reproduce classical relativity tests in flat, Euclidean space. It raises the question: Is space-time curvature valid? At this point the elementary question that should have been asked long ago by scientists and non-scientists alike is: *With any reasonable definition of space, how can one "curve" it?* (If you have trouble visualizing curved space, try curved time!) Curved space-time appears to be, and always to have been, as Tom Phipps casually remarked, an oxymoron!

In Table 1 appended here is a summary of how conventional relativity fails and how the flat space time, local and cosmic time treatment gives common sense results in its place.

Concept	Variable Mass	Proper Time	Relativistic	Common Sense
Primary reference frame	√	√	X	ave. over detection = reference
flat (Euclidean) space	√	√	X	space defined as direction
no singularities (black holes)	√	√	X	clocks run fast and slow
no fields (action at a distance)	√	√	X	causality
$mass \neq f(v)$		√	X	$M \to \infty$ as $v \to c$
$mass = f(t)$	√		X	Mach, e.m. speed $= c$
no dark matter	√		X	high redshifts not velocity
no big bang, expansion of space or faster than light inflation	√		X	something cannot come from nothing, space cannot expand
	cosmological	terrestrial	historical	
	Hoyle Narlikar Arp	Van Flandern Phipps, Gill Selleri, Drew Montanus Galeczki	Einstein Academia Media	

Table 1. Some of the most important concepts in modern physics and cosmology are listed in the first column. The next three columns show whether variable mass, proper time, or relativistic physics support or violate these concepts. The last column gives the common sense (operational definition) of the concepts. Finally, at the bottom of the columns are a few of the names associated with the three analytical systems. (From *Acta Scientiarum*, in press).

Gravity

After this long preamble we finally come to the point: If space is not curved by the presence of mass (as per Einstein)—then what causes gravity? We are forced by the solution which explains the redshift dependence on age of matter to look for another cause of gravity. If masses do not move on prefixed tracks in space then there is no hope of having the instaneously acting component of gravity by guiding them with the exchange of some electromagnetic wave travelling with speed c.

Since the time of the 18th century Genevan physicist, Le Sage, many people have considered what is apparently the only alternative to 'pulling' gravity, *i.e.*, 'pushing gravity'. My attention, however, was called to it belatedly by an article in Tom Van Flandern's Meta Research Bulletin. The key point for me was that its force behaved "inversely as the square of the separation," a point which I had not bothered to work out. The force (be with you) is transmitted by a surrounding sea of much faster than light gravitons. Van Flandern (1998) calculates $> 2 \times 10^{10}\, c$. So we can have as 'nearly instantaeneous' action as we wish and yet not abandon the concept of causality.

Of course it is interesting to comment on some of the doctrinal problems of the imminently deceased relativity theory. Are inertial and gravitational mass the same? Since the atoms of a feather and of a lead ball are made of the same electrons, protons and neutrons, we will have—to some orders anyway—the same force applied by the absorption from the surrounding sea of gravitons. So the equivalence principle holds. But only if the absorption of gravitons, and subsequent impetus, is proportional to inertial mass.

My own working hypothesis for gravity now is that gravitons are very low mass particles with a huge de Broglie wavelength compared to photons. Since their wavelength is so long they have much less interaction with the intergalactic medium. So they far exceed the normal velocity of light in 'vacuum' (*i.e.*, the vacuum that light in our locality of the universe sees). In other words the photon is transmitted through the average cosmic false vacuum, material vacuum or zero point energy field—to use just a few names given to the old fashioned concept of 'aether'. But the graviton interacts with much less of this molasses and hence moves much faster. One might speculate that there is a vast amount of matter in the universe which radiates at very long wavelengths.

Perhaps it is time to wander back to the observations with our new hypothesis in hand. Since the particles of matter in the universe grow as they age and communicate with ever more distant parts of the universe they have to receive information. In the variable mass theory this electromagnetic communication is at the speed of light, c. The gravitons travelling much faster than the speed of light, however, must also carry information. (No one could argue that knowledge of the direction of an adjoining mass is not information). So the old relativistic shibboleth—"information cannot be transmitted faster than the speed of light"—falls by the wayside. Recent experiments with entangled quantum states are also indicating this.

As the inertial mass of particulate matter grows with time, in order to conserve momentum it must slow its velocity with respect to the primary reference frame. This is an important contribution of the new physics because the observations show that newly created, high redshift quasars are initially ejected as a near zero mass plasma with very high velocities and then grow in mass, drop in redshift and slow in velocity until they eventually form groups of slightly younger companions to the parent galaxy. This is observationally established and can only be explained by the variable mass theory.

The condensation of low mass plasma into a coherent body in the new theory forms an interesting contrast to condensation of galaxies in the 78-year-old Big Bang theory. Bernard Bligh (2000) has shown thermodynamically that the hot Big Bang cannot cool and condense into galaxies because its expansion is not constrained. As experience would dictate, a hot gas just diffuses. The situation with the near zero mass plasma is different, however, in that the growing mass of its constituent particles slows their velocities, thereby cooling their temperature. In addition, the growing mass increases the pressure toward condensing into a gravitationally bound body.

Now that we reference the primary reference frame we are reminded that this is yet another strike against the hallowed relativity theory, which is supposed to have no primary reference frame. But the existence of the microwave background certainly reminds us that an average over the detectable universe certainly represents an obvious, primary reference frame. Moreover, laboratory experiments, including those on the Sagnac effect by Selleri and others, reveal the presence of such a frame.

The objection by Feynman to pushing gravity, which was brought to my attention by John Kierein, was that objects in orbital motion such as the earth would experience resistance from increased graviton flux in the direction of their motion. The answer, without computation, seems to be that this effect would only come into action at very high orbital speeds because of the very high speed of the gravitons. But, in general, it should be noted that my observational experience sheds doubt on any extragalactic velocities greater than about 300 km/sec. (rotational velocities in galaxies). This would imply that older objects must come very close to rest with respect to—what else but a primary, or universal reference frame.

Quantization

An unexpected property of astronomical objects (and therefore an ignored and suppressed subject) is that their properties are quantized. This first appeared when William Tifft showed that the redshifts of galaxies occurred in certain preferred values, *e.g.*, 72, 144, 216, *etc.* km/sec. Later William Napier demonstrated a periodicity of 37.5 km/sec with great accuracy. The outstandingly important, empirical implication to draw from these by now exceedingly well established observations is that the individual velocities of galaxies must be less than about 20 km/sec; otherwise the sharp quantizations would be blurred. In turn this implied very little motion in a primary reference frame.

For the quasars, Geoffrey Burbidge noticed soon after the first redshifts began to accumulate that there was a preferred value about resdhift $z = 1.95$. As more redshifts accumulated it became clear that the whole range of extragalactic redshifts was significantly periodic. K.G. Karlsson showed that they fit the formula

$$(1+z_n) = (1+z_0) \times 1.23^n.$$

This was interpreted by Arp in terms of the variable mass theory by hypothesizing that as the electron masses grew with time they increased through permitted mass states which stepped by a factor of 1.23.

The most astonishing result was then pointed to by Jess Artem, that the same quantization ratio that appeared in quasar redshifts appeared in the orbital parameters of the planets in the solar system. This first manifested itself in the ratio of planetary semi-major axes occurring in some high power of n in 1.23^n.

This also appeared to be true of the ratio of planetary and lunar masses and even solar and electron masses.

Shortly afterward, O. Neto in Brazil, Agnese and Festa in Italy, L. Nottale in France and A. and J. Rubčić in Croatia independently began pointing out similarities to the Bohr atom in the orbital placement of the planets. Different variations of

$$\text{Bohr-like radius} = n^2 \text{ or } n^2 + 1/2n$$

fit the planetary semi-major axes extremely well with rather low 'quantum' numbers n. Most recently I have learned of a modification to the Titius-Bode law by Walter Murch where the

$$\text{planetary radii} = 1 + 2^n + 2^{n-1}.$$

This latter law fits the observed planetary positions exceedingly well for $n = -1$ to 6 with an average deviation of only 2.4 percent.

Which of these empirical laws is correct or whether they are all different approximations of a more fundamental law is a mystery at this moment. But it is clear that the properties of the planets are not random and that they are in some way connected to quantum mechanical parameters, both of which are connected to cosmological properties.

Just to try to tie some of the above results together, in what is obviously an inadequate theory, let us suppose that the planetary system started as some kind of analogue to an atom. In the variable mass theory the matter starts out from zero mass but the basic unit of charge never changes. Therefore the seed planets would be placed according to Bohr atom rules. As time goes on their inertial masses grow, but in steps which are governed by communication with their cosmic environment. Very soon the charge aspect of the planet is over-whelmed by its inertial mass aspect and it is thereafter governed by the currently observed gravitational laws.

Expanding Earth

As long ago as 1958, S. Carey reported detailed geological data which implied the earth had been expanding. K.M. Creer (1965) was one of many who showed how accurately the continents fitted together in the past and M. Kokus (1994) calculated how the observed sea floor spreading in the mid Atlantic ridge supported this interpretation. Naturally without an identifiable physical cause most scientists abandoned these empirical conclusions in favour of the theory that there was nothing of significance to explain. It is appropriate to quote Creer, however: "For an adequate explanation we may well have to await a satisfactory theory of the origin and development of the universe." The vari-able mass theory is a candidate to fulfill that prophecy.

But how does Le Sage gravity enter this picture? I would suggest the following trial hypothesis. If much faster than light gravitons are pushing massive bodies toward each other, then they must be transmitting an impulse which could be described as energy. Is it possible that these gravitons are depositing energy or creating mass in the interior of the earth which is causing energy or creating mass in the interior of the earth which is causing it to expand?

There are two attractive features of this suggestion. In the Olympia meeting (1993) there were calculations that the mass of the earth had to be increasing. The problem was, however, that the mass had to be increasing too fast. To quote J.K. Davidson (Olympia Meeting, p. 299): "The current expansion rate is very rapid and gives rise to questions like, how is the extra mass being created (it seems to be occurring in the core as there is no evidence at the surface); will the earth ultimately explode and form another asteroid belt or will it become a Jupiter then a sun...." At that meeting I reminded the Geophysics section of the fact that the extragalactic quantization evidence showed that as matter evolved it must jump rapidly from one quantized particle mass value to the next highest. The obvious implication is that this would be a natural explanation for the varying rate of expansion of the earth.

The second attractive feature of the variable mass theory is that the research of Tom Van Flandern (1993) indicates that planets explode. It has always been clear that where a giant planet should exist between Mars and Jupiter there is instead a belt of rock fragments called the asteroids. But Van Flandern's careful work on the problem of Mars (which should in all continuity be much larger rather than much smaller than the earth) shows that it has suffered a fragmenting explosion leaving visible effects on one face. So there is evidence that this happens in the solar system. In fact there is visible evidence that it happens in galaxies as well (Arp, 1998, 1999).

The Current State

The most intriguing problem to me now is to combine the features of the variable mass solution with the features of the pushing gravity models. The Machian communication of the variable mass solution with matter at increasing distances offers a solution for the quantization values as reflecting discrete drops in mean density as we proceed outward in a hierarchical universe (Narlikar and Arp, 2000). But that communication is electromagnetic at the velocity of light. Is it possible to transfer the periodically increasing mass with photons that resonate with the frequency of the electrons and protons in the matter under consideration? Or does this resonance frequency of the electron, for example (Milo Wolff, 1995), just make it possible for the much smaller, much faster than light gravitons to deposit new mass in older material.

As important as the details are, the observations overall seem now to generally require new matter to continually materialize at various points in the universe. Balance, if necessary, could be obtained from feedback mechanisms between the intergalactic aether and long wavelength radiation from present matter (I presume). The greatest part of the progress independent researchers have made in the past decades, in my opinion, has been to break free of the observationally disproved dogma of curved space time, dark matter, Big Bang, no primary reference frame and no faster than light information.

References

Apeiron, winter-Spring 1991, pp 18-28.

H. Arp, 1998, *Seeing Red: Redshifts, Cosmology and Academic Science*, Apeiron, Montreal.

H. Arp, 1999, *ApJ* **525**, 594.

H. Arp, H. Bi, Y. Chu and X. Zhu, 1990, *Astron. Astrophys.* **239**, 33.

B. R. Bligh, 2000, "*The Big Bang Exploded*," 4 St. James Ave., Hampton Hill, Middlesex, TW12 1HH, U.K.

K.M. Creer, 1965, *Nature* **205**, 539.

M. Kokus, 1994, private communication.

J. Narlikar and H. Arp, 2000, "Dynamics of Ejection from Galaxies and the Variable Mass Hypothesis," in preparation.

Olympia Meeting, 1993, *Frontiers of Fundamental Physics*, "Geophysics," pp 241-335, eds, Barone, M. and Selleri, F., (Plenum, New York and London).

T. Van Flandern, 1993, *Dark matter, Missing Planets and New Comets*, North Atlantic Books, Berkeley.

T. Van Flandern, 1998, "The Speed of Gravity- What the Experiments Say," *Phys. Lett. A* **250**, 1.

M. Wolff, 1995, "A Wave Structure for the Electron," *Galilean Electrodynamics* **6**, No. **5**, 83.

Gravity in the Century of Light

Sources, Construction and Reception
of Le Sage's Theory of Gravitation

James Evans[*]

1. Introduction

The history of gravitation theories provides excellent opportunities for investigating what "explanation" means, and has meant, in physics. There are two reasons for this. First, the phenomena to be accounted for by a successful theory of (Newtonian) gravity are easily described and understood, which is not the case, for example, with electrodynamics. Second, there were very few additions to these phenomena for two hundred years. The shifting fortunes of gravitation theories in the eighteenth and nineteenth centuries were largely due to causes other than shifts in the empirical evidence. Each generation of physicists, or natural philosophers, sought to place universal gravitation in the context of its own worldview. Often this entailed an effort to reduce gravitation to something more fundamental. What is deemed fundamental has, of course, changed with time. Each generation attacked the problem of universal gravitation with the tools of its day and brought to bear the concepts of its own standard model.[1]

The most successful eighteenth-century attempt to provide a mechanical explanation of gravity was that of Georges-Louis Le Sage (1724-1803) of Geneva.[2] (Fig. 1.) Like many good Newtonians of the time, Le Sage was an atomist: he wished to explain all the properties of matter in terms of collisions and conglomerations of atoms. But he went further than most, for he believed that even gravity could be explained in this way. Le Sage's effort reduced gravitation to the eighteenth century's most austere physical notion, that of mass points, or atoms, in the void.

Le Sage's theory is an especially interesting one, for several reasons. First, it serves as the prototype of a dynamical explanation of Newtonian gravity. Second, the theory came quite close to accomplishing its aim. Third, the theory had a long life and attracted comment by the leading physical thinkers of several successive generations. Le Sage's theory therefore provides an excellent opportunity for the study of the evolution of attitudes toward physical explanation. The effects of national style in science and generational change take on a new clarity.

---

[*] Department of Physics, University of Puget Sound, 1500 North Warner, Tacoma, WA 98416 USA

Pushing Gravity: new perspectives on Le Sage's theory of gravitation
edited by Matthew R. Edwards (Montreal: Apeiron 2002)

Fig. 1. Georges-Louis
Le Sage (1724-1803), in
an eighteenth-century
engraving. Photo cour-
tesy of Bibliothèque pub-
lique et universitaire, Ville
de Genève.

2.   Le Sage's Theory in Bare Outline

Le Sage imagines that the observable universe is bathed in a sea of ultramundane corpuscles—called ultramundane (*ultramondain*) because they impinge on us from outside the known universe. These corpuscles have the following properties: minute mass, enormous speed, and complete inelasticity. Now, all apparently solid objects, such as books and planets, are mostly void space. Consequently, gross objects absorb but a minuscule fraction of the ultramundane corpuscles that are incident upon them.

From these premises Le Sage deduces an attractive force between any two gross objects. Imagine two macroscopic bodies, as in the top portion of Fig. 2. Let us refer to the body on the left as L and the body on the right as R. Ultramundane corpuscles rain on these bodies from both left and right. A small fraction of the corpuscles incident from the left is absorbed by L. Therefore, R stands *in the shadow* of L: Body R receives fewer corpuscles from the left than it does from the right because of the screening action of L. Consequently, R will be pushed toward the left by the uncompensated corpuscles that are incident from the right. In the same way, L also stands in the shadow of R and experiences an effective force towards the right. The two bodies which appear to *pull* on one another are actually *pushed* together. To complete the picture, we must now imagine ultramundane corpuscles incident on the bodies, not just from the left and right, but along all possible trajectories. Le Sage's theory can be made quantitative, as he certainly intended it to be. With the right auxiliary assumptions it does produce an attraction of two bodies in direct proportion to the product of their masses and in inverse proportion to the square of the distance between them.[3]

The goal of this article is to set Le Sage's theory in historical context. We shall begin by surveying attitudes towards gravity as they developed in the century preceding Le Sage. Then we shall turn to Le Sage's intellectual development, his construction of his theory, and his efforts to win a hearing for it. Finally, we shall examine the reception of the theory by Le Sage's contemporaries.

3. Explaining Gravity: From Descartes to Huygens and Newton

In Paris, on several consecutive Wednesdays of the year 1669, the newly established Royal Academy of Sciences held a debate on the cause of weight.[4] Gilles Personne de Roberval read the first memoir on the subject on August 7.

Fig. 2. Pairs of macroscopic bodies traversed by currents of ultramundane corpuscles. From Le Sage's *Essai de chymie mécanique*. Photo courtesy of the Library of the Royal Society, London.

Roberval divided physical thinkers into three schools: (1) some hold that weight resides in a heavy body; (2) others make it common and reciprocal between the heavy body and the body towards which it gravitates; (3) yet others make it an effect of a third body, which pushes the heavy body. All attempts at establishing a mechanism naturally belong to the third school of thought. As Roberval pointed out, the thinkers of this school all have recourse to a subtle body which moves with extreme rapidity, which insinuates itself among the particles of larger bodies, and thus produces the effects of weight and levity. Roberval pointed out the following difference between the thinkers of the third school and those of the other two camps. Those who ascribe weight to the very nature of the heavy body, or to the common nature of two bodies, make weight the cause of motion; but those of the third school want motion to be the cause of weight. Roberval also remarked that all three opinions were the products of pure thought and had nothing solid to support them. But the first two schools had this advantage, that once postulating the quality, they explained everything without effort. But the third school, after postulating its subtle fluid, still had a good deal of work to do. For his own part, Roberval suspected that men might lack the special sense required to know anything of this subject, in the same way that the blind cannot know anything of light or colors.

The next Wednesday, Nicolas Frenicle asserted that one must admit the reality of attraction. He pointed out analogies between weight and the attraction of a magnet for iron, of amber for dry things, and of drops of mercury for one another. But one week later, Jacques Buot objected to those who spoke of a virtue or desire for union between the particles of a body. No one, he said, had ever conceived the cause of such desires or affections in inanimate things. He then turned to the vortex theory of Descartes.

In his *Principles of Philosophy* (1644) Descartes had imposed upon natural philosophy stringent new rules of explanation.[5] Descartes banished the occult qualities of the medieval scholastics, such as sympathy, affinity and attraction (characteristic of Roberval's first two schools of thought), and insisted that all natural phenomena be explained by the impact of contiguous bodies upon one another. This way of thinking about nature came to be called "mechanical philosophy." According to Descartes, the planets are carried around the Sun by a vortex (*tourbillon*) of celestial fluid. The weight of a body at the surface of the Earth is also due to a vortex of celestial fluid. This subtle fluid, seeking to recede from the center of its vortex, impels the ordinary terrestrial matter towards the center. In one of his published letters, Descartes even described a demonstration to illustrate his theory of weight. Fill a round vessel with fine lead shot. Among this shot place some pieces of wood, lighter and larger than the shot. If you then turn the vessel rapidly, "you will find that this small shot will drive all these pieces of wood ... toward the center of the vessel, just as the subtle matter drives the terrestrial bodies."[6] Descartes realized that in his explanations of celestial and terrestrial phenomena he had granted himself considerable freedom to invent invisible mechanisms. To forestall his critics, he claimed that he offered these mechanisms only as hypotheses. Moreover, even if these hypotheses happened to be false, they could still be valuable. A false hypothesis that successfully accounts for the phenomena could be as useful as the truth itself.[7] Nevertheless, Jacques Buot, in his discourse of August 21, 1669, accepted Descartes' explanation of weight as fully established.

Christiaan Huygens read his own paper on August 28. Huygens' contribution was an important one, for he was the first to suggest a mechanism for gravity that was supported by calculation. He brought to bear his own new theorem on circular motion in order to estimate the speed of the matter in the ethereal vortex. In this he raised the argument over the cause of weight to a new level—a fact not immediately appreciated by his contemporaries. He raised the level of discourse in another way, by his avoidance of circularity of thought in his explanation and his criticism of Descartes for just such a failing. Huygens pointed out that while Descartes' demonstration experiment certainly works, it works only because the lead and wood have different densities. That is, Descartes had to assume inherent differences in weight—which were supposed to be a product of the explanation, not a part of the premise. Although Huygens stressed that his theory of weight was different from that of Descartes, it nevertheless was certainly in the Cartesian tradition. In 1690, Huygens published his *Discourse on the Cause of Weight*, in which he presented his theory of gravity, reworked and expanded, but unchanged in its essence.[8]

In this debate at the Paris Academy, which occurred nearly two decades before the publication of Newton's *Principia*, we can already see the shape of the larger and more vociferous debate that followed the enunciation of the law of universal gravitation. Newton chose his title carefully and meant it as a rebuke to Descartes: these were not vague and sloppy "principles of philosophy" but rather *Mathematical Principles of Natural Philosophy*. In the preface to the first (1687) edition Newton asserted that the whole burden of philosophy is "to discover the forces of nature from the phenomena of motions and then to demonstrate the other phenomena from these forces."[9] To the second edition of 1713 he added the celebrated General Scholium, in which he feigned no hypotheses about the cause of gravity: "For whatever is not deduced from the phenomena must be called a hypothesis; and hypotheses, whether metaphysical or physical, or based on occult qualities, or mechanical, have no place in experimental philosophy."[10] In renouncing metaphysical and occult qualities, Newton was only endorsing what Descartes had begun. But in attacking physical or mechanical hypotheses, he was attacking Descartes himself and the whole school of Cartesian mechanical philosophy.

It was possible for Newton to make a point of renouncing mechanical hypotheses because the plan of his *Principia* did more or less correspond to the burden of natural philosophy: induction of the inverse-square law of gravitational attraction from the phenomena, and deduction of new phenomena from the force law. But Newton's rejection of hypotheses in the General Scholium was also partly a rhetorical device, introduced to answer the critics of the first edition of the *Principia* who complained that he had not given the cause of gravity, and that he had even reintroduced the occult forces of the medieval scholastics.

Newton himself was certainly not the positivist that later generations made of him. In his youth he was steeped in the vortices of Descartes and he abandoned them only after a struggle. While composing the *Principia*, Newton still thought the vortices at least to be worth refuting as a mechanical cause of gravity. At the end of Book II he took pains to show they could not be made consistent with Kepler's laws of planetary motion. But even then Newton did not cease speculating about the cause of gravity. In his *Opticks* he was inclined to attribute the effects of gravity to the same ethereal medium as was responsible for the refraction of light. Newton held that this ether was most rare inside bodies and that it increased in density with distance from the surface of a body. Thus, the ethereal medium was far denser in the outer parts of the solar system than in the vicinity of the Sun. According to Newton, if the elastic force of this medium is sufficiently great, "it may suffice to impel bodies from the denser parts of the medium towards the rarer, with all that power which we call gravity."[11]

The intellectual heritage of Newton was therefore ambiguous. The Newton of the *Principia* had renounced mechanical hypotheses as vain speculation and had asserted that it was enough to be able to calculate the effects of gravity. The Newton of the *Opticks*, confronted by a host of new optical phenomena, was far more speculative: so little was known about the nature of light that one *had* to seek explanations below the surface of the visible phenomena. In the development of eighteenth-century epistemology, it was the Newton of the *Principia* who weighed most heavily. This is clear, for example, in the article "Hypothesis" published in the *Encyclopédie* of Diderot and d'Alembert.[12] The article takes a sensible middle ground, saying that there are two excesses to avoid in the matter of hypotheses—either to put too much faith in them, as did Descartes, or to proscribe them entirely. According to the *Encyclopédie*, Newton and especially his disciples fell into this contrary error. "Disgusted with the suppositions and errors with which they found the philosophical books filled, they protested against *hypotheses*, they tried to render them suspect and ridiculous, calling them the poison of reason and the plague of philosophy." The *Encyclopédie* points out, accurately, that Newton himself used hypotheses (what else is the principle of universal gravitation?). But the key point is that Newton was *believed* to have been unalterably opposed to the use of hypotheses in natural philosophy. As the eighteenth century progressed, there was a decided shift toward the positivistic position. This did not happen all at once. But by the time Le Sage began to promote his mechanical theory of gravity, principled agnosticism about the cause of gravity was well on its way to becoming the majority position among the first rank of physicists. As we shall see, this attitude had major consequences for the reception of Le Sage's theory.[13]

4. Sources and Development of Le Sage's Theory

Georges-Louis Le Sage was educated at a private grammar school and then at the Collège de Genève. But his education was greatly supplemented at home through the efforts of his father, who stressed languages and—after a fashion—the sciences. The father, also called Georges-Louis Le Sage, was a teacher of philosophy, a writer of books, a man of strong opinions, skeptical of pretentious learning, rankled by the power of privilege in Genevan political affairs. His influence over his son's development was considerable for both good and ill. On the one hand, he read works in Latin and in English with his son and drove him to study hard. But he was strong-willed and overbearing and Le Sage never fully escaped from his domination until his father's death. A strong sense of the father's personality can be had from his *Hazarded Thoughts on Education, Grammar, Rhetoric and Poetics*, in which his philosophy of education is expressed in a series of caustic aphorisms:

> There is a great deal of charlatanry in the notebooks from which the professors crib to their pupils. Sometimes these are only disguised copies of books already published, unknown to the pupils; and often these notebooks fall into contempt, as soon as they are published.

> Systems that fix one's ideas favor the laziness of masters and disciples, and are contrary to the search for truth.

> The fruits that one draws from algebra are not of a sufficiently general usage to make this science enter into the ordinary course of studies.

> In the renovation of philosophy, the great aid that Galileo, Kepler, Descartes and others had drawn from geometry in order to improve physics made many people believe that the study of geometry rendered the mind exact and capable of reasoning well on everything. But the oddities that one has seen certain mathematicians produce on matters that do not have quantity as the object clearly make one see the opposite. There are no people more distracted, and less capable of applying themselves to the affairs of civil life, than the poets and the geometers.

> Physics is necessary to Great Lords so that they may protect themselves against two sorts of people to whom they are continually exposed: empirics and chemists.[14]

Le Sage *père* also wrote a textbook of physics, the first to be published at Geneva.[15] However, he reassured his readers that he would spare them any mathematics. Le Sage's physics textbook therefore consists of a series of short sections surveying subjects of traditional interest. Although a reader of Le Sage's textbook would not have learned up-to-date physics—let alone the mathematical methods of physics—the book is interesting in its Cartesi-Newtonian stance. Thus, Le Sage père prefers to explain weight in terms of vortices. But on the controversial issue of the shape of the Earth, he favors Newton's spheroid flattened at its poles. This is all the more remarkable because Le Sage's textbook of physics was published in 1732, before the famous expedition to Lapland by the French Academy of Sciences decisively settled the question of the Earth's shape. It seems that the hand of Descartes weighed less heavily in francophone Geneva than in France.

Nevertheless, the physics textbook of Le Sage *père* was, in its essence, a collection of facts and pronouncements. Apparently, his conversation was of the same nature. He liked to express his decisions in proverbs or maxims, which he used as unanswerable arguments to shut off discussion. The father, in short, had no sympathy for protracted lines of reasoning or for anything systematic in education. System was what the young Georges-Louis craved. When they read English together, the son would ask his father for the meanings of the roots of words that they encountered. This information the father refused to give, on the grounds that the root changed its meaning in composition. And when the young Georges-Louis set up his little scientific experiments, he found that his apparatus was not respected by the household. Nevertheless, the father helped to stimulate Georges-Louis' interest in natural philosophy by pointing out curious phenomena to him and by his oracular remarks upon them.

The boy began to read Lucretius, in Latin, with his father at the age of thirteen and was profoundly affected by the ancient atomist. The Greek school of atomic physical theory was founded in the fifth century B.C. by Leucippus and Democritus; but, apart from a few quotations by later writers, nothing of their work survives. The most important Greek atomist is Epicurus (341-270 B.C.), who elaborated the atomic theory of Democritus and who also introduced a major ethical component into his philosophy, even going so far as to make physics subservient to ethics. Lucretius (c. 99-55 B.C.) was the author of *De rerum natura* (On the Nature of Things), a verse exposition of the philosophy of Epicurus, with considerable emphasis on his physical doctrines. The Latin poem was popular in the Enlightenment for its exaltation of scientific rationalism and its denunciation of traditional religion as the principal source of mankind's fear of death and of the gods. That Le Sage's father was fond of Lucretius is clear from the frequent citations of the Roman poet in his textbook of physics.

Not only the rationalism of Lucretius but also the atomic doctrine itself appealed to the boy's imagination. Lucretius was bold in inferring facts about the invisible world of the very small from the phenomena of everyday life. Atoms are invisible, but so are many other things whose effects show them to be corporeal, such as wind. That invisibly small bodies do in fact exist is clear from the phenomenon of scent, from the evaporation of water, and from the wearing away of the right hands of metal statues, over the years, as passers-by grasp them for good luck. That void exists is clear as well, or else bodies could not be penetrated, nor would it be possible for things to move. The porosity of objects and the existence of atoms of different sizes is clear from the fact that light can penetrate horn, but water cannot. How else can this be explained but by supposing that the atoms of light are smaller than those of water?[16]

Arguments of just this sort had currency in eighteenth-century mechanical philosophy. In principle, Descartes himself was not an atomist, for he believed neither in void spaces nor in the existence of irreducibly small, fundamental constituents of matter. Nevertheless, in many of his explanations of phenomena

Descartes had recourse to mechanisms involving invisible particles. And some of Descartes' contemporaries developed mechanical philosophies that were forthrightly corpuscularian, Pierre Gassendi being a notable example. The ancient atomic philosophy of Lucretius resonated strongly in many eighteenth-century minds.

Already at the age of thirteen Le Sage began to wonder about gravity. When he asked his father why the Earth doesn't fall, his father replied, "It is fixed by its own weight," and added that he ought to find it even more amazing to see other objects fall. In his teens, Le Sage enrolled at the Academy of Geneva, where he learned some mathematics under Cramer and some physics under Calandrini.[17] While at the academy he achieved celebrity by refuting a supposed quadrature of the circle. Near the end of his academic studies he met Jean-André Deluc in the mathematics classes. They became good friends and maintained a constant correspondence. Deluc recorded a conversation that occurred about this time: Le Sage pointed out that a horse which appears to *pull* a cart is actually *pushing* against the breast-piece of the harness.

After Le Sage left the Academy, his father pressed him to choose a vocation. What attracted Georges-Louis above all else were philosophy and physics. His mother and father, who disagreed about all else, were united in opposition. To them, the situation of a man of letters was the least desirable of all. This situation, to which the father felt himself reduced and to which the son certainly would be reduced, amounted to living on the proceeds of a few private lessons. The son would have to choose a real career. Georges-Louis hesitated between theology and medicine and eventually decided on the latter. His father sent him to study at Basle. He spent a year at the university, without great benefit. But while there, he happened to hear Daniel Bernoulli, in an inaugural lecture, discuss the possible existence of certain magnitudes so enormous or so small that they revolt the imagination. At a later stage of his development, Le Sage was to draw on the corpuscular theory of gases in the 10th chapter of Bernoulli's *Hydrodynamics*.[18]

After his year in Basle, Le Sage went to Paris to continue his medical studies. At his father's insistence, he refrained from studying higher mathematics. But in Paris the deficiencies of his education in physics and mathematics began to dawn on him. In a letter to his father, after listing several very well known books of physics that he had never read, he added that the situation was still worse when it came to mathematics. Here he entered into great detail in order to disabuse his father, who still flattered himself that he had taught the boy quite enough to battle with the *savants* of Paris. Some of the things he did not know, Georges-Louis wrote, were for these *savants* only the A, B, C of mathematics. However, he won friends and respect by demonstrating the falsity of a supposed perpetual motion machine.

Quite by accident, he came across a copy of La Caille's *Elementary Lessons in Astronomy*, which he found at a friend's house, on the mantle of a fireplace. After reading through some of the articles, he read the conclusion, where

La Caille set down the obligation of the physicist: to explain all of astronomy in terms of mechanics. This grand idea echoed in his mind for weeks. And whenever he thought about it, he saw as a means of explanation only his atoms.

As at Basle, Le Sage supplemented his allowance by tutoring. When he abruptly lost his position with a wealthy family, he found time to take up his old meditations on the cause of gravity. Then, on January 15, 1747, at 11:30 in the evening, he wrote to his father:

> Eureka, Eureka. Never have I had so much satisfaction as at this moment, when I have just explained rigorously, by the simple laws of rectilinear motion, those of universal gravitation, which decreases in the same proportion as the squares of the distances increase. I had already four years ago a new idea on the mechanism of the universe: only two things impeded me—the explanation of the repulsion that one observes in the particles of certain elements and the law of the square of the distances. Now I found the first of these things the day before yesterday, and the second only a moment ago. The whole almost without seeking it and even in spite of myself.[19]

He finished his letter with a dream: "perhaps this will win me the prize proposed by the Academy of Paris on the theory of Jupiter and Saturn."

His father's response was to cut short his stay in Paris, although he had not yet finished his medical studies. When Le Sage returned to Geneva, his father pressed him to begin a medical practice, in spite of Georges-Louis' protests that he did not know anything about medicine. The father precipitated matters by inserting in a paper printed at Geneva a notice that read: G.-L. Le Sage, young physician of Geneva, offers his service to the public. Now this advertisement caused a scandal, for it flouted Genevan law. Le Sage's mother v. as a native of Geneva, but his father was not. (He had emigrated from France as a Protestant refugee from religious persecution.) Consequently, although Le Sage himself had been born in Geneva to a mother born in Geneva, he was not of bourgeois status. As a member of a lower legal class (the class of *natifs*), he was forbidden by law to practice the professions, including medicine. Although this law had been in temporary abeyance, his father's advertisement outraged the authorities, who restored it to its former force and handed down a formal prohibition against Le Sage's practice of the profession of medicine. This shock opened the eyes of his father, who finally gave up trying to direct him.

This run-in with the magistrates was also a contributing cause in the composition of a political pamphlet by Le Sage's father. A pamphlet titled *The Spirit of the Laws* and consisting of 103 aphorisms appeared in Geneva in 1752. Though anonymous, and clearly borrowing its title from the famous book of Montesquieu, the pamphlet was soon traced to Georges-Louis Le Sage père. The Small Council (the executive governing body of Geneva) found that the pamphlet contained "dangerous maxims against Religion and the Government" and decreed that the pamphlet should be suppressed and all copies of it withdrawn. In truth, there was little of religious import in the pamphlet, except a plea for religious tolerance, in emulation of the English, and an expression of preference for natural religion. The truly seditious part of the pamphlet was its attack on aristocracy and hereditary privilege: "Every perpetual privilege which is not useful to the Generality is an injustice. Such were the privileges of the patricians among the Romans.... If all men are born equal, a privilege which is an exception to the law is contrary to natural law."[20]

If young Georges-Louis were really to pursue a career in medicine, one hope yet remained: to get hold of enough money to purchase bourgeois status. To Georges-Louis there seemed but one way to do it: win the prize for 1748 offered by the Paris Academy for a treatment of the theory of irregularities in the motions of Jupiter and Saturn. Le Sage sent in a hastily composed piece, called *Essai sur l'origine des forces mortes* (Essay on the origin of dead forces), which bore the epigraph "plus ultra." Le Sage ignored the prize topic and instead outlined his theory of gravity. But it was all for naught, since his contribution arrived too late and was refused by the Academy's secretary, Fouchy. A memoir by Euler was crowned—a memoir that actually treated the prize question and that brought to bear the whole power of contemporary mathematical methods. No better demonstration could be wished of Le Sage's isolation from the real concerns and methods of mid-eighteenth-century mathematical physics.

Four years later, the Academy of Sciences announced a second prize competition on the same subject. Le Sage, still full of hope, reworked and sent once more to the Academy his *Essai sur l'origine des forces mortes*. This time it bore as brave epigraph two lines from Lucretius:

Debent nimirum praecellere mobilitate
Et multo citius ferri quam lumina solis.

Most certainly they must be of exceeding swiftness
and must be carried far more quickly than the light of the Sun.

Lucretius, *De rerum natura II*, 161-162
(trans. Rouse).

As before, Le Sage's goal was the explanation of gravity itself and he ignored the prize question except in its most general connection with his own topic. After a long delay, he learned the inevitable—Euler had won again[21]—and Le Sage finally renounced all hope of a career in medicine.

When the chair of mathematics came empty at the Academy of Geneva, Le Sage aspired to fill it. In those days, however, candidates for academic positions at Geneva were required to participate in a public competition. Le Sage, afflicted with a debilitating timidity, withdrew from the competition. Throughout his life, he made ends meet by living with the utmost frugality and by giving private lessons in mathematics. Georges-Louis Le Sage settled into the life from which his father had most wished to preserve him, that of an impoverished man of letters.

Around this time, Le Sage learned he had been anticipated in his principal idea, the explanation of attraction by rectilinear impact. It was his former professor, Gabriel Cramer, who told him about Fatio. Nicolas Fatio de Duillier

(1664-1753) was born at Basle, but his family settled near Geneva and obtained bourgeois status in 1678. By the age of seventeen Fatio had invented a new method for measuring the distance between the Earth and the Sun and had offered an explanation of the ring of Saturn. He became well known for his development of J.D. Cassini's explanation of the zodiacal light. After living in Paris and in Holland, in 1688 he settled in England and was named a member of the Royal Society. By 1689 he had become a close friend of Isaac Newton. The exact nature of their relationship has been the subject of controversy—some holding that they were lovers, others that Newton may only have been Fatio's "alchemical father." In any case, their four-year-long relationship was intense and its rupture played a role in Newton's mental breakdown of 1693. After that, Fatio turned to millennialism and prophecy and became closely involved with the Camisard refugees from France. He collaborated in the printing and distribution of a book of the prophecies of Elie Marion, a book that was attacked as both blasphemous and seditious. This led in 1707 to Fatio's trial and condemnation to the pillory. In December of that year he was exposed for one hour on two successive days at Charing Cross and at the Royal Exchange, with a notice attached to his hat: "Nicolas Fatio convicted for abetting and favouring Elias Marion, in the wicked and counterfeit prophecies, and causing them to be published, to terrify the queen's people." After his release, he wandered as a missionary across Europe, as far as Asia Minor, eventually resettling in England in 1712. However, Fatio did not completely abandon his scientific interests, for he published some minor works on navigation and other subjects late in his life.[22]

Fatio had in 1690 presented to the Royal Society of London a corpuscular theory of gravity remarkably like that of Le Sage.[23] However, Fatio had not worked out the consequences of his hypotheses in detail, and in any case he had never published his treatise.[24] Late in his life, Fatio returned to this subject. In 1729 he composed a Latin poem on the cause of weight, in the style of Lucretius, which he submitted to a scientific competition of the Paris Academy of Sciences. When this failed, he conceived the hope of dedicating this poem to the Royal Society of London.

Since neither of Fatio's works on the cause of weight were published—neither the French-language treatise of 1690 nor the Latin poem of 1729—one may well ask how Le Sage's teacher, Gabriel Cramer, learned of Fatio's theory. Apparently, the connection was as follows. Fatio's elder brother had, around 1700, made a copy of Fatio's treatise on the cause of weight. When the brother died in 1720, this copy passed to his nephew and heir, Jean-Ferdinand Calandrini of Geneva. Another member of the Calandrini family, Jean-Louis Calandrini (1703-1758), was Cramer's fellow teacher at the Academy of Geneva. Cramer became sufficiently interested in Fatio's theory to use it as a source of theses for his students.[25] Indeed, in 1731 Cramer's student Jalabert defended at Geneva thirty-seven *physico-mathematical theses concerning weight*.[26]

The academic custom of defense of theses descended from the disputations of the medieval universities. In the eighteenth century these affairs served two different purposes. Some disputations were only for exercise ("exercitationis causa"). Others were doctoral disputations ("disputatio inauguralis" or "pro gradu"), held to establish the fitness of the student for the doctorate. In either case, the list of theses, or positions, to be defended was published and the defense itself was a public event in which the student was examined orally. Rarely were these lists of theses intended to be original contributions to learning. Customs varied from place to place and evolved with time. In the seventeenth century, the theses were generally written by the professor under whose presidency the theses were defended, even though in the published document the student might be identified as "author." Not surprisingly, the theses of a disputation often paralleled the contents of a professor's course, perhaps with the addition of a few original theses at the end, contributed by the student with the professor's approval. Sometimes a professor held a series of disputations (each at a different date and with a different student) on a common subject, and after conclusion of the series published the whole thing as a textbook. As the eighteenth century wore on, there was a shift toward the writing of the theses by the student.[27]

In Cramer's examination of Jalabert on weight, it appears that the majority of the 37 theses were composed by Cramer himself and that they reflected the contents of a course Jalabert had taken from him. Most of the 37 theses concerned theories elaborated by Copernicus, Kepler, Descartes, Malebranche, Newton and others. But the final few theses bore on the theory of Fatio, without, however, mentioning him by name. It seems that for Jalabert himself, the ultimate cause of weight was theological.

After learning of Fatio, Le Sage scrupulously gave him credit in all his writings and often mentioned Cramer and Jalabert as well. Moreover, Le Sage went to great trouble to collect some of Fatio's papers, which Pierre Prévost deposited in the library at Geneva after Le Sage's death. There they still remain. Le Sage even began to gather materials to assist him in writing a life of Fatio, which he never completed.[28] Le Sage's interest in preserving Fatio's memory was no doubt strengthened by the fact that Fatio had connections to Geneva. But when Le Sage learned of a dissertation by a German physician named Redeker[29] with similar ideas about weight, he took care also to mention this predecessor.

These, then, were Le Sage's principal influences: Le Sage père, Lucretius, Daniel Bernoulli, La Caille, Fatio, and, of course, Newton. The haphazard nature of his preparation reflects not only his isolation, but also his mental disorganization, which was a fundamental aspect of his personality. Le Sage wrote much but published little. Indeed, he was almost incapable of finishing a treatise. He strove to meet every imaginable objection. Worse, his memory failed him and he found himself rewriting fragments of a composition that he had begun, laid aside, then utterly forgotten. He jotted his thoughts down on the backs of playing cards, which he kept in separate envelopes and boxes labeled with thematic titles. There still exist in the archives of the University of Geneva some 35,000 of Le Sage's annotated playing cards, many of them indecipherable.[30] Among his writings was a collection of jottings headed "on the immiscibility of my thoughts with those of others."

5.   Gravitation and Generation

Shortly after his return to Geneva, Le Sage became a friend of Charles Bonnet (1720-1793), who provided him encouragement and moral support. Like Le Sage, Bonnet was educated at the Academy of Geneva. But because he was several years older than Le Sage, they do not appear to have become close until later. Bonnet's first scientific work was in entomology. He produced a sensation in the early 1740s with his discovery that the aphid reproduces parthenogenetically (*i.e.*, "by virgin birth"). After Abraham Trembley's discovery of animal regeneration in the polyp, or fresh-water hydra, Bonnet demonstrated that fresh-water worms also could regenerate when cut into pieces. The polyp posed a difficulty in classification: was it plant or animal? On the one hand it reproduced by budding and could regenerate itself from cuttings, which seemed plant-like. On the other hand, it was capable of motion and obviously fed by ingestion. But for Bonnet the most vexing problem posed by the polyp was metaphysical: if both halves of a cut polyp could become intact animals, what did this say about the existence of animal soul?[31]

A childhood illness had left Bonnet practically deaf. And in 1745 he became nearly blind. He led a sedentary existence, scarcely leaving his wife's estate at Genthod, except for short visits to Geneva. In his later work, Bonnet turned increasingly to theory, partly because of his own metaphysical predisposition, but partly because the loss of his sight left him unable to pursue the experimental and observational approach that had characterized his early work. In his *Considerations on Organized Bodies*,[32] Bonnet took a highly speculative and hypothetical approach to explaining the mysteries of generation and development. A number of reviewers of this book complained that it was full of *conjectures*.

Bonnet's most widely read work was his *Contemplation of Nature*. This was not a technical report of his researches, but rather a popular meditation on the Great Chain of Being, which links the Creator to all His creatures. The inanimate and the animate form a scale of insensibly small steps, from rocks and crystals to plants to simple organisms to sensate and intelligent animals. The polyp naturally serves as the link between plant and animal. In the preface to *Contemplation of Nature*, Bonnet responds to the attacks on his earlier work on generation and to the complaints that he hypothesized too freely. "What author," he asks, "has distinguished more carefully than I the facts from their consequences, immediate or mediate?" The accusation that he had muddied the distinction between the facts and his own conjectures clearly vexed him—he "who had so often protested against the abuse of conjectures and of hypotheses."

Bonnet mentions two great enigmas that physicists and natural historians have so far been unable to penetrate: the cause of weight and the mystery of generation. And here he inserts a sympathetic reference to Le Sage's attempt to find the true cause of gravity, without, however, mentioning Le Sage by name:

> The great NEWTON abstained from seeking the cause of weight. An estimable physicist [Le Sage] modestly tries to explain it; he has recourse to an ingenious hypothesis, which happily satisfies the phenomena, & which he nevertheless gives only for what it is. Our zealous writers immediately put him on trial, condemn him without understanding him, praise to the point of breathlessness the reserve of NEWTON, which they understand no better, and finish by declaiming against the Spirit of System.[33]

According to Bonnet, the Naturalist or the Physicist ought to confront his critics with these words: "I beg the true physicists to tell me if I have so far reasoned correctly, if I have violated the facts, if I have contradicted my principles." Bonnet ends by pleading: "To banish entirely from physics the art of conjecture would be to reduce us to pure observation; and what use would these observations be to us, if we were not to draw from them the least consequence?"

In Charles Bonnet, then, Le Sage found a kindred spirit—a fellow Genevan who felt one had to take risks to infer the order of nature behind the facts of observation, and who felt that he had been unfairly criticized for doing so, that he had been lumped together with vain and careless systematizers. Le Sage and Bonnet maintained a lively correspondence. Their conversations and letters were full of corpuscles. Bonnet took to signing his own letters *Anaxagoras* and to addressing Le Sage sometimes as *Leucippus*, but more often as *Democritus*. Le Sage spoke continually of writing a great *History of Weight*, which would treat the whole history of attempts to explain gravity, from antiquity to the eighteenth century, culminating in Le Sage's own final explanation. Bonnet urged him to leave off revising and to *publish*. Bonnet pleaded with Le Sage to ignore the ancient adage of Horace, that one should correct a work for nine years before publishing: it was enough to correct it for nine months.[34]

6.   Winning a Hearing

The first published sketch of Le Sage's theory had appeared in the popular miscellany *Mercure de France* in May, 1756. In the February issue, an anonymous academician of Dijon had published an article that ascribed gravity to the action of light. The author did not sign his piece, preferring not to attach his name to the theory until he could develop it more fully. In his response, Le Sage agreed with the academician on the necessity of attributing gravity to a rectilinear impulsion (as opposed to the circular or vortical impulsion that characterized the theories of Descartes and Huygens). But he gently criticized the academician for not having done his literature search, and for failing to cite earlier theories of the same sort, most notably that of Jean Bernoulli. Le Sage then thoroughly refuted Bernoulli's theory. At the close of the piece, Le Sage explained how the academician might improve a gravitation theory based on rectilinear impulsion and, in so doing, briefly outlined his own theory of gravity, while giving most of the credit to Fatio.[35]

In 1758 the Academy of Rouen held a prize competition on the following subject: "To determine the affinities that exist between mixed principles, as begun by Geoffroy[36]; and to find a physico-mechanical system for these affinities." The point of the competition was to explain chemical affinity. But Le Sage, like many of his time, believed that one explanation would be found to underlie both the laws of chemistry and the law of universal gravitation—a point of view that persisted well into the nineteenth century. Accordingly, Le Sage's *Essay on Mechanical Chemistry*,[37] submitted for the competition, is an attempt to account for chemical affinity by the same mechanism that explains universal gravitation.

In the introduction to this work, Le Sage remarks that chemists are not comfortable with algebra and that he will therefore explain his theory in ordinary language, relegating a few calculations to the back of the work. The basic phenomenon to be explained is *attraction*. According to Le Sage, attraction is called *gravitation* if the bodies are separated from one another and *cohesion* if they are in contact. Thus gravity, cohesion and chemical affinity are all aspects of a single more general phenomenon. Le Sage attempts to lead his readers inexorably through a sequence of arguments that develop all the features of his theory of attraction:

- Whenever we have discovered the true cause of some change in state of a body, we have found that *it is due to impulsion*. For example, the rise of a column of water in a pump is due to the pressure of the air. Thus it is reasonable to suppose that the approach of two attracting bodies toward one another is actually due to the impulsion of some sort of invisible matter. This argument takes its strength from the following axiom: "similar effects come from similar causes." Or, if we prefer, we may regard it as a proof by analogy, which, according to Le Sage, is the strongest kind of proof in physical reasoning.
- Because the matter that produces the attractions of bodies does not offer sensible resistance to their motion, its parts must give free passage to them. Thus, *the invisible matter must be fluid*.
- This fluid must travel faster than the bodies it causes to accelerate. Because the acceleration of a falling body does not cease even when the body is moving rapidly, *the speed of the fluid must be very great*. In remarks added to the *Mechanical Chemistry* after the period of the competition, Le Sage used an argument from planetary motion to show that the speed of the fluid must be at least 10^{13} times the speed of light. And here he again quoted those lines from Lucretius: "Most certainly they must be

of exceeding swiftness/ and must be carried far more quickly than the light of the Sun."

- Since all bodies fall toward the center of the Earth, the fluid must be able to move through a single space simultaneously in all directions. Thus the parts of the fluid must be isolated from one another. *This fluid therefore consists of discrete corpuscles*, which do not interfere with one another in the least.

- Curvilinear motion is forced. Once the generator of the force is removed, curvilinear motions immediately become rectilinear. Since the corpuscles of the fluid do not interfere with one another, but move with complete freedom, *their paths must be rectilinear*. And here Le Sage could not resist inserting a remark about the wrong-headedness of the old doctrine of vortices.

- The weights of objects do not sensibly decrease under roofs. Thus, *the corpuscles must be very small*, or subtle, and roofs must be porous. Indeed, *the pores of bodies must be a very great proportion of the bodies themselves*, so that the corpuscles have nearly free passage through the bodies. For the gravitation of celestial bodies is very nearly in proportion to the quantity of their matter, and this could not be the case if the outer layers of a body absorbed a sensible fraction of the incident corpuscles.

Thus Le Sage has led us inexorably to "corpuscles, isolated, very subtle, which move in straight lines, in a great number of different directions, and which encounter very porous bodies. *Voilà*, therefore, the only possible material cause of attraction."

Le Sage believes that the final cause of the corpuscles that produce the effects of gravity is an incorporeal being, who launched them into motion at the moment of creation. In view of the enormous speed of the corpuscles, those that reach the Earth today must have traveled an immense distance since the beginning of the world. Those that will reach us tomorrow will have traveled an even more immense distance. Since these corpuscles come to us from outside the known universe, they are called *ultramundane*.

Le Sage deduces the inverse-square law simply by the following verbal argument. Imagine a *physical point*, that is, a small spherical region of space, traversed by currents of ultramundane corpuscles traveling in all directions. The number of corpuscles that cross a unit of area on the surface of this small sphere will be spread out over a correspondingly larger area on the surface of a larger surrounding sphere, in such fashion that the number crossing through a unit area will fall off as the inverse square of the distance. And this is exactly analogous to the law of the decrease of the intensity of light.

After developing the general principles of attraction in the course of his discussion of gravitation, Le Sage turns to cohesion. The basic phenomenon to be explained is the fact that two bodies made of the same substance attract more strongly than two bodies made of different substances. Thus two drops of oil, or two drops of water, will attract each other and unite, which is not the

Fig. 3. Pierre Prévost (1751-1839), Le Sage's pupil and disciple. Oil portrait by F. Langlois after a drawing by Mme. Munier-Romilly. Photo courtesy of Bibliothèque publique et universitaire, Ville de Genève. It was Prévost who read Le Sage's *Newtonian Lucretius* before the Academy of Berlin and who published some of Le Sage's works after Le Sage's death.

case for a drop of oil and a drop of water. Moreover, even when we consider the attraction of like for like, different substances manifest this attraction with different forces. For example, two drops of oil attract one another with greater force than two drops of water of the same size. In his *Mechanical Chemistry* Le Sage accounts for chemical affinity by introducing ultramundane corpuscles of various sizes, as well as pores of various sizes in ordinary bodies, as shown in Fig. 2. Attraction is strongest for bodies that have similar pores. This represents an obvious generalization of his theory of gravity.

The *Essay on Mechanical Chemistry* was the first complete exposition of Le Sage's theory of gravity. The essay was crowned by the Academy of Rouen for its treatment of the second (theoretical) part of the prize question. In 1761, Le Sage had copies of the essay printed, but it never was published in any regular way. Le Sage hoped that it would eventually form a part of a collection of related essays that might be published as a book. This never happened, so Le Sage contented himself with giving copies of *Mechanical Chemistry*, from time to time, to those he hoped would be interested, usually with a hand-written title page placed over the printed treatise. There is a copy of *Mechanical Chemistry* in the library of the Royal Society of London that was sent by Le Sage in 1774. The printed treatise is accompanied not only by the hand-written title page but also by an elaborate hand-written synopsis, which doubles as a table of contents. Apparently, Le Sage realized that his argument in *Mechanical Chemistry* was too long for most readers. The handwritten synopsis is a useful and concise addition.

As mentioned above, Le Sage won the prize for the second, or theoretical, part of the competition on the nature of affinity sponsored by the Academy of Rouen. The first, or experimental, part of the competition was won by Jean-Philippe de Limbourg, a physician of Liège, who had his own treatise printed in 1761.[38] At the end of his book, Limbourg included a general account of the ideas in Le Sage's *Mechanical Chemistry*. This was the first published discussion of Le Sage's theoretical views by another writer. About thirteen years later, a chemist and apothecary named Demachy discussed both of these treatises on affinity. But Demachy did not have a copy of Le Sage's *Mechanical Chemistry*, and based his account of Le Sage's theory on the synopsis that had been given by Limbourg.[39] Le Sage complained bitterly of the short shrift he had been given by Limbourg, as well as of the inaccuracies in Demachy's account, based as it was on the imperfect summary by Limbourg.[40] Here we see foreshadowed the fate of Le Sage's system. It was, throughout its life—and this includes the period of its nineteenth- and twentieth-century revivals—more often talked about than read in the original. But a large part of the responsibility for this rests with Le Sage himself for his failure to publish.

The *Essay on Mechanical Chemistry* is burdened with much that is irrelevant to gravitation. A more succinct exposition of the theory is Le Sage's *Newtonian Lucretius*, which in 1782 was read by his pupil and disciple, Pierre Prévost, before the Royal Academy of Berlin, where Prévost was resident as a member.[41] (See Fig. 3.) Le Sage seeks to combine the principles of atomism (hence Lucretius) with those of Newton. The paper is organized around a fanciful conceit: Le Sage describes how the ancient atomists of the Lucretian school might have hit upon the law of Newtonian gravitation if they had only followed Le Sage's train of thought. This mode of exposition could hardly have helped Le Sage win adherents. Nevertheless, *Newtonian Lucretius* was the chief published form of the theory available to Le Sage's contemporaries. It bore as epigraph a quotation from Fontenelle's elegy of Cassini:

> In every matter, the first systems are too limited, too narrow, too timid. And it seems that truth itself is the reward only of a certain boldness of reason.

The most systematic account of Le Sage's theory is his *Mechanical Physics*,[42] which was pieced together from his notes and drafts by Pierre Prévost after Le Sage's death. However, the *Mechanical Physics* was not published until 1818, it does not seem to have been widely read, and it had little effect on the debate over Le Sage's theory of gravitation.

7. Reception of the Theory: Attitudes toward Explanation in Physics

Le Sage's most effective manner of promoting his system was not by publication, but rather by private letter. He argued for the ultramundane corpuscles in a lively correspondence that included most of the scientific luminaries of his day. For this reason, Le Sage's voluminous correspondence is an excellent resource for the study of eighteenth-century attitudes toward hypotheses in physics. In 1774, Le Sage sent a copy of his *Mechanical Chemistry* to Matthew Maty, secretary of the Royal Society of London. Le Sage also sent to Maty a long letter[43] in which he recounted the frustrations he had experienced in trying to win a hearing for his theory. Le Sage gives a perceptive and often touching account of the reactions he had provoked and of the objections he had attempted to answer. He writes that when he tried to lead certain enlightened persons to accept his mechanism, he "sensed on their part an extreme repugnance quite independent of its more or less perfect accord with the phenomena."

Some correspondents insisted on an *analogy*. That is, Le Sage was asked to point to another physical phenomenon in which similar principles were at work. "And, not having found in my mechanism a perfect analogy with any known mechanism, except only a considerable analogy with light, I despaired of ever being able to convince those people."

Some of those to whom Le Sage tried to communicate his theory "found it easier to pass judgement on *hypothesis* [itself] than to examine my distinction between solid hypotheses and those which are not. And one continued to spout at me gravely with the most trivial commonplaces against hypotheses taken in a very vague sense."

Other critics wished Le Sage to prove that gravity "is not an *essential quality* of matter, nor ... the immediate effect of divine will." To satisfy the scruples of these people, he had to "go back to metaphysics," which he "had abandoned a very long time ago."

Others maintained that even if he had established the reality of his system, he "still would have satisfied only a vain curiosity, which is no longer in fashion in this century, in which one devotes oneself only to useful knowledge." To answer these people, Le Sage felt compelled to examine the *advantage* that physics and metaphysics would draw from his making known the nature and cause of gravity.

It is indeed possible to find most of these responses in letters from the leading philosophers of the day to Le Sage. Leonhard Euler is a good example of those who asked for analogies and then remained unimpressed by what Le Sage could produce. When people complained to Le Sage that they could neither visualize nor accept the currents of ultramundane particles traversing every small volume of space simultaneously in hundreds of thousands of different directions, he tried to soothe them by offering an analogy to light. Particles of light stream constantly in all directions, without disturbing one another in the least. Euler was not assuaged. He wrote bluntly:

> Without engaging myself in an examination of whether such an infinity of currents in all directions would be possible, or could continue for a single instant without disturbing itself, I remark only that the proof drawn from the movement of light has no weight with me, since I am convinced that light is not at all hurled from luminous bodies, but that it is propagated from them in the same manner as sound from sonorous bodies, without anything really escaping from bright bodies.[44]

In a debate by correspondence that stretched over several years, Euler had begun by agreeing with Le Sage on the importance of banishing from physics attraction and cohesion, along with the ancient occult qualities. He congratulated Le Sage for his efforts, but held out for waves in an ethereal fluid as the probable mechanism of gravity. Le Sage made Euler admit that the properties of the light-carrying ether were incapable of explaining gravity too. But then Euler fell back on a second ether, much more subtle and elastic, for the explanation of gravity. Finally, he could no longer contain his disgust:

> And so you will excuse me, Monsieur, if I still feel a very great repugnance for your ultramundane corpuscles; and I would always rather admit my ignorance of the cause of gravity than to have recourse to hypotheses so strange.[45]

For *metaphysical* objections to Le Sage's theory, we can find no richer source than the letters of Roger Boscovich to Le Sage. Boscovich granted that in his *Mechanical Chemistry* Le Sage had succeeded where Descartes, Huygens and Bulfinger had all failed: he had explained how gravity could be produced by the impulsion of a material substance that still produced no sensible resistance to motion.[46] But Boscovich withheld approval. This most radical of atomists found Le Sage's system "unnatural" and branded it an arbitrary hypothesis. Moreover, Boscovich objected that each ultramundane corpuscle served a function only during the very short time that it was in the act of colliding with a heavy object, and that this was a minuscule fraction of the corpuscle's duration. But Boscovich's strongest aversion to the theory was due to the extraordinary number of ultramundane corpuscles required. Since heavy bodies stopped but a tiny fraction of the corpuscles incident upon them, the great majority of corpuscles were superfluous, for they never collided with any heavy object. This implied an extravagant wastefulness on the part of the Creator. In vain did Le Sage respond that one could suppress all the superfluous corpuscles once one admitted perfect foresight on the part of the Creator: He need only have created those corpuscles that had the right initial conditions of velocity and position actually to encounter some heavy object in the course of their travels.

If we can discern any pattern in the objections of Le Sage's correspondents it is this. Many of the older mathematicians and philosophers—people who had been born between 1700, say, and 1720—were willing to debate the physical mechanism responsible for gravitation. They were still mopping up after the great battle that had banished occult qualities from physics. Gravitation had to be reducible to mechanics: this was an article of their faith. However, most people who took this point of view already subscribed to some other mechanical system and were therefore unlikely to be converted to Le Sage's views. So we have seen in the cases of Euler and Boscovich.

The most sympathetic of Le Sage's correspondents of this generation was Daniel Bernoulli, who was pleased to see Le Sage drawing on his corpuscular theory of gases. And, like many of his contemporaries, Bernoulli was sympathetic to the effort to reduce gravity to mechanics. But, while heaping general praise upon Le Sage, Bernoulli withheld approval of his system.[47] Bernoulli considered his own corpuscular theory of gases to be unproved, "a pure hypothesis, and even a rather gratuitous hypothesis."[48] And so he could hardly agree with Le Sage that the existence of ultramundane corpuscles had been proved beyond a reasonable doubt.

Younger people—those born in the 1730s and 1740s—were accustomed to using gravitational attraction as a demonstrated fact without troubling themselves over its causes. They had become convinced of the fruitlessness of pursuing mechanical hypotheses that always were more or less arbitrary and that were not susceptible of proof. The battle that had expunged occult qualities from physics belonged to the remote past. These younger physicists simply had little interest in the underlying cause of gravitation and little confidence that the cause could be discovered. This attitude is often called *Laplacian*, but we find it already present in people who reached maturity well before Laplace.

A good example is provided by the response of the French astronomer, Jean-Sylvain Bailly. After receiving a lengthy letter in which Le Sage explained his system, Bailly replied in friendly form and praised Le Sage for the profundity of his subject and his reasoning. And yet, we encounter a note of irony in his praise and an unanswerable rebuff in his confession of faith:

> I do not flatter myself, Monsieur, to delve as you do into the principles of Nature; I have, at most, the strength to follow you. But I have followed you with pleasure; and, not being strong enough to make you objections, I limit myself to making you my profession of faith. I am a Newtonian: I am even led to believe that gravity is a property of matter....[49]

Bailly complacently indicated a willingness to accept an ethereal fluid that reduced gravitation to impulsion, "provided that this fluid explains everything and without effort." But, clearly, a man ready to accept gravity as an inherent property of matter was going to have a low tolerance for effort in any sort of mechanical explanation.

8. Laplace's Response and Implications for Celestial Mechanics

Pierre-Simon Laplace (1749-1827) was the foremost mathematical physicist of his generation. He is best known for his *Celestial Mechanics*, which appeared in five volumes between 1799 and 1825 and which put this science on a new and more systematic foundation. Although Laplace never gave Le Sage's theory serious consideration, he was influenced by it to explore two effects that would represent departures from the Newtonian theory: a finite speed of propagation of gravity and a resistive force experienced by the planets in their orbits. Le Sage's friend and compatriot, Jean-André Deluc, was in Paris in 1781, where he was on friendly terms with Laplace and tried to interest him in Le Sage's theory. Laplace declined to be draw in, but did admit to an interest in exploring the resistive force implicit in Le Sage's sea of corpuscles:

> Before pronouncing on this subject, I have taken the course of waiting until M. Sage has published his ideas; and then I propose to pursue certain ana-lytical researches that they have suggested to me. As for the particular sub-ject of the secular equations of the motion of the planets, it has appeared to me that the smallness of that of the Earth would imply in the *gravific* fluid a speed incomparably greater than that of light, and all the more considerable as the Sun and the Earth leave a freer passage to this fluid, which conforms to the result of M. Sage. This prodigious speed, the immense space that each fluid molecule traverses in only a century, without our knowing where it comes from or where it goes or the cause that has put it into motion—all that is quite capable of terrifying our weak imagination; but in the end, if one ab-solutely wants a mechanical cause of weight, it appears to me difficult to imagine one which explains it more happily than the hypothesis of M. Sage....[50]

Indeed, it is not difficult to show that Le Sage's hypothesis leads to an effective attractive force F_{att} that conforms to Newton's law of gravitation. If M_1 and M_2 are the masses of two infinitesimal bodies, the force that one exerts upon the other is

$$F_{att} = \frac{kM_1M_2}{r^2},$$

where r is the distance between the bodies and k is a constant that depends upon properties of the sea of ultramundane corpuscles. It turns out that k, the constant of universal gravitation, is given by

$$k = \frac{nm}{4\pi}v^2f^2,$$

where m is the mass of a single ultramundane corpuscle, n is the number of corpuscles per unit volume of space, v is the speed of the corpuscles (assumed for simplicity to be the same for all) and f is a (presumably universal) constant with dimensions of area/mass. f is the cross-sectional area for collision pre-sented to the corpuscles by a macroscopic object of unit mass. (Here it must be emphasized that Le Sage himself never published such formulas.)

As we have seen, in Le Sage's system, apparently solid objects must be made mostly of empty space. In his *Mechanical Physics*, Le Sage speculated that the atoms of ordinary matter are like "cages"—that is, they take up lots of space, but are mostly empty. In this way, ordinary objects block only a tiny fraction of the ultramundane corpuscles that are incident upon them. Other-wise, as Le Sage himself points out, merchants could change the weights of their stuff by arranging it in wide, thin layers (in which case it would weigh more) or in tall piles (in which case it would weigh less). More significantly for precision measurement, the gravitational attraction of the Moon toward the Earth would be diminished during a lunar eclipse because of the interposition of the Earth between the Sun and the Moon, a phenomenon that has never been noticed by the astronomers. Thus, in order to have a theory consistent with the phenomena, f must be so small that even planet-sized objects absorb a negligible fraction of the corpuscles incident upon them. The constant of universal gravitation k can be made to agree with the facts no matter how small we make f, provided that we suitably increase n or v.

There is an unwanted side effect in Le Sage's system, to which Laplace refers. Planets traveling through the sea of corpuscles will be slightly retarded. This is the effect to which Laplace refers under the rubric of *secular equations*. A body of mass M_1 moving through the sea of ultramundane corpuscles will experience a resistive force F_{res} that is proportional to the speed u of the body:

$$F_{res} = \frac{4}{3} M_1 fnmvu.$$

The resistive force is directed oppositely to the body's velocity u. (Again, Le Sage himself did not publish such a formula.) Since no resistance of this kind had been detected, it was necessary to insist that the resistive force suffered by a planet be much smaller than the attractive force exerted by the Sun on the planet. Thus, if we let M_1 denote the mass of a planet and M_2 that of the Sun, we require

$$F_{res}/F_{att} \ll 1.$$

Upon substitution of the expressions for the forces, we obtain

$$\frac{u}{v} \frac{r^2}{fM_2} \ll 1.$$

M_2, u and r (the mass of the Sun, the speed of the planet and the radius of the planet's orbit) are not adjustable. Thus we are led to the conclusion that the speed v of the corpuscles must be very large. Moreover, since we need f to be very small, we are forced to make v even greater. This is what Laplace meant when he said that the smallness of the secular equation of the Earth "would imply in the gravific fluid a speed incomparably greater than that of light, and all the more considerable as the Sun and the Earth leave a freer passage to this fluid." The prodigious velocity required for Le Sage's corpuscles appears, more than many other features of the theory, to have repelled Laplace.

Some years later, after the publication of Laplace's *Exposition of the System of the World*, Le Sage wrote to express his disappointment that Laplace had not discussed his mechanical theory of gravity. Laplace's reply drew a clear boundary between his generation's way of doing physics and the old mechanical philosophy espoused by Le Sage:

> If I have not spoken in my work of your explanation of the principal of universal weight, it is because I wanted to avoid everything that might appear to be based upon a system. Among philosophers, some conceive of the action of bodies upon one another only by means of impulsion and, to them, action

at a distance seems impossible. Your ingenious manner of explaining universal gravitation, in proportion to the masses and in reciprocal proportion to the square of the distances, should satisfy these philosophers and bring them to admit this great law of nature, which they would reject despite the observations and all the calculations of the geometers, if it were well demonstrated to them that it could result from impulsion.

Other philosophers, on the contrary, admit their ignorance on the nature of matter, of space, of force and of extension, and trouble themselves little about first causes, seeing in attraction only a general phenomenon which, being subjectable to a rigorous calculation, gives the complete explanation of all the celestial phenomena and the means of perfecting the tables and the theory of the motion of the stars. It is uniquely under this point of view that I have envisaged attraction in my work.

Perhaps I have not had enough consideration for the first philosophers of whom I have just spoken, in not presenting to them your manner, as simple as ingenious, of bringing the principle of weight back to the laws of impulsion; but this is a thing that you have done in a manner leaving nothing to be desired in this regard. However, I propose to calculate in my *Treatise on Celestial Mechanics* the deteriorations that must result from your hypotheses in the long run in the mean motions and the orbits of the planets and the satellites.[51]

Laplace did, indeed, include calculations in the fifth volume of his *Celestial Mechanics* which grappled with some of the consequences of Le Sage's theory. But even here Laplace did not see fit to mention Le Sage by name.[52]

9. Le Sage's Legacy

Modern historians of science often do not know what to do with Le Sage. Many regard Le Sage's system as bizarre or even worse. One writer has characterized it as "imprecise, qualitative and even retrogressive."[53] But Le Sage's contemporaries did not deny that his system accomplished its aim, *i.e.*, that its premises did, indeed, result in Newtonian gravitation. And, contrary to the impression given by some recent writing, Le Sage was a good Newtonian and he fought hard in one of the last rear-guard actions of the anti-Newtonians.

In 1773 Le Sage unmasked as frauds two purported experiments reported in the *Journal des Beaux-Arts & des Sciences* by a mysterious Jean Coultaud and a certain Mercier. These writers claimed to have performed pendulum experiments on mountains in the Alps, near villages that they named, in which a pendulum was found to swing more rapidly at the summit of a mountain than near the mountain's base. These results led Coultaud and Mercier to the conclusion that the weights of objects *increase* with their distance from the center of the Earth, in accordance with some versions of Cartesian vortex theory. This claim was rebutted by leading Newtonians, including d'Alembert and Lalande, who attributed the anomalous results to localized density variations. Le Sage went a long step farther. He began an investigation, making use of his network of correspondents, friends and relatives. Le Sage proved that the experiments had never taken place and that "Coultaud" and "Mercier" were fictitious persons. Le Sage scored a victory for Newtonian gravitation in one of the strangest controversies of the day.[54] This detective work helped win him election as a foreign member of the Royal Society of London. He had already been named a *correspondant* of the Paris Academy of Sciences. Thus, it is clear that his contemporaries regarded him as a legitimate member of the international community of physicists, even though very few of them endorsed his system.

The views of some modern writers that Le Sage was an apostate anti-Newtonian, and that his system was only qualitative, derive partly from Le Sage's failure to clothe his exposition in adequate mathematical dress, and partly from the peculiarities of his character and his manner of exposition, which made him seem strange in his own day and which make him appear even more so today. Equally important, Le Sage's theory and Le Sage's methods of argument were in conflict with the prevailing anti-hypothetical epistemology of his day, as we have seen by examining his scientific correspondence. Most of Le Sage's converts were people who knew him personally and who had some connection with Geneva. Examples include Deluc, Prévost and the English experimental scientist and radical politician, Charles Stanhope, whose son was a pupil of Le Sage's at Geneva. Horace-Bénédict de Saussure, although not exactly a convert, did discuss Le Sage's theory in his physics courses at the Academy of Geneva.

In spite of the defects and obscurity of Le Sage's publications, he succeeded in making his theory widely known through correspondence. The international scientific connections of Geneva helped to a great extent. Moreover, Geneva was an important destination and stopping point for well-heeled travelers of all sorts, including those with interests in the sciences.[55] It is likely that most *savants* who passed through Geneva over a period of two generations heard something of Le Sage's theory. By 1770 his theory was well enough known in France to be the subject of a disputation at Lyon. There a student named Sigorgne defended some theses under the presidency of Professor P.-F. Champion combating the opinions of Le Sage on attraction.[56] This was not what Le Sage would have wished, of course, but at least it meant that his theory was being noticed.

Le Sage's friends did their part to popularize his ideas. As we have seen, Prévost was responsible for the publication of *Newtonian Lucretius* in the French-language memoirs of the Berlin Academy. Deluc harangued Laplace about the system in a series of letters. And, of course, Prévost saw Le Sage's posthumous *Mechanical Physics* through the press in 1818. Moreover, both Deluc and Prévost mentioned Le Sage's system in some of their own published works. In his *Researches on the Modifications of the Atomosphere* (1772), Deluc made a number of sympathetic references to Le Sage and his theory.[57] More significantly, Prévost in his *On the Origin of Magnetic Forces* (1788), gave a brief but coherent overview of Le Sage's theory, made a case for its importance, and pleaded with his readers to suspend judgment until Le Sage had a chance to publish his own proofs of the theory.[58]

Both Deluc's and Prévost's books received translations into German.[59] Indeed, it was largely from the German translation of Prévost's book that the philosopher F.W.J. von Schelling learned of Le Sage's theory. In Germany, the mechanical physics of Le Sage was usually seen as a rather repellant competitor to the dynamical view of nature proposed by Kant and most famously developed by Schelling under the rubric *Naturphilosophie*. For Schelling, Le Sage's theory was simply anathema. Thus Schelling devotes long parts of his *Ideas for a Philosophy of Nature* to an attack on Le Sage's view of the world. Schelling mocks Le Sage for merely showing "that the fall of bodies can be very intelligibly explained by reference to things that we know nothing whatever about." Moreover, Schelling criticizes Le Sage's whole approach to knowledge with this complaint: "The mechanical physics begins with *postulates*, then erects *possibilities* upon these postulates, and finally purports to have constructed a system that is beyond all doubt."[60] This was not quite fair to Le Sage, who believed that he had carefully applied the method of exclusion to eliminate all other possible explanations of gravity. Only a few German writers of the older generation, who deplored the excesses of both Romanticism and metaphysics, tended to be sympathetic to Le Sage. This was the case with the physicist Georg Christoph Lichtenberg, who was attracted to Le Sage's theory.[61] In the Germany of *Naturphilosophie* Lichetenberg was, of course, a lonely exception. Nevertheless, the prominence of Schelling's attack on Le Sage's theory at least guaranteed that it would not be forgotten.

In Britain, Le Sage's views were helped by the relocation of Jean-André Deluc. For in 1773 Deluc moved to England, where, the following year, he took the official position of Reader to Queen Charlotte, the wife of George III. As a scientist of reputation and a fellow of the Royal Society, he had many opportunites to enlighten his English friends on the cause of gravity. In Britain, as well as in France and Germany, Le Sage's theory became a part of the common knowledge of physical thinkers. If his works were rarely read, his ideas nevertheless remained in circulation. Le Sage's theory even enjoyed a brief revival in the Victorian period because of the enthusiasm of William Thomson, Lord Kelvin.[62]

As we have seen, Le Sage's theory of the ultramundane corpuscles failed to affect mainstream thinking about gravity. However, Le Sage's ideas about discrete gases (of which the ultramundane corpuscles are a special case) did have a remarkable influence in the development of one branch of physics—the theory of thermal equilibrium, especially in the case of phenomena involving radiant heat. Around 1790, Marc-Auguste Pictet of the Academy of Geneva discovered an astonishing fact: *radiant cold* could be reflected and focused by mirrors in the same way as radiant heat. In his experiment, Pictet used a pair of concave tin mirrors facing one another across a distance of 10 feet. A sensitive air thermometer was placed at the focus of one mirror. When a flask of snow was placed in the focus of the second mirror, the thermometer immediately descended. This experiment posed quite a puzzle. Some thinkers were used to regarding cold as a mere negative, a privation of heat. Under this view it was difficult to see how cold could be radiated and reflected. Nearly everyone regarded thermal equilibrium as a static situation. Two objects in thermal equilibrium were like two springs in contact, each under the same tension. Pierre Prévost explained the paradoxical experiment by introducing the idea of dynamic equilibrium. According to Prévost, two objects in thermal equilibrium constantly emit and absorb particles of heat in a balanced, mutual exchange. Prévost took this idea, as he tells us himself, directly from Le Sage, and used it to explain Pictet's experiment in complete detail.[63] Pictet's experiment on the radiation and reflection of cold was the immediate stimulus for the researches of Benjamin Thompson, Count Rumford, into a whole host of thermal phenomena.

Acknowledgement

I am grateful to Christiane Vilain, Frans van Lunteren and Rienk Vermij for insights into eighteenth-century academic customs, to Roger Hahn for alerting me to a letter of Laplace, to Theodore Feldman for information about Le Sage's relations with Jean-André Deluc, and to Alfred Nordmann for communications about Lichtenberg's interest in Le Sage. The University of Puget Sound generously provided research support that made it possible to consult rare publications. Thanks are also due to the efficient and helpful staffs of the Bibliothèque Publique et Universitaire de Genève and the Library of the Royal Society (London) for providing microfilm copies of manuscripts.

Notes

[1] "The standard model" is, of course, a term of late twentieth-century particle physics. John Heilbron has applied this term in a useful way to the set of widely accepted physical tenets of the late eighteenth century. J.L. Heilbron, *Weighing Imponderables and Other Quantitative Science around 1800. Historical Studies in the Physical and Biological Sciences*, Supplement to Vol. 24, Part 1 (1993). See especially pp. 5-33. For a discussion of gravitation theory as the embodiment of a worldview, see F.H. van Lunteren, "Gravitation and Nineteenth-Century Worldviews," in P.B. Scheurer and G. Debrock, eds., *Newton's Scientific and Philosophical Legacy* (Dordrecht: Kluwer, 1988). For more detail, see the same author's doctoral dissertation, *Framing Hypotheses: Conceptions of Gravity in the 18th and 19th Centuries* (Rijksuniversiteit Utrecht, 1991).

[2] For Le Sage the best biographical source, on which all later accounts depend, is the book by Le Sage's pupil and disciple, Pierre Prévost, *Notice de la vie et des écrits de George-Louis Le Sage de Genève* (Genève: J. J. Paschoud, 1805). Useful brief notices are found in the following works. Jacques Trembley, ed., *Les savants genevois dans l'Europe intellectuelle du XVIIe au milieu du XIXe siècle* (Genève: Editions du Journal de Genève, no date but c. 1987), pp. 117-119, 413. Frank A. Kafker and Serena L. Kafker, *The Encyclopedists as individuals: a biographical dictionary of the authors of the* Encyclopédie. Studies on Voltaire and the Eighteenth Century **257** (Oxford: Voltaire Foundation, 1988), pp. 223-226. By far the most important source of unpublished manuscripts is the large collection of Le Sage papers at the Bibliothèque Publique et Universitaire de Genève (cited below as BPU).

[3] For other discussions of Le Sage's theory see the following. Samuel Aronson, "The Gravitational Theory of Georges-Louis Le Sage," *The Natural Philosopher* **3** (1964) 51-74. William B. Taylor, "Kinetic Theories of Gravitation," *Annual Report of the Board of Regents of the Smithsonian Institution for the Year 1876* (Washington: Government Printing Office, 1877), 205-282, on pp. 217-221. However, Taylor mistakenly brushes aside Le Sage's theory as not meeting its goals. The survey by S. Tolver Preston, "Comparative Review of some Dynamical Theories of Gravitation," *Philosophical Magazine*, 5th Series, **39** (1895) 145-159, is still useful, although Preston's evaluations of the

merits of the various theories can safely be ignored. These sources provide citations of many nineteenth-century discussions of Le Sage's theory, including the attempted revival of the theory by William Thomson, Lord Kelvin, and the subsequent criticism by Maxwell. For this episode the key sources are William Thomson, "On the Ultramundane Corpuscles of Lesage," *Philosophical Magazine*, 4th Series, **45** (1873), 321-345 and J.C. Maxwell, "Atom," *Encyclopædia Britannica* (1875 and later editions), reprinted in W. D. Niven, ed., *The Scientific Papers of James Clerk Maxwell*, 2 vols. (Cambridge: Cambridge U. P., 1890), Vol. 2, 445-484.

[4] An account of the debate, with texts of the communications, is available in *Oeuvres complètes de Christiaan Huygens publiées par la Société Hollandaise des Sciences*, Vol. 19 (La Haye: Martinus Nijhoff, 1937), pp. 628-645.

[5] René Descartes, *Les principes de la philosophie*, in *Oeuvres de Descartes*, ed. by Charles Adam and Paul Tannery, Vol. IX-2 (Paris: J. Vrin, 1978). The *Principles of Philosophy* was written in Latin and was published in 1644 under the title *Principa philosophiae*. The first publication of the French translation was in 1647.

[6] Descartes to Mersenne, 16 octobre 1639, in *Oeuvres de Descartes*, Vol. II, pp. 593-594. This letter was first published by Clerselier in 1659, in the second volume of his edition of *Lettres de M Descartes*.

[7] Descartes, *Principes de la philosophie*, Part 3, Paragraph 44, in *Oeuvres de Descartes* (Ref. 5), Vol. IX-2, p. 123.

[8] Christiaan Huygens, *Discours de la cause de la pesanteur* (Leiden: Pierre vander Aa, 1690), reprinted in *Oeuvres complètes de Christiaan Huygens*, Vol. 21 (1944).

[9] Isaac Newton, *The Principia: Mathematical Principles of Natural Philosophy*, trans. by I. Bernard Cohen and Anne Whitman (Berkeley: University of California Press, 1990), p. 382. Newton restated the same position near the end of Query 28 of the *Opticks*.

[10] Newton, *Principia*, trans. Cohen and Whitman, p. 943.

[11] Isaac Newton, *Opticks*, based on the fourth edition of 1730 (New York: Dover, 1952). Query 21, pp. 350-351. In Newton's view, then, gravity is a sort of hydrostatic force, and not a dynamical one as in the theory of Huygens. The first edition of *Opticks* appeared in 1704. Later editions differed largely in the expansion of the Queries. Query 21 first appeared in the second English edition of 1717.

[12] "Hypothèse," *Encyclopédie, ou dictionnaire raisonné des sciences, des arts et des métiers*, Vol. 8 (Paris: 1765), pp. 417-418. This article was written by the abbé Jean-Baptiste de La Chapelle, one of the principal contributors on mathematics.

[13] For a philosophical perspective on Le Sage's confrontation with the anti-hypothetical epistemology of his day, see: Larry Laudan, "George-Louis LeSage: A Case Study in the Interaction of Physics and Philosophy," in *Akten des II. Internationalen Leibniz-Kongresses Hanover, 17-22 Juli 1972*, vol. 2 (Wiesbaden: F. Steiner, 1974), pp. 241-252. Larry Laudan, "The medium and its message: a study of some philosophical controversies about ether," in G.N. Cantor and M.J.S. Hodge, eds., *Conceptions of Ether* (Cambridge: Cambridge U.P., 1981).

[14] Georges-Louis Le Sage (père), *Pensées hazardées sur les études, la grammaire, la rhetorique, et la poëtique* (La Haye: Jean Van Duren, 1729), pp. 59, 74, 101, 100, 104. The dates of Le Sage père are 1684-1759. For useful remarks on the place of Le Sage *père* and *fils* in Genevan scientific culture, see Burghard Weiss, "Zur Newton-Rezeption der Genfer Aufklärung," *Philosophia Naturalis* **23** (1986) 424-437.

[15] Georges-Louis Le Sage (père), *Cours abrégé de physique, suivant les derniers observations des Académies Royales de Paris & de Londres* (Genève: Frabri & Barrillot, 1732).

[16] Lucretius, *De rerum natura*, ed. and trans. by W.H.D. Rouse, revised by M.F. Smith, 2nd ed., Loeb Classical Library (Cambridge: Harvard U. P. ; London: William Heinemann, 1975), Book 1, lines 265-357; Book 2, lines 381-397.

[17] The mathematician Gabriel Cramer (1704-1752) is best known for "Cramer's rule" and other work on determinants. Jean-Louis Calandrini (1703-1758) helped edit a Latin edition of Newton's *Principia*, published at Geneva, 1739-1742, to which he added several chapters of commentary. He claimed to have discovered, six years before Clairaut, Newton's error in the treatment of the motion of the lunar apogee. A valuable account of the cultural matrix of Genevan science, including a discussion of education under Cramer and Calandrini, is given by Virginia P. Dawson, *Nature's Enigma: The Problem of the Polyp in the Letters of Bonnet, Trembley and Réaumur*, Memoirs of the American Philosophical Society **174** (Philadelphia: 1987), pp. 51-83.

[18] Daniel Bernoulli, *Hydrodynamica, sive de viribus et motibus fluidorum commentarii* (Strasbourg: Johann Reinhold Dulsecker, 1738). *Hydrodyanmics by Daniel Bernoulli and Hydraulics by Johann Bernoulli*, trans. by Thomas Carmody and Helmut Kobus (New York: Dover, 1968).

[19] Prévost, *Notice de la vie* (Ref. 2), pp. 50-51.

[20] André Gür, "Un précédent à la condamnation du *Contrat social*: l'affaire Georges-Louis Le Sage (1752)," *Bulletin de la Société d'Histoire et d'Archéologie de Genève* **14** (1968) 77-94.

[21] Euler's piece that won the prize awarded for 1752 was called "Recherches sur les irrégularités du mouvement de Jupiter et de Saturne" and was published in *Recueil des pièces qui ont remporté les prix de l'Académie Royale des Sciences*, Vol. 7 (Paris: Panckoucke, 1769). Euler's piece that won the prize for 1748 was called "Recherches sur les inégalités du mouvement de Saturne et de Jupiter." It was printed in 1749. It is found bound at the end of some, but not all, copies of Vol. 6 of the *Recueil* (1752).

[22] The most complete biographical study is Charles Andrew Domson, *Nicolas Fatio de Duiller and the Prophets of London: An Essay in the Historical Interaction of Natural Philosophy and Millennial Belief in the Age of Newton* (Ph. D. dissertation, Yale University, 1972). Domson argues that Fatio's religious fanaticism, which is usually described as a tragic falling away from Newtonianism, was actually a consequence of the influence of Newton himself.

[23] For more on Fatio's theory and Newton's view of it, see the article by Frans van Lunteren in this volume. For the text of Fatio's treatise (never published in his lifetime), see Bernard Gagnebin, "De la cause de la pesanteur: Mémoire de Nicolas Fatio de Duiller présenté à la Royal Society le 26 février 1690," *Notes and Records of the Royal Society of London* **6** (May, 1949) 105-160.

[24] It must also be said that Fatio's explanation is difficult to follow, since he postulates several orders of particles in nature, with varying degrees of elasticity and hardness. On the one hand, he insists that either the corpuscles responsible for the effects of weight or the bodies that they impinge upon must be like perfect springs. On the other hand, he insists that there must be inelasticity somewhere, in order to produce a loss of motion in the corpuscles. See Gagnebin, "De la cause de la pesanteur" (Ref. 23), pp. 128-129. Inelasticity is, indeed, the key idea. For if the interactions are perfectly elastic, they will not produce an effective attractive force between two macroscopic bodies. Air molecules are a concrete realization of a sea of *elastic* corpuscles: obviously, ordinary objects immersed in the atmosphere are not pressed together.

[25] This trajectory was constructed by Horst Zehe, *Die Gravitationstheorie des Nicolas Fatio de Duiller* (Hildesheim: Gerstenberg Verlag, 1980), p. 279.

[26] Gabriel Cramer, *Theses Physico-Mathematicae de Gravitate, ..., quas Deo dante, sub Praesidio D.D. Gabrielis Cramer, tueri conabitur Johannes Jallabert, Author* (Genevae: 1731). For a brief discussion of this document of 27 pages, see Zehe, *Die Gravitationstheorie des Nicolas Fatio* (Ref. 25), pp. 279-280. Cramer's student, Jean Jalabert (1712-1768), was ordained a minister and became a theologian. But in 1737 he took the chair of experimental physics at Geneva and is best known for his work on electricity.

[27] For these remarks about academic customs I am indebted to a manuscript by Rienk Vermij, provisionally titled *The Reception of Copernicanism in the Dutch Republic 1575-1750* and soon to be published by Edita, the publishing department of the Royal Dutch Academy of Arts and Sciences.

[28] Le Sage's materials for a biographical notice of Fatio are preserved in Geneva, BPU, Ms. 2043.

[29] [Franz Albert Redeker], *Franc. Alb. Redekeri...De causa gravitatis meditatio* (Lemgoviae: ex off. Meyeriana, 1736).

[30] Le Sage's playing cards have been but little studied. Many of the envelopes into which Le Sage organized them were labeled with categories of his own psychological self-examination. For a fascinating psychological portrait of Le Sage based on some of these cards, see Bernard Gagnebin, "Un maniaque de l'introspection rélévé par 35,000 cartes à jouer: Georges-Louis Le Sage," in *Mélanges d'histoire du livre et des bibliothèques offerts à monsieur Frantz Calot* (Paris: d'Argences, 1960), pp. 145-157.

[31] A good brief account of these experiments and their consequences for eighteenth-century metaphysics and physiology is given by Thomas L. Hankins, *Science and the Enlightenment* (Cambridge: Cambridge U. P., 1985), pp. 130-145.

[32] Charles Bonnet, *Considérations sur les corps organisés, où l'on traite de leur origine, de leur développement, de leur réproduction....* (Amsterdam: Marc-Michel Rey, 1762).

[33] Charles Bonnet, *Contemplation de la nature*, 2nd ed., 2 vols. (Amsterdam: Marc-Michel Rey, 1769), Vol. 1, p. vi. The first edition was published in 1764.

[34] Bonnet to Le Sage, 20 juillet 1766, quoted in Prévost, *Notice* (Ref. 2), pp. 331-332. Bonnet to Le Sage, 12 novembre 1773, quoted in Prévost, *Notice*, p. 342.

[35] [Le Sage], "Letter à un académicien de Dijon, dont il a paru dans le Mercure de Février un Système du monde, où l'on explique, par l'impulsion d'un fluide, les phénomenes que M. le Chevalier Newton a expliqués par l'attraction," *Mercure de France*, May 1756, 153-171.

[36] The essential problem of chemical affinity is that a certain substance may combine easily with some substances but not with others. Suppose there are two substances A and B in combination. And suppose that A has a stronger affinity with a free substance C. If the combination AB is placed in proximity with C, then C will combine with A, leaving B free. Etienne-François Geoffroy (1672-1731) was the first to systemize such chemical knowledge in a table of affinities. Etienne-François Geoffroy, "Table des différens rapports observés entres différens substances," *Mémoires de l'Académie Royale des Sciences* for 1718 (published in 1719), 202-212.

[37] *Essai de chymie méchanique* (privately printed; no place; no date). Le Sage wrote this piece for the prize competition of the Academy of Rouen in 1758. After it was crowned, Le Sage had it printed in 1761. The printed version was substantially revised from the version originally submitted to the academy.

[38] Jean-Philippe de Limbourg, *Dissertation de Jean-Philippe de Limbourg, docteur en medecine, sur les affinités chymiques, qui a remporté le prix de physique de l'an 1758, quant à la partie chymique, au jugement de l'Académie Royale des Sciences, Belles-Lettres & Arts, de Rouen* (Liège: F. J. Desoer, 1761). Limbourg's summary of Le Sage's theory is found on pp. 70-87.

[39] Jacques-François Demachy, *Recueil de dissertations physico-chymiques présentées à différentes académies par M. de Machy, des Académies de Berlin & de Rouen, & celle des curieux de la nature, Démonstrateur de Chymie au Jardin des Apothicaires, & Maître Apothicaire de Paris* (Amsterdam and Paris: Monory, 1774).

[40] "Lettre écrite à l'auteur de ce recueil par M. Lesage de Genève," *Observations sur la Physique* **2** (1774) 244-246.

[41] Le Sage, "Lucrèce Newtonien," *Nouveaux Mémoires de l'Académie Royale des Sciences et Belles-Lettres, Année 1782* (Berlin, 1784) 404-427. Reprinted in Pierre Prévost, *Notice de la vie et des écrits de George-Louis Le Sage de Genève* (Genève: J.J. Paschoud, 1805). English translation in S.P. Langley, "The Le Sage Theory of Gravitation," *Annual Report of the Board of Regents of the Smithsonian Institution for the Year Ending June 30, 1898* (Washington: Government Printing Office, 1899) pp. 139-160.

[42] Le Sage, *Physique mécanique*, in Pierre Prévost, *Deux traités de physique mécanique, publiés par Pierre Prévost, comme simple éditeur du premier et comme auteur du second* (Genève: J.J. Paschoud, 1818).

[43] Le Sage to Maty, 18 avril 1774. Royal Society; Letters & Papers VI, 199.

[44] Euler to Le Sage, 16 avril 1763. Quoted in Prévost, *Notice* (Ref. 2), 382-386.

[45] Euler to Le Sage, 18 septembre 1765. Quoted in Prévost, *Notice* (Ref. 2), 389-390.

[46] Boscovich to Le Sage, 13 juillet 1771. Quoted in Prévost, *Notice* (Ref. 2), 354-360.

[47] Daniel Bernoulli to Le Sage, 28 mars 1761. Geneva, BPU, Ms. Suppl. 512, f. 70.

[48] Daniel Bernoulli to Le Sage, 15 avril 1767. Geneva, BPU, Ms. Suppl. 512, f. 72.

[49] Bailly to Le Sage, 1 avril 1778. Quoted in Prévost, *Notice* (Ref. 2), 299-301.

[50] Laplace to J.-A. Deluc [octobre, 1781]. In the Le Sage papers, Geneva, BPU; Ms. Suppl. 513, f. 260.

[51] Laplace to Le Sage, 17 germinal an V (= 6 April 1797). Geneva, BPU, Ms. Suppl. 513.

[52] Pierre-Simon Laplace, *Traité de mécanique céleste*, vol. 5 (Paris: Bachelier, An VII-1825. Reprinted, Bruxelles: Culture et Civilisation, 1967). On the possibility of a diminution of the attraction by the interposition of other bodies, see Book XVI, Ch. 4, pp. 403-407.

[53] J.L. Heilbron, *Electricity in the 17th and 18th Centuries* (Berkeley: U. of California Press, 1976), p. 76. J.B. Gough, too, has suggested that Le Sage's system achieved only an approximation to Newton's law of universal gravitation: see Gough, article "Le Sage," in C.C. Gillispie, ed., *Dictionary of Scientific Biography* (New York: Scribner, 1970-1980).

[54] James Evans, "Fraud and Illusion in the Anti-Newtonian Rear Guard: The Coultaud-Mercier Affair and Bertier's Experiments, 1767-1777," *Isis* **87** (1996) 74-107. In this paper, I have suggested that the fraudulent papers by "Coultaud" and "Mercier" were actually written by Hyacinthe-Sigismonde Gerdil (1718-1802), theologian, Cartesian philosopher, later a cardinal of the Catholic church, and, in the last years of his life, a candidate for the papacy. For a defense of Gerdil and another possibil-

ity, see Massimo Germano, *Scienza impura nel seculo dei lumi* (Torino: Levrotto & Bella, 1998), as well as an exchange of letters in *Isis* **90** (1999) 95-96.

[55] For a list of foreign scientists who spent some time in Geneva between 1791 and 1822, see René Sigrist, *Les origines de la Société de Physique et d'Histoire Naturelle (1790-1822)*, Mémoires de la Société de Physique et d'Histoire Naturelle de Genève, Vol. 45, Fasc. 1 (1990), pp. 209-212. For a sociological study of networks linking the Genevans with one another, as well as with foreign scientists, see Cléopâtre Montadon, *Le développement de la science à Genève aux XVIIIe et XIXe siècles* (Vevey: Editions Delta, 1975).

[56] Papiers relatifs aux thèses soutenues à Lyon le 12 juin 1770. Geneva, BPU, Ms. 2048.

[57] Jean-André Deluc, *Recherches sur les modifications de l'atmosphère* (Genève: 1772), Vol. I, pp. 166-167, 229; Vol. II, pp. 368-369, 435-438. Deluc's title page bears a quotation from Lucretius: "There are also a number of things for which it is not enough to name one cause...." (*De rerum natura*, VI, 703-704). That is, when we cannot be sure of the cause of some phenomenon, we should try to consider all the possible causes.

[58] Pierre Prévost, *De l'Origine des forces magnétiques* (Genève: Barde, Manget et Cie, 1788), pp. 33-39.

[59] Jean-Andre De Luc, *Untersuchungen über die Atmosphäre und die zu Abmessung ihrer Veränderungen dienlichen Werkzeuge*, trans. by Joh. Sam. Traugott Gehler (Leipzig: Müller, 1776-1778). Pierre Prévost, *Vom Ursprunge der magnetischen Kräfte*, trans. by David Ludewig Bourguet (Halle: Waisenhaus, 1794).

[60] Friedrich Wilhelm Joseph von Schelling, *Ideas for a Philosophy of Nature*, trans. of ed. of 1803 by Errol E. Harris and Peter Heath (Cambridge: Cambridge U. P., 1988), pp. 168 and 161. See also Reinhard Lauth, "Die Genese von Schellings Konzeption einer rein aprioristischen Physik und Metaphysik aus der Auseinandersetzung mit Le Sages spekulativer Mechanik," *Kant-Studien* **75** (1988) 75-93.

[61] See Paul Hahn, *Georg Christoph Lichtenberg und die exakten Wissenschaften. Materialien zu seiner Biographie* (Göttingen: Vandenhoeck & Ruprecht, 1927) and Armin Hermann, "Das wissenschaftliche Weltbild Lichtenbergs," in Helmut Heissenbüttel, ed., *Aufklärung über Lichtenberg* (Göttingen: Vandenhoeck & Ruprecht 1974), pp. 44-59.

[62] For this episode, see the article by Matthew Edwards in this volume.

[63] For an account of this paradoxical experiment and Prévost's explanation of it, see James Evans and Brian Popp, "Pictet's experiment: The apparent radiation and reflection of cold," *American Journal of Physics* **53** (1985) 737-753. For more detail on Rumford's use of the experiment, see Hasok Chang, "Rumford and the Reflection of Radiant Cold: Historical Reflections and Metaphysical Reflexes," *Physics in Perspective* (in press). A broader study of Genevan physics in the spirit of Le Sage and Prévost is given by Burghard Weiss, *Zwischen Physikotheologie und Positivismus: Pierre Prévost (1751-1839) und die korpuskularkinetische Physik der Genfer Schule* (Frankfurt am Main: Verlag Peter Lang, 1988).

Nicolas Fatio de Duillier on the Mechanical Cause of Universal Gravitation

Frans van Lunteren[*]

Attempts to explain Newton's universal attraction of material bodies date back to the early reception of Newton's *Principia* (1687). In a sense, Newton himself had opened the door to the causal issue. For in the *Principia* Newton repeatedly stressed that he did not conceive of attraction in a physical sense, that is as an immediate action of one body upon another. 'Attraction' was to be understood as merely a shorthand expression for the tendency of material bodies to approach one another, whatever the cause of this tendency. It might, as far as Newton was concerned, arise from 'the action of the aether or of the air, or of any medium whatever'.[†]

But Newton's disclaimers carried little weight. It would be hard for any reader to believe that the author was really open to the notion of bodies being driven to one another by a material fluid. For one, Newton rejected all dense fluids as being incompatible with the unhindered motion of planets and other bodies. His theory of planetary motion required a space that contained little, if any matter. How could an extremely tenuous fluid exert the immense power needed to move the massive planets towards the sun? Moreover, if Newton really believed that bodies were 'pushed' or 'impelled' rather than 'attracted', why use the controversial word 'attraction'? Finally, what kind of fluid or mechanism would be able to account for the mutual endeavour of objects as small as the least particles of matter in accordance with a precise mathematical relationship?[‡]

Yet some readers did not take mechanical explanation and universal attraction to be incompatible conceptions. The first conspicuous attempt to elucidate the physical cause of Newtonian gravity was made in 1690 by a gifted young Swiss mathematician and natural philosopher named Nicolas Fatio de Duillier. His current repute hinges less on his scientific advancements than on his choice of friends. For some years he was an intimate of Isaac Newton, or rather *the* intimate of Newton. The nature of their relationship and its sudden ending have been the subject of much speculation among historians.[§]

---

[*] Institute for the History and Foundations of Science, Department of Physics and Astronomy, Utrecht University, Utrecht, The Netherlands

[†] F. van Lunteren, *Framing hypotheses: Conceptions of gravity in the 18th and 19th centuries* (unpublished dissertation: Utrecht, 1991) 22-23; I.B. Cohen (ed.), *Isaac Newton's Philosophiae naturalis principia mathematica* (Cambridge, 1972) 298.

[‡] Van Lunteren, *Framing hypotheses*, 23-24, 28-29, 44, 46, 50-51, 60.

[§] F. Manuel, *A portrait of Isaac Newton* (Cambridge, Mass., 1968) 191-212; R. Westfall, *Never at rest: a biography of Isaac Newton* (Cambridge, 1980) 493-497, 516-517, 528-533, 538-539.

In 1699, some years after the breach, Fatio caused a scandal by hinting publicly that Leibniz had stolen the invention of the calculus from Newton. This step triggered a series of events that eventually would bring Leibniz and his supporter Johann Bernoulli into a bitter priority conflict with Newton and his British allies, above all John Keill.[*] Another seven years later Fatio joined the French Camisards. The leaders of this radical Huguenot sect from the Cevennes had been exiled from France. They roamed the streets of London, prophesying the imminent millennium, holding seances and speaking in tongues. The local authorities, concerned about the public display of religious zeal, brought Fatio and his co-religionists to trial. Their sentence involved public humiliation: they were to stand on the scaffold with a paper denoting their offences.[†]

Although Fatio had swiftly managed to make a reputation for himself as a mathematician, his theory of gravity failed to gain approval. His contemporaries either ignored or dismissed his causal explanation. After Fatio's death his compatriot Georges-Louis Le Sage rescued it from complete oblivion. The latter, having developed similar views on the cause of gravity, honoured Fatio as his prime precursor. This, however, was to be only the first of a series of resurrections of the theory.[‡] Few theories have met with so much resistance or even scorn and yet have shown such resilience. This fact in itself justifies an account of its first inception.

The story, moreover, is not without interest even setting aside the later fate of the theory. For Fatio's theory emerged from close interactions with the two most renowned mathematicians and natural philosophers of his time: Isaac Newton and Christiaan Huygens. As we will see, Fatio's theory of gravitation was to a large extent the outcome of earlier attempts to reconcile Newton's theory of gravity with that of Huygens. Unfortunately, his synthesis seems to have convinced neither of his mentors. Yet, unlike Huygens, Newton may well have been mildly sympathetic to Fatio's ideas on gravitation, at least for some time. But it is hard to tell whether such appreciation concerned the theory itself or its author. For his judgement changed radically after the rift.

This then is the story of the genesis of Fatio's theory and its reception by his contemporaries. The first part of this essay contains a brief sketch of Fatio's life, with special emphasis on his connections to Huygens and Newton. Subsequently, we will discuss some pre-Newtonian explanations of terrestrial gravity, including those of Fatio and Huygens. His conversion to Newton's theory resulted in an attempt to combine Newtonian mathematical attraction with Huygens' physical mechanism. Flawed as this attempt may have been, it con-

---

[*] For a full account of the priority dispute, see A.R. Hall, *Philosophers at war: the quarrel between Newton and Leibniz* (Cambridge, 1980).

[†] H. Zehe, *Die Gravitationstheorie des Nicolas Fatio de Duillier* (Hildesheim, 1980) 43-47.

[‡] For Le Sage's theory, see the article by James Evans in this volume. Later attempts to revive the theory are discussed in the article by Matthew Edwards .

tained the seeds of his subsequent theory of gravitation. The last part discusses the reception of Fatio's theory.[*]

Seeking patronage

Nicolas Fatio de Duillier was born in Basel in 1664. The son of a wealthy Swiss landowner, he first received private tuition at home and afterwards continued his studies at the *Académie* in Geneva. His main mentor at the Genevan academy was the philosopher Jean-Robert Chouet. Chouet had broken the scholastic tradition at the academy, until then a centre of Calvinist scholarship, by introducing such novelties as Cartesian philosophy and demonstration experiments. It was probably through his influence that Fatio renounced an ecclesiastic career, disregarding the explicit wish of his father, and instead focussed on mathematics and natural philosophy.[†]

Interrupting his theological studies at the age of eighteen, Fatio moved to France to assist Domenico Cassini, the famous head of the Royal Observatory. He stayed in Paris for a year and a half. The death of Colbert, the academy's main patron, probably prompted him to return to his home town. Back in Geneva he applied his astronomical skills in a series of geodetic measurements. The proximate aim of the work, which he undertook in collaboration with his brother, was the design of a new map of the lake of Geneva and its surroundings. The ultimate goal was to gain scientific recognition abroad and perhaps even membership in the Parisian academy.

Fatio also studied the zodiacal light, a phenomenon discovered by Cassini at the time that Fatio was in Paris. His observations resulted in an ingenious theory, which he communicated to Cassini and other acquaintances. Although Cassini presented these letters to the French academy, their effect was not what Fatio had hoped for. The members were irritated by Fatio's circumspection in securing his priority. For Fatio had already sent a manuscript containing his theory to a Parisian journal, while postponing publication until his observations provided greater clarity.[‡]

With his chances in Catholic France dwindling, Fatio placed his hopes in protestant Europe. Having heard of a French plot against the Prince of Orange, he travelled to Holland in the spring of 1686 to inform the Prince of the pending dangers. The Dutch authorities handsomely rewarded Fatio by promising him a mathematical professorship in The Hague on behalf of the state. The latter would involve a yearly stipend of twelve hundred florins. While waiting for this prospect to materialise, Fatio entered into a close cooperation with Christiaan Huygens, Europe's leading mathematician. It was probably Huygens who had testified to Fatio's mathematical competence.[§]

[*] This paper is largely based upon Zehe's aforementioned study.
[†] B. Gagnebin, 'De la cause de la pesanteur: Mémoire de Nicolas Fatio de Duillier', *Notes and Records of the Royal Society of London* 6 (1949) 106-107; C.A. Domson, *Nicolas Fatio de Duillier and the prophets of London* (New York, 1981) 4-11; Zehe, *Die Gravitationstheorie*, 2-3.
[‡] *Ibid.*, 4-15.
[§] *Ibid.*, 15-19.

At the time Huygens was working on two specific topics, the first being his theory of gravity and the second his method of determining the tangent to certain mathematical curves. As in Paris, Fatio adapted to the interests of his new mentor, while trying to move ahead. His own solution to the tangent problem, worked out in collaboration with Huygens, made a strong impression on the latter and cemented their relationship. In a similar vein the ambitious Fatio would eventually develop his own theory of gravity, taking that of Huygens as a starting point.

When in the spring of 1687 the Dutch authorities still failed to deliver, Fatio decided to spend the summer in England. In London he was quick to associate himself with the leading members of the Royal Society, among them Robert Boyle. While visiting the meetings of the Society, he was informed of a forthcoming work by the Cambridge mathematician Isaac Newton that would revolutionise natural philosophy. In June Fatio was proposed for membership of the Royal Society. The final decision on his admittance, however, was not taken before the end of the year. The delay forced Fatio to extend his stay in Britain. Only in the spring of 1688 was he formally admitted as a member of the Society.

In the following months he lectured the Society on various subjects, including Huygens' theory of gravity. His new prominence did not, however, procure him a salaried position. But in the spring of 1689 Fatio saw his chances multiply. The Glorious Revolution had placed the Prince of Orange on the British throne, and Fatio soon moved in courtly circles. More than once he was offered a position as secretary to one of King William's diplomats. Yet he declined these offers, as they did not match his ambitions. The only patron he was willing to serve was his close friend John Hampden, the son of the king's chancellor. But unfortunately Hampden fell out of favour with the court, thereby diminishing Fatio's prospects.[*]

Fatio and Newton

When in the late spring of 1689 Huygens paid his first visit to England, Fatio escorted his friend about the capital. He was also present at the Royal Society meeting where Huygens and Newton met for the first time. It probably also served as the occasion for Fatio's introduction to Newton. The encounter had a strong impact on both men. Before long Fatio openly expressed his veneration of Newton, 'the most honourable man I know, and the ablest mathematician who has ever lived'. Newton's letters to Fatio show that the affection was mutual and in Newton's case exceptionally strong. The scrutiny of Newton's *Principia* convinced Fatio of the failure of all theories based upon Cartesian vortices, including Huygens' theory of gravity.[†]

In March 1690 Fatio presented his own theory of gravity to the Royal Society. Two days later Newton came over to London and spent a month in the

---

[*] *Ibid.*, 19-25.
[†] Westfall, *Never at rest*, 493-495

company of Fatio. Fatio took care to obtain Newton's signature at the bottom of the paper that he had presented, as well as that of Halley. Together Fatio and Newton studied Huygens' recently published *Traité de la Lumière*, which also contained Huygens' views of gravity as well as some brief comments on Newton's theory.[*]

Later that spring, having accepted a position as a private tutor, Fatio accompanied his pupil on a trip to the Netherlands. Here he repeatedly visited Huygens, with whom he discussed his own theory of gravity as well as his mathematical innovations. After the death of the young man entrusted in his care Fatio returned to England in September 1691.[†] Upon his return, Fatio and Newton immediately resumed contact. Fatio ignored his brother's advice to compose a book on his theory of gravity and instead started work on a new edition of Newton's *Principia* in which he meant to include his own theory. By adding extensive comments to Newton's forbidding mathematics, he hoped to make the work more accessible. But the task proved to be more demanding than he had expected and in fact it never materialised.[‡]

As the correspondence between Newton and Fatio makes clear, Fatio came to share Newton's interests in alchemy and biblical prophecies. It has been suggested that it was Newton who set Fatio on the course leading to his religious extravaganza.[§] In early 1693 Newton invited Fatio to come over to Cambridge and take the chambers adjacent to his own. He even offered him an allowance. At the time Fatio was considering a voyage to Geneva to settle his affairs after the death of his mother. Although he was strongly tempted by Newton's offer, he did not move to Cambridge. Fatio and Newton met in London in the summer of 1693, but their relationship seems to have come to a sudden end later that year. In September of the following year Fatio admitted to Huygens that he had not heard of Newton for seven months. Whatever its cause, the rupture between both men was never fully healed.[**]

Meanwhile Fatio had declined offers for professorships in Amsterdam and Wolfenbüttel, the latter coming from Leibniz. As he explained, he lacked the required 'knowledge, health, and diligence'.[††] Instead Fatio once again accepted a private tutorship in early 1694, spending most of the following years in Oxford. Only in January 1698, during a trip to Holland, did he part company with his young protégé. In June Fatio returned to London, where he spent the following year. Here he resumed his mathematical studies, solving a problem set by Johann Bernoulli four years earlier.[‡‡] The problem in question was that of the brachistochrone, or the curve of quickest descent.

---

[*] Gagnebin, 'De la cause de la pesanteur', 115-116; Westfall, *Never at rest*, 496.

[†] Zehe, *Die Gravitationstheorie*, 25-27.

[‡] *Ibid.*, 27, 30-32.

[§] Domson, *Nicolas Fatio de Duillier*, 37, 42-43, 48-52, 55-66.

[**] Westfall, *Never at rest*, 531-533, 538-539.

[††] Domson, *Nicolas Fatio de Duillier*, 41; Zehe, *Die Gravitationstheorie*, 34.

[‡‡] *Ibid.*, 35.

Within a few months following Bernoulli's public challenge, the problem had been solved by Europe's foremost mathematicians, being, apart from Johann himself and his brother Jakob, L'Hôpital, Leibniz and Newton. In response to the various solutions, Leibniz had remarked that he had correctly predicted the names of those capable of tackling the problem. Fatio, who had not bothered with mathematics for years, was deeply hurt by the implicit suggestion of impotence. In 1699 Fatio published a small mathematical tract, in which he expounded his own solution to the Bernoulli-problem as well as those to other mathematical questions. He boasted that the invention of his own version of the calculus had been independent of Leibniz' publications. He added that Newton's letters and manuscripts proved Newton to be the first inventor. He also insinuated that Leibniz, notwithstanding his own priority claims, had actually 'borrowed' some vital insights from Newton.[*]

The accusation may have helped to at least partly restore the relationship with Newton. Three years later, again tutoring in London after a two-year stay in Geneva, Fatio was mentioned by Gregory as being among those to whom Newton had promised to publish his own mathematical methods as well as his work on optics. In 1704 Gregory noted that Newton was trying watches with jewel bearings made by Fatio, and in 1706 Gregory mentioned a manuscript by Fatio on comets that he had seen. Fatio repeatedly visited the meetings of the Royal Society, now under Newton's presidency. Apparently, he was still active in scientific circles.[†]

But in the course of 1706 Fatio sealed his scientific fate. That year he joined the Cévenol prophets, becoming a secretary to Elie Marion, one of the leaders of the movement. Fatio did not restrict himself to keeping records of miracles and divine messages. He even seems to have made a public attempt to raise a man from the dead. His punishment did not serve to sober him. In 1710 he left London to accompany Marion on a missionary tour through Europe, bringing them as far as Constantinople. By the time he returned to London his reputation as a mathematician and philosopher had been effectively ruined.[‡]

Subsequent attempts to renew contacts with the Royal Society did not meet with success. In spite of some new papers on mathematics, astronomy and technological innovations, Fatio failed to regain scientific respectability. He died in May 1753, ninety years old, and little more than a curiosity.

Mechanical explanations of terrestrial gravity

For a better understanding of the nature and genesis of Fatio's theory of gravity, we must first consider pre-Newtonian accounts of the cause of terrestrial gravity. In the course of the seventeenth century philosophers came to reject

---

[*] Hall, *Philosophers at war*, 104-109, 118-121; Zehe, *Die Gravitationstheorie*, 35-40.

[†] Manuel, *A portrait of Isaac Newton*, 205-206; D. Gjertsen, *The Newton handbook* (London & New York, 1986) 198; Westfall, *Never at rest*, 654.

[‡] Domson, *Nicolas Fatio de Duillier*, 83-92; Zehe, *Die Gravitationstheorie*, 43-46; For Newton's mixed attitude towards the Camisards, see M. Jacob, 'Newton and the French Prophets', *History of science* 16 (1978) 134-142, and Westfall, *Never at rest*, 654-655.

the traditional view of gravity as a natural tendency of solid and fluid bodies to move downwards. The mechanical philosophy did not tolerate the attribution of such quasi-active properties to material objects. As the followers of Gassendi and Descartes stressed time and again, inanimate matter is unable to initiate motion. Therefore the cause of gravity must consist in an external agent that pushes heavy bodies downward. Apparently the particles of this material, though insensible agent impinge upon heavy bodies, thereby transferring part of their motion to the grosser particles of the falling body.[*]

Most seventeenth-century mechanical accounts of gravity fit in either of two broad categories, the one reaching back to Descartes, the other to Gassendi. In both cases we are confronted with a circulation of subtle matter. In Descartes' cosmology contiguous whirlpools of insensible, subtle matter fill the universe. Solar vortices carry planets around suns; planetary vortices move moons around planets. The planetary vortices allow for a natural explanation of gravity. For according to Descartes, a terrestrial body owes its gravity to the downward pressure of subtle matter circulating in the terrestrial vortex.

In a certain sense, bodies at the surface of the earth are light rather than heavy, due to the spinning of the earth. If the space surrounding the earth had been empty, all terrestrial parts not firmly attached to one another would fly off towards the heavens. But as the subtle matter encompassing the earth moves with a speed exceeding that of terrestrial bodies, it has a stronger centrifugal tendency. In Descartes' stuffed world, the only way it can recede from the centre is by pushing slower bodies downwards. The resultant force upon terrestrial bodies, known as their weight, depends upon the proportion of their pores, penetrated by subtle matter, to their solid parts.[†]

The second type of gravitational mechanism consists in an upward and downward stream of subtle matter. In this scenario, the main task is to account for the fact that the downward stream has a stronger effect upon terrestrial bodies than its upward moving counterpart. One may assume that the descending particles move with greater speed, or that they are coarser than the ascending particles. The latter solution was of course based upon the analogy with rain or hail. Newton's earliest views on gravity belong to this category, as did those of Fatio.[‡]

Both kinds of explanation suffer from serious drawbacks. Two flaws mark the Cartesian theory. Firstly, a unidirectional terrestrial vortex would impel heavy objects towards the terrestrial *axis* rather than towards the *centre* of the earth. Secondly, one would expect the rapidly rotating torrents of subtle matter to drag the falling body along the tangent. This would seem to preclude a perfectly vertical fall. As we will see, Huygens' vortical theory of gravity was based upon the awareness of these shortcomings.[§]

---

[*] Van Lunteren, *Framing hypotheses*, 6-9.

[†] *Ibid.*, 9; R. Descartes, *Principia Philosophiae* [1644], in Descartes, *Œuvres* (13 vols., Paris, 1964-74[2]) IX, 210-215.

[‡] Van Lunteren, *Framing hypotheses*, 18-19, 39-40.

[§] *Ibid.*, 17.

But the notion of a gravitational hail also has its problems. We have already noticed the asymmetry between the upward and downward currents. But even more problematic is the cause of this circulatory motion. Whence the downward motion of the gravitational particles? It is no use to explain the gravity of terrestrial bodies by appealing to the gravity of the subtle fluid. Yet, few philosophers were discouraged by such difficulties. They either ignored these problems or they invented ingenious *ad hoc* explanations.

Fatio and Huygens on terrestrial gravity

In a manuscript composed in 1685, Fatio expounded his thoughts on the nature of gravity. He spoke of a 'fierce current of exceptionally subtle matter', that flows from all possible directions towards the centre of the earth, pushing all bodies downward. The larger their surface and their quantity of matter, the greater the impact of the current. According to Fatio, the speed of the current far exceeds that of falling bodies. This assumption was required by Galileo's law of falling bodies, which makes the increment of speed independent of the momentary speed of a falling object.

When the subtle matter reaches the centre of the earth, the central fire attenuates it. Its parts are broken down into smaller pieces. Thus energised and rarefied the subtle matter flows outward. In its attenuated form it lacks its former power to move terrestrial bodies. Elsewhere Fatio suggested that this outward motion of particles, caused by the central fire, effects the sucking down of grosser particles, filling the vacated places of the former. Although fully aware of the hypothetical nature of his theory of gravity, Fatio did point to what he saw as empirical support. Experiments with the airpump by Boyle and Huygens suggested that under certain circumstances the height of a mercury column in a glass tube could far exceed the customary value, attributed to the pressure of the air.[*]

Within two years Fatio learnt of another explanation of gravity. In early 1687 Fatio was copying some of Huygens' manuscripts. In his notebook he commented on those pieces that were of special interest to him. In February he expressed his appreciation for Huygens' theory of gravity. Huygens had presented this theory to the French Academy in 1669, but until then postponed publication. Huygens assumed that the spherical space, which included the earth and its atmosphere, contained a fluid 'diversely agitated in all directions with much rapidity'. As other matter surrounded this space, the fluid was unable to leave the sphere. As a result its particles described large circles around the centre of the earth in all possible directions.

Huygens countered the objection that these motions would oppose each other with the argument that the extreme smallness and the large mobility of the particles could account for the preservation of the multidirectional agitation, as in the case of boiling water. Heavy bodies plunged into this fluid would

---

[*] H. Zehe, *Die Gravitationstheorie*, 88-95.

not acquire any sensible horizontal motion, due to the rapid succession of the impulses. He agreed then with the essential point of the Cartesian theory, namely that the centripetal tendency of heavy bodies is due to the exceeding centrifugal tendency of the particles of the celestial matter.[*]

By patching up Descartes' theory of gravity, Huygens lost the simplicity and the unity of the Cartesian conception. For the multidirectional vortex was in Huygens' view surrounded by a unidirectional vortex, responsible for the motion of the moon. He also left intact the Cartesian solar vortex. Such multiplication of vortices did not put Fatio off. He even suggested an extension of Huygens' multidirectional vortex so as to be superimposed upon the Cartesian vortices, even in the case of the solar vortex. In his view the concerted action of both vortices would account for the fact that all planets circulate more or less in the same plane and in the same direction.

Yet, in his notes Fatio did not restain his doubts about all vortical explanations of gravity. As he made clear he failed to see how the centrifugal tendency of the fluid would suffice to push bodies downward, whereas the direct, horizontal collisions of the fluid particles did not exert the least sensible pressure upon those bodies. In his earlier theory, these collisions had played the central role in the gravitational mechanism. His enthusiasm for Huygens' theory may have been genuine; it was certainly not unqualified.[†]

Reconciling Newton and Huygens

In July 1688 Fatio was requested to present Huygens' theory of gravity to the members of the Royal Society. They were probably eager to know how the views of Europe's leading natural philosopher related to Newton's recently published conceptions. In the mean time Fatio had read the *Principia*. His initial reservations with regard to Newton's principle of attraction had given way to unqualified acceptance. Such acceptance was facilitated by the fact that, unlike others, Fatio saw no insuperable discrepancy between Newtonian attraction and mechanical explanation. For in his lecture at the Royal Society, Fatio attempted to combine Newton's attraction with what he regarded as a modified form of Huygens' theory.

In the first part of his lecture Fatio expounded Huygens' original theory of gravity. He now dismissed the notion that bodies were pressed downwards by partly intercepting a vertical current of particles as absurd. For it would be impossible to account for such a current; and neither was it clear what would happen to these particles when they reached the centre of the earth. Therefore the only natural explanation of terrestrial gravity would involve circular motions around the centre of the earth. What followed were the details of Huygens' theory.[‡]

---

[*] *Ibid.*, 71-83; Van Lunteren, *Framing hypotheses*, 17-18; *Œuvres Complètes de Christiaan Huygens*, 23 vols. (The Hague, 188-1950) vol. XIX, 628-639.

[†] H. Zehe, *Die Gravitationstheorie*, 96-100.

[‡] *Ibid.*, 102-113.

In the second part of the lecture he suggested a modification of the theory which would enable it to account for the Newtonian attraction between all material bodies. To this end he transferred the centrifugal tendency of the subtle matter from the neighbourhood of celestial bodies to that of solid material particles. He gave two different accounts of this tendency. The first anticipated his ultimate theory of gravity. Consider an infinite number of extremely small particles flying in all possible directions through empty space. Assume moreover that these particles take up only a marginal part of space. According to Fatio the presence of much larger solid spherical particles will change the motion of the subtle particles in such a way as to make them flee these solid bodies. For all particles moving away from a solid body will keep on doing so, whereas those particles *approaching* the solid body will face an imminent change of motion because of its presence. After the collision they will likewise flee the solid body.[*]

This account will strike the modern reader as seriously flawed. For by intercepting a particle the solid body will indeed augment the number of particles moving away from the body at that side, but it will also diminish the number of particles moving away at the opposite side of the body. Moreover, a centrifugal *motion* of particles moving *rectilinearly* through empty space is something very different from a centrifugal *tendency* in a *rotating* fluid, where such centrifugal motion is prohibited. Fatio may well have been aware of the weaknesses in his first account for he immediately suggested a 'better' explanation of the centrifugal tendency, being in fact the one proposed by Huygens and now transferred to the microscopic realm.

According to Fatio, the resulting centrifugal tendency would produce a dilution of the subtle matter (which he now considered to be elastic) in the neighbourhood of solid bodies. The density of subtle matter in the space between two neighbouring bodies would thereby be diminished. As a consequence, these bodies would suffer a stronger pressure on the external sides and therefore tend to approach one another. As a result all material bodies, consisting of these gross, spherical particles, would tend to approach one another in accordance with Newton's theory.[†]

But the latter theory also had its problems. Here the difficulty is to account for the multidirectional circular motions of the subtle particles. If space were indeed almost empty, as Fatio now believed, then why would these particles move in curved trajectories? As we will see, before long Fatio would relinquish the second explanation in favour of a modified version of the first.

Huygens' objections

Meanwhile Huygens had worked out his own compromise. His attitude towards Newton's theory was ambivalent. He accepted Newton's claim that an inverse square centripetal force, rather than a Cartesian vortex produced plane-

---

[*] *Ibid.*, 114-117.
[†] *Ibid.*, 117-121.

tary motion. But he dismissed Newton's mutual attraction of all material bodies in the universe. In his view, such an attraction was both unwarranted and redundant. Instead, he extended his explanation of terrestrial gravity to the solar realm. It only remained to investigate the cause of the inverse-square diminution of the centripetal force with increasing distance from the sun, 'a new and remarkable property of gravity'.[*]

He clarified his objections in his *Discours sur la cause de la pesanteur*, published in 1690 as an appendix to his *Traité de la lumière*:

> That is something I would not be able to admit because I believe that I see clearly that the cause of such an attraction is not explainable by any of the principles of mechanics, or of the rules of motion. Nor am I convinced of the necessity of the mutual attraction of whole bodies, since I have shown that, even if there were no earth, bodies would not cease to tend towards a centre by that which we call gravity.[†]

A point that troubled Huygens was the inference, implicit in Newton's analysis, that the unhindered motion of the planets and comets required that the celestial spaces contained little if any matter, the very point that was conceded by Fatio. This conclusion seemed to shut the door to Huygens' explanation of gravity and, above all, his doctrine of light. For in Huygens view, expounded in the *Traité*, light consisted in pulses transmitted by contiguous particles of the ubiquitous subtle matter. As Huygens argued, the subtlety of this matter does not imply that its parts are separated by large distances. Instead he suggested that the particles 'touch each other, but that their tissue is rare and interspersed with a great number of small void spaces.'[‡] Being an atomist Huygens did not have any serious objections to the void.

Huygens ended his discussion of Newton's theory with a repetition of his mechanistic creed: 'It would be different, of course, if one would suppose that gravity is a quality inherent in corporeal matter. But that is something which I do not believe that M. Newton would admit because such a hypothesis would move us far away from Mathematical or Mechanical Principles.' In truth Huygens, like other continental philosophers, was sceptical with regard to Newton's adherence to mechanical principles. As he confided to Leibniz in 1690, he was not satisfied by Newton's theory of the tides, or by all the other theories that Newton built on his 'Principle of Attraction, which to me seems absurd.'[§]

Unlike Fatio, then, Huygens was both unwilling and unable to follow Newton all the way. He did not believe in the possibility of a mechanical explanation of Newton's attraction, and Newton's evacuation of space conflicted with his cherished theories of light and gravity, both of which required mutual contact between contiguous particles. Neither did he see any need for Newton's attraction, because his own mechanical account of a celestial centripetal force sufficed to explain all relevant phenomena. As we will see similar considera-

---

[*] Van Lunteren, *Framing hypotheses*, 44; *Œuvres Complètes de Christiaan Huygens*, XXI, 472.
[†] *Ibid.*, 471.
[‡] *Ibid.*, 473.
[§] *Œuvres Complètes de Christiaan Huygens*, IX, 538.

tions precluded him from accepting Fatio's new theory of gravity, first disclosed in a letter to Huygens in 1690.

Fatio's theory of universal gravitation

In the summer of 1689 Fatio had discussed his views on gravity with Huygens, who at the time was visiting London. While reading Huygens' *Discours* in early 1690, Fatio realised that he had failed to convince Huygens of the validity of his approach. He may have entertained a hope that Huygens would comment favourably on his ideas in his new book. Huygens' failure to do so triggered some new considerations from Fatio's side. Commenting on Huygens' book in a series of letters, Fatio re-entered the subject of gravity, eventually disclosing his new ideas. As he emphasised, he had finally cleared his theory of all possible objections. He suggested that Huygens' reserve was due to the same difficulty that had bothered him for some time.[*]

Part of the theory may seem familiar. He resumed the supposition of very subtle particles, speeding rectilinearly through empty space in all possible directions. To this hypothesis, he added the crucial assumption that these particles would lose a small part of their motion whenever they collided with gross material bodies. He claimed that these assumptions would result in Newton's gravitational action in accordance with an inverse-square law.

The argument ran more or less as follows. Consider only those particles that will collide at a certain point on the surface of an impenetrable solid sphere. As they move in converging currents, the force of these currents will be inversely as the square of the distance. After the collision these same particles will move away from this point in diverging currents, again with a force inversely as the square of the distance. Due to the loss of motion, however, the latter force will be somewhat smaller than the former. At large distances the dimensions of the sphere become negligible and the net result will be a centripetal force, inversely as the square of the distance. Adding to this the assumption that material bodies are extremely porous, Fatio could also account for the mass dependency of gravitation and the lack of gravitational screening by interposed material bodies.[†]

Now comes the aforementioned difficulty. Fatio originally believed that his assumption of a loss of motion would imply an increasing accumulation of subtle matter in the neighbourhood of gross material bodies. But he finally came to realise that the extent of condensation would be finite, and that it would be established almost immediately without any further increase. Moreover, as he later realised, it could be reduced to any desired amount if one increased the velocity of the gravific particles.[‡]

---

[*] Fatio to Huygens, March 6, 1690 in: *Œuvres Complètes de Christiaan Huygens*, IX, 384; Zehe, *Die Gravitationstheorie*, 130.

[†] *Œuvres Complètes de Christiaan Huygens*, IX, 384-386; Zehe, *Die Gravitationstheorie*, 134-138.

[‡] *Œuvres Complètes de Christiaan Huygens*, IX, 387; Zehe, *Die Gravitationstheorie*, 140-142, 147, 154.

In March 1690 Fatio read a copy of his letter to Huygens at a meeting of the Royal Society. He asked Edmond Halley, at that time secretary to the Society, to sign each page of the paper. Some weeks later he also received Newton's signature. In the manuscript that bears these signs Fatio had added a few considerations to the content of the letter. He argued explicitly for an infinitesimally small density of the subtle matter. The gravitational force being proportional to both the velocity squared and the density, one could diminish the density to an arbitrary extent, by introducing a compensating increase in the velocity. For most practical purposes, Fatio's gravitational fluid was indistinguishable from empty space.[*]

In a later supplement to the theory Fatio calculated the resistance experienced by a spherical body moving through his gravific fluid. His result was a resistance that was proportional to both the velocities of the particles and their density. Given the fact that the force exerted by the particles was proportional to the density and the *square of the velocity*, one could easily arrive at an arbitrarily small resistance for any given force by decreasing the density and increasing the velocity.[†]

The contemporary reception of Fatio's theory

The few philosophers with first-hand knowledge of the theory were hardly impressed by Fatio's exercise. Hooke, who had attended the Royal Society meeting, noted his reaction in his diary: 'Facio [Fatio] read his own hyp[othesis] of Gravity, not sufficient.' The following week he condescendingly referred to Fatio as the 'Perpet[ual] Motion man'.[‡] Halley was later said to 'laugh at Mr Fatios manner of explaining gravitation.'[§] Fatio likewise failed to convince Huygens. In a letter written in reply to Fatio's exposition, Huygens heaped up a number of objections. In Huygens' view, either the subtle matter would have to be annihilated at the central body, or no central force would arise. For the receding current would equal the approaching current. Moreover, without the annihilation, he could not see why the subtle matter would converge on the central body.

Fatio replied that he did not assume all subtle matter to converge on the central sphere. As the particles moved in all possible directions only a very small part would actually move towards the sphere. For his explanation of gravity, however, it sufficed to take only those particles into consideration. As far as the other objection was concerned, Fatio argued that an arbitrarily small loss of motion at each collision could produce the same force as the total annihilation of any given velocity. For the central force varied as the difference of the squares of the initial and the final velocities. For a fixed difference and an

---

[*] Gagnebin, 'De la cause de la pesanteur', 115-116, 129-134.

[†] Zehe, *Die Gravitationstheorie*, 249-250.

[‡] R. Hooke quoted in G.E. Christianson, *In the presence of the Creator: Isaac Newton & his times* (New York & London, 1984) 345.

[§] D. Gregory quoted in I. Newton, *The Correspondence* (Cambridge, 1959-1977) 7 vols., vol. III, 191.

increasing initial velocity, the final speed would approach the initial speed indefinitely. He also stressed that an arbitrary small amount of subtle matter, if sufficiently split up and agitated, could produce all the required attractive forces in the solar system.[*]

As is clear from the marginal notes that Huygens added to Fatio's letter, he was not impressed by Fatio's rebuttal. Still he did not take up the subject again in his correspondence. They probably discussed the matter when Fatio visited Huygens in the Netherlands. Whatever the nature of these discussions, they left Fatio with the impression that he had convinced Huygens of the soundness of his theory. As Huygens' subsequent letters to L'Hôpital and Leibniz prove, the belief was erroneous. Huygens held on to his conviction that Fatio's theory implied an accumulation of matter at the attracting body.[†]

The inappropriateness of some of Huygens' criticisms leads one to suspect an utter lack of interest. He completely misrepresented the theory by comparing it to the theory of gravity of Varignon. The latter had explained terrestrial gravity by an elastic fluid surrounding the earth. The motion of an object at a certain distance from the earth was determined by the length of the columns of subtle matter below and above the object, both exerting a pressure on the object proportional to the length of the column. Near the surface the upper column, being much longer, exerted a far greater pressure, thereby pushing bodies downward. There is hardly any resemblance with Fatio's theory.[‡]

Fatio's unusual assumptions probably sufficed to make the theory unpalatable to Huygens and other followers of the mechanical creed. The vacuity of space around and within material bodies, the extreme velocities that Fatio granted to his subtle particles, all this contradicted mechanical common sense, and even worse, the physical theories cherished by all these natural philosophers. Leibniz, another correspondent of Fatio, noted disapprovingly that Fatio regarded his doctrine of empty space not as a hypothesis, but as an indisputable truth. To Leibniz, as to most Cartesians, empty space was anathema.[§]

The sole exception to this general dismissal may well have been Isaac Newton. In a private memorandum, written at a much later date, Fatio boasted of Newton's consent:

> Sir Isaac Newton's Testimony is of the greatest weight of any. It is contained in some additions written by himself at the End of his own printed Copy of the first edition of the Principles, while he was preparing for a second Edition. And he gave me leave to transcribe that testimony. There he did not scruple to say "That there is but one possible Mechanical cause of Gravity, to wit that which I had found out..."[**]

---

[*] Huygens to Fatio, March 21, 1690 & Fatio to Huygens April 21, 1690, in: Œuvres Complètes de Christiaan Huygens, IX, 391-393, 407-412.

[†] Ibid., 412, Œuvres Complètes de Christiaan Huygens, vol. X, 354, 613.

[‡] Van Lunteren, Framing hypotheses, 19-20, 42-43.

[§] Zehe, Die Gravitationstheorie, 174.

[**] Newton, The Correspondence, III, 69-70.

Newton on Fatio's theory

When Fatio returned to England in 1692, he still had not published his theory of gravity. In fact he had lost the manuscript. In time, however, he managed to retrieve it. Meanwhile he had put his hopes on Newton. A new and enlarged edition of the *Principia* would be the ideal vehicle for the disclosure of his causal explanation.

Newton began his revision of the *Principia* immediately after its publication. He entered the alterations in several copies of the book, allowing some of his intimates to see and even transcribe them. Fatio actually transmitted a list of Newton's emendations directly to Huygens, who passed them on to Leibniz. In turn, Fatio also scrutinized the work for author's and printer's errors, jotting down his own improvements.[*]

In December 1691 Fatio informed Huygens of his intentions to prepare a new edition and see it through the press. He planned to add extensive commentaries to make the work more accessible. He expected the task to take him two or three years. News of the new edition spread rapidly. Both Huygens and Leibniz considered Fatio to be well qualified for the job.[†] At the time Fatio was writing to Huygens, the mathematician David Gregory, another young intimate of Newton, testified to Fatio's plans of including his own theory in the intended second edition:

> Mr Fatio designs a new edition of Mr Newtons book in folio wherin among a great many notes and elucidations, in the preface he will explain gravity acting as Mr Newton shews it doth, from the rectilinear motion of particles the aggregate of which is but a given quantity of matter dispersed in a given space. He says that he hath satisfied Mr Newton, Mr Hugens & Mr Hally in it.[‡]

Although Fatio may well have misjudged the opinions of Halley and Huygens, solid evidence supports his claim of Newton's favourable attitude. A draft addition in Newton's hand to his discussion of the vacuity of the celestial spaces in Book III of the *Principia* praises both theory and its author.

> They are mistaken therefore who join the least particles of bodies together in a compact mass like grains of sand or a heap of stones. If any particles were pressed together so densely, the gravitating cause would act less towards the interior ones than towards the exterior ones and thus gravity would cease to be proportional to the [quantity of] matter. Other textures of the particles must be devised by which their interstices are rendered more ample. And these are the necessary conditions of an Hypothesis by which gravity is to be explained mechanically. The unique hypothesis by which gravity can be explained is however of this kind, and was first devised by the most ingenious geometer Mr. N. Fatio. And a vacuum is required for its operation since the more tenuous particles must be borne in all directions by motions which are

---

[*] I.B. Cohen, *Introduction to Newton's 'Principia'* (Cambridge, 1971) 162, 177-179.
[†] *Ibid.*, 177-179.
[‡] *Ibid.*, 180

rectilinear and very rapid and uniformly continued and these particles must experience no resistance unless they impinge upon denser particles.[*]

However, as Fatio knew well enough, Newton entertained doubts about a mechanical cause of gravitation. As Fatio later admitted, 'he would often seem to incline to think that Gravity had its Foundation only in the arbitrary Will of God.'[†] Indeed, Newton seems to have planned the incorporation in his *Principia* of extensive references to ancient sources, supportive of the view that God, being omnipresent, activated the entire cosmos. As Gregory recorded in a memorandum:

> The plain truth is that he believes God to be omnipresent in the literal sense
> […] But if this way of proposing this his notion be too bold, he thinks of do-
> ing it thus. What cause did the Ancients assign of Gravity[?] He believes
> that they reckoned God the cause of it, nothing else, that is no body being
> the cause, since every body is heavy.[‡]

And at some unknown date Gregory added to his note on Fatio's claim of Newton's and Halley's consent: 'Mr. Newton and Mr. Hally laugh at Mr Fatios manner of explaining gravitation'.[§] Perhaps Newton changed his mind with regard to the merits of Fatio's theory. It is not unlikely that the proposed tribute to Fatio stemmed primarily from the strong affection that Newton felt for his young protege. After the break-up, Newton never mentioned Fatio's theory again. In the second edition of the *Principia*, appearing as late as 1713, he incidentally dismissed all mechanical theories of gravity.

> [Gravity] must proceed from a cause that penetrates to the very centres of
> the sun and the planets, without suffering the least diminution of its force;
> that operates not according to the quantity of the surfaces of the particles
> upon which it acts (as mechanical causes used to do), but according to the
> quantity of the solid matter which they contain.[**]

Let us compare this argument with his previous comments on Fatio's theory. At that time he saw no difficulty in combining the empirically determined proportionality of gravity to mass with a mechanical explanation, as long as one accepted the extreme rarity of solid matter within ponderable bodies. In fact, Newton still adhered to this conception of matter. By now however he extended his requirements of a mechanical explanation from the penetration of bodies to that of the ultimate solid parts of matter. This was of course a condition that no mechanical theory could meet, Fatio's theory being no exception.

But the proportionality of gravitation and mass does not strictly imply the latter condition. As long as the ultimate particles of matter, or atoms, all share the same ratio of surface area to volume Newton's objection loses its force. Now, it may have been that Newton's dismissal was merely rhetorical and only

---

[*] Newton in A.R. Hall & M. Boas Hall (ed.) *The unpublished scientific papers of Isaac Newton* (Cambridge, 1962) 315.

[†] Newton, *The Correspondence*, III, 70.

[‡] W.G. Hiscock, *David Gregory, Isaac Newton and their circle: Extracts from David Gregory's Memoranda 1677-1708* (Oxford, 1937) 29-30.

[§] Newton, *The Correspondence*, III, 191.

[**] I. Newton, *Mathematical principles of natural philosophy* (Berkeley, 1962) 546.

reflected his unwillingness to consider mechanical causes. On the other hand the objection may have stemmed from a solid, but unprovable conviction that the ultimate particles of matter differ in size or figure, an assumption that would render his argument valid.

And even when in 1717 Newton did suggest a material cause of gravitation in the third edition of his *Opticks*, his fluid did not resemble that of Fatio in any respect. For its activity did not derive from the rapid motions of the particles, but rather from the repulsive forces between the static particles.[*] It seems therefore safe to conclude that whatever Newton's original views of Fatio's theory, he eventually became as sceptical as other contemporaries.

The further development of the theory

The lukewarm reactions to his work did not undermine Fatio's faith in his theory of gravity. In his view the theory was as indubitable and as well established as Newton's law of gravitation, to which it formed a natural supplement. He regarded Newton's work as essentially incomplete without his own physical account of Newton's mathematical principle of gravitation.

In the further course of his life Fatio returned to his theory at several occasions. In 1696 he composed a manuscript in quarto entitled 'On the cause of gravity' during his stay in Oxford as a tutor of a young nobleman. In the 40-page manuscript he refined and expanded his theory, without changing anything in its physical assumptions. The additions were concerned with the structure of atoms required by the proportionality of gravity and mass and the free passage of light through glass and crystal in each and every direction; with the pressure exerted by the gravific particles on a solid plane; and above all with the concept of infinity as applied to the velocity and rarity of the fluid.[†]

In 1700, while staying in Geneva, Fatio entered a correspondence with Jacob Bernoulli. The latter probably considered any enemy of his brother a likely ally. When Fatio's theory cropped up in the correspondence, Jacob, intrigued by the hints that Fatio had dropped, begged Fatio for a full account: 'I am dying of impatience to see your theory of gravity'. Eventually Fatio did send a detailed account. From the following correspondence it is clear that the theory caused Bernoulli severe difficulties. Finally, Bernoulli praised the essay as providing solid proof of Fatio's talents and never addressed the subject again. After Fatio's return to England the correspondence seems to have come to an end.[‡]

In 1706 Fatio added some new paragraphs to his manuscript. His subsequent flirtation with religious heterodoxy did not put a stop to his natural philosophical ambitions. After his missionary wanderings through Europe ending in 1712, he resumed his mathematical and philosophical studies. In 1716 he left London to settle in Maddersfield. His research now focussed on alchemy, the

---

[*] I. Newton, *Opticks* (New York, 1952) Queries 17-24.
[†] Gagnebin, 'De la cause de la pesanteur', 119; Zehe, *Die Gravitationstheorie*, 34-35.
[‡] *Ibid.*, 177-180.

cabbala and theological speculations. In 1728 he wrote an obituary for Isaac
Newton. Subsequent attempts to regain his repute in learned circles met with
little success. In the same year 1728 he competed for the prize set by the Paris
academy for a physical explanation of celestial gravitation. Fatio's submission,
a Latin poem in the style of Lucretius, was passed over by the judges. Instead
they awarded a theory based upon Cartesian vortices. An adaptation of the
poem, sent to the Royal Society in 1730, met with a similar fate. Attempts to
procure a readership for his theory through subscription likewise failed.[*]

Meanwhile, a copy of Fatio's manuscripts had come into the hands of the
Genevan professor Gabriel Cramer. In 1731 Cramer published a dissertation
consisting of 37 theses on gravity, to be defended by his student Jallabert. Of
the 37 theses the last eight contained a summary of Fatio's theory, without
however mentioning his name. It was also Cramer who in 1749 drew Le Sage's
attention to Fatio's theory.[†]

The final occasion for Fatio to return to his theory of gravity was in 1742.
Again he polished his earlier arguments without adding anything meaningful.
If he was still pondering the publication of the intended 'Treatise on the cause
of gravity', such plans were soon thwarted by a stroke causing paralysis.
Fatio's *magnum opus* never materialised. When Fatio died in 1753 his theory
seemed to have disappeared with its author. Yet by this time Le Sage was already working on its revival.[‡]

Conclusion

Fatio's ideas on the cause of gravity fell on barren soil. In the course of time
philosophers were more and more divided along partisan lines. Those who kept
insisting upon mechanical explanations filled the universe with matter in vortical motion; those who swore by the void invoked 'active principles'. Fatio's
theory of gravity appealed to neither group. In the eighteenth century those
who accepted Newton's universal gravitation took it for an irreducible principle, the cause of which was unfathomable. If pressed they would either hint at
an inherent, although not essential property bestowed upon matter by God at
the creation, or at a direct and continuous manifestation of God's will. Even the
French and Germans eventually came to adopt such views.[§]

It seems unlikely then that a published version of Fatio's theory would
have made much of a difference. Perhaps philosophers would have been somewhat more careful in dismissing all mechanical accounts of universal
gravitation. Three arguments pervaded among the public dismissals of all mechanical explanations of gravity. A fluid offering no resistance to the motion of
bodies cannot exert a sensible power upon these bodies; gravity, being proportional to mass, must pervade the inner substance of bodies; the force does not

[*] *Ibid.*, 47-48.
[†] *Ibid.*, 279-280.
[‡] *Ibid.*, 49-50.
[§] Van Lunteren, *Framing hypotheses*, 84-90.

depend upon the velocity of the attracted bodies. As we have seen Fatio's theory was not vulnerable to any of these objections.[*]

Yet it seems likely that such objections should be seen as a symptom, rather than the cause of the dissatisfaction with mechanical theories. The former preference for mechanical explanation was now seen to rest upon prejudice. Given the fact that we know nothing of the essence of matter, it was said, how can we decide that attraction (in a physical sense) is less conceivable than impulse. In the words of Maupertuis, pleading the Newtonian cause in the Paris Academy in 1732: 'Is it more difficult for God to make two remote bodies tend or move towards one another, than to wait, in order to move it, until a body has been encountered by another?'[†]

Given our state of ignorance, philosophers added, it seemed best to heed Newton's 'Hypotheses non fingo'. For without any empirical clues it would be useless to speculate on the cause of gravitation. This profound insight found its most plastic expression in Voltaire's writings:

> Those philosophers who create systems with regard to the secret construction of the universe are like our travellers who go to Constantinople, and talk about the serail: they have only seen its outside, and yet pretend to know what the sultan does with his favourites.[‡]

[*] *Ibid.*, 71, 86-87, 90.

[†] P.L.M. de Maupertuis, *Œuvres* (Lyon, 1756) I, 93-94.

[‡] Voltaire, *Elémens de Philosophie de Newton* (Neuchatel, 1773) 390-391.

Newton's Aether-Stream Hypothesis and the Inverse Square Law of Gravitation[*]

E.J. Aiton, M.Sc., Ph.D.[†]

[...]

When he was writing the *Principia*, Newton was anxious to convince Halley that he had learnt nothing from Hooke. In a letter to Halley dated 20 June 1686, Newton claimed that the inverse square law for the attraction was implied in his unpublished essay, 'An Hypothesis explaining the Properties of Light discoursed of in my severall Papers',[‡] communicated to Oldenburg in 1675 and registered in the Royal Society.

In this document, Newton developed the hypothesis of a universal aether, explaining not only the properties of light but also the action of various forces, such as the electric, magnetic and gravitational forces. The aether causing gravity was not identical with the optical aether but something thinly diffused through it, of a tenacious and elastic nature. Just as vapours condense on solid surfaces, Newton supposed, the earth condenses so much of the gravitational aether, or 'spirit' as he termed it,[§] as to cause it to descend from above with great velocity:

> 'In which descent it may beare downe with it the bodyes it pervades with force proportionall to the superficies of all their parts it acts upon; nature makeing a circulation by the slow ascent of as much matter out of the bowells of the Earth in an aereall forme which for a time constitutes the Atmosphere, but being continually boyed up by the new Air... riseing underneath, at length... vanishes againe into the aethereall Spaces,...and is attenuated into its first principle'.[**]

In his letter of 20 June 1686 Newton suggested to Halley that if he considered the nature of the hypothesis, he would find

> 'the gravity decreases upward and can be no other from the superficies of the Planet than reciprocally duplicate of the distance from the center, but downwards that proportion does not hold'.[††]

Newton also remarked that he had never extended the inverse square proportion inside the earth, and had suspected that it did not hold exactly down to the surface until he had demonstrated this the previous year[‡‡], whereas Hooke, to whom he referred obliquely as a bungler, erred in extending the inverse square proportion down to the centre. Hooke did not in fact extend the inverse square

---

[*] This is an abridged version of an article originally published in *Annals of Science*, **25**, 255-260 (1969). Permission to reprint it was given by Taylor & Francis (http://www.tandf.co.uk/journals).

[†] Didsbury College of Education, Manchester.

[‡] *Correspondence*, vol. *i*, pp. 362-386.

[§] *Ibid.*, p. 365.

[**] *Ibid.*, p. 366.

[††] *Correspondence*, vol. *ii*, p. 440.

[‡‡] *Ibid.*, p. 435.

Pushing Gravity: new perspectives on Le Sage's theory of gravitation
edited by Matthew R. Edwards (Montreal: Apeiron 2002)

61

law to the centre of the earth; moreover, in one of his letters to Newton,[*] he remarked that in discussing such a possibility he was only considering a hypothetical case that he did not believe to be true. Newton also referred Halley to Sir Christopher Wren; for he was almost confident that Wren knew the inverse square law two years before the date of Hooke's letter, and the absence of a statement of the law in Hooke's Cometa (1678) showed that of the three, Hooke was the last to know it.[†]

Commenting on the hypothesis in a further letter to Halley, Newton explained how the inverse square law followed. In the hypothesis, Newton wrote, he had supposed

> '...that the descending spirit acts upon bodies here on the superficies of the earth with force proportional to the superficies of their parts, which cannot be unless the diminution of its velocity in acting upon the first parts of any body it meets will be recompensed by the increase of its density arising from that retardation. Whether this be true is not material. It suffices that 'twas the Hypothesis. Now if this spirit descend from above with uniform velocity, its density and consequently its force will be reciprocally proportionall to the square of its distance from the center. But if it descend with accelerated motion, its density will every where diminish as much as its velocity increases, and so its force (according to the Hypothesis) will be the same as before, that is still reciprocally as the square of its distance from the center'.[‡]

Although the increase in density of the gravitational aether on entering bodies was needed to explain the dependence of weight on mass, the optical aether was supposed to be less dense in the interior of bodies than in free space. Newton evidently soon recognized the inconsistency of supposing such different properties for the two aethers; for in a letter to Boyle, four years later, he replaced the aether-stream explanation of gravity by another depending on a supposed increase in size of the particles with distance from the centre of the earth, both inside the earth and in free space. As the larger particles were less apt to be lodged in the pores of bodies, these endeavoured to make way for the smaller particles below, thus displacing the body downwards.[§] In the second English edition of the Opticks (1717) Newton suggested yet another explanation: he supposed the density of the aether to increase with distance from the earth, the elastic force of the aether impelling bodies towards the less dense parts.[**]

None of these speculations amounts to an explanation of universal gravitation. The nearest approach is to be found in the elastic-aether hypothesis of the Opticks, in which the heavenly bodies, supposed, like the earth, to be centres of low aether density, were impelled towards one another by the expansive force of the aether. This symmetry was not explicitly extended to terrestrial bodies; these bodies were impelled towards the earth, but evidently the earth

---

[*] Ibid., p. 309.
[†] Ibid., p. 435.
[‡] Ibid., p. 447.
[§] Ibid., p. 295.
[**] Newton, Opticks, Dover Publications, 1952, Query 21.

was not similarly impelled in the opposite direction, neither were terrestrial bodies impelled towards one another. It is true that the density of the optical aether was less in the interior of bodies than outside, but the density gradient extended only a short distance.

Newton's first explicit statement of the principle of universal gravitation was given in the *Principia*,[*] but the principle was implied in the calculation of the attraction of a sphere, achieved, as Newton remarked in a letter to Halley,[†] in 1685. The idea of universal gravitation had indeed already been conceived by Descartes, who erroneously attributed it to Roberval.[‡] An explanation of universal gravitation, evidently acceptable to Newton,[§] was presented to the Royal Society in 1690 by Nicolas Fatio de Duillier.[**] As conceived by Fatio, the aether consisted of rapidly moving particles so widely scattered that their straight paths were rarely impeded by mutual collisions.[††] Gravity was caused by the inelastic collisions of the aether particles with gross bodies, not only the earth and heavenly bodies but also '*les Atomes qui les composent*'. Two opposite streams were envisaged, one towards the body, the other away from the body, the latter consisting of particles rebounding with reduced speed or emerging, again with reduced speed, after traversing the interior of the body.[‡‡] Huygens objected that the inward stream would not form unless the aether condensed in the body, and this he regarded as impossible.[§§]

In the correspondence with Halley, Newton's argument rested exclusively on the aether-stream hypothesis. A constant inward stream of S particles per unit time, moving with speed v, at a distance r from the centre would have a density $\rho = S/(4\pi r^2 v)$. In his commentary, Newton explains that, if the aether stream descends with accelerated motion, the density decreases everywhere as much as the velocity increases, so that the force in free space would be the same as if the velocity were constant. This implies that Newton supposed the force to be proportional to the density and the velocity: that is, in the notation already introduced, to $S/(4\pi r^2)$, which is independent of the velocity of the aether stream. Also Newton explains that, in meeting bodies near the surface of the earth, the loss of momentum of the individual particles is compensated by

---

[*] *Principia*, Book III, prop. 7.

[†] *Correspondence*, vol. *ii*, p. 435.

[‡] See E. J. Aiton, 'The Cartesian Theory of Gravity', *Ann. Sci.*, 1959, **15**, 30.

[§] See A. R. Hall and M. B. Hall, *Unpublished Scientific Papers of Isaac Newton*, London, 1962, p. 313.

[**] B. Gagnebin, 'De la cause de la pesanteur: mémoire de Nicolas Fatio de Duillier', *Notes and Records of the Royal Society of London*, 1949, **6**, 105-160. Two years earlier, Fatio had read a memoir to the Royal Society on Huygens's theory of gravity, but he seems to have rapidly assimilated Newton's ideas. On Huygens's theory, see E. J. Aiton, *loc. cit.*, pp. 34 ff.

[††] The aether of Newton's *Opticks* is of the kind envisaged by Fatio rather than the continuous fluid of Newton's own aether-stream hypothesis. See Query 28.

[‡‡] Gagnebin, *loc. cit.*, p. 127.

[§§] Huygens, *Œuvres complètes de Christiaan Huygens*, La Haye, 1888-1950, vol. ix, pp. 391-393. Moreover, the loss of speed of the aether in the inelastic collisions and the consequent running down of the system was unacceptable to Huygens. Thus he remarked that, even if the two streams did form, their effects would cancel.

an increase in density of the aether stream, so that the force is constant throughout the body. Thus the force of the aether stream is not diminished by meeting bodies; ρv is constant both in free space and in the interior of bodies. The inverse square law would indeed hold to the centre of the earth if the compensating increase in density were not checked. Evidently Newton did not consider an explanation of how the departure from the inverse square law inside the earth followed from his hypothesis to be necessary, confident that Halley would recognize the obvious implication that the increase in density was offset to some extent by the removal of particles from the aether stream owing to condensation.[*]

The force with which bodies were impelled by the aether stream was similar to the resistance of a fluid to the motion of solid bodies through it, discussed in Book II of the *Principia*, and was proportional to the momentum communicated.[†] The principal difference was that the aether penetrated the body so that the force was proportional to the volume, whereas in the case of fluids such as air and water, the resistance was proportional to the surface on which the fluid impinged. In the *Principia*, Newton considers the cases of resistance proportional to the velocity and to the square of the velocity. Although experiments had shown that the second case corresponded to reality, Newton evidently intended Halley to believe that, in 1675 he supposed the resistance to be proportional to the velocity.

An evaluation of Newton's claims in the letters to Halley may now be attempted. Although, as Newton admitted, the hypothesis was 'one of my guesses which I did not rely on',[‡] his argument rested on the premise that, in its implications, the hypothesis reliably reflected his exact scientific views. As interpreted by Newton himself, the aether-stream hypotheses implies the inverse square law in free space, whether the velocity of the aether-stream is constant or accelerated, and moreover implies a departure from this law in the interior of the earth owing to the reduction of the aether stream by condensation. Granting his premise, Newton could therefore claim the aether-stream hypothesis as evidence that in 1675 he believed the inverse square law to hold in free space, but did not assume its validity to the centre of the earth. Nevertheless his assertion that Hooke failed to recognize this limitation of the inverse square law was untrue, as was clear from one of Hooke's letters in his possession.[§] [...]

---

[*] In a letter to the author, dated 17 January 1969, Professor L. Rosenfeld accepts this interpretation in place of that given in his article, 'Newton and the law of gravitation', *Archive for History of Exact Sciences*, 1965, **2**, 365. Professor Rosenfeld has also made a reappraisal of Newton's aether hypotheses in a new article, 'Newton's views on aether and gravitation', which he has kindly allowed the author to read in typescript.

[†] *Principia*, Book II, Scholium, Section 1.

[‡] *Correspondence*, vol. *ii*, p. 440.

[§] *Ibid.*, p. 309.

Le Sage's Theory of Gravity: the Revival by Kelvin and Some Later Developments

Matthew R. Edwards[*]

An account is given of the attempts by Kelvin and later authors to revive Le Sage's theory of gravity. Predictions of Le Sage's theory in relation to shielding and eclipse experiments, as well as some possible links to relativity and cosmology, are briefly discussed.

Introduction

One of the oldest mechanical theories of gravity of which we have knowledge is that of Georges-Louis Le Sage, proposed in the mid-eighteenth century.[†] Le Sage's theory reached its zenith of popularity in the late nineteenth century, when it was shown by Kelvin to be compatible with the then newly discovered kinetic theory of gases. It stood alone among the mechanical theories of gravity of the day in its ability to reproduce Newton's law exactly. By the turn of the century, however, the theory had been thoroughly discredited, most notably by Maxwell, and today is generally considered of historical interest only. Feynman, for example, refers to the theory as a sort of primitive stepping stone in the early evolution of physics (Feynman *et al.*, 1963).

In this article, I briefly examine some of the later attempts to revive Le Sage's theory, beginning with its expression by Kelvin. An underlying focus is to discern whether the reasons for its dismissal by the physicists of the day were entirely valid. Our discussion of recent Le Sage-type models will be brief, as many of them appear elsewhere in this book.

Early History of Le Sage's Theory

Details of the early history of Le Sage's theory may be found in Le Sage's own paper, "*Lucrèce Newtonien*" (Le Sage, 1784), Kelvin's paper (Kelvin, 1873) and numerous later accounts (Taylor, 1877; Darwin, 1905; Aronson, 1964; Roseveare, 1982; Van Lunteren, 1991; see also the articles by Van Lunteren and Evans in this volume). The following account is drawn primarily from Aronson (1964).

Le Sage proposed that gravity is caused by the continuous bombardment of ordinary matter by "ultramundane corpuscles" originating from the depths of

---

[*] Gerstein Science Information Centre, University of Toronto, Toronto, Ontario, Canada, M5S 3K3. E-mail: matt.edwards@utoronto.ca

[†] Many years earlier Nicolas Fatio de Duillier proposed a similar theory, in which Newton expressed a sympathetic interest for some time. Fatio's contribution is discussed in the paper by Van Lunteren in this book.

Pushing Gravity: new perspectives on Le Sage's theory of gravitation   65
edited by Matthew R. Edwards (Montreal: Apeiron 2002)

space. So small were these corpuscles and so porous the structure of ordinary matter that the vast majority of particles, like the neutrinos of modern physics, passed unhindered through even massive bodies such as the Earth. Le Sage proposed separately that the corpuscles were miniscule relative to their separation; that their motions were rectilinear; that they rarely if ever interacted; that their motions could be regarded as equally dense streams moving in all directions; and that their velocities were extremely high. The latter postulate allowed the frictional resistance of the corpuscular sea to bodies in motion through it to be kept insensibly small relative to the attractive force. In order that the gravitational force be proportional to the mass of a body, rather than its cross-sectional area, Le Sage postulated moreover that the basic units of ordinary matter were highly porous to the corpuscles. In some of his writings he referred to them as cage-like structures, in which the diameters of the "bars" were small relative to the dimensions of the "cages". An isolated body in this medium would be shelled uniformly from all directions and would thus experience no net force upon it. In a system of two or more bodies, however, the mutual shading of corpuscles would result in an apparent force of attraction between the two bodies.

A critical aspect of the model, which was recognized by Le Sage and would later lead to grave difficulties, related to the nature of the collisions between the corpuscles and the units of ordinary matter. The collisions could not be entirely elastic, for in this case the shading effect would be exactly nullified by corpuscles rebounding from the shading mass to strike the shaded one. Instead, Le Sage proposed that the particles were either carried away at reduced velocities or else stuck to the bars of the cage-like units of matter.

With these postulates, Le Sage was able to show that his mechanism could reproduce Newton's law of gravitation. The following argument is taken from Preston (1877). Let A and B be two masses separated by a distance R. Consider the force which B by virtue of its shading effect exerts on A. The particles impinging on A may be viewed as originating from a spherical surface with radius R centred about A. The number of particles ordinarily striking A, if B were absent, is proportional to the cross-sectional area of A and hence, by the assumption of A's cage-like structure, to its mass. With B present, however, a fraction of particles is intercepted which varies directly with the cross-sectional area of B, and hence B's mass, and indirectly with the surface area of the sphere, which is proportional to R^2. The attractive force is thus proportional to the product of the masses over the square of the separation. Similarly, A exerts an equal and opposite force on B.

Due to their *ad hoc* and somewhat unusual formulation, Le Sage's ideas were not well-received during his day (see Evans, this volume). Le Sage, however, was completely undeterred by his critics and spent the greater part of his life developing epistemological arguments to defend his theory. According to Laudan (1981), it is Le Sage's efforts to advance the "method of hypothesis", which is today taken for granted, that were his major contribution, not the theory itself.

The Revival by Kelvin

After Le Sage, the theory fell into a historical pattern typical for this theory, which can be characterized as general oblivion punctuated by isolated introductions of variant forms. Since long intervals frequently lapsed between these renewals, the latter have very often lacked historical context. This pattern persists to the present day. The many and complex threads of Le Sage's successor theories in the eighteenth and nineteenth centuries are discussed in fine detail by Van Lunteren (1991).

An exception to this general pattern of neglect was a surge of interest in the 1870's, when Kelvin updated the work by demonstrating a close analogy with the kinetic theory of gases (Kelvin, 1873).[*] All of the various postulates introduced by Le Sage concerning the gravitational corpuscles (rectilinear motion, rare interactions, *etc.*) could be collected under the single notion that they behaved as a gas. Kelvin thus stated that:

> ... inasmuch as the law of the inverse square of the distance, for every distance, however great, would be a perfectly obvious consequence of (Le Sage's) assumptions, were the gravific corpuscles infinitely small and therefore incapable of coming into collision with one another, it may be extended to as great distances as we please, by giving small enough dimensions to the corpuscles relatively to the mean distance of each from its nearest neighbour. The law of masses may be extended to as great masses as those for which observation proves it (for example, the mass of Jupiter), by making the diameters of the bars of the supposed cage-atoms constituting heavy bodies, small enough. Thus, for example, there is nothing to prevent us from supposing that not more than one straight line of a million drawn at random towards Jupiter and continued through it, should touch one of the bars. Lastly, as Le Sage proves, the resistance of his gravific fluid to the motion of one of the planets through it, is proportional to the product of the velocity of the planet into the average velocity of the gravific corpuscles; and hence, by making the velocities of the corpuscles great enough, and giving them suitably small masses, they may produce the actual forces of gravitation, and not more than the amount of resistance which observation allows us to suppose that the planets experience.

In this single passage, Kelvin at the same time touches on three potentially problematic aspects of Le Sage's theory. The range of the gravitational force would be proportional to the mean free path of the Le Sage corpuscles, which in turn would be governed by their diameters and numerical densities. While Kelvin states here merely that this range could be placed beyond observational limits if the corpuscles were imagined sufficiently small, Preston subsequently seized upon this aspect of the theory as one of its major attractions.

---

[*] According to Brush (1976), it was in fact the theories of Le Sage and Hartley which paved the way conceptually for the kinetic theory.

Preston recognized that a finite range of the gravitation was crucial to the notion of a gravitationally stable universe.

In the same passage, Kelvin also notes that the potentially observable deviations from Newton's law due to 'self-shading' of corpuscles in large planets, for example, can be minimized by extending their porosity to as great proportions as necessary, by imagining that the cage bars of Le Sage's atoms were sufficiently small. This aspect of Le Sage's model was also appreciated by others, such as Maxwell (1875) and Poincaré (1918), who incorporated it in their calculations. Kelvin also adopts Le Sage's explanation for the imperceptible resistance experienced by bodies in motion through the corpuscular medium. The velocities of the corpuscles can be imagined so great that the ratio of a body's velocity to the average corpuscular velocity can be effectively reduced to zero, thereby eliminating the calculated resistive force (see also Darwin, 1905). I shall argue below that this approach, though seemingly innocuous, may actually have retarded the development of the theory.

Kelvin's major contribution to the debate lay in the thorny problem of the nature of collisions between Le Sage corpuscles and ordinary bodies. Whereas Le Sage had argued that these collisions must be wholly or partially inelastic, to avoid the aforementioned difficulty of rebounding corpuscles, Kelvin suggested that elastic collisions might be feasible if, following Clausius' notion of vibrational and rotational energies in gas molecules, the translational energies of Le Sage corpuscles after collision were given over to these other modes. In this way, the total energy of the system would be conserved. Le Sage's theory had been criticized for requiring an endless expenditure of energy from the outside. Moreover, the translational energies of the corpuscles could be restored in later collisions between corpuscles, as Clausius had shown that the translational component of kinetic energy in a gas remains in a constant ratio to the total kinetic energy. There would thus be no need for a 'gravitational death' of the Universe owing to the progressive loss of translational kinetic energy of corpuscles.[*]

At this point, the historical picture becomes more complicated. Maxwell's evaluation of the Kelvin-Le Sage theory was to become, according to Aronson, a turning point ultimately leading to the overthrow of the theory. Maxwell's critique appeared in the Ninth Edition of the Encyclopaedia Britannica under the title 'Atom' in 1875. After presenting a lucid account of the revised theory and noting its potential promise, Maxwell condemned it on thermodynamic grounds, stating that the temperature of bodies must tend to approach that at which the average kinetic energy of a molecule of the body would be equal to the average kinetic energy of an ultramundane corpuscle. Maxwell assumed that the latter quantity was much greater than the former and thus concluded

---

[*] Kelvin and Aronson both cite Le Sage as also predicting a gravitational collapse of the Universe for these same reasons. But for Le Sage, a finite duration of the Universe was dictated by other factors specific to his own model (James Evans, personal communication).

that ordinary matter should be incinerated within seconds under the Le Sage bombardment. He next gave the following proof to support this assessment:

> Now, suppose a plane surface to exist which stops *all* the corpuscles. The pressure on this plane will be $p = NMu^2$ where M is the mass of corpuscle, N the number in unit of volume, and u its velocity normal to the plane. Now, we know that the very greatest pressure existing in the universe must be much less than the pressure p, which would be exerted against a body which stops all the corpuscles. We are also tolerably certain that N, the number of corpuscles which are at anyone time within one unit of volume, is small compared with the value of N for the molecules of ordinary bodies. Hence, Mu^2 must be enormous compared with the corresponding quantity for ordinary bodies, and it follows that the impact of the corpuscles would raise all bodies to an enormous temperature.

As noted by Preston (1877), the questionable assumption with Maxwell's argument is that the value of N for corpuscles is much smaller than N for ordinary bodies. Preston argued that, on the contrary, the value of N for corpuscles might be made as large as desired if the value for M was correspondingly smaller. In this way, the Le Sage pressure could be maintained despite the low kinetic energies of the individual corpuscles. What Maxwell thought of this rebuttal may not be known; he died just two years after Preston's paper appeared, in 1879. Some authors, however, such as Aronson, apparently believe that Maxwell had the last word on the subject.

An unusual development came with the abandonment of Kelvin's theory by Kelvin himself. Here it should be emphasized that Kelvin had great ambitions for the theory. For him, the Le Sage theory complemented his dynamical scheme based on vortex atoms which was intended to account for all physical phenomena. When for various reasons he was forced to abandon his dynamical scheme in favour of an elastic-solid ether, Le Sage's theory was apparently dropped as well. By 1881, his assessment of the Le Sage theory was gloomy:

> Le Sage's theory might easily give an explanation of gravity and of its relation *to inertia of masses,* on the vortex theory, were it not for the essential aeolotropy of crystals, and the seemingly perfect isotropy of gravity. No finger-post pointing towards a way that can possibly lead to a surmounting of this difficulty, or a turning of its flank, has been discovered, or imagined as discoverable (Kelvin, 1881).

A postscript to the Kelvin-Le Sage theory was issued by G. H. Darwin (1905), who drew an analogy between Le Sage's mechanism and the newly appreciated phenomenon, discovered by Poynting, whereby two radiating spheres would repulse one another.[*] In his paper, Darwin calculated the gravitational force between two bodies at extremely close range to determine if geometrical effects would lead to a deviation from Newton's law. He concluded that only in the instance of perfectly inelastic collisions, or in the case that Kelvin's compensatory mechanism were operating and *all* translational ki-

---

[*] A possible indication of the decline of the Kelvin-Le Sage model by 1905 is evident in Darwin's statement in his paper that his calculations were mostly done years earlier, and that it was only Poynting's work which now prompted him to publish.

netic energy was given up by corpuscles after collision with bodies, would Newton's law stand up.

From this brief summary, it is apparent that several closely interconnected problems frustrated the development of Le Sage's theory, problems which have also plagued Le Sage-type models ever since. These relate to the thermodynamic question and the likelihood of a frictional drag and gravitational aberration effect. The complications introduced by these problems are illustrated in the analysis of Poincaré (1918), who concluded that the Le Sage corpuscles must travel with such high velocities, some 10^{24} times c, that the Earth would be incinerated in seconds. Like other critics of the Le Sage theory, Poincaré failed to address the modifications introduced by Kelvin and Preston.

At the same time, there are other disquieting features of Kelvin's revised theory. If, as Darwin calculated, *all* the translational kinetic energy had to be converted to other modes after collisions, then a steady accrual of Le Sage corpuscles in the vicinity of masses would surely result. Secondly, the solution adopted by both Le Sage and Kelvin to the resistance problem—the invocation of arbitrarily high corpuscular velocities—effectively divorces the theory from both Special and General Relativity, in which the quantity c is pervasive. It would seem more satisfactory if the Le Sage corpuscles possessed this average speed. Kelvin's modification thus appeared to sequester the gravitational force from the other forces. The Le Sage corpuscles operated within a sphere of their own, such that Kelvin's grand scheme of integrating the forces of nature could not be realized.

The combined influence of the many negative assessments, perhaps in conjunction with a general shift away from mechanical ether theories, appear to have led to a progressive loss of interest in the Le Sage-Kelvin theory. Still, Le Sage's theory was not without its supporters even up to the turn of the century and beyond. The status of Le Sage's theory at this time was summarized by Van Lunteren (1991, p. 276):

> In spite of the blows which Maxwell dealt the theory of Le Sage, the debate surrounding this model continued until after the turn of the century. Most contributions to the debate were critical, but the very fact that so many prominent physicists took pains to criticize the theory in itself attests to its prominence. Le Sage's theory was certainly the most conspicuous explanation of gravitation. For many critics the theory embodied the very notion of a dynamical theory of gravitation. Refuting the theory was sometimes regarded to constitute a proof of the inexplicability of gravitation. It was also most reminiscent of the crude materialism of the ancient atomists.

Le Sage's Theory in the Twentieth Century

In the twentieth century Le Sage's theory was more or less entirely eclipsed by Einstein's General Relativity. Just as in the previous centuries, isolated efforts to improve the theory have nonetheless been made. Several of these attempts are discussed or reprinted elsewhere in this volume and, for this reason, will not be examined at length here. In some cases these theories have had only a very limited exposure. If there is a common thread amongst the twentieth century theories, it is that the main obstacles that faced Kelvin in his day are still in need of resolution today.

Soon after the revival by Kelvin, many authors, including Lorentz (1900) and Brush (1911), attempted to substitute electromagnetic waves for Le Sage's corpuscles. Many of the most recent efforts have continued in this vein. The earliest such theory was due to Lorentz (1900). Assuming that space is filled with radiation of a very high frequency, Lorentz showed that an attractive force between charged particles (which might be taken to model the elementary subunits of matter) would indeed arise, but only if the incident energy were entirely absorbed. This situation thus merely reinforced the previous difficulties noted above in Le Sage's own theory and served to discourage further research along this line. In essence, this same problem has continually thwarted all subsequent Le Sage-type models.

One possible difficulty of electromagnetic Le Sage models is connected to the problem of gravitational aberration. As pointed out initially by Laplace and later by many others, it would appear that the gravitational force would need to be propagated at a velocity $\gg c$ to avoid introducing forces into astrophysics that are known not to exist (see also Van Flandern, this volume). At the same time, other authors (*e.g.*, Poincaré, 1906 (cited in Roseveare, 1982); Jaakkola, 1996) had expressed the view that within the Galaxy and Solar System such forces may be compensated for by others and that aberration effects in these settings may thus not arise.

The Theory of Majorana

In an unusual development, Le Sage's theory in this century became intertwined with an alternative theory of gravitation, also involving shading effects, proposed by Q. Majorana (1920). The history of Majorana's theory is detailed in two papers in this volume by Martins and will only be briefly discussed here. Majorana took as a starting assumption that a material screen set between two other bodies would diminish the force of attraction between the latter due to gravitational absorption by the screen. This state of affairs might be most readily envisioned if the gravitational force was caused by "a kind of energical flux, continually emanating from ponderable matter". The situation might then be analogous to the absorption of light in passage through a semi-transparent medium. His view thus differed sharply from Le Sage's, in that matter itself, rather than the remote regions of space, are the source of the gravitational fluxes. A complication of Majorana's theory was that bodies must be continually losing energy as a result of the gravitational emission. In a famous set of experiments Majorana found evidence for gravitational shielding of the same magnitude as would be consistent with astrophysical data. Majorana was aware of Le Sage's theory and in one set of experiments tried to distinguish which of the theories was correct, his own or Le Sage's. As shown by Martins (this volume), however, a clear distinction between Le Sage and Majorana using shielding experiments may be impossible *even in principle*.

The phenomenon uncovered by Majorana initially attracted considerable interest, especially from A. A. Michelson. Upon publication of an article by the astronomer H. N. Russell (1921), however, Michelson apparently lost interest and Majorana's work was largely neglected by physicists. Russell first demonstrated that, in order that large deviations from Kepler's laws not occur under Majorana's theory, the inertial masses of bodies must remain at all times proportional to the gravitational masses. Russell then went on, however, to show that even granted this proportionality, a major problem arose in the case of the tides, the solar tides in particular being some 370 times greater on the side of the Earth facing away from the Sun compared to the side facing the Sun. This criticism was subsequently attacked by Radzievskii and Kagalnikova (1960, reprinted here) and Shneiderov (1961b). The details of Russell's analysis are complex and were never fully accepted by Majorana, who felt that the whole question of tidal forces and measurements needed closer examination. Russell's paper is discussed further below in connection with General Relativity.

Since the time of Majorana's experiments, a number of laboratory investigations have been conducted in an effort to duplicate Majorana's findings (for a review, see Gillies, 1997; see also Unnikrishnan and Gillies, this volume). While these studies have failed to detect an effect of the same magnitude as Majorana's, it should be noted that none have employed Majorana's beam balance technique of quick, successive measurements where the shielding mass was first present, then absent. The latter-day studies have instead often relied on highly sensitive torsion balances featuring many electrical components. The suitability of torsion balances for detecting extremely tiny deviations from the norm was discussed by Speake and Quinn (1988). The major difficulty with such balances, in their view, is that such small weights must be used, due to the inherent weakness of the fibre, that non-gravitational noise, chiefly of seismic or thermal origin, may mask the miniscule deviations sought.

An experimental apparatus which *may* be suitable for replicating Majorana's work is the Zürich apparatus for measuring G (see Unnikrishnan and Gillies, 2000, and references therein). The Zürich experiment involves the deployment of large shielding masses in a manner highly reminiscent of Majorana's experiments. While data from the Zürich experiment do not at the moment appear to support Majorana (Unnikrishnan and Gillies, 2000, but see also Dedov *et al.*, 1999), a direct replication of Majorana's experiments in an effort to decide this important issue would be highly desirable.

Recently, support for the theories of Majorana and Le Sage has come from a different direction. A puzzling aspect of gravitation has long been the inability of researchers to precisely determine the value of the gravitational constant, G. This difficulty continues to motivate efforts in this area, such as the aforementioned Zürich experiment. In a detailed study, however, Dedov *et al.* (1999) consider the effects of the Earth's screening action in such experiments according to the theories of Le Sage and Majorana. The authors conclude that the Earth's screening effect, which would have a different mathematical form depending on the specific experiment, does account for the observed variations in the measured value of G.

A few decades ago there was an upsurge of interest in Majorana's work due to speculation that gravitational shielding might be associated with the so-called "fifth force" (Fischbach *et al.*, 1988). More recently, renewed interest has followed experiments involving rotating semiconductors hinting at some type of gravitational absorption (for discussions of the latter, see the papers by Unnikrishnan and Gillies and Hathaway in this volume).

Eclipse Experiments

Observational evidence for gravitational absorption has also been sought during solar and lunar eclipses, with findings both for and against being reported (for reviews, see Gillies, 1997, Martins, 1999 and Borzeszkowski and Treder, this volume). In these studies, however, it is not entirely clear what the predicted effects should be for Le Sage's theory. In the case of a gravimeter passing through totality during a solar eclipse, for example, we would need to compute separately the attenuation effects for four bodies—the Earth, the Sun, the Moon and the gravimeter. In practice, such computations are extremely difficult and a comprehensive treatment under Le Sage's theory has yet to be done.

On the other hand, it would appear that a Le Sage-type mechanism could possibly account, at least qualitatively, for the gravitational effects reported during a recent total solar eclipse in China (Wang *et al.*, 2000; but see also Unnikrishnan *et al.*, 2001; Unnikrishnan and Gillies, this volume). Using a spring-mass gravimeter during the solar eclipse of March 9, 1997, Wang *et al.* observed a decrease in surface gravity of 7 μgal at two times, one immediately before the onset of the eclipse and one just after the eclipse. At the height of the eclipse, however, there was no effect.

At first glance this result appears to be the opposite of what one might expect under Le Sage's theory. From the standpoint of the Earth, in Le Sage's theory, the Moon and Sun immediately before and after the eclipse screen off a greater quantity of the total background flux of Le Sage particles (or waves) than during the eclipse. This is because the flux passing through the Moon during the eclipse has already been attenuated while passing through the Sun. The two shadows 'cancel' each other partly at this time leading to an increased flux hitting the Earth compared to the situation immediately before and after the eclipse. We might thus expect an *increase* in the surface gravity of the Earth during the eclipse according to Le Sage's theory.

During a total eclipse, however, it is important to note that only a small region of the Earth, along the path of totality, is encompassed at any one time in the eclipse cone of shadow. It is only in this region that there is an increased flux of Le Sage particles or waves from the direction of the Moon. This allows for a very different interpretation of the gravimeter readings (this interpretation was suggested by Roberto de Andrade Martins, personal communication). Consider the situation just before the gravimeter passes into the cone of shadow. At this time the Earth under the shadow experiences a repulsive force from the direction of the Sun-Moon system. A small acceleration is imparted to the Earth, which is recorded as a slight decrease in surface gravity by the nearby gravimeter not yet under the shadow. As the shadow passes directly over the study site, both the gravimeter and the column of Earth beneath it are now exposed to the *same* increased flux and pushing force. There is thus no change in the relative acceleration between the Earth and the gravimeter and no anomaly at this time. As the cone of shadow passes to the other side of the study site, the Le Sage flux on that side increases and the gravimeter again records the slight acceleration of the Earth. This could account for the curious 'before-and-after' effect in the Chinese study. In eclipses where the study site does not experience totality, it would be expected under this mechanism that just one peak would be observed, corresponding to the period when the region of totality passes closest to the study site. In this respect, a single-peak decrease of 10-12 μgal was reported by Mishra and Rao (1997) for a solar eclipse in India in 1995. In this instance the study site only experienced 80 per cent totality.

Recent Le Sage-Type Theories

Despite the general emphasis on Majorana's rather than Le Sage's theory, the latter has cropped up in new forms several times in the last half-century. A partial listing of these newer theories would include the works of Radzievskii and Kagalnikova (1960), Shneiderov (1943, 1961a), Buonomano and Engel (1976), Adamut (1976, 1982), Veselov (1981), Jaakkola (1996) and Van Flandern (1999). As many of these theories are discussed more fully elsewhere in this book, and in some cases reprinted, the present brief discussion will be limited to Shneiderov.

In a very ambitious model, Shneiderov (1943, 1961a) argued that Le Sage did not take into account the progressive character of the absorption of a ray of gravitons as it passed through a body. He named his own theory, which corrected this supposed deficiency, the "exponential theory" of gravity. Shneiderov's approach is similar in some respects to that of Radzievskii and Kagalnikova (1960), but contains a few assumptions which are not well explained. Shneiderov was most interested in exploring the geological consequences of his theory and attempted to link his work to the internal heating of planets and to Earth expansion (see Kokus, this volume). At the end of his 1961 article the editor of the Italian journal indicated his enthusiasm for Shneiderov's theory by issuing a call for papers for a conference devoted to it. Whether or not such a conference ever came to pass I have been unable to discern.

In a separate paper, in which he attacked Russell's criticism of Majorana's theory, Shneiderov (1961b) proposed an experiment to test the validity of

Majorana's and his own theory. It is unclear whether any such experiment has ever been attempted. The details of the proposed experiment were as follows:

> An accurate balance is put into a vacuum casing. A light, evacuated, and hermetically sealed spherical shell is suspended from one arm of the balance. Suspended in the spherical shell, at its center is a light receptacle with 50 g of liquid mercury in it. A counterweight is put on the scale of the other arm to balance the instrument. The mercury is evaporated to fill the shell uniformly. The weight of the shell filled with 50 g of mercury vapor should be greater than when the mercury is in the liquid state, and the arm of the balance supporting the sphere should, therefore, go down if the exponential theory of gravitation were correct.

Shneiderov calculated that the ratio of the mass of mercury in the vapour state to its mass in the liquid state would be $1 + 5.143 \times 10^{-11}$. A possible complication in Shneiderov's experiment is the unknown effects of the change of phase from liquid to vapour.

Shneiderov also attempted to account for the electrostatic force between charges in his model (Shneiderov, 1961a). Unlike bulk matter, which was mostly porous to radions (his term for Le Sage's particles), electrons in his scheme intercepted the entire incident flux of radions. To Shneiderov, this accounted for the enormously greater strength of the electrostatic force over gravity. In a similar vein, Jones (1987) and more recently Byers (1995) have given arguments supporting Le Sage-type shielding as the source of the strong force binding nucleons. These notions are consistent with an electromagnetic unification of all the forces and particles of nature, an occasional theme in Le Sage-type theories.

Le Sage Gravity and General Relativity

Some possible links between Le Sage gravity and GR are also evident. Near a large body, such as the Sun, an object necessarily experiences a reduced Le Sage pressure from the direction of the body. If the 'Le Sage frame' were defined as one in which the velocities and numerical densities of Le Sage corpuscles or waves are the same in all directions, then it is apparent that such a frame in the vicinity of the Sun would be 'falling' towards it. This suggests a Le Sage formulation of GR, in which changing Le Sage pressures near masses provide the physical basis for the mathematically derived expressions related to the 'curvature of space'. In this respect, it should be noted that Einstein considered a gravitational ether, which would differ fundamentally from the electromagnetic ethers of Fresnel and Lorentz, to be necessary to account for the inertia and acceleration of bodies (see Kostro, 2001).

Given the close connections between the theories of Le Sage and Majorana (see Martins, this volume), some comments by Russell on Majorana's theory may also be relevant in this light. As noted above, Russell published an article highly critical of Majorana's theory. Russell did not express unease with Majorana's experimental findings, however, and in the same article made the following interesting suggestion:

> But what then becomes of Professor Majorana's long and careful series of experiments? If their result is accepted, it seems necessary to interpret it as showing that the *mass* of one body (his suspended sphere of lead) was diminished by the presence of another large mass (the surrounding mercury); that the effect was a true change in mass (since inertial mass and gravitational mass are the only kinds of mass we know of); and that it depended on the proximity of the larger mass, and not upon any screening action upon the earth's gravitation. Strange as this notion may seem, it is not inherently absurd. Indeed, if the phenomena of gravitation and inertia may be accounted for by assuming that the four-dimensional "world" possesses certain non-Euclidean properties, or "curvature", both in the presence of matter and remote from it, it is not very surprising if the curvature induced by one mass of matter should be modified to some degree by the superposition of the curvature due to another, so that the effects were not exactly additive.

Clearly, the tiny effect found by Majorana was viewed by Russell as a possible manifestation of the then newly proposed theory of General Relativity.

Le Sage gravity, in view of Russell's interpretation above, could shed light on one of the unsolved problems of GR. In the Newtonian model, the total energy E_t of a gravitating pair of masses, such as the Moon and the Earth, can be expressed as

$$E_t = E_k + E_p,$$ (1)

where E_k is the kinetic energy of the two bodies and E_p is the potential energy. E_p tends to increase with increasing separation, while E_k tends to decrease. But as energy is associated with mass in GR, a difficulty arises since E_p cannot be tied to a specific point in the system (Bondi, 1991). The concept of shielded or 'hidden' mass may prove useful in this context. Rather than regarding the two masses as separate, independent units, as in Newtonian theory, they may be treated as a single mass, which may be dispersed in space to a greater or lesser degree. The expression for the total mass of the system, M_t, may be given as

$$M_t = M_{ap} + M_s,$$ (2)

where M_{ap} is the apparent mass of the bodies, in the sense of Majorana, and M_s is the shielded or hidden mass. The apparent mass of the two bodies will be seen to vary in precisely the same way as the potential energy, increasing to a maximum at infinite separation. Conversely, M_s will tend to increase as the two bodies approach each other. Thus, the motion from a lower to a higher orbit can be viewed as the creation of 'new' mass, as shielded portions of the bodies become exposed to Le Sage corpuscles.

Such an interpretation of mass could have implications for cosmology. As noted above, under either the Le Sage or Majorana theories, celestial objects like the Sun have M_{ap} reduced relative to the situation that they were finely distributed throughout space. As Majorana showed, for very large bodies, in which the attenuation of the gravitational flux might approach 100 per cent, M_{ap} becomes proportional to the cross-sectional area, and thus to R^2. In such cases the core regions of the bodies receive no corpuscles at all from the external surroundings. The core of a body in this case would not be held in place by its own self-gravitation, but by the gravitational pressure of the outer shell. M_{ap} of the core would fall to zero. Outside the domain of gravity, and perhaps the other forces as well, the core region would exist as a kind of reservoir of unrefined matter and energy.

The hidden reservoirs of degraded matter might then give rise to unusual physical and cosmological phenomena. Large 'black hole'-type objects, for example, might remain stable until an external event, such as a stellar collision, disrupts the equilibrium of forces. Ruptures of the shell might then lead to jetting of core material into the surrounding space, which in turn could give rise to new hydrogen atoms and subsequently new stars and galaxies. Such a sequence might correspond in a general sense to the theory of formation of quasars outlined by Arp (1998, see also this volume). In this way equilibrium might be attainable between the processes of hydrogen consumption (in stars) and hydrogen renewal (in quasar formation) in a static Universe.

References

Adamut, I.A., 1976. "Analyse de l'action gravitationelle du rayonnement électromagnétique sur un système de corps. Une théorie électrothermodynamique de la gravitation", *Nuovo Cimento B* **32**, 477-511.

Adamut, I.A., 1982. "The screen effect of the earth in the TETG. Theory of a screening experiment of a sample body at the equator using the earth as a screen", *Nuovo Cimento C* **5**, 189-208.

Aronson, S., 1964. "The gravitational theory of Georges-Louis Le Sage", *The Natural Philosopher*, **3**, 51.

Arp, H.C., 1998. *Seeing Red:Redshifts Cosmology and Academic Science*, Apeiron, Montreal.

Bondi, H, 1991. "Gravitation", *Curr. Sci.* **63**, 11-20.

Brush, C.F., 1911. "A kinetic theory of gravitation", *Nature*, **86**, 130-132. The same article also appeared in *Science*, **33**, 381-386.

Brush, S.G., 1976. "The kind of motion we call heat", *Studies in Statistical Mechanics*, Vol. 6, North-Holland Publishing Co., Amsterdam, pt. 1, pp. 21-22, 48.

Buonomano, V. and Engel, E., 1976. "Some speculations on a causal unification of relativity, gravitation, and quantum mechanics", *Int. J. Theor. Phys.* **15**, 231-246.

Byers, S.V., 1995. "Gravity, inertia and radiation" (website article, http://home.netcom.com/~sbyers11/).

Darwin, G.H., 1905. "The analogy between Lesage's theory of gravitation and the repulsion of light", *Proc. Roy. Soc.* **76**, 387-410.

Dedov, V.P., *et al.*, 1999. "Gravitational screening effect in experiments to determine *G*", *Meas. Tech.* **42**, 930-941.

Feynman, R.P., *et al.*, 1963. *The Feynman Lectures on Physics, Vol. 1*, Addison-Wesley Publishing Co., Menlo Park, Ca., Sections 7-7.

Fischbach, E. *et al.*, 1988. "Possibility of shielding the fifth force", *Phys. Rev. Lett.* **60**, 74.

Gillies, G.T., 1997. "The Newtonian gravitational constant: recent measurements and related studies", *Rep. Prog. Phys.* **60**, 151-225.

Jaakkola, T., 1996. "Action-at-a-distance and local action in gravitation: discussion and possible solution of the dilemma", *Apeiron* **3**, 61-75. Reprinted in this book.

Jones, W.R., 1987. "How the ether replaces relativity", in *Progress in Space-Time Physics 1987* (J.P. Wesley, ed.), Benjamin Wesley, Blumberg, Germany, pp. 66-82.

Kelvin, see Thomson, W.

Kostro, L., 2001. *Einstein and the Ether*, Apeiron, Montreal.

Laudan, L., 1981. *Science and Hypothesis*, Reidel, Dordrecht, pp. 118-123.

Le Sage, G.-L., 1784 (for the year 1782), "Lucrèce Newtonien", *Memoires de l'Academie Royale des Sciences et Belles Lettres de Berlin*, 1-28.

Lorentz, H.A., 1900. *Proc. Acad. Amsterdam,* **ii,** 559. A brief treatment in English appears in *Lectures on theoretical physics, Vol. 1*(1927), MacMillan and Co., Ltd., 151-155 (an edited volume of translations of a lecture series by Lorentz).

Majorana, Q., (1920). "On gravitation. Theoretical and experimental researches", *Phil. Mag.* [ser. 6] **39**, 488-504.

Martins, de Andrade, R., 1999. "The search for gravitational absorption in the early 20th century", in: *The Expanding Worlds of General Relativity* (Einstein Studies, vol. 7) (eds., Goemmer, H., Renn, J., and Ritter, J.), Birkhäuser, Boston, pp. 3-44.

Maxwell, J.C., 1875. "Atom", *Encyclopedia Britannica, Ninth Ed.,* pp. 38-47.

Mishra, D.C. and Vyaghreswara Rao, M.B.S., 1997. "Temporal variation in gravity field during solar eclipse on 24 October 1995", *Curr. Sci.* **72**, 782-783.

Poincaré, H., 1906. "Sur le dynamique de l'électron", *Rend. Circ. mat Palermo* **21**, 494-550.

Poincaré, H., 1918. *Science and method,* Flammarion, Paris. An English translation was published as *Foundation of Science*, Science Press, New York, 1929.

Preston, S.T., 1877. "On some dynamical conditions applicable to Le Sage's theory of gravitation", *Phil. Mag.*, fifth ser., vol. 4., 206-213 (pt. 1) and 364-375 (pt. 2).

Radzievskii, V.V. and Kagalnikova, I.I., 1960. "The nature of gravitation", *Vsesoyuz. Astronom.- Geodezich. Obsch. Byull.,* **26** (33), 3-14. A rough English translation appeared in a U.S. government technical report: FTD TT64 323; TT 64 11801 (1964), Foreign Tech. Div., Air Force Systems Command, Wright-Patterson AFB, Ohio (reprinted here).

Roseveare, N.T., 1982. *Mercury's Perihelion from Le Verrier to Einstein*, Oxford University Press, Oxford.

Russell, H.N., 1921. "On Majorana's theory of gravitation", *Astrophys. J.* **54**, 334-346.

Shneiderov, A.J., 1943. "The exponential law of gravitation and its effects on seismological and tectonic phenomena: a preliminary exposition", *Trans. Amer. Geophys. Union*, 61-88.

Shneiderov, A.J., 1961a. "On the internal temperature of the earth", *Bollettino di Geofisica Teorica ed Applicata* **3**, 137-159.

Shneiderov, A.J., 1961b. "On a criticism of Majorana's theory of gravitation", *Bollettino di Geofisica Teorica ed Applicata* **3**, 77-79.

Speake, C.C. and Quinn, T.J., 1988. "Detectors of laboratory gravitation experiments and a new method of measuring *G*", in *Gravitational Measurements, Fundamental Metrology and Constants*, (eds. V. De Sabbata and V.N. Melnikov), Kluwer, Dordrecht, pp. 443-57.

Taylor, W.B., 1877. "Kinetic theories of gravitation", *Annual Report of the Board of Regents of the Smithsonian Society*, 205-282.

Thomson, W. (Lord Kelvin), 1873. "On the ultramundane corpuscles of Le Sage", *Phil. Mag.*, 4th ser., **45**, 321-332.

Thomson, W. (Lord Kelvin), 1881. *Roy. Inst. Gr. Brit. Proc.* **9**, 520-521.

Unnikrishnan, C.S. and G. T. Gillies, 2000. "New limits on the gravitational Majorana screening from the Zürich *G* experiment", *Phys. Rev. D* **61**, 101101(R).

Unnikrishnan, C.S., Mohapatra, A.K. and Gillies, G.T., 2001. *Phys. Rev. D* **63**, 062002.

Van Flandern, T., 1999. *Dark Matter, Missing Planets and New Comets, 2nd ed.*, North Atlantic Books, Berkeley, Chapters 2-4.

Van Lunteren, F.H., 1991. Framing Hypotheses: Conceptions of Gravity in the 18th and 19th Centuries, PhD thesis (Rijksuniversiteit Utrecht).

Veselov, K.E., 1981. "Chance coincidences or natural phenomena", *Geophys. J.* **3**, 410-425. Reprinted in this book

Wang, Q.-S. *et al.*, 2000. "Precise measurement of gravity variations during a total solar eclipse", *Phys. Rev. D* **62**, 041101(R).

The Nature of Gravitation[*]

V.V. Radzievskii[†] and I.I. Kagalnikova

Introduction

The discovery of the law of universal gravitation did not immediately attract the attention of researchers to the question of the physical nature of gravitation. Not until the middle of the 18th century did M.V. Lomonosov [1] and several years later, Le Sage [2,3], make the first attempts to interpret the phenomenon of gravitation on the basis of the hypothesis of 'attraction' of one body to another by means of 'ultracosmic' corpuscles.

The hypothesis of Lomonosov and Le Sage, thanks to its great simplicity and physical clarity, quickly attracted the general attention of naturalists and during the next 150 years served as a theme for violent polemics. It gave rise to an enormous number of publications, among which the most interesting are the works of Laplace [4], Secchi [5], Leray [6], W. Thomson [7], Schramm [8], Tait [9], Isenkrahe [10], Preston [11, 12], Jarolimek [13], Vaschy [14], Rysanek [15], Lorentz [16], D. Thomson[‡] (cited in [17]), Darwin (18), H. Poincaré [19, 20], Majorana [21-25], and Sulaiman [26,27].

In the course of these polemics, numerous authors proposed various modifications to the theory of Lomonosov and Le Sage. However, careful examination of each of these invariably led to conclusions which were incompatible with one or another concept of classical physics. For this reason, and also as a result of the successful elaboration of the general theory of relativity, interest in the Lomonosov–Le Sage hypothesis declined sharply at the beginning of the 20th century and evidently it would have been doomed to complete oblivion if, in 1919-1922, the Italian scientist Majorana had not published the results of his highly interesting experiments. In a series of extremely carefully prepared experiments, Majorana discovered the phenomenon of gravitational absorption by massive screens placed between interacting bodies, a phenomenon which is easily interpreted within the framework of classical concepts of the mechanism of gravitation, but theretofore did not have an explanation from the point of view of the general theory of relativity.

The famous experimenter, Michelson [28], became interested in the experiments of Majorana. However, his intention to duplicate these experiments faded, evidently as a result of the critical article by Russell [29], in

___
[*] This paper is a corrected version of U.S. government technical report FTD-TT-64-323/1 + 2 + 4 [AD-601762]. The original article in Russian appeared in: *Bull. Vsesoyuz. Astronomo-Geod. Obschestva*, No. 26 (33), pp. 3-14, 1960. Reprinted with permission of V.V. Radzievskii.
[†] Present address: Nizhnii Novgorod Pedagogical University, Nizhnii Novgorod, Russia.
[‡] Editor's note: The D. Thomson mentioned in this paper possibly refers to W. Thomson

which it was shown that if Majorana's gravitational absorption really did exist, then the intensity of ocean tides on two diametrically opposite points on the earth would differ almost 400 fold. On the basis of Russell's calculation, Majorana's experimental results were taken to be groundless in spite of the fact that the experimental and technical aspect did not arouse any concrete objections.

In acquainting ourselves with the whole complex of pre-relativity ideas about the nature of gravitation, we were compelled to think of the possibility of a synthesis of the numerous classical hypotheses, such that each of the inherent, isolated, internal contradictions or disagreements with experimental data might be successfully explained. The exposition of this 'synthesis', *i.e.*, a unified and modernized classical hypothesis of gravitation created primarily from the work of the authors cited above and supplemented only to a minimum degree by our own deliberations, is the main problem of this work. The other motive which has impelled us to write this article is that we have discovered the above mentioned objections of Russell against Majorana's experimental results to be untenable: from the point of view of the classical gravitation hypothesis no differential effect in the ocean tides need be observed. Therefore we must again emphasize that Majorana's experimental results deserve the closest attention and study. It seems to us that duplication of Majorana's experiments and organization of a series of other experiments which shed light on the existence of gravitational absorption are some of the most urgent problems of contemporary physics. Positive results of detailed experiments could introduce substantial corrections into even the general theory of relativity concerning the question of gravitational absorption, which within the framework of this theory still remains a blank spot.

Evidently a strict interpretation of the Majorana phenomenon is possible only from the position of a quantum-relativistic theory of gravitation. However, insofar as this theory is still only being conceived, it seems appropriate, as a first approximation, to examine an interpretation of this problem on the basis of the 'synthetic hypothesis' presented below, especially as the latter includes the known attempts at a theory of quantum gravitation. We shall begin with a short exposition of the history of the question.

1. Discussion of the Lomonosov-Le Sage hypothesis

According to the Lomonosov-Le Sage hypothesis, outer space is filled with 'ultracosmic' particles which move with tremendous speed and can almost freely penetrate matter. The latter only slightly impedes the momentum of the particles in proportion to the magnitude of the penetrating momentum, the density of the matter, and the path length of the particle within the body.

Thanks to spatial isotropy in the distribution and motion of the ultracosmic particles, the cumulative momentum which is absorbed by an isolated body is equal to zero and the body experiences only a state of compression. In the presence of two bodies (*A* and *B*) the stream of particles from body *B*, impinging on body A, is attenuated by absorption within body B. Therefore, the surplus of the flux striking body A from the outer side drives the latter toward body B.

In connection with the Lomonosov-Le Sage hypothesis, the question of the mechanism of momentum absorption immediately arises. Generally speaking, the following variants are possible:

1. The overwhelming majority of particles pass through matter without loss of momentum, and an insignificant part are either completely absorbed by the matter or undergo elastic reflection (Schramm [8]). Evidently, in the first case, constant 'scooping' of ultracosmic particles by matter must take place, leading to a secular decrease in the gravitation constant. In addition, as can easily be shown, an inadmissible rapid increment of the body's mass in this case must occur if the speed of the ultracosmic particles is close to that of light. In the second case, as Vaschy [14] showed, the reflected particles must compensate for the anisotropy in the motion of the particles which was created by the interacting bodies. In other words, the driving of the bodies in this case would be completely compensated for by the repulsion of the reflected particles and no gravitation would result.

2. All particles passing through matter experience something like friction, as a result of which they lose part of their momentum owing to a decrease in speed (Le Sage [2, 3], Leray [6], Darwin [18], and others). Evidently in this case there would also be a gradual weakening of the gravitational interaction of the bodies (Isenkrahe [10]).

A way out from the described difficulty was made possible by the proposal of Thomasin (cited in [19, 17]), D. Thomson (cited in [17]), Lorentz [16], Brush [30], Klutz [31], Poincaré [19, 20], and others for a new modification of the Lomonosov-Le Sage hypothesis, according to which the ultracosmic particles are replaced by extremely hard and penetrating electromagnetic wave radiation. If in this case we assume that matter is capable of absorbing only primary radiation and radiated secondary radiation, which still possesses great penetrating power, then the Vaschy effect (repulsion of secondary radiation) may be eliminated.[*]

The next question which arises in connection with the Lomonosov-Le Sage hypothesis concerns the fate of the energy which is absorbed by the body along with the momentum of the gravitational field. As Maxwell [32] and Poincaré [19, 20] have shown, if we attribute to gravity a speed not less than the speed of light, then in order to ensure the gravitational force observed in nature it is necessary to accept that momentum is absorbed which is equal to an amount of energy that can transform all material into vapor in one second.

---

[*] However, in order that a secular decrease in the gravitation constant does not occur it is necessary to suppose that the quanta of secondary radiation, after being radiated, decompose to primary radiation and, as a consequence, at some distance, depending on the duration of their lives, the gravitational interaction between bodies approaches zero.

However, these ideas lose their force when the ideas of Thomasin, D. Thomson, and Lorentz are considered, according to which the absorbed energy is not transformed into heat, but is reradiated as secondary radiation according to laws which are distinct from the laws of thermal radiation.

There was still one group of very ticklish questions connected with the astronomical consequences of the Lomonosov-Le Sage hypothesis. As Laplace had shown [4], the propagation of gravitation with a finite speed must cause gravitational aberration, giving rise to so many significant disturbances in the motion of heavenly bodies that it would be possible to avoid them only if the propagation velocity of gravitation exceeded the velocity of light by at least several million times.

Poincaré [20] directed attention to the fact that the motion of even an isolated body must experience very significant braking as a result first of the Doppler effect (head-on gravitons become harder and consequently have more momentum than ones which are being overtaken) and second, the mass being absorbed sets the body in motion and a part of the body's own motion is communicated to the mass. In order for this braking not to be detected by observation, it is necessary to assume that the speed of gravitational radiation exceeds the speed of light by 18 orders. This idea of Poincaré is considered to be one of the strongest arguments against the Lomonosov-Le Sage hypothesis.

Not long ago a modification to the Lomonosov-Le Sage hypothesis was suggested by the Indian academician Sulaiman [26, 27].

According to this hypothesis, an isolated body A radiates gravitons in all possible directions isotropically, experiencing a resultant force equal to zero. The presence of a second body B slows the process of graviton radiation by body A more strongly, the smaller the distance between the bodies. Therefore the quantity of gravitons being radiated from the side of the body A facing body B will be less than from the opposite side. This gives rise to a resultant force which is different from zero and tends to bring body A and body B together.

Further, Sulaiman postulated invariability of the graviton momentum with respect to a certain absolute frame of reference. Here the moving body must experience not braking, but rather acceleration coinciding with the direction of speed which compensates the braking influence of the medium.

Sulaiman's hypothesis is very interesting. Unfortunately, it does not examine the question of decreasing mass of the radiating bodies or the question of the fate of the radiated gravitons.

As can easily be shown by elementary calculation, so that the impulse being radiated by the body can secure the observed force of interaction between them, it is necessary that they lose their mass with an unacceptably great speed. It is completely clear that no combination of longitudinal and transverse masses can save the thesis. There is a well-defined relationship between the relativistic expressions of the momentum and the energy [33], and it is impossible to imagine that a body radiating energy E (*i.e.*, mass E/c^2) could with this momentum radiate more than E/c.

If we suppose that the radiation of the mass is compensated by the reverse process of graviton absorption, then we return to a more elementary variant of the Lomonosov-Le Sage hypothesis. Graviton absorption and the screening effect which is inescapably linked with it guarantee a gravitational attraction force without the additional concept of anisotropic graviton radiation by one body in the presence of another.

2. Majorana's experiment, Russell's criticism

Majorana did not insist in his investigations on a concrete physical interpretation of the law of gravitation. He simply started from the supposition that if there is a material screen between two interacting material points A and B, the force of their attraction is weakened by gravitational absorption of this screen [21, 22, 25]. As in the Lomonosov-Le Sage hypothesis, Majorana took attenuation of the gravitational flux to be proportional to the value of the stream itself, the true density of the substance being penetrated by it, and the path length through the substance. The proportionality factor h in this relationship is known as the absorption coefficient. It is evident that with the above indicated supposition the relationship of the gravitational flux value to the path length must be expressed by an exponential law.

Let us imagine a material point which is interacting with an extended body. Since any element of this body's mass will be attracted to the material point with a force attenuated by screening of that part of the body which is situated between the element and the material point, on the whole the heavy mass of this body will diminish in comparison with its true or inert mass.

In his work [21], Majorana introduced a formula for the relationship between the heavy (apparent) mass M_α and the inert (true) mass M_υ of a spherical body of radius R and a constant true density δ_υ

$$M_\alpha = \psi M_\upsilon = \frac{3}{4}\left[\frac{1}{u} - \frac{1}{2u^3} + e^{-2u}\left(\frac{1}{u^2} + \frac{1}{2u^3}\right)\right]M_\upsilon, \qquad (1)$$

where $u = h\delta_\upsilon R$.

Expanding (1) into a series, it is easy to see that when $u \to 0$, $M_\alpha \to M_\upsilon$ and when $u \to \infty$, $M_\alpha \to \pi R^2/h$. From this

$$h \le \frac{\pi R^2}{M_\alpha}. \qquad (2)$$

Applying the result of (2) in the case of the sun, which is a body with the most reliably determined apparent weight, Majorana obtained

$$h \le 7.65 \cdot 10^{-12} \ CGS. \qquad (3)$$

To experimentally determine the absorption coefficient h it is theoretically sufficient to weigh some "material point" without a screen and then determine the weight of this "material screen" after placing it in the center of a hollow sphere. If in the first case we obtain a value m, then in the second case we will register a decreased value as a result of gravitational absorption by the walls of the hollow sphere

$$m_\alpha = me^{-h\delta l} \cong m(1 - h\delta l), \qquad (4)$$

where δ is the density of the material from which the screening sphere is made, and l is the thickness of its walls. Designating ε as the weight decrease $m - m_\alpha$, we easily find that

$$h = \frac{\varepsilon}{m\delta l}. \qquad (5)$$

To determine the absorption coefficient value by formula (5), Majorana began, in 1919, a series of carefully arranged experiments, weighing a lead sphere (with a mass of 1,274 gm) before and after screening with a layer of mercury or lead (a decimeter thick).

After scrupulous consideration of all the corrections it turned out that, as a result of screening, the weight of the sphere had decreased in the first series of experiments by 9.8×10^{-7} gm, which, according to (5), yields $h = 6.7 \times 10^{-12}$. In the second series of experiments, $h = 2.8 \times 10^{-12}$ was obtained.

As already mentioned, in 1921 Russell came out with a critical article devoted to Majorana's work.

Assuming that the interaction force between two finite bodies is expressed by the formula

$$F = \frac{Gm_1\psi_1 m_2\psi_2}{r^2}, \qquad (6)$$

where, in accordance with expression (1)

$$\psi = \frac{3}{4}\left[\frac{1}{u} - \frac{1}{2u^3} + e^{-2u}\left(\frac{1}{u} + \frac{1}{2u^3}\right)\right],$$

and assuming at first that the decrease in weight as a result of self-screening occurs while leaving the inert masses unchanged, Russell obtained on the basis of (6) the third law of Kepler in the form

$$\frac{a_1^3}{a_2^3} = \frac{T_1^2}{T_2^2}\left[\frac{\psi_1}{\psi_2}\right]. \qquad (7)$$

The value of ψ, calculated by Russell with the absorption coefficient $h = 6.7 \times 10^{-12}$ found by Majorana for several bodies of the solar system, is equal to:

Sun:	0.33	Mars:	0.993
Jupiter:	0.951	Moon:	0.997
Saturn:	0.978	Eros:	1.000
Earth:	0.981		

From this it follows that the true density of the sun is not 1.41, but 4.23 g/cm^2.

Using the above tabulated values of ψ and Kepler's law, Russell showed convincingly that the corresponding imbalance between the heavy and inert masses of the planets would lead to unacceptably great deflections of their motions. In order that the deflection might remain unnoticed, it would be necessary for the absorption coefficient h to be 10^4 times less than the value found by Majorana. From this Russell came to the undoubtedly true conclusion that if as a result of self-screening the weight decrease found by Majorana did occur, then there would have to be a simultaneous decrease in their inert masses.

Russell made this conclusion the basis of the second part of his article, which was devoted mainly to investigation of the question of the influence of gravitational absorption on the intensity of lunar and solar tides. Following Majorana's ideas, Russell suggested that a decrease in attraction and necessarily also a decrease in the inert mass of each cubic centimeter of water in relation to the sun or moon would occur only if they were below the horizon. If this is admitted, then sharp anomalies in the tides must be observed, *viz.*, the tides on the side of the earth where the attracting body is located must be less intense (2 times for lunar tides and 370 times for solar tides) than on the opposite side of the earth. In conclusion Russell contended that his calculations demonstrated the absence of any substantial gravitational absorption and that consequently Majorana's results are in need of some other interpretation. Russell himself, however, did not come to any conclusions in this regard.

While acknowledging the ideas presented in the first part of Russell's work to be unquestionably right, we must first of all state that the self-screening effect and the weight decrease associated with it cannot be seen as a phenomenon which is contradictory to the relativistic principle of equivalence: any change in a heavy mass must be accompanied by a corresponding change in the inert mass of the body. But is it possible to agree with the results of the second part of Russell's article, according to which gravitational absorption on the scale discovered by Majorana is contradicted by the observation data of lunar and solar tides? Let us remember that Russell came to this conclusion starting from the freshly formed Majorana hypothesis of gravitational absorption only under the condition that the attracting bodies are on different sides of the screen. Meanwhile, application of the Lomonosov-Le Sage hypothesis, which painted a physical picture of gravitational absorption, leads, as we will show in the following section, to conclusions which are completely compatible with Majorana's experimental results and with the concepts set forth in the first part of Russell's article, but at the same time, all of the conclusions about tide anomalies lack any kind of basis. Skipping ahead somewhat let us say in short that according to the Lomonosov-Le Sage hypothesis, the weakening of attraction between two bodies must occur when a screen intersects the straight line joining them, regardless of whether there are gravitational bodies on various sides or on one side of this screen.

3. The 'Synthetic' Hypothesis

Let us suppose that outer space is filled with an isotropic uniform gravitational field which we can liken to an electromagnetic field of extremely high frequency. Let us designate ρ as the material density of the field, keeping in mind with this concept the value of the inert mass contained in a unit volume of space. Evidently the density of that part of the field which is moving in a chosen direction within the solid angle $d\omega$ is $\rho(d\omega/4\pi)$. Under these conditions a mass of

$$d\mu = dS\rho \frac{d\omega}{4\pi} c ,$$ (8)

carrying a momentum

$$dp = dS\rho \frac{d\omega}{4\pi} c^2$$ (9)

will pass through any area element dS in its normal direction within the solid angle $d\omega$ in unit time.

The mass flux (8) will fill an elementary cone, one cross section of which serves as the area element dS. At any distance from this area element, let us draw two planes parallel to it which cut off an elementary frustrum of height dl, and let us imagine that the frustrum is filled with material of density δ. It is evident that the portion of the flux (8) absorbed by this material will be

$$d(d\mu) = d\mu \, h\delta \, dl$$ (10)

or

$$d(d\mu) = h\rho c \frac{d\omega}{4\pi} dm ,$$ (11)

where $dm = \delta \, dS \, dl$ is the mass of the elementary frustrum.

Let us imagine a 'material point' of mass m in the form of a spherical body of density δ and of sufficiently small dimensions so that it is possible to neglect the progressive character of the absorption within it and to consider that the absorption proceeds in conformity with formula (11). Let us divide the section of this spherical body into a number of area elements and construct on each of them an elementary cone with an apex angle $d\omega$. Applying formula (11) to these cones, and integrating with respect to the whole mass of the material point, we obtain

$$\Delta(d\mu) = h\rho c \frac{d\omega}{4\pi} m .$$ (12)

Formula (12) determines the value of the absorbed portion of the field mass which has passed in unit time through a cone with an apex angle $d\omega$, which is circumscribed around a sufficiently small spherical body of mass m.

To obtain the total rate of increment in the mass of the point, it is necessary to take into consideration absorption of the field impinging on it from all possible directions, which is equivalent to integration (12) over the whole solid angle ω. This gives

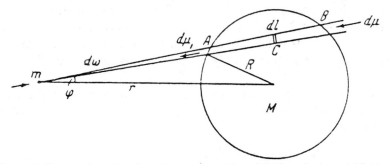

Figure 1. Diagram for calculation of mass absorption of the flux of a material field.

$$\frac{dm}{dt} = h\rho cm .$$ (12′)

Returning to formula (10), imagine that the field flux inside the cone circumscribed around material point m penetrates the material throughout the finite section of the path $AB = l$ (Fig. 1).

Integrating (10) from B to A, we obtain an expression which determines the total absorption within the cone AB when $\delta = $ const

$$\left(d\mu\right)_1 = d\mu e^{-h\delta l} .$$ (13)

Let $d\mu$ be the mass of the field striking cone AB from side B, and $(d\mu)_1$ be the mass of the field exiting this cone and impinging on body m. The decrease in the mass of the flux because of absorption in AB is equivalent to the decrease in its density up to the value

$$\rho_1 = \rho e^{-h\delta l} .$$ (14)

Thus from the left a flux of density ρ [its absorbed portion is expressed by formula (12)] strikes material point m, and from the right, a flux of density ρ_1. The portion which is absorbed will be

$$\Delta\left(d\mu\right)_1 = h\rho c e^{-h\delta l}\frac{d\omega}{4\pi}m .$$ (15)

Calculating (15) and (12) and multiplying the result by c, we obtain a vector sum of the momentum absorbed by point m in unit time equal to the value of the force dF, from which point m is 'attracted' to cone AB.

$$dF = h\rho c^2 \frac{d\omega}{4\pi}\left(1 - e^{-h\delta l}\right) .$$ (16)

It would not be hard to show that with such a force cone AB is 'attracted' to point m.

Setting $l = dl$ in (16) we obtain the attraction force of point m to a cone of elementary length

$$d\left(dF\right) = h^2\rho c^2 \frac{d\omega}{4\pi}m\delta dl .$$ (17)

As can be seen, force (17) at the assigned values of δ, $d\omega$, and dl depends neither on the distance between point m and the attracting elementary frustrum, nor on the mass of the latter. This result corresponds completely to the data of Newton's theory of gravity and is explained by the fact that the mass of the frustrum being examined is directly proportional to the square of its distance from point m.

Differentiating (16) with respect to l, we obtain the value of the attraction force of point m to element C of cone AB, which also does not depend on the position of this element

$$d(dF) = h^2 \rho c^2 \frac{d\omega}{4\pi} m e^{-h\,\delta\,l} \delta\, dl \ . \tag{18}$$

Comparison of (18) and (17) shows, however, that element C attracts point m with a weakened force and the degree of its weakness depends on the general thickness l of the screening material, regardless of whether point m and element C are on different sides or on the same side of the screen. The latter result is mathematical evidence of the groundlessness (within the framework of the Lomonosov-Le Sage hypothesis) of the critical ideas in the second part of Russell's article.

Let us now determine the total attraction force of material point m to a spherical homogeneous body of mass M. Multiplying the right side of (16) by $\cos\psi$ for this purpose and taking into account that $l = 2\sqrt{R^2 - r^2 \sin^2\psi}$ and $d\omega = 2\pi \sin\psi \, d\psi$, we easily find that

$$F = \frac{h\rho c^2 m}{2} \int\limits_{0}^{\arcsin\frac{R}{r}} \left(1 - e^{-2h\delta\sqrt{R^2 - r^2\sin^2\psi}}\right) \cos\psi \, \sin\psi \, d\psi = \frac{h^2 \rho c^2}{4\pi} \frac{m\psi M}{r^2} \ , \tag{19}$$

where

$$\psi = \frac{3}{4}\left[\frac{1}{u} - \frac{1}{2u^3} + e^{-2u}\left(\frac{1}{u^2} + \frac{1}{2u^3}\right)\right] , \tag{20}$$

in which $\mu = h\delta R$.

As has already been noted above, $\psi \cong 1$ whence follows that the value

$$G = \frac{h^2 \rho c^2}{4\pi} \tag{21}$$

plays the role of a gravitational constant. The value ψ which depends on progressive gravitational absorption within the body M must be considered to be the weight decrease coefficient of the latter.

In correspondence with the later experiments of Majorana, let us suppose that the coefficient of gravitational absorption is

$$h = 2.8 \cdot 10^{-12} \ . \tag{22}$$

Then on the basis of (21) we easily find that

$$\rho = 1.2 \cdot 10^{-4} \ g \ cm^{-3} \ . \tag{23}$$

Such a relatively high material density for outer space cannot meet objections, since the material of the gravitational field can almost freely penetrate any substance and is noticeable only in the form of the phenomenon of gravitational interaction of bodies. Now let us see how this business fares with the Doppler and aberration effects. It is quite evident that if the material behaves like a 'black body', *i.e.*, if it absorbs gravitational waves of any frequency equally well, then the Doppler effect will cause inadmissibly intense braking of even an isolated body moving in a system, relative to which the total momentum of the gravitational field is equal to zero. Therefore, we are forced to admit that matter absorbs gravitational waves only within a definite range of frequencies Δv which is much greater than the Doppler frequency shift caused by motion, and at the same time substantially overlaps that region of the field spectrum adjacent to Δv, whose intensity may be considered to be more or less constant. It is easy to see that under these conditions, a moving body will not experience braking, just as a selectively absorbing atom moving in an isotropic field with a frequency spectrum having a surplus overlapping the whole absorption spectrum of the atom, does not exhibit the Poynting-Robertson effect.

Actually, in system Σ which accompanies the atom, the observer will detect from all sides absorption of photons of the same frequency corresponding to the properties of the atom. From the point of view of this observer, the resulting momentum borne by the photons which are absorbed by the atom will be equal on the average to zero. The mass of photons being absorbed in system Σ is not set in motion and therefore does not derive any momentum from the atom. On the other hand an observer in system S relative to which the field is isotropic will detect that the moving atom is overtaken by harder photons and is met by softer photons. In other words it will seem to him that the atom absorbs a resulting momentum which differs from zero and is moving in the direction of the motion of the atom and compensates the loss of momentum, which is connected with the transmission of its absorbed mass of photons.

In this manner the observer in system S will also fail to observe either braking or acceleration of the atom's motion.

As concerns the effect of aberration, according to the apt remark of Robertson [34], which is completely applicable to a gravitational field, consideration of this phenomenon is the worst method of observing the Doppler effect. Actually, an isolated body such as the sun is a sink for the gravitational field being absorbed and a source for one not being absorbed. Since we are interested only in the form, we may say that in the presence of a body, something analogous to distortion of the gravitational field occurs; at each point of the field there arises a non-zero resulting momentum directed towards the center of the sink. Evidently such a momentum may collide with any other body in a direction towards this center. The very fact of motion, as follows from the aforementioned considerations, cannot cause the appearance of a transversal force component.

Thus it is possible to see that the modernized Lomonosov-Le Sage hypothesis presented here is not in conflict with a single one of the empirical facts which up to now have been discussed in connection with this hypothesis. At the same time, of course, it is impossible to guarantee that a more detailed analysis of the problem will not subsequently lead to discovery of such conflicts.

The Lomonosov-Le Sage hypothesis not only makes it possible to easily interpret the Majorana phenomenon, but also in clarifying the essence of gravity opens up perspectives for further investigations of the internal structure of matter and for a study of the possibility of controlling gravitational forces, and consequently the energy of the gravitational field. To illustrate the power of the energy, it suffices to recall that in the Majorana experiments the weight of the lead sphere, when introduced into the hollow sphere of mercury, decreased by 10^{-6} gm, which is equivalent to the liberation of twenty million calories of gravitational energy.

Most recently the authors have become aware of the experiments of the French engineer Allais who discovered the phenomenon of gravitational absorption by observations of the swinging of a pendulum during the total solar eclipse on June 30, 1954. In connection with this we feel compelled to mention that towards the end of the 19th century, the Russian engineer I.O. Yarkovskiy [35] was busying himself with systematic observations of the changes in the force of gravity, which resulted in the discovery of diurnal variations and a sharp change in the force of gravity during the total solar eclipse on August 7, 1887.

References

1. M.V. Lomonosov. *Polnoye sobraniye sochineniy*, Vol. 1. Izd. AN SSSR.
2. G.-L. Le Sage. *Nouv. Mém. de l'Acad. de Berlin*, 1782.
3. *Deux traités de physique mécanique*, publiés par Pierre Prévost. Genève–Paris, 1818.
4. Laplace. *Oeuvres*, v. IV.
5. A. Secchi. *L'unita delle forze fisiche*, 1864.
6. Leray. *Comptes rendus*, 69, 615, 1869.
7. W. Thomson. *Proc. Roy. Soc. Edinburgh* 7, 577, 1872.
8. H. Schramm. *Die allgemeine Bewegung der Materie als Grundursache der Erscheinungen*. Wien, 1872.
9. P.G. Tait. *Vorlesungen über einige neuere Fortschritte der Physik*. Braunschweig, 1877.
10. G. Isenkrahe. *Das Rätsel der Schwerkraft. Kritik der bisherigen Lösungen des Gravitationsproblems*. Braunschweig, 1879.
11. T. Preston. *Philosophical Magazine*, 4, 200, 364, 1877; 15, 391, 1881.
12. T. Preston. *Sitzungsber. Akad. Wiss., Wien*, 87, 795, 1883.
13. A. Jarolimek. *Wien. Ber.*, 88, 897, 1883.
14. M. Vaschy. *Journ. de phys.*, (2), 5, 165, 1886.
15. Rysanek. *Rep. de phys.*, 24, 90, 1887.
16. H.A. Lorentz. *Mém. de l'Acad. des Sci. d'Amsterdam*, 25, 1900.
17. Z.A. Tseytlin. *Fiziko-khimicheskaya mekhanika kosmicheskikh tel i system*. M.–L., 1937.
18. G.H. Darwin. *Proc. Roy. Soc. London*, 76, 1905.
19. H. Poincaré. *Sci. et méthode*. Paris, 1918.
20. H. Poincaré. *Bull. Astronomique*, 17, 121, 181, 1953.

21. Q. Majorana. *Atti Reale Accad. Lincei*, **28**, 2 sem., 165, 221, 313, 416, 480, 1919.
22. Q. Majorana. *Atti Reale Accad. Lincei*, **29**, 1 sem., 23, 90, 163, 235, 1920; *Philos. Mag.*, **39**, 488, 1920.
23. Q. Majorana. *Atti Reale Accad. Lincei*, **30**, 75, 289, 350, 442, 1921.
24. Q. Majorana. *Atti Reale Accad. Lincei*, **31**, 41, 81, 141, 221, 343, 1922.
25. Q. Majorana. *Journ. phys. et radium*, **1**, 314, 1930.
26. S.M. Sulaiman. *Proc. Acad. Sci. India*, **4**, 1, 1934; **4**, 217, 1935.
27. S.M. Sulaiman. *Proc. Acad. Sci. Unit. Prov.*, **5**, 123, p. 2, 1935.
28. A.A. Michelson. *Atti della Soc. per il progresso della scienza, Congresso di Trieste*, settembre, 1921.
29. H.N. Russell. *Astrophys. Journ.*, **54**, 334, 1921.
30. C.F. Brush. *Proc. Amer. Phys. Soc.*, **68**, 1, 55, 1929.
31. H. Klutz. *Techn. Engng. News*, **35**, No. 1, 1953.
32. J.C. Maxwell. *Encyclopedia Britannica*, 9 ed., v. 3, 46, 1875.
33. (English translation erroneous for this reference)
34. H. Robertson. *Monthly Notices of Roy. Astron. Soc.*, **97**, 423, 1937.
35. I.O. Yarkovskiy. *Vsemirnoye tyagateniye, kak sledstviye obrazovaniya vesomoy materii*. Moskva, 1889.

Gravity

Tom Van Flandern[*]

All known properties of gravity can now be modeled in a deterministic way starting with a unit, or "quantum," of gravity called the "graviton." The key to a successful and complete model is recognizing the need for two different media operating at vastly different scales. One of these, the contiguous "light-carrying medium" (elysium), provides the relativistic properties usually attributed to "space-time curvature," but through the vehicle of refraction instead of curvature. The other medium is that of the discrete, super-minute, strongly faster-than-light, force-carrying agents we here call gravitons. These latter provide all the Newtonian properties of gravity. This complete model also implies several new properties of gravity not yet recognized by current physics. However, a brief survey of observational data suggests no conflict with, and indeed some support for, the existence of these new properties.

Introduction

As Isaac Newton remarked so eloquently in the 17th century, the logical mind, competent in philosophical matters, finds it inconceivable that one object might act on another across a gulf of space without some intermediaries passing between the objects to convey the action. The alternative would require some form of magic, an effect without a cause. As such, it would violate the *causality principle*, one of the fundamental Principles of Physics. These principles have a higher status than the so-called "laws of physics," such as Newton's Universal Law of Gravitation. Such laws may change as knowledge increases. By contrast, the Principles of Physics are deductions about nature so closely related to pure logic that a definite observed violation of one of them would bring into question the very nature of the reality we live in (objective, external *vs.* dream-like or virtual). [1]

Of course, nothing about nature requires that the individual agents conveying an action be observably large or otherwise suitable for detection by any human-built apparatus. At one time, single air molecules (the conveyors of common sound waves) were unknown to science, although bulk sound was easily detectable. Likewise, the photon, or unit of light, was once unknown, although humankind was able to perceive bulk light long before forming cogent ideas about its true nature.

When we consider the forces of nature, the same principles undoubtedly apply. Newton explicitly made no hypothesis about the fundamental nature of gravity, leaving open the question of the agents that convey it (usually called "gravitons"). When Newtonian gravity was replaced by Einstein's general relativity (GR), two possible interpretations of the nature of gravity came with it:

[*] Meta Research, P.O. Box 15186, Chevy Chase, MD 20825-5186

Pushing Gravity: new perspectives on Le Sage's theory of gravitation
edited by Matthew R. Edwards (Montreal: Apeiron 2002)

93

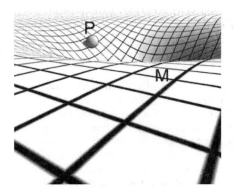

Figure 1. Rubber sheet analogy for gravity. Source mass M makes dent in "space-time" sheet, causing target body at P to roll "downhill" toward M.

the *field* and the *geometric*. In recent years, the latter has tended to become dominant in the thinking of mathematical relativists. In the geometric interpretation of gravity, a source mass curves the "space-time" around it, causing bodies to follow that curvature in preference to following straight lines through space. This is often described by using the "rubber sheet" analogy, as shown in Figure 1.

However, it is not widely appreciated that this is a purely mathematical model, lacking a physical mechanism to initiate motion. For example, if a "space-time manifold" (like the rubber sheet) exists near a source mass, why would a small particle placed at rest in that manifold (on the rubber sheet) begin to move toward the source mass? Indeed, why would curvature of the manifold (rubber sheet) even have a sense of "down" unless some force such as gravity already existed? Logically, the small particle at rest on a curved manifold would have no reason to end its rest unless a force acted on it. However successful this geometric interpretation may be as a mathematical model, it lacks physics and a causal mechanism.

GR also recognizes a field interpretation of its equations. "Fields" are not well defined in regard to their basic structure. Yet they clearly represent a type of agent passing between source and target, able to convey an action. As such, the field interpretation has no intrinsic conflict with the causality principle of the sort that dooms the geometric interpretation. However, all existing experimental evidence requires the action of fields to be conveyed much faster than lightspeed. [2]

This situation is ironic because the reason why the geometric interpretation gained ascendancy over the field interpretation is that the implied faster-than-light (ftl) action of fields appeared to allow causality violations. A corollary of special relativity (SR) is that anything propagating ftl would be moving backwards in time, thereby creating the possibility of altering the past and causing a logical paradox. For example, an action in the present, propagated into the past, might create a condition that prevented the action from coming into existence in the present, thereby eliminating the action propagating into the past, which restores the original situation, *etc.*, in an endless loop of causality contradiction. The causality principle excludes effects before causes because of just such logical paradoxes.

Yet the field interpretation of GR requires ftl propagation. So if SR were a correct model of reality, the field interpretation would violate the causality

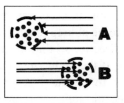

Figure 2. A: Force applied to exterior of body is resisted by each internal constituent. B: If a force is applied to every constituent, it does not matter how many there are.

principle, which is why it fell from popularity. However, it has only recently been appreciated that SR may be a valid mathematical theory in agreement with most experimental evidence, yet still be an invalid theory of physics. This is because an infinite number of theories that are mathematically equivalent to SR exist. [3] One of these, Lorentzian Relativity (LR), has been shown to be in full accord with all eleven independent experiments that test SR in the lightspeed or sub-lightspeed domains, yet does not forbid ftl propagation in forward time, as SR does. [4] If LR (for example) were a better physical theory than SR, then ftl propagations in forward time are allowed, and the field interpretation of GR would not imply any causality violations after all.

Our task here then is to follow this line of inquiry—the field of interpretation of GR combined with LR—and combine it with the logical need for agents to convey an action, to develop a model of gravity that is complete in its fundamentals, right down to the nature and properties of the unit of gravity, the hypothetical graviton.

How gravitons can give Newtonian properties of gravity

Gravity has properties unlike most other forces of nature. For example, its effect on a body is apparently completely independent of the mass of the affected body. As a result, heavy and light bodies fall in a gravitational field with equal acceleration. This is contrary to our intuitions based on experience with other types of forces. We have come to expect that a heavy body will resist acceleration more than a light one. But gravity does not behave that way. It is as if gravity was oblivious to the law of inertia.

However, on closer inspection, this property is not so surprising after all. Our intuitions are based on experience with mechanical, electric, magnetic, radiation, and other forces, most of which act directly on only part of a body; for example, only on its surface, or only on its charged particles. That action then creates pressure waves that pass through the entire body, forcing other parts of the body not acted on by the force to respond also. Hence, we see the origin of the property of "inertia," or resistance to motion—the effect of an active force is diluted as each affected part of a body contacts its unaffected neighbors and requires them to change their state of motion also. See Figure 2A. In general, the greater the mass of the body, the greater will be the ratio of the number of molecules unaffected directly by the force to the number directly affected; for example, the ratio of interior molecules to surface molecules. This increased ratio requires the effect of the force to be diluted over more molecules, creating the appearance of a greater resistance to motion.

Gravity or any force that lacks this property and is able to accelerate bodies of all masses with equal ease must necessarily be a force able to reach every molecule and every significant constituent of a body directly, so that no dilution occurs. Under such conditions, it would not matter if the body were made of bound or unbound particles. If such a force is carried by agents (*e.g.*, gravitons), those agents must be so tiny that they easily pass through what appears to us to be solid matter, thereby making every bit of the body (interior or surface) equally accessible to the agents. See Figure 2B. For example, neutrinos are such an entity, because they can so easily pass through the entire Earth without being noticed, only occasionally hitting something and being absorbed. However, the number of neutrinos in the universe is far too small for those entities to qualify as the agents carrying gravitational force.

Another familiar property of Newtonian gravity is that its intensity drops off with the square of distance from the source. However, anything that spreads in two spatial dimensions while propagating through a third will have this same property. If a force is carried from a source by agents, the excess agents (for a repulsive force) or shortage of agents (for an attractive force) will spread in two dimensions while propagating through a third. Hence, such a force will normally have the inverse square property.

The preceding remark also gives us a hint about why gravity is always an attractive force. If sources of gravity block gravitons instead of emitting them, and all bodies are immersed in a graviton sea (much like air molecules), then it immediately follows that gravity will always be an attractive force.

These three properties of gravity—its proportionality to the mass of the source, its inverse square behavior, and its always-attractive character—are the properties described by Newton's Universal Law of Gravitation. Newton did not discuss the independence of gravitational acceleration from the mass of the target body. Instead, he blended the gravitational acceleration formula with his second law of motion and arrived at a formula for gravitational force, proportional to the product of the source and target masses. It would have been better for the development of understanding if Newton had left the law of gravitation as a formula for acceleration. This is because, in astrophysical systems, we can observe accelerations, but not forces. The latter must be inferred from the accelerations using Newton's second law. Inspection will quickly show that the second law is used to get both the theoretical law and the forces inferred from observations, but is needed in neither place. If Newton had published an acceleration law instead of a force law, it would be more evident that bodies of all masses fall at the same rate in a gravitational field (ignoring their back effect on the body generating that field).

This was the understanding of the behavior of gravity in the 18th century, when Le Sage wrote his papers on the "graviton" model (without using that word). He was able to explain the basic Newtonian properties using a universal sea of fast-moving agents. Then masses, although nearly transparent to gravitons, shadow one another from some graviton impacts by absorbing some of them. This results in the masses being pushed toward one another by the excess numbers of graviton impacts from the direction of their outer surfaces, not balanced by the absorbed gravitons missing in the shadow between the bodies.

Although the model could indeed explain the Newtonian properties of gravity, it defied the wisdom of the times to expect that ordinary matter could be transparent to these graviton agents. Additional objections included the absence of a drag force as bodies moved through this graviton sea and the problem of disposing of the heat that graviton absorptions would deposit in masses. We will deal with these objections after the model is more fully explicated.

How gravitons can give relativistic properties of gravity

The key to understanding relativity in a "quantum gravity" context (*i.e.*, using gravitons) is to be familiar with the flat-space interpretation of GR, and to appreciate that the medium responsible for the transmission of light waves is not the graviton medium. The speed at which waves propagate through any medium is always close to the speed of motion of the principal constituents of that medium. For example, for a gas, the wave speed is $\sqrt{5/3}$ of the speed of the particles in that gas. But as we have seen, gravitons must travel many orders of magnitude faster than light, making the wave speed in the graviton medium also much faster than light. Moreover, the graviton medium consists of discrete entities, much like air molecules, which can transmit longitudinal waves such as sound but not transverse waves such as light.

So the graviton medium and the "light-carrying medium" (LCM, which we will alternately call "elysium" because of its phonetic similarity to "the LCM," using the Greek name for the afterlife world of great bliss) must be separate and distinct media. But they occupy the same space at the same time. This is only possible if they differ greatly in the scales they operate on. For example, the ocean may be thought of as a medium of contiguous water molecules at one scale, or as a medium of discrete baryons at a much smaller scale, both occupying the same space at the same time.

Given an elysium medium distinct from the graviton medium, it follows that elysium will be affected by gravity, just as all matter of larger scales than gravitons must be. Two possibilities arise that are, for our purposes, equivalent. Elysium might be a compressible medium, in which case it will become denser near masses because of compaction by gravitons. Or elysium might be an incompressible medium, in which case pressure rises with medium depth near masses. In either case, the increased density or increased pressure will give rise to refraction phenomena for any waves passing through elysium. (Consider that an inflated object, submersed in water to an arbitrary depth, heads straight for the surface when released even though the water density is essentially constant with depth. This shows that pressure gradients produce effects analogous to density gradients.) These elysium waves would be electromagnetic waves— "light," for short—by definition of elysium.

This means that light passing the Sun will be bent by refraction in elysium. Changes in the density/pressure of elysium need only be proportional to changes in gravitational potential; *i.e.*, gravity will force elysium to form equipotential surfaces, just as it forces the Earth, and other bodies whose shape is determined by gravity and spin, to have equipotential surfaces.

For a more detailed understanding, we first note that the velocity of anything propagating through a medium of variable density is inversely proportional to the square root of medium density—a general wave property derived in many elementary physics texts. We will also need the following notation: When comparing observable phenomena for a stationary body at different gravitational potentials, the relativistic clock-slowing, meter-stick-contraction factor is $s = \sqrt{1 - 2\mu/rc^2}$, where $s \leq 1$ and the gravitational potential, $-\mu/r$ (where r is distance from the Sun and μ is a constant equal to the product of the universal gravitational constant times the mass of the source of gravity), is proportional to changes in medium density. (Because gravitational potential has an arbitrary zero point, the expression for potential used here really represents a change in gravitational potential from that applicable to the reference master clock.)

Quoting the principles outlined by Eddington [5]: "Light moves more slowly in the material medium than in a vacuum, the velocity being inversely proportional to the refractive index of the medium. The phenomenon of refraction is in fact caused by a slowing of the wave-front in passing into a region of smaller velocity. We can thus imitate the gravitational effect on light precisely, if we imagine the space around the Sun filled with a refracting medium which gives the appropriate velocity of light. To give the velocity $c(1 - 2\mu/rc^2)$, the refractive index must be $1/(1 - 2\mu/rc^2)$, or, very approximately, $1 + 2\mu/rc^2$." Note that Eddington's factor $1 - 2\mu/rc^2$ equals s^2 in our notation.

The same phenomenon, changes in the density/pressure of elysium proportional to changes in gravitational potential, is responsible for two other GR effects as well: gravitational redshift and radar time delay. The former is normally manifested by the slowing of clocks in stronger gravitational potentials; the latter by the slowing of propagation of radar signals between planets. These are exactly analogous to the refraction phenomenon, which is itself a consequence of the slowed propagation speed for lightwaves in denser elysium.

Wave velocity through elysium is $\propto (1 - 2(\phi - \phi_0)/c_0^2) \propto \sqrt{\rho_0/\rho}$, where ϕ is the gravitational potential and ρ the density of the medium at the wave location; and ϕ_0 is the gravitational potential, ρ_0 the density, and c_0 the wave speed of the medium at the reference location, typically at infinity. The speed of "matter waves" depends on elysium density: wave speed $c = c_0 s^2$, where c_0 is the speed of the wave at the reference location (*e.g.*, infinity), and $s^2 = 1 - 2(\phi - \phi_0)/c_0^2$. The respective formulas for the relativistic effects are: $f_0 s$ for gravitational redshift, where f_0 = frequency outside the gravitational field; and $2(1 - s^2)$ for light-bending. [6] To first order in the potential, these are identical to the GR formulas.

These details have been worked out many times before, which is why we feel justified in keeping the details somewhat sketchy in this paper. See, for example, the review article by Fernando de Felice [7] That author notes that Einstein himself first suggested the idea that gravitation is equivalent to an optical medium. From the abstract, "… Maxwell's equations may be written as if they were valid in a flat space-time in which there is an optical medium … this medium turns out to be equivalent to the gravitational field. … we find that the language of classical optics for the 'equivalent medium' is as suitable as that of Riemannian geometry." Nine earlier authors who have worked on this problem are cited in the text.

The relativistic in-plane rotation of elliptical orbits ("advance of perihelion") effect is a bit different from these phenomena affecting light because it affects material bodies. A satisfactory explanation for this effect using a Le Sagian gravity model has been lacking. Just as Mercury's mass makes no significant contribution to its own perihelion motion, any mass change or momentum change for Mercury should also have no effect on its perihelion motion. Indeed, if matter could always be treated as an ensemble of particles with purely ballistic motion, elysium would not contribute anything to perihelion advance.

However, electrons are not particles with purely ballistic motions. Electrons have strong wave-like properties, and are the main reason that light is considered an "electromagnetic" phenomenon. Indeed, one of Louis de Broglie's chief contributions to physics was demonstrating that ordinary matter has wave properties too. We are therefore obliged to consider that orbiting bodies will be influenced by the density of the elysium that they travel through because of the influence of elysium on their electrons.

Qualitatively, therefore, the elliptical motion of orbiting bodies is slowed most by elysium near perihelion, where that medium is densest; and is slowed least near aphelion, where elysium is sparsest. This velocity imbalance (relatively slower at perihelion, relatively faster at aphelion) rotates the ellipse forward, which is what an advance of perihelion means. See Figure 3, where the advance with each revolution is exaggerated by a factor of one million.

As we have seen, this speed-change concept works well for purely wave phenomena, and allows the elysium concept to predict the first three tests of GR exactly because of its effect on the speed of light. Analogously for the predominately ballistic motion of a planet or other body, the effect of elysium is to slightly slow the ballistic velocity that the orbiting body would otherwise have because of the material body's DeBroglie wave properties. Electrons in matter propagate through elysium at speed c determined by the local mean density of elysium. The forward speed of the matter creates an effective increase in the density of elysium by the factor $(c \pm v)/c$, where the sign determines the direction of the matter with respect to the direction of electron propagation. See Figure 4.

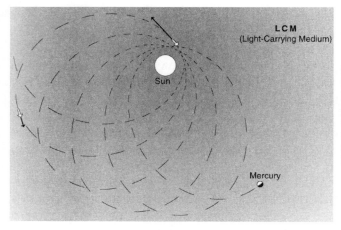

Figure 3. How the increasing density of a light-carrying medium (elysium) toward the Sun causes Mercury's elliptical orbit to precess forward. Artwork by B. Starosta.

The relativistic clock-slowing, meter-stick-contraction factor is $1/\gamma$, where $\gamma = 1/\sqrt{1 - v^2/c^2}$, $\gamma \geq 1$, and v is the ballistic velocity of a body. Analogous to wave velocities being slowed by the factor s^2, ballistic velocities are slowed by the factor $1/\gamma^2$ because of the increased effective density of elysium. And the slowed electrons exert electrostatic force on the atoms to slow their forward ballistic speed by a like amount. From that starting point, the rigorous derivation of the perihelion motion formula follows standard celestial mechanics perturbation formulas. [8] We have previously detailed these steps [9], and answered questions about them [10]. Here we will only repeat the implied correction (2nd term below) to the formula for Newtonian gravitational acceleration (1st term below) that gives rise primarily to an advance of the perihelion (or more generally, the pericenter) of orbits:

$$\ddot{\vec{r}} = -\frac{GM}{r^3}\vec{r} - \frac{3v\dot{v}}{c^2}\vec{v} \tag{0.1}$$

Here, G is the gravitational constant, M the mass of the attracting body, r is the distance of some test particle from the attracting body, v is the velocity of the test particle, arrows over variables indicate vectors, and dots over variables indicate time derivatives. The correction term yields the same perihelion advance formula as GR to second order in velocity. However, significant differences with GR may arise when two or more significant masses mutually interact.

GR predicts other minor effects as well; and these too have their counterparts in this flat-space model. "Frame dragging" occurs when the inertial frame for the axis of a rotating body is "dragged" by the "curvature of space-time." In

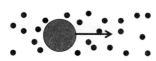

Figure 4. The faster a body moves through elysium, the more elysium constituents it encounters per unit time; and vice versa. For ballistic motion of bodies, this is the physical equivalent of wave motion through denser (or sparser) elysium. This slows (or speeds up) the net forward propagation speed of electrons, which slightly slows (or speeds up) the ballistic motion of the entire body relative to the expected results from the forces applied.

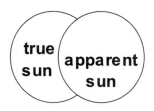

Figure 5. The true, instantaneous Sun and the Sun we see from Earth by its arriving light differ in their positions with respect to the distant stars by 20 arc seconds or 0.0001 radians. Gravity accelerates the Earth toward the true Sun, not toward the direction its light comes from.

our Le Sage-type model, we can always substitute "elysium" for "curvature of space-time," and expect an identical result to first order in the gravitational potential. The concept of "frame-dragging" now becomes one of a rotating body moving ballistically through a medium while it orbits another body. This obviously generates a small torque, the effect of which is to precess the spin axis of the rotating body.

GR also predicts "gravitational waves." In our Le Sagian model, these are waves in elysium generated by the orbital motion of one body (a target of gravity) around another (a source of gravity). As such, these will be seen to be indistinguishable from very-long-wavelength electromagnetic waves. That point of clarification may be helpful to all physicists. Both lightwaves and gravitational waves have been described as "disturbances of space-time." Now we see that they are as alike as radio and optical waves; *i.e.*, they are waves in the same medium, having the same speed but differing in wavelength. In all cases, it is important to appreciate that gravitational waves have no connection with the conveyance of gravitational forces or of changes in those forces. [11]

Additional properties of gravity implied by gravitons

A Newtonian or Einsteinian gravitational field is a mathematical construct that has an infinite range. However, if gravitons are the carriers of the force of gravity, then gravity cannot have an infinite range because, sooner or later, the gravitons will strike something and cease to convey their message from the source. If nothing else gets in the way sooner, each graviton will travel until it hits another graviton and gets scattered. The average or "root-mean-square" (rms) distance that a graviton travels before hitting another graviton is, by definition, the characteristic range of gravitational force in Le Sage-type models. That range must obviously be very large, because we see gravity operating apparently undiminished over at least the scale of globular clusters. However, we do not have any secure knowledge about gravitation operating at the scale of galaxies and clusters of galaxies, the dynamics of which have frequently been questioned.

Another curious property of gravity is its apparently instantaneous action. By way of contrast, light from the Sun requires about 500 seconds to travel to the Earth. So when it arrives, we see the Sun in the sky in the position it actually occupied 500 seconds ago rather than in its present position. (See Figure 5.) This difference amounts to about 20 seconds of arc, a large and easily measurable amount for astronomers.

From our perspective, the Earth is standing still and the Sun is moving. So it seems natural that we see the Sun where it was 500 seconds ago, when it emitted the light now arriving. From the Sun's perspective, the Earth is moving. It's orbital speed is about 10^{-4} c, where c is the speed of light. So light from the Sun strikes the Earth from a slightly forward angle because the Earth tends to "run into" the light. The forward angle is 10^{-4} radians (the ratio of Earth's speed to light speed), which is 20 arc seconds, the same displacement angle as in the first perspective. This displacement angle is called *aberration*, and it is due entirely to the finite speed of light. Note that aberration is a classical effect, not a relativistic one. Frame contraction and time dilation effects are four orders of magnitude smaller, since they are proportional to the square of the ratio of speeds.

Now we naturally expect that gravity should behave similarly to light. Viewing gravity as a force that propagates from Sun to Earth, the Sun's gravity should appear to emanate from the position the Sun occupied when the gravity now arriving left the Sun. From the Sun's perspective, the Earth should "run into" the gravitational force, making it appear to come from a slightly forward angle equal to the ratio of the Earth's orbital speed to the speed of gravity propagation.

This slightly forward angle will tend to accelerate the Earth's orbital speed because it is an attractive force, and one that does not depend on the mass of the affected body. A similar effect is observed when the force in question is the pressure of sunlight, which of course repels instead of attracting, thereby slowing the Earth's orbital speed. However, that force does depend on the mass of the affected body, so that for bodies of Earth's size it is negligible. Bodies small enough to notice, such as dust particles, tend to spiral into the Sun as a consequence of this deceleration, which in turn is caused by the finite speed of light. This whole process is called the *Poynting-Robertson* effect.

But observations indicate that none of this happens in the case of gravity! There is no detectable delay for the propagation of gravity from Sun to Earth. The direction of the Sun's gravitational force is toward its true, instantaneous position, not toward a retarded position, to the full accuracy of observations. And no perceptible change in the Earth's mean orbital speed has yet been detected, even though the effect of a finite speed of gravity is cumulative over time. Gravity has no perceptible aberration, and no Poynting-Robertson effect—the primary indicators of its propagation speed. Indeed, Newtonian gravity explicitly assumes that gravity propagates with infinite speed.

A Le Sage model of gravity has other properties beyond GR. Ordinary matter is highly transparent to gravitons. But if matter becomes dense enough, gravitons can no longer flow freely through it, or perhaps even penetrate it at all. This is called "gravitational shielding." It is useful to think of a swarm of bees flying in front of the Sun. If the bee swarm is sparse, each bee blocks a bit of sunlight, and the total blockage is proportional to the number of bees. However, if the swarm is dense, some bees are in the shadow of other bees, and hence do not add to the total light blockage. In an analogous way, if matter is dense enough, not all of it contributes to the body's external gravitational field at every instant because some of the body's internal matter may lie in the graviton shadow of other bits of the body.

In the extreme case where gravitons are all absorbed, matter in the center of a body does not get the chance to absorb any gravitons, and therefore contributes nothing to the body's external field or the force of gravity near it. In such a case, the body's gravitational mass, as measured by its external field, would not be equal to its inertial mass, which would still be contributed to by all matter in the body. This is a violation of the equivalence principle, which equates gravitational and inertial mass for all bodies.

As we shall see when we examine the experimental evidence and objections in later sections, this implied violation for dense states of matter causes no difficulties. However, it does limit how strong any gravitational field or force can become, yielding a maximum acceleration when the graviton flux from one side is completely blocked. This natural limit, preventing forces from becoming infinite, guarantees that nature will contain no singularities because of the unlimited collapse of overly dense bodies. All such collapses must eventually cease, leaving a body with the maximum possible external gravity field. So the predicted end state of highly collapsed matter is not a "black hole," but rather a body of high gravitational redshift. Bodies of that description are seen—certain types of quasars—for which considerable evidence exists that the high redshifts are not cosmological in nature. [12] We see now that they may be gravitational in nature.

Another new property of this two-media-type of Le Sagian gravity model is that material bodies should experience drag or resistance to motion through elysium. Clearly, any such resistance is slight because planets show no apparent signs of it as they orbit the Sun. But this causes the model no difficulties. It merely sets constraints on media constituent properties. If we arrived at constraints from various considerations that contradicted one another, that would falsify the model under discussion. But we do not presently have any circumstance where such a contradiction is suggested.

Finally, we need to consider that, as gravitons are absorbed by a mass, such events must transfer heat to the mass. If the mass did not radiate away this heat, it would soon melt, then vaporize from excess heat. So ordinary masses must be in thermal equilibrium with the graviton medium, radiating as much heat back into space as the masses continually absorb. We should also note that, if gravitons were only absorbed but never re-radiated, the universe would be running down as gravitons became depleted, and the gravitational constant would be decreasing with time.

The relationships among gravitons, the gravitational constant, heat flows from masses, and drag forces through the graviton medium, are mathematically developed by Slabinski [25]. Historically, absorbed graviton models and scattered graviton models were developed separately. The latter led to no net force (as Slabinski's paper proves). The absorbed-graviton models had a severe difficulty with heat flow because, if all gravitons must be absorbed to produce a net force, then the heat is so great that it soon vaporizes the receiving mass. Slabinski shows the answer to this dilemma. When some gravitons are absorbed, that produces an asymmetry for the far more numerous scattered gravitons that allows them to produce a net force too. Then scattered gravitons are the main contributors to the gravitational constant, while the relatively rare absorbed gravitons are the main contributors to heating of masses. In the following paragraphs, we will describe qualitatively what these mathematical conclusions may mean in physical terms.

Imagine a vast, unlimited field of small meteoroids moving at random. Now add two relatively large comets to this field. If collisions between meteoroids and comets were perfectly elastic, each rebounding meteoroid on one side of a comet would exactly replace the missing continuation of a rebounding meteoroid on the opposite side. So the field of meteoroids would remain essentially the same as it would have been if the comets were not present. No net force on the comets occurs. However, if the comets completely absorb impacting meteoroids, then meteoroids are lost from the system. More meteoroids are absorbed on each comet's outer surface than on its inner surface (the one facing the other comet) because some meteoroids absorbed by the other comet never make it to the first comet's inner surface. In this case, the comets feel a net force pushing them toward one another.

This analogy illustrates the way gravitons (replacing meteoroids) interact with units of matter (replacing comets). To make the analogy better, we must introduce an extended halo of small asteroids orbiting the nucleus of each comet. These asteroids are the counterparts of elysium in the actual model, which acts as a sort of extended atmosphere around a matter unit. The new feature is that collisions with the comet nucleus or with any of its orbiting cloud of asteroid satellites by meteoroids will produce a net force on the entire comet cloud. If the total mass of the satellites is comparable to or greater than the mass of the comet nucleus, then all collisions of meteoroids with satellites will contribute more to the net force on the comet than collisions with the nucleus because the asteroid satellites have a greater cross-sectional area exposed to collisions. The greater cross-sectional area assures more total collisions on the satellites than if they were collected into a single mass. In general, the more finely the satellites are broken up without loss of total mass, the greater will be the excess of the resulting contribution to net force on the comet from the satellites.

The importance of this to our model is that meteoroid impacts on the comet nucleus, like graviton impacts on a unit of matter, leave a heat residue; whereas meteoroid impacts on asteroid satellites, like graviton impacts on the elysium cloud around a unit of matter, contribute to the net force on the nucleus without heating it. The elysium cloud then absorbs the main heat generated by graviton impacts. But that heat is harmlessly (and undetectably) carried away as heated elysium packed near a unit of matter is exchanged with cooler elysium from the general pool of elysium filling space.

Referring again to Slabinski's article, we can now identify gravitons impacting a unit of matter with "absorbed gravitons," and gravitons impacting the denser elysium cloud around a unit of matter (mostly not absorbed or only partially absorbed) with "scattered gravitons." Both contribute to the gravitational constant. The latter are far more numerous than the former. But only the "absorbed gravitons" contribute to the heating of matter because the elysium heating is quickly dissipated into the general reservoir of elysium, which has already reached its own thermodynamic equilibrium with the gravitons. Just as our planetary electromagnetic radiation budgets were not complete until we could measure contributions from all wavelengths, the gravitational energy budgets will not be complete until we can measure the portions carried away by elysium.

So heat is deposited by gravitons, then is leisurely lost as the elysium circulates and freshens in separate activities that are not part of the graviton absorption/scattering process. This brings to mind the heat generated by a refrigerator. Most of it must be siphoned off and dumped to allow the important part of the process to operate. The net result is just what we need to make the Le Sage graviton model work. The gravitational constant (Slabinski's eqn. 16) depends on the products of absorption and scattering coefficients, the latter being huge compared to the former. Meanwhile, the heat flow (Slabinski's eqn. 19) depends only on the absorption coefficient (the part of the heat absorbed by matter instead of by elysium), and is therefore miniscule in comparison. We simply neglect the presently undetectable part of the thermodynamic cycle representing elysium heat. This neglect seems safe around matter of ordinary densities. But for high matter densities, the free flow of elysium might be impeded. We cannot help but wonder if elysium heat might play a crucial role in raising the temperature of the Sun's core, or perhaps even the solar corona, to many millions of degrees.

The implications of this model reach deeply into many areas of physics. For example, the existence of elysium heat created by gravitons implies a minimum temperature in equilibrium with the graviton medium for all unshielded matter. It then follows that "absolute zero" could be lowered even further by shielding from gravitons.

Observational evidence for new properties
Speed of gravity

To obey the several constraints required of graviton models, these entities must propagate very much faster than lightspeed. The following list (taken from [11]) summarizes experiments related to the speed of gravity.

1. a modern updating of the classical Laplace experiment based on the absence of any change in the angular momentum of the Earth's orbit (a nec-

essary accompaniment of any propagation delay for gravity even in a static field);

2.   an extension of this angular momentum argument to binary pulsars, showing that the position, velocity, and acceleration of each mass is anticipated in much less than the light-time between the masses;

3.   a non-null three-body experiment involving solar eclipses in the Sun-Earth-Moon system, showing that optical and "gravitational" eclipses do not coincide;

4.   planetary radar ranging data, which measures the orbital acceleration of the Earth relative to the Sun (the common focus of the orbits of Earth and the other planet), showing that the direction of Earth's gravitational acceleration toward the Sun does not coincide with the direction of arriving solar photons;

5.   neutron interferometer experiments, showing a dependence of acceleration on mass, and therefore a violation of the weak equivalence principle (the geometric interpretation of gravitation); [13]

6.   the Walker-Dual experiment, showing in theory that changes in both gravitational and electrostatic fields propagate faster than the speed of light, c, a result reportedly given preliminary confirmation in a laboratory experiment.

7.   An earlier laboratory experiment ([14], with summary description in [15]) showed that charges respond to each other's instantaneous positions, and not to the "left-behind potential hill," when they are accelerated. This demonstrates that electrodynamic forces must likewise propagate at faster than lightspeed more convincingly than earlier experiments showing angular momentum conservation.

8.   A new laboratory experiment at the NEC Research Institute in Princeton claims to have achieved propagation speeds of 310 c. [16] This supplements earlier quantum tunneling experiments with similar results. [17] It is still in considerable doubt whether these experiment types using electromagnetic radiation can truly send information faster than light. [18] Whatever the resolution of that matter, the leading edge of the transmission is an electromagnetic wave, and therefore always travels at lightspeed. However, such experiments have served to raise public consciousness about the faster-than-light-propagation concept.

Of all these experiments, #(2)—the binary pulsars—places the strongest lower limit to the speed of gravity: $2 \times 10^{10} c$. This satisfies all known constraints on gravitons.

Parameterizing the speed of gravity by the symbol V, then the best available approximation we now have is $V = \infty$. But however large it may be, logic requires that V be finite to avoid violations of the causality principle. So when its value can finally be estimated, the Newtonian law of gravitation (the 1st term below) will be modified by the addition of the 2nd term:

$$\ddot{\vec{r}} = -\frac{GM}{r^3}\vec{r} + \frac{GM}{Vr^2}\vec{v} \qquad (1.1)$$

As before, G is the gravitational constant, M the mass of the attracting body, r is the distance of some point from the attracting body, and v is the velocity of an orbiting test particle.

Finite range of gravity

Mutual collisions of gravitons cause back-scattering into graviton shadows that diminish the long-range force of gravity faster than the inverse square law does. At sufficiently great distances, the gravity of a mass essentially disappears. The following formula for gravitational acceleration represents the modification of the Newtonian law of gravity needed to account for the range limitation effect in Le Sage-type gravity models. It assumes that back-scattering into the shadow between bodies occurs uniformly with distance, and at a rate that is proportional to the size of the shadow's particle deficit:

$$\ddot{\vec{r}} = -\frac{GM}{r^3}\vec{r}\; e^{-(r/r_G)} \qquad (1.2)$$

In this formula, r_G is the characteristic range of gravity (the root mean square distance a particle travels before collision), and e is the base for natural logarithms. This reduces to the Newtonian gravity formula as r_G approaches infinity.

This modified gravitation law has strong consequences for large-scale structures such as galaxies or clusters of galaxies. For details of how this law explains galaxy shapes and dynamics better than the conventional law, and without need of "dark matter," see [19]. The same reference also explains how this law provides a physical basis for the presently empirical Tully-Fisher relation between spin rate and intrinsic luminosity.

One observational test we can apply is to note that, for the largest scales, our modified law operates in an effectively inverse linear fashion with distance. Mainstream astronomers assume that the inverse square Newtonian law of gravity still holds, so they infer the existence of invisible "dark matter" in amounts that, for unknown reasons, must increase radially in galaxies with distance r from the center, thereby canceling one power of r in the inverse square attraction of the center. These astronomers speak of the M/L ratio of galaxies, where M is mass and L is luminosity or light. This would be unity if most mass were luminous, but is generally much larger because of inferred dark matter.

The observed situation is summarized in Figure 6, taken from [20]. This illustrates the inferred M/L ratios over a variety of scales. Note that the general trend is linear (corresponding to exponential in a non-logarithmic plot), even over 3-4 orders of magnitude in scale. The mean trend line in this figure would intercept the horizontal axis $M/L = 1$ (the value when Newtonian gravity governs and there is no "dark matter") at about 3000 light-years or 1 kiloparsec (kpc). This provides us with an estimate of r_G.

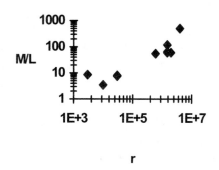

Figure 6. Log-log plot of M/L (mass-to-light ratio) versus r (scale-size in light-years). Source: [20]

Additional observations in the solar system also allow a test of this concept. A finite range of gravity would result in a gravitational constant progressively decreasing away from the Sun. The largest observable consequence would be an apparent rotation of the radar reference frame (whose inertial frame is determined by dynamics) with respect to the optical reference frame (inertial frame determined by distant stars). The predicted effect would cause the radar mean motion of the Earth's solar orbit to exceed its optical mean motion by $0.71/r_G$ in units of arc seconds per century, where r_G is in kpc. Such a discrepancy is actually observed, has a magnitude of just about this size, and has remained an unexplained puzzle over the past decade. [21] This independent derivation of a possible cause for the effect not only lends support to the basic idea of particle models for gravity, but also concurs with the earlier estimate that r_G is probably close to 1 kpc.

Gravitational shielding

Let a "matter ingredient" (MI) be defined as a unit of matter dense enough that no gravitons can pass through it without absorption. But since MIs, by definition, totally absorb all flux particles that strike them, there must exist some density of matter so great that it lacks space between MIs, and through which no flux particles can penetrate. Other matter behind such a solid wall of MIs could absorb no flux particles, and therefore could not contribute to the gravitational field of the body it resides in.

For particle gravity, this means that dense matter might have more than one matter ingredient (MI) along the same path of a flux particle, but only the first MI encountered absorbs the flux particle. If matter were sufficiently dense, no flux particles could penetrate beyond a certain depth, and only the outer layers of a body would contribute to its external gravitational field. The body's gravitational mass and its matter content would be different. The ratio of gravitational to inertial mass would depart from unity—a condition not at all in conflict with the results of Eötvös-type experiments because those experiments are not truly sensitive to detecting such differences, despite a widespread contrary impression. [22] Galileo's "tower of Pisa" experiment showed that all masses fall at the same rate in a much stronger gravitational field such as the Earth's. So they must do the same even if their gravitational and inertial masses are highly unequal. Such an inequality would change the inferred forces, but not the observed accelerations, of falling bodies. Eötvös-type experiments look only for acceleration differences between different types of masses falling in

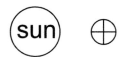

Figure 7. An intermediate body can block part of the gravitational effect of a large mass on a small test body.

the Earth's field—differences that the Galileo experiment showed cannot realistically exist.

Discussed in physical terms, an electromagnetic or mechanical force can normally be applied directly only to the surface of a body. The surface MIs or molecules are accelerated, and they in turn press against the next layer of matter particles further in, and so on. The force must be transmitted from molecule to molecule by a pressure wave that spreads and dilutes the force as it propagates through the body. For this reason, the greater the number of molecules to which the force must be transmitted, the greater is the resistance of the body to the force applied. By contrast, we see that Le Sage gravitons normally have equal access to each and every MI in a body, and therefore tend to accelerate each of them by the same amount. As a result, the total acceleration of a body will be the same as the acceleration of each MI in the body, no matter how many MIs the body is composed of. This is why normal dynamical motions in response to gravitational forces are independent of the inertial mass of the affected body.

However, when two or more MIs line up along the path of a graviton able to encounter only one of them, the corresponding theoretical effect is called "gravitational shielding" because a portion of the gravitational field that would exist in Newtonian gravity is blocked or shielded. At a point in space, the gravitational acceleration induced by a body of mass M at a distance r when another body intervenes is:

$$\ddot{\vec{r}} = -\frac{GM}{r^3}\vec{r}\; e^{-s_G \int \rho\, dr} \tag{1.3}$$

where ρ is the density of the intervening body over the short distance dr, the integral must be taken through the intervening body along the vector joining the point in space and body M, and s_G is the shielding efficiency factor in units of cross-sectional area over mass. If such shielding exists in nature, then gravitational acceleration does have a small dependence on the matter content of the affected body, violating the Einstein equivalence principle.

To test for such an effect in nature, one needs to examine a test body orbiting near a relatively dense intermediate mass, where the intermediate mass occasionally intervenes in front of a more distant large mass. (See Figure 7.) We then seek evidence that the distant mass exerts less than its full effect on the test body at times when the intermediate mass is aligned between the other two. But there is no *a priori* way to be certain how big this effect (the size of s_G) might be, because it depends on the amount of empty space between MIs in planetary and stellar interiors.

What is probably the most suitable test case for this effect in the solar system arises from the two Lageos artificial satellites. The Earth's core provides

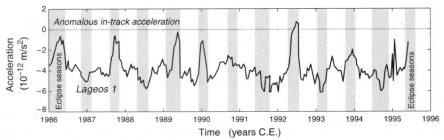

Figure 8. Lageos I data. Shading denotes eclipse seasons.

the dense intermediate mass, and the Sun is then the large distant mass. Both satellites are in orbits high enough, and the 400-kg satellites are massive enough, to be very little affected by most non-gravitational forces such as atmospheric drag or solar radiation pressure. And both satellites are covered all over their outer surfaces with retro-reflectors that bounce back light along the incoming direction. This enables these satellites to have their positions measured by laser ranging from ground stations. In that way, the orbits can be determined with a precision on the order of a centimeter or better.

Lageos 1 has been in orbit for over 20 years, and Lageos 2 for less than 10 years. Both are in nearly circular orbits roughly an Earth radius high, and circle the globe roughly once every four hours. Lageos 1 revolves retrograde with an inclination of 110°, which causes its orbit plane to precess forward. Lageos 2 is in a direct orbit with an inclination of 53°, precessing backward. As a consequence, Lageos 2 has "eclipse seasons"—periods of time when the satellite enters the Earth's shadow on every orbit for up to 40 minutes—that are more frequent and more variable in length than for Lageos 1. Then as precession changes orbit orientation, each satellite may go many months continuously in sunlight, without eclipses. For Lageos 2, it is possible for two consecutive eclipse seasons to merge into one long season, as happened in late 1994 through early 1995.

The significance of eclipses for this discussion is that these are periods when any gravitational shielding effect that may exist would be operative. Of course, several other types of non-gravitational forces also operate only during eclipses. Solar radiation pressure shuts off only during eclipses, as does much of the thermal radiation from the Earth. Light, temperature, and charged particles are all affected, and at the one centimeter level, these must all be considered.

Both Lageos satellites exhibit anomalous in-track accelerations that were unexpected. See Figure 8 and Figure 9, showing this effect for each satellite. [23] The anomalous in-track acceleration (negative because it operates just as a drag force would) in units of 10^{-12} m/s^2 is plotted against year. Eclipse seasons are indicated. An average negative acceleration throughout the data can be explained as a combination of radiation, thermal, and charge drag forces. But the data shows substantial deviations from this average drag, especially during eclipse seasons, and these are not so easily explained. [24]

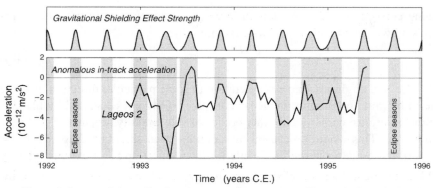

Figure 9. Lageos 2 data. Shading denotes eclipse seasons. Theoretical gravitational shielding effect appears above observed anomalous acceleration for comparison.

Some factor, perhaps rocket exhaust at the time of injection into orbit, may have dirtied the satellite surface and caused albedo variations that might accelerate the satellite during eclipses. Lageos 2 was launched with care to avoid any repetition of such problems. Yet the preliminary data available so far suggest that the anomalous acceleration during eclipse seasons is still present. This increases the suspicion that the cause might be gravitational shielding. The top portion of Figure 9, placed above it for easy comparison, shows the theoretical gravitational shielding effect, calculated with the single parameter $s_G = 2 \times 10^{-18}$ cm^2/g. The amplitude of the effect would be essentially the same for Lageos 1 and Lageos 2. Lageos 1 is affected by radiation forces and other effects that sometimes reinforce and sometimes go counter to the hypothetical shielding effect. But the data clearly allows, though it does not require, a gravitational shielding effect. It is still possible that some other unknown cause mimics the gravitational shielding effect.

Graviton drag

Bodies that move at different speeds must suffer drag from the graviton medium. This drag would be the same on each individual co-moving MI, so it would not matter how many MIs were involved, or how big each mass was. Each co-moving body, big or small, would experience the same graviton drag, so relative orbits would not change and the drag would not be noticed. But bodies moving with different speeds would experience slightly different drag, although this would be a tiny effect because it would be proportional to v/V (orbital speed of one body around another divided by the speed of gravity).

So orbiting bodies have extra drag due to their extra velocity relative to their parent. The general formulas for drag are worked out in reference [25]. They are interpreted in terms of cosmological factors and assigned numerical values in reference [26]. We need to introduce a drag coefficient d_G that can be related to cosmological parameters (defined just before the "predictions" section below) through $d_G = 8\pi G \rho_B / 3H_0 = \Omega_B H_0 \approx 8.5 \times 10^{-20}$ /s. Then the fol-

lowing correction to the Newtonian force law producing an in-track deceleration is all we need to allow for basic graviton drag:

$$\ddot{\vec{r}} = -\frac{GM}{r^3}\vec{r} - d_G\vec{v} \qquad (1.4)$$

The Sun might also have acceleration in some particular direction in space
caused by graviton drag on its dense core that would not be shared by planets,
moons, asteroids, comets, and other bodies of substantially less density than the
Sun's core. This would be caused by a combination shielding/drag effect, the
result of more matter in the Sun's interior than shows up in its external gravity
field. Such a combination effect might behave as $d_G\,\vec{v}\,s_G\int\rho\,dr$, where the integral is taken through the Sun, and v refers to the unknown speed of the Sun
relative to the mean graviton field. If the effect exists, it should reveal itself as
an apparent acceleration of Earth (and all other solar system bodies) in the opposite direction. Such an acceleration would contribute to perihelion motion
and/or to a secular eccentricity change. It might also show up in new comet orbits, because of their very long periods, as a possible directional dependence of
the original (pre-planetary perturbations) reciprocal semi-major axes, $(1/a)_{orig}$.
This should be checked for when we have enough high-quality new comet orbits. This type of effect can occur in Le Sagian gravity because the gravitational mass and the inertial mass of the Sun need not be even approximately
equal.

Heat flows

The absorption of gravitons would produce internal heat within planets through
processes that would presumably manifest themselves as, for example, radioactivity and spontaneous emission of photons. Unfortunately, we cannot predict
the total amount of such heat without knowing the mass, speed, absorption efficiency, and flux of gravitons. However, we do know something about the
relative behavior of such heat flows for bodies of different mass.

Observed lunar and planetary excess heat flow data is given in Table 1.
[27,28,29,30] In Le Sagian gravity models, the excess heat generated by graviton absorption would be directly proportional to each planet's mass. No other
factor should matter unless internal densities were so high as to cause gravitational shielding and elysium trapping, in which case masses and calculated heat
absorptions would be larger than our estimates. The question for us here is
whether the observed excess heat flows are consistent with the Le Sage model
predictions. We can ascertain that by examining the proportionality of the "excess internal heat" and "mass" columns in Table 1, in which absorbed values
are calculated and emitted values are inferred from observations.

At a glance, we see that the proportionality is not very close. However, a
possible clue to the reason for this appears in the "excess heat per cm^2" column, which measures the excess of escaping heat over absorbed solar heat per
square centimeter of planetary surface area. If the masses are multiplied by

Table I. Excess heat flows for entire body (units: erg/s $\times$ 10^{20}; last column: erg/s/cm^2)

Planet	Ab-sorbed heat	Emitted heat	Ratio: emitted to absorbed heat	Excess internal heat	Mass	Excess heat per cm^2
Moon				0.11 ± 0.03	0.012	29 ± 7
Earth	12,110	12,113	1.00026	3.2 ± ?	1	63 ± ?
Jupiter	49,933	83,400	1.67 ± 0.09	33,500 ± 4500	318	5440 ± 730
Saturn	10,167	18,100	1.78 ± 0.09	7,900 ± 900	95	2010 ± 210
Uranus	518	551	1.064 ± 0.062	33 ± 32	14.6	42 ± ?
Neptune	201	529	2.52 ± 0.37	328 ± 74	17.2	433 ± 100

about 19 as a proportionality factor, the resulting values are within one sigma of the last column values for the three largest planets in our table.

The principal contributor to the excess heat must be something that increases with planet surface area instead of planet mass. If it is indigenous, heat from elysium trapping would be the most reasonable guess. If the heat source is exogenous, then heating by meteors is a neglected factor with quite closely the right qualitative behavior, and one that would affect the three largest planets most. Uranus and Earth would have less contribution from meteors both because of smaller masses and because both are far from the major meteor sources: the main asteroid belt and the trans-Neptunian objects. Uranus is likewise special, and its heat flow subject to underestimation, because its axis of rotation is tilted 98° to its orbit plane. So at most times, planet rotation does not allow Earth or spacecraft observations to measure heat emissions from its entire surface. Sometimes only heat flow from one polar region can be seen, and that seems likely to under-represent heat flow from the whole planet.

For the Moon, probes implanted by astronauts were placed at two different landing sites at a depth that was insulated from "daily" (actually monthly) temperature fluctuations, so they presumably measure only heat from the interior. And the Moon has no atmosphere, so the figure will not be contaminated by meteors, clouds, or other possible heat traps. And its density is too low for significant elysium trapping. However, we can't be certain that these two sites are representative of heat flow over the entire lunar surface. For example, lunar mascons and inhomogeneous distribution of radioactive materials inside the Moon might cause the heat flows to vary from place to place; and the lunar farside, so visually different from the nearside, has no heat flow measurements from Earth or by astronauts. Nonetheless, these lunar probe measures agree (within their errors) with values measured from Earth in microwave data for the visible side of the Moon. And of all the values in the table, these are the most likely to be a purely Le Sagian gravity effect. So the lunar data suggests that a scale factor of 9×10^{20} erg/s/Earth-mass, multiplied by mass, would give the Le Sagian contribution to heat flow.

If we use this same scale factor with the other masses, we arrive at plausible Le Sagian heat flow estimates that are consistent with the measured values combined with a hypothetical contribution from meteor heating or elysium trapping. Only for Earth and Uranus do we get values too high compared to measures; but in view of the uncertainties for these two planets in particular, this does not create difficulties for the hypothesis. However, at this time we have data of insufficient accuracy to draw any firm conclusion about Le Sagian heat flow. We simply note that a major cause of excess heat flow for planets is apparently non-Le Sagian, and may be meteoric heating or elysium trapping.

Objections to classical graviton models

Models featuring gravitons have been debated for the better part of three centuries. The following is a list of the various objections raised, and how those objections are answered in the present model.

- If particle collisions with matter are perfectly elastic, momentum is conserved and no (gravitational) net force will result. [25] (Answer: Particle collisions must be inelastic or partially absorbed and partially scattered. Particles may lose velocity and absorbed particles will raise the temperature of the impacted mass.)
- The temperature of matter would be continually raised by particle collisions. (Answer: Matter must re-radiate absorbed energy approximately isotropically to maintain a net force and a temperature equilibrium. In fact, in the late 19th century, Kelvin suggested that atomic vibrations caused by graviton collisions would in turn pump up graviton velocities and in so doing would reduce the temperature of matter until a steady state was reached. Here we propose that excess heat is carried off by elysium flow.)
- Particles must travel very rapidly to convey the necessary momentum to matter, yet produce no detectable frictional resistance to motion. (Answer: The minimum particle speed consistent with the lack of detectable aberration is $2 \times 10^{10}\,c$. This high speed is also consistent with the lack of detectable friction because frictional drag is proportional to the mean speed of gravitons, whereas gravitational force is proportional to the square of that speed. [25])
- Matter must be mostly empty space to make shielding effects very small. J.C. Maxwell used the analogy of two swarms of bees blocking light. If either swarm is too dense, the light-blocking effects are not simply additive. (Answer: It is now accepted that matter is mostly empty space. Ordinary matter yields forces that are additive. Super-dense matter might produce non-additive effects.)
- The range of the force between bodies cannot be infinite because of the backscatter of graviton particles colliding with other graviton particles. (Answer: The range of gravitational force may in fact be limited to about a kiloparsec.)
- Graviton-graviton collisions would damp mean graviton velocities, even for elastic collisions. (Answer: Mean graviton velocities are increased by a

compensating amount through the Meta Cycle [26], whereby lightwaves from spontaneously emitted photons lose energy to the graviton medium, causing the photons to redshift.)

- If gravitons were not extremely small compared to their mean free path, the resulting inverse square force would be proportional to the body's cross-sectional area rather than its mass. (Answer: The gravitons are many orders of magnitude smaller than quantum particles, yet have a mean free path on the order of a kiloparsec.)

In the late 19th century, the merits of such models were debated by Maxwell and Kelvin. [31] Kelvin postulated that the velocity lost by gravitons would be compensated by an increase in the rotation and vibration of the gravitons. Maxwell showed that solution was invalid. Maxwell then argued that thermodynamics requires that the temperature of bodies must tend to approach that at which the average kinetic energy of a molecule of the body would be equal to the average kinetic energy of a graviton. However, Maxwell's subsequent proof that, contrary to the requirement of thermodynamics, the kinetic energy of gravitons must always exceed that of molecules rests on an invalid assumption about the relative numbers of gravitons and molecules, and ignored the possibility that most of the heating of molecules might be quickly carried away and dissipated by elysium.

What now seems clear from thermodynamic considerations is that, if molecules had a greater kinetic energy than gravitons, then gravitons would gain energy after a rebound, resulting in a force of repulsion between bodies. This might turn out to be relevant for understanding the origin of electrical forces. In the present model, we propose absorption and scattering of gravitons rather than elastic or inelastic rebounds. The absorptions are later followed by isotropic emission of that absorbed energy as photons, which later redeposit their energy into the graviton medium. The thermodynamic books are indeed balanced, but only when averaged over long times, large volumes, and a huge range of scale. In the short term, molecules do absorb gravitons and slowly heat up. The key to a successful model is therefore that directed absorption be converted into isotropic re-emission as body temperature reaches equilibrium with the surroundings. (It is ironic that Kelvin did not note this consequence of the Le Sage theory when later discussing the age of the Earth, arguing that it would lose all its internal heat and freeze in just 40×10^6 years.)

Kelvin also noted how work could be extracted from the gravitational field: Orient one domino-shaped matter ingredient (MI) vertically. Alternatively, one can simply take two spherical MIs and place one atop the other. Raise this MI (or pair) to some height in Earth's gravitational field. Next, rotate the MI (or pair) parallel to the ground. Finally, release it (them). Less energy is required to raise the MI than is gained in the drop. See Figure 10.

This effect arises from gravitational shielding—an effect that applies to individual MIs by definition, but not in general to large assemblies of them, which are mainly empty space. On a larger scale, one could theoretically build

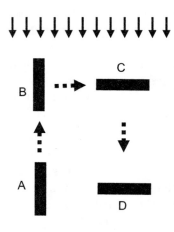

Figure 10. In a vertical graviton wind, if an elongated graviton-impenetrable block is raised, re-oriented, then dropped, net energy may be extracted because more gravitons aid its fall than resist its uplift.

a gravitational shield of super-dense matter. This shield could then operate on the same principle as a windmill or sail does in air, using the continual "graviton wind" blowing down-ward toward Earth that holds us in place (be-cause Earth blocks some counterpart gravitons from coming up). Like the sail on a sailboat, if it is made of coarse yarn, little wind energy can be extracted; whereas if it is made of material that air molecules cannot penetrate, all the wind energy can be extracted. Then by "tacking," we can redirect that wind energy in the desired di-rection, doing useful work.

The ability to do work with a gravitational field presents the possibility of building a "per-petual motion machine." It "merely" requires being able to create super-dense matter—a process still unavailable to physics at the be-ginning of the 21st century. However, argu-ments of principle about perpetual motion (if one does not take "perpetual" too literally) should now be settled in their favor because of the possibility that real gravitons may exist.

"Gravitons," as we use the term here, should not be confused with the hy-pothetical spin-2 gravitons of quantum physics. The latter are related to the concept of "curved space-time," and as such might be identified with the unit constituent of elysium, but certainly not with the agents carrying gravitational force. The reason for the failure of quantum physics to successfully model gravitation at a quantum level using these entities should now be readily evi-dent: two completely different media are needed for elysium (the light-carrying medium) and for the gravitational-force-carrying agents.

Direct measurements of the speed of radio signals through near-Earth space in the Global Positioning System (GPS) show no detectable speed varia-tions down to the level of at most 12 m/s. From that, we can conclude that ely-sium does not rotate with the Earth (as first shown by the Michelson-Gale ex-periment in 1925). The classical Sagnac experiment of 1913 indicates that ely-sium also does not rotate with a spinning laboratory platform, which is why a Michelson-Morley-type experiment on a rotating platform does detect fringe shifts. Therefore, elysium constituents must be quite small compared to atomic nuclei—something we might already have inferred from their lack of detection by experiments. Although gravitons cause elysium to "pool" and get denser near masses, we can infer that fresh elysium is continually replacing old ely-sium in such pools. If it were not, the pools would necessarily eventually ac-quire the angular momentum of whatever mass they are interacting with.

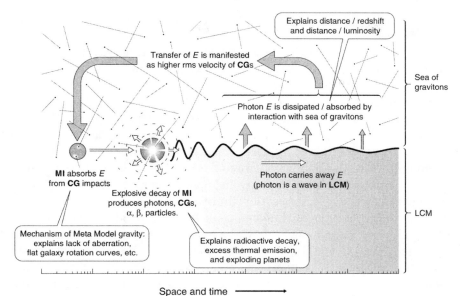

Figure 11. The Meta Cycle balances the books so that the universe does not run down or have its media gradually consumed. E = energy; CG = "classical graviton"; MI = "matter ingredient"; LCM = light-carrying medium (elysium).

Completion of a classical graviton model

We will now examine how elysium and graviton media fit into the larger picture, and how nature balances its books, conserving energy and momentum and not consuming its media.

Figure 11 is a schematic for the universe at our scale. It begins with a universal flux of high-speed "classical gravitons" (CGs) in a discrete medium. Occasionally, as in the lower left portion of the diagram, a "matter ingredient" (MI—the largest unit of matter able to absorb gravitons) swallows a colliding graviton, removing a bit of flux and energy from the CG medium and transferring it to the MI. The momentum it transfers propels the MI, which would happen even for a perfectly elastic, non-absorbent collision. The net propulsion of the MI caused by arriving CGs from all directions is its gravitational acceleration, which will be toward any large mass that blocks a substantial number of CG impacts on the MI from that direction. The speed of the CGs is so fast (at least 20 billion times lightspeed) that the direction of the acceleration coincides with the true, instantaneous direction of the nearby large mass, without aberration, to the accuracy we can presently measure. If the large mass is sufficiently far away (more than a few kiloparsecs, for example), stray CGs may get scattered to fill in for some of the missing ones blocked by the mass, diluting its gravitational force.

Gradually, from accumulated CG impacts, the MI accretes mass and energy and heats up. This process continues until the MI passes some critical threshold and explosively releases the excess stored energy and/or mass. The explosion energy may produce a shock wave through elysium, which would then appear to observers on our scale to be the spontaneous emission of a photon (a lightwave impulse). The same phenomenon on a much larger scale might be called a planetary explosion or a nova.

Alternatively, the exploding MI may eject mass. This would appear to observers on our scale to be particle decay, releasing an alpha or beta particle or a gamma ray. On a larger scale, we might describe similar phenomena as the ejection of a neutron star or a planetary nebula in a supernova explosion. Tiny bits from the MI explosion will return to the CG flux, restoring their numbers. The more conspicuous phenomena would appear cumulatively to be what we call radioactivity and excess heat flow from large masses.

A spontaneously emitted photon, as it leaves the body of which the MI was a part, propagates through space as a lightwave. Normally, it then encounters nothing except the CG medium. But whenever two media interact, friction can occur. Analogously to transverse water waves interacting with an air medium above them, the waves will lose energy back to the resisting medium, causing the waves to diminish in frequency (and amplitude) and grow in wavelength. In other words, they redshift (and get intrinsically fainter) as they travel. This provides a natural mechanism for the redshift of light traveling cosmological distances. CGs are so small compared to lightwaves that no significant scattering or refraction of light occurs. This removes the main objection against so-called "tired light" models as an explanation for cosmological redshift. And the effect of friction on lightwave amplitude that accompanies the effect on frequency brings supernova and other data into excellent agreement with predictions of this model—something that cannot be said for more simplistic "tired light" models. [32]

This mechanism also restores the energy to the CG medium lost when the gravitons were absorbed by the MI that emitted this lightwave. The extra energy becomes a faster rms speed for the gravitons, balancing the books for the slower CGs returned to the universal flux when the MI exploded. When a fresh MI condenses and forms from the debris of the interstellar medium, the original configuration is fully restored in detail. Numbers, energy, and momentum all balance. The universe is neither heating up nor running down on balance, when sampled over sufficiently long periods and sufficiently large volumes of space over a sufficient range of scales.

Two additional points are deserving of comment. According to the second law of thermodynamics, entropy (or disorder in the universe) is always increasing. We can see that, sampled only at certain scales, entropy will indeed always appear to increase. However, sampled at scales where gravity dominates, entropy always appears to decrease (i.e., the order of the universe increases). So when the phenomena are mechanical, electromagnetic or nuclear (strong or weak), all natural processes are explosive or destructive, and order can be increased only by doing work. However, on scales where gravity is the dominant force operating, gravity tends to condense bodies and form galaxies, stars, and planets out of highly disordered clouds of gas and dust. That is creating order from disorder, an anti-entropic process. Only by doing work, as in a planetary, nova, or supernova explosion, can disorder be obtained again from the order imposed by gravity. But when the complete Meta Cycle is considered, both entropic and anti-entropic processes participate, leaving no net change in the entropy of the universe. This is consistent with a universe that is infinite in size and age.

We described above the model's mechanism for producing cosmological redshift of light. But because we have a specific mechanism that deductively requires redshift, rather than a mechanism inductively derived to explain the observed redshift, we find our mechanism has other implications than just the redshift of lightwaves. The CG medium will resist all motions of the lightwaves. This means that their transverse wave motions will be resisted and lose energy at the same rate as the longitudinal wave motions. The physical meaning of the transverse amplitude of lightwaves corresponds to intensity. Specifically, the intensity of a lightwave is proportional to its amplitude squared. So if energy of a lightwave is lost in proportion to $(1+z)^{-1}$, then amplitude decreases at this same rate, and intensity decreases as $(1+z)^{-2}$, where z = redshift. This happens to be very close to the observed rate of brightness change with redshift in cases (such as bright galaxies) where redshift is primarily cosmological. The Big Bang predicts a $(1+z)^{-4}$ decrease, and must invoke *ad hoc* evolutionary effects to match observations. However, other lines of evidence indicate that no such strong evolutionary effects exist. [32]

If we pull together all the contributions (1.1), (1.2), (1.3), (1.4) from possible new properties of gravity, and invoke the modifications (0.1) to the old laws implied by this two-media model, we arrive at a new form of the law of gravity—the Le Sagian universal law of gravitation:

$$\ddot{\vec{r}} = -\frac{GM}{r^3}\vec{r}\,e^{-(r/r_G)-s_G\int\rho\,dr} - \left(\frac{3v\dot{v}}{c^2}+d_G\right)\vec{v} \qquad (2.1)$$

Supplementing Newton's universal gravitational constant G, (2.1) introduces three new gravitational parameters, all of which can be related to the properties of gravitons and elysium:

- r_G is the rms distance between graviton collisions, estimated to be 1 kpc $\approx$ 3.09×10^{19} m.
- s_G is the graviton shielding coefficient, estimated to be 2×10^{-19} m^2/kg.
- d_G is the graviton drag coefficient = $8\pi G\rho_B/3H_0 = \Omega_B H_0$, where G is the universal gravitational constant $\approx 6.672 \times 10^{-11}$ m^3/s^2/kg, ρ_B is the average baryonic matter density of the universe $\approx 3.0 \times 10^{-28}$ kg/m^3, H_0 is the Hubble constant ≈ 60 km/s/Mpc $\approx 1.94 \times 10^{18}$/s, and Ω_B is the ration of the baryonic density of the universe to the critical density ≈ 0.044. From these values, d_G is estimated to be $\approx 8.5 \times 10^{-20}$/s.

Predictions

Le Sagian particle gravity was designed to explain the basic characteristics of Newtonian gravity: induced test particle accelerations toward a source mass, proportional to the source mass, and falling off with the square of distance from that source mass. As we have seen, if a light-carrying medium (elysium) is included, then our Le Sagian model yields all classical general relativity effects as well without need of adjustable parameters: light slowing and bending, gravitational redshift, and the in-plane precession of elliptical orbits. This last effect arises from a single term in Le Sagian gravity, but needs a combination of three effects in GR, giving Le Sagian gravity the edge in simplicity. [9] Differences between these models arise in second-order terms in gravitational potential, and these can be used in future comparative testing of both models.

However, Le Sagian gravity is a specific model that arises primarily from logic applied to physics constrained by physical principles. In short, it is a deductive model developed forward from a classical physics starting point, not an inductive model developed by working backwards from observations. As such, the model makes many specific predictions of phenomena that have no counterparts in Newtonian or relativistic gravitation models. Among these are propagation speeds far faster than light, a finite range for gravitational force, the possibility of gravitational shielding, graviton drag, and heat flow from masses.

Experimental results already are at least consistent with, and in some cases outright favor, the existence of each of these not-yet-officially-recognized phenomena. Additional astrophysical and laboratory experiments over the next few years should firm up the case for or against the model for each of these phenomena. In particular, solar system tests may confirm the characteristic range of gravity suggested by galactic dynamics and cosmology; gravitational shielding may be confirmed in Lageos or other data; planetary excess heat flows may be better determined; and the propagation speed of gravity and graviton drag might be detected. Moreover, a different perihelion advance rate for two large masses is predicted, and binary pulsars may soon show which prediction is right. Investigations for the impact on stellar evolution models have yet to begin, but one can already foresee that the gravitational shielding effect in the interior of stars will likely lower the predicted output of solar neutrinos. This lower-than-expected emission rate has been a mystery for standard stellar evolution models for a generation. Moreover, gravitational shielding effects that limit the strength of the external gravity fields of supermassive bodies may allow indefinitely large masses ("supermassive stars") to exist in stable form. Such bodies would have very high intrinsic redshifts, much as quasars (whose true nature is still a matter of conjecture) are observed to have.

Clearly, this Le Sage-type particle-gravity model with two media makes so many novel yet testable predictions that it must surely be falsified quite soon unless it is truly an improvement over existing models. But then, the same thing was true two centuries ago, and the model is still standing today.

Conclusion

> SAGREDO: But of what kind and how great must we consider this speed of light to be? Is it instantaneous or momentary or does it, like other motion, require time? Can we not decide this by experiment?
>
> SIMPLICIO: Everyday experience shows that the propagation of light is instantaneous; for when we see a piece of artillery fired, at great distance, the flash reaches our eyes without lapse of time; but the sound reaches the ear only after a noticeable interval.
>
> Galileo's Two New Sciences

Herein, we continually adopt the point of view that "unseen" and "undetected" do not equate to non-existent. In so doing, we find considerable value for the understanding and visualization of phenomena in hypothesizing the existence of media and units of media as agents for the conveyance of physical forces. For a full exposition of gravitation, we require two such media— elysium and gravitons. We show how these interact to produce all the properties of Newtonian gravity and of GR. We also develop several new properties, and show the experimental status of each. No implied property is in any distress from experiment or observation; and some potentially provide new insights to the interpretation of observations. Moreover, no objection to this Le Sage-type model survives close scrutiny because all such objections can be answered by setting constraints on the properties of the units of the two media, and none of these constraints are mutually contradictory. The model remains falsifiable by finding a constraint that does contradict other known constraints, and/or by the failure of specific predictions that distinguish this model from competing models. Such predictions will be testable in the short-term future.

We require of new models that they conform to the following precepts: models must be contradicted by nothing known, must add new insights and understanding of nature, and must make predictions feasible to test, the failure of which will falsify the model. On all counts, the complete model of gravitation presented herein meets these criteria. It therefore deserves a place on the scientific table for continued comparison with future observations and experiments in competition with all other scientifically viable models.

References

[1] Van Flandern, T. (2000), "Physics has its principles," *Meta Res. Bull.* 9, 1-9.
[2] Van Flandern, T. (1998), "The speed of gravity—What the experiments say," *Phys. Lett. A* 250, 1-11.
[3] Selleri, F. (1996), "Non-invariant one-way velocity of light," *Found. Phys.* 26, 641-664.
[4] Van Flandern, T. (1998), "What the Global Positioning System tells us about relativity," in *Open Questions in Relativistic Physics*, F. Selleri, Ed., Apeiron, Montreal, 81-90.
[5] Eddington, A.E. (1920), *Space, Time and Gravitation*, 2nd ed. (reprinted 1987), Cambridge Univ. Press, Cambridge, 109

[6]   Hatch, R. (1999), "Gravitation: Revising both Einstein and Newton," *Galilean Electrodyn.* 10, 69-75.

[7]   de Felice, F. (1971), "On the gravitational field acting as an optical medium," *Gen. Rel. Grav.* 2, 347–357.

[8]   Danby, J.M.A. (1988), *Fundamentals of Celestial Mechanics*, 2nd edition, Willmann-Bell, Richmond, Ch. 11.

[9]   Van Flandern, T. (1999), "The Perihelion Advance Formula," *Meta Res. Bull.* 8, 9-15.

[10] Van Flandern, T. (1999), "Follow-up to the Perihelion Advance Formula," *Meta Res. Bull.* 8, 24-29.

[11] Van Flandern, T. (2000), "The speed of gravity—Repeal of the speed limit," submitted to *Phys. Lett. A*; preprint available at <http://metaresearch.org>, "cosmology" tab, "gravity" sub-tab.

[12] Arp, H.C. (1998), *Seeing Red*, Apeiron, Montreal.

[13] Greenberger, D.M. and Overhauser, A.W. (1980), *Sci. Amer.* 242 (May), 66.

[14] Sherwin, C.W. and Rawcliffe, R.D. (1960), Report I-92 of March 14 of the Consolidated Science Laboratory, Univ. of Illinois, Urbana; obtainable from U.S. Department of Commerce's Clearinghouse for Scientific and Technical Information, document AD 625706.

[15] Phipps, T.E., Jr. (1986), *Heretical Verities*, Classic Non-fiction Library, Urbana, 273-282.

[16] Wang, L.J., Kuzmich, A., and Dogariu, A. (2000), *Nature* 406, 277-279.

[17] Heitmann, W. and Nimtz, G. (1994), *Phys. Lett. A* 196, 154.

[18] Weiss, P. (2000), *Sci. News* 157, 375.

[19] Van Flandern, T. (1996), "Possible new properties of gravity," *Astrophys. Space Sci.* 244, 249-261.

[20] Wright, A.E., Disney, M.J., and Thompson, R.C. (1990), "Universal gravity: was Newton right?," *Proc. Astr. Soc. Australia* 8, 334-338.

[21] Standish, E.M. (1995), *Jet Propulsion Laboratory*, Pasadena, <ems@tolstoy.jpl.nasa.gov>, private communication.

[22] Van Flandern, T. (1995), "Are gravitational and inertial masses equal?," *Meta Res. Bull.* 4, 1-10.

[23] Thanks to Erricos Pavlis at NASA Goddard Space Flight Center for supplying this data.

[24] Rubincam, D.P. (1990), "Drag of the Lageos satellite," *J. Geophys. Res.* 95, 4881-4886.

[25] Slabinski, V.J. (1998), "Notes on gravitation in the Meta Model," *Meta Res. Bull.* 7, 33-42. An adaptation of the same paper titled "Force, Heat, and Drag in a Graviton Model" appears elsewhere in this book.

[26] Van Flandern, T. (1998), "The Meta Cycle," *Meta Res. Bull.* 7, 43-47.

[27] Heiken, G.H., Vaniman, D.T. and French, B.M., eds. (1991), *Lunar Sourcebook*, Cambridge Univ. Press, New York, 28.

[28] Encrenaz, T. and Bibring, J.P., eds. (1995), *The Solar System*, 2nd ed., Springer-Verlag, New York, 216-217:

[29] 1995 data from <http://atmos.nmsu.edu/jsdap/encyclopediawork.html>.

[30] Thanks to Alan G. Archer <photoget@teleport.com> for supplying the preceding two references.

[31] North, J.D. (1965), *The Measure of the Universe*, Clarendon Press, Oxford.

[32] Van Flandern, T. (1999), *Dark Matter, Missing Planets and New Comets*, 2nd ed., North Atlantic Books, Berkeley, 400-401.

Artwork (figures 1, 3, 8, 9, 11) courtesy of Boris Starosta (http://starosta.com)

Force, Heat and Drag in a Graviton Model[*]

Victor J. Slabinski[†]

Starting from a basic premise, gravitons interacting with matter, we derive rigorous formulas to relate three macroscopic physical properties (force, heat, and drag) to parameters describing graviton properties. Classical objections to graviton models are that no force exists if all gravitons are scattered, and the generated heat would vaporize masses if all gravitons are absorbed. The formulas derived here allow the placement of constraints on the graviton parameters. When gravitons are partly absorbed and partly scattered, parameter values exist consistent with the observed gravitational constant, the observed low excess heat flows from planets, and drag small enough to be still undetected.

1. Can the Scattering of Gravitons Produce Any Gravitational Force?

Consider that space is filled with gravitons that all move (for simplicity in the analysis) with the same very large speed v_g with respect to some rest frame. Let N = number of gravitons per unit volume of space (when far from any material, deflecting bodies) per unit solid angle for their directions of travel. We will assume that N is independent of incident direction. Then let A_{scat}, A_{abs} = cross-sectional area for scattering and absorption of gravitons by a mass particle, respectively. We assume the cross-sectional areas are proportional to the mass m of the deflecting or absorbing particle, so

$$A_{scat} = K_{scat}\, m \qquad (1)$$

$$A_{abs} = K_{abs}\, m \qquad (2)$$

where K_{scat}, K_{abs} = constants of proportionality.

Now let m_g = mass of a single graviton. Then consider the flux of gravitons which pass through the interaction cross-section ($A_{scat} + A_{abs}$) of the particle as shown in Figure 1 and which would continue to move in a straight line to an (imaginary) test area A_{test} *if the interaction did not occur*. These gravitons would move with directions within the solid angle $d\Omega$ subtended by A_{test} about m,

$$d\Omega = \frac{A_{test}}{r^2} \qquad (3)$$

where r = distance of test area from particle.

---

[*] Adaptation of an article first published in *Meta Research Bulletin* 7, 33-42 (1998) – see "Publications" tab at <http://metaresearch.org>.

[†] 3457 South Utah Street, Arlington, VA 22206. Present address: U.S. Naval Observatory, Washington, DC 20392-5240

Pushing Gravity: new perspectives on Le Sage's theory of gravitation
edited by Matthew R. Edwards (Montreal: Apeiron 2002)

123

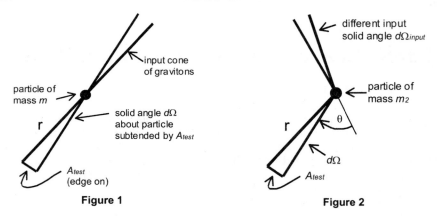

Figure 1　　　　　　　　　　　　　**Figure 2**

The flux of gravitons passing the particle (number per unit time per unit cross-section per unit solid angle) is Nv_g. The flux within the required input solid angle is $(Nv_g)d\Omega$. The rate at which gravitons within the required solid angle intersect the interaction cross-sectional area of the particle is then

$$R_{\substack{direct\\loss}} = (Nv_g)d\Omega(A_{scat} + A_{abs}); \tag{4}$$

this is the rate at which the presence of the mass particle decreases the direct input of gravitons onto A_{test}.

The gravitons *absorbed* by the mass particle presumably have their energy converted to heat and thus produce no further interactions. (The force on the particle due to their change of momentum will be treated later.) The gravitons *scattered* by the mass particle have their direction of travel changed through some angle θ, but I assume the magnitude of their velocity is still v_g. There will be some statistical distribution to the deflection angles θ given by some function $f(\theta)$ = fraction of scattered gravitons deflected through an angle θ per unit solid angle about θ. Symmetry in the scattering about the input direction is assumed. All we know about f is that the fraction of particles scattered through angles between θ and $(\theta + d\theta)$ is $f(\theta)(2\pi \sin\theta \, d\theta)$, so

$$\int_0^\pi f(\theta) 2\pi \sin\theta \, d\theta = 1 \tag{5}$$

Some gravitons incident on the mass particle within a different input solid angle $d\Omega_{input}$ as shown in Figure 2 will be scattered through an angle θ into the solid angle $d\Omega$ so that they pass through the test area. The rate at which gravitons with directions within $d\Omega_{input}$ are scattered (in all directions) by the mass particle is $(Nv_g)d\Omega_{input}A_{scat}$. The fraction of these that then pass through A_{test} is $f(\theta)d\Omega$. The rate at which gravitons are scattered toward A_{test} is thus

$$dR_{\substack{scattered\\in}} = \left[(Nv_g)d\Omega_{input}A_{scat}\right]f(\theta)d\Omega \tag{6}$$

To find the total rate at which gravitons are scattered toward A_{test}, we integrate over all input directions. We set

$$d\Omega_{input} = 2\pi \sin\theta \, d\theta \tag{7}$$

and then integrate over all θ to find

$$R_{scattered \atop in} = \int_{\theta=0}^{\pi} dR_{scattered \atop in} = \left(Nv_g\right) d\Omega \, A_{scat} \int_0^{\pi} f\left(\theta\right) d\Omega_{input}$$

$$= \left(Nv_g\right) d\Omega \, A_{scat} \int_0^{\pi} f\left(\theta\right) 2\pi \sin\theta \, d\theta = \left(Nv_g\right) d\Omega \, A_{scat} \tag{8}$$

where we have used Eq. (5). Eqs. (4), (8), (3), and (2) then allow us to find the rate by which the presence of a particle with mass m_2 decreases the input of gravitons onto A_{test} as

$$R_{net \atop loss} = R_{direct \atop loss} - R_{scattered \atop in}$$

$$= \left(Nv_g\right) d\Omega \, A_{abs} \tag{9}$$

$$= \frac{Nv_g A_{abs}}{r^2} A_{test} = \frac{Nv_g K_{abs} m_2}{r^2} A_{test}$$

We have the surprising result that scattering of gravitons by the mass particle causes no decrease in the rate at which gravitons reach A_{test}!

Let A_{test} now be the position of a particle of mass m_1; the decrease in graviton flux (number of particles per unit time per unit area) due to m_2 is

$$\mathcal{F}_{decrease} = R_{net \atop loss} \Big/ A_{test}$$

$$= \frac{Nv_g K_{abs} m_2}{r^2} \tag{10}$$

We compute the force $\vec{F}_1$ on m_1 due to the graviton flux using $\vec{F}_1 = -$ (rate of change of graviton momentum from interactions with m_1)

$$= -\sum_i \left(d\vec{p}_i / dt\right) \tag{11}$$

where the summation extends over all solid angles about m_1 and $d\vec{p}_i / dt$ = rate of change of momentum of gravitons incident within a small solid angle $d\Omega_i$ about m_1. For gravitons with an incident direction given by a unit vector $\hat{u}_i$, the momentum change for an absorbed graviton = (final momentum) – (incident momentum) $= \left(0 - m_g v_g\right) \hat{u}_i$ while the (average) momentum change for a scattered graviton

$$= \left(m_g v_g \left\langle \cos\theta \right\rangle - m_g v_g\right) \hat{u}_i$$

$$= -m_g v_g \left(1 - \left\langle \cos\theta \right\rangle\right) \hat{u}_i$$

where

$$\left\langle \cos\theta \right\rangle = \int_0^{\pi} f\left(\theta\right) \left(2\pi \sin\theta \, d\theta\right) \cos\theta \tag{12}$$

Then

$$\frac{d\vec{p}_i}{dt} = \mathcal{F}_i \left[-A_{abs,1} m_g v_g - A_{scat,1} m_g v_g \left(1 - \left\langle \cos\theta \right\rangle\right)\right] \hat{u}_i \tag{13}$$

where $\mathcal{F}_i$ is the incident flux in solid angle $d\Omega_i$.

$$\mathcal{F}_i = \left(Nv_g\right)d\Omega_i \qquad (14)$$

for all solid angle elements *except* the one which contains m_2; for that element

$$\mathcal{F}_{m2} = \left(Nv_g\right)d\Omega_i - \mathcal{F}_{decrease} \qquad (15)$$

We form the solid angle elements $d\Omega_i$ such that diametrically opposite (about m_1) elements are equal. Such pairs have oppositely directed $\hat{u}_i$ values, so $d\bar{p}_i/dt$ from the pair are equal in magnitude and opposite in direction by Eqs. (13) and (14), and thus cancel in the Eq. (11) summation. An exception is the pair that includes m_2 within one element. If $\hat{u}_{2,1}$ is the unit vector from m_1 toward m_2, that pair gives the only non-zero contribution in Eq. (11) so

$$\bar{F}_1 = \left[\left(N v_g d\Omega_i\right)\hat{u}_{2,1} - \left(N v_g d\Omega_i - \mathcal{F}_{decrease}\right)\hat{u}_{2,1}\right]$$

$$\times\left[A_{abs,1} + A_{scat,1}\left(1 - \langle\cos\theta\rangle\right)\right]m_g v_g \qquad (16)$$

$$= \frac{N m_g v_g^2 K_{abs} m_2}{r^2}\hat{u}_{2,1}\left[K_{abs} + K_{scat}\left(1 - \langle\cos\theta\rangle\right)\right]m_1$$

where we have used Eqs. (10), (1), and (2). This has the form of Newton's Law of Gravitation

$$\bar{F}_1 = \frac{G m_1 m_2}{r^2}\hat{u}_{2,1} \qquad (17)$$

with the gravitational constant G given by

$$G = N m_g v_g^2 K_{abs}\left[K_{abs} + K_{scat}\left(1 - \langle\cos\theta\rangle\right)\right] \qquad (18)$$

Eq. (18) gives one relation of graviton parameters to a known physical constant. By inspection, we see that if $K_{abs} = 0$, the gravitational constant unconditionally goes to zero, and there is no net force. But if $K_{scat} = 0$, the force is proportional to K_{abs}^2. This requires that K_{abs}^2 be large enough to produce gravitational force by itself, which in turn implies a heat build-up in masses from the continual absorption of energy (see next section). However, when both absorption coefficients are non-zero, then the scattering coefficient can make the major contribution to the gravitational constant while contributing little or nothing to the heating of masses.

If this seems puzzling, we point out that at m_2, only the absorption cross-section affects the flux of gravitons that appear to be coming from the vicinity of m_2. At m_1, there is then a deficiency of gravitons coming from the m_2 direction. The resulting net excess of gravitons coming from the direction opposite to the m_2 direction now causes a net force on m_1. The momentum transfer to m_1 due to this excess depends both on absorption of part of the excess and on scattering of part of the excess. The latter force contribution gives the K_{scat} term in Eq. (16).

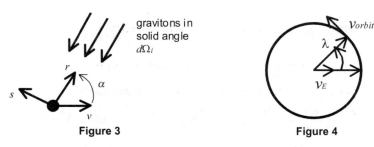

Figure 3   Figure 4

2. How Much Heat Is Produced by Graviton Absorption?

The absorption of gravitons means their kinetic energy goes into heating material bodies. The rate at which gravitons are absorbed by a body of mass m is

$$N v_g \left(\text{total solid angle about body}\right) A_{abs} = N v_g \, 4\pi \, K_{abs} m$$

Each absorbed graviton gives up a kinetic energy of $\frac{1}{2} m_g v_g^2$, so the rate H at which gravitons heat up the body is

$$H = \left(2\pi \, N \, m_g v_g^{3} K_{abs}\right) m \tag{19}$$

The Earth and Moon give off internal heat usually ascribed to internal radioactivity. If we assume this is due to absorbed gravitons instead, Eq. (19) could be used to put a bound on the parameters of the theory. See section 4 for some numerical bounds based on this and other constraints derived here.

3. How Much Drag Results from Motion through the Graviton Sea?

Consider a particle moving with a velocity $\bar{v}$ with respect to the "rest" frame in which the graviton flux is isotropic with respect to direction. Consider the gravitons incident on the particle from a solid angle $d\Omega_i$ at an angle α from $\bar{v}$, as seen in the rest frame as shown in Figure 3. The incident graviton flux is $N v_g d\Omega_i$ in the rest frame; due to its motion, the particle sees a flux (to first order in v/v_g) of $N \, d\Omega_i \left(v_g + v\cos\alpha\right)$. Each graviton's momentum is $m_g \left(-v_g \hat{r}\right)$ in the rest frame; as seen from the particle, its momentum is $m_g \left(-v_g \hat{r} - \bar{v}\right)$. The time rate of change of graviton momentum in this solid angle, due to interaction with the particle, is (by analogy with Eq. (13) and (14))

$$d\left(\frac{d\bar{p}}{dt}\right) = N \, d\Omega_i \left(v_g + v\cos\alpha\right)\left[A_{abs} + A_{scat}\left(1 - \langle\cos\theta\rangle\right)\right] m_g \left(v_g \hat{r} + \bar{v}\right)$$

$$\cong N \, d\Omega_i \left[A_{abs} + A_{scat}\left(1 - \langle\cos\theta\rangle\right)\right] m_g \left[v_g^2 \hat{r} + v_g v(\hat{v} + \hat{r}\cos\alpha)\right] \tag{20}$$

to first order in v/v_g. If we consider all solid angles between α and $(\alpha + d\alpha)$, the component of momentum change normal to the unit vector $\hat{v}$ averages to zero and we get (with $d\Omega_i = 2\pi \sin\alpha \, d\alpha$)

$$d\left(\frac{d\vec{p}}{dt}\right) = N\,2\pi\sin\alpha\left[A_{abs} + A_{scat}\left(1 - \langle\cos\theta\rangle\right)\right]$$

$$\times m_g\left[v_g^2\cos\alpha + v_g v\left(1 + \cos^2\alpha\right)\right]\hat{v}\,d\alpha \tag{21}$$

By Eqs. (11), (1), and (2) then, the drag force on the particle is

$$\vec{F}_{drag} = -\int_{\alpha=0}^{\pi} d\left(\frac{d\vec{p}}{dt}\right) = -\frac{16\pi}{3}N\,m_g v_g\left[K_{abs} + K_{scat}\left(1 - \langle\cos\theta\rangle\right)\right]m\vec{v} \tag{22}$$

Consider a satellite in a circular orbit about the Earth as shown in Figure 4.

$$\vec{v} = \vec{v}_E + \vec{v}_{orbit} \tag{23}$$

where $\vec{v}_E$ is the Earth's velocity with respect to the rest frame and $\vec{v}_{orbit}$ is the satellite's velocity along its orbit. Using this expression in Eq. (22) and computing the average drag force *along the orbit* gives

$$\langle\vec{F}_{drag} \bullet \hat{v}_{orbit}\rangle = \frac{1}{2\pi}\int_0^{2\pi}\left(\vec{F}_{drag} \bullet \hat{v}_{orbit}\right)d\lambda$$

$$= -\frac{16\pi}{3}N\,m_g v_g\left[K_{abs} + K_{scat}\left(1 - \langle\cos\theta\rangle\right)\right]m v_{orbit} \tag{24}$$

This last equation gives another test of graviton theory because no drag from the graviton medium has yet been detected observationally.

4. Numerical Limits

Using the constraint equations (18), (19), and (24) derived here, together with cosmological parameters and experimental limits on the speed of gravity (Van Flandern, 1998a), the following are the strongest numerical constraints we can determine (Van Flandern, 1998b):

$$Nm_g < 2.3\times10^{-63}\,\text{cm}^{-3}\text{g} \tag{25}$$

$$K_{abs}v_g = 10^{13}\,\text{cm}^3\text{g}^{-1}\text{s}^{-1} \tag{26}$$

$$v_g > 6\times10^{20}\,\text{cm s}^{-1} \tag{27}$$

$$K_{abs} < 1.7\times10^{-8}\,\text{cm}^2\text{g}^{-1} \tag{28}$$

$$\frac{K_{scat}}{K_{abs}} > 2.9\times10^{29} \tag{29}$$

Other constraints we can derive are less severe, and are therefore consistent with the above. Hence, a range of graviton parameters exists that allows graviton models to be viable.

References

Van Flandern, T. (1998a). "The speed of gravity – What the experiments say," *Phys.Lett. A* **250**, 1-11.

Van Flandern, T. (1998b). "The Meta Cycle," *Meta Research Bull.* **7**, 43-47. [Availability information at <http://metaresearch.org>.]

Gravitation as a Compton Effect Redshift of Long Wavelength Background Radiation

John Kierein[*]

A background of very long wavelength radiation is predicted from a static universe with a Compton effect redshift. The interaction of this radiation with massive bodies produces gravity in a 'push' process as suggested by Brush.

1. Introduction

The idea that gravity is a push from the outside rather than a pull has a long history (see, for example, Aronson, 1964). It is a satisfying theory because it provides a mechanism for gravity that eliminates the magical "action at a distance" mystique about the attraction of masses. Le Sage's "ultramundane particles" (highly penetrating particles coming from beyond the Earth) provide a physical connection that pushes masses together in an inverse square law identical to Newton's gravitational force [Ref 2]. Richard Feynman (1963), in his popular *Feynman Lectures*, describes the excitement that people feel when they discover this idea because of the enlightened insight it provides them. He then proceeds to explain why it is his belief that this idea cannot be correct.

In this paper, we revive the ideas of Le Sage with a modern view. This view comes about as a consequence of static universe models that contain a redshift. One such model is the one in which the redshift is due to the Compton effect rather than the Doppler effect (Kierein, 1988, 1990). The Compton effect explains intrinsic redshifts on the sun as well as quasar redshifts (Compton, 1923; Kierein and Sharp, 1968).

2. Compton Effect Redshift

In this model, there are electrons, positrons and other free particles between galaxies. As light travels through this transparent medium, it loses energy to these free particles in the following manner.

Hubble's law observes that $z = \Delta\lambda/\lambda = HD$ or:

$$\Delta\lambda = HD\lambda, \tag{1}$$

where $\Delta\lambda$ is the redshifted change in wavelength, λ is the original wavelength, D is the distance to the object, and H is "Hubble's constant" of proportionality (H is sometimes conventionally expressed as H/c for convenience for the Doppler interpretation).

[*] 2852 Blue Jay Way, Lafayette, CO 80026. E-mail: Bigbangiswrong@angelfire.com. Website: http://www.angelfire.com/az/BIGBANGisWRONG/index.html

Pushing Gravity: new perspectives on Le Sage's theory of gravitation
edited by Matthew R. Edwards (Montreal: Apeiron 2002)

If one interprets this law as being due to multiple Compton effect interactions of photons starting at the distance D and interacting with an intervening medium of free particles (such as electrons) of density ρ particles per cubic centimeter, then

$$\Delta\lambda = (\Delta\lambda_i)(N_i),\tag{2}$$

where $\Delta\lambda_i$ is the shift per interaction given by the familiar Compton formula

$$\Delta\lambda_i = \frac{h(1-\cos\theta)}{mc}.\tag{3}$$

In this expression h is Planck's constant, m is the mass of the particle (electron), c is the velocity of light and θ is the angle of deflection of the photon velocity vector. N_i in equation 2 is the number of Compton interactions occurring, so that cos θ is the "average cos θ" observed over the large number of interactions involved.

Now:

$$N_i = (N_t)T,\tag{4}$$

that is, the number of interactions equals the integrated probability, N_t, that an interaction is occurring at any time, times the total time of travel, T, where

$$T = \frac{D}{c}.\tag{5}$$

Now:

$$N_t = \frac{\sigma\rho\lambda c}{\lambda_c},\tag{6}$$

where σ is the Thomson cross section (in the case where the particle is the electron), and λ_c is the Compton wavelength of the particle $= h/mc$.

Thus, from equations 4, 5 and 6:

$$N_i = \frac{\sigma\rho\lambda cD}{\lambda_c c}\tag{7}$$

and from equations 2, 3 and 7, with substituting and canceling:

$$\Delta\lambda = \sigma\rho(1-\cos\theta)D\lambda.\tag{8}$$

Thus, from equations 1 and 8:

$$H = \sigma\rho(1-\cos\theta)\tag{9}$$

This interesting result shows that the 'large cosmological constant', H, can be expressed in terms of the 'smaller' Thomson cross-section constant so familiar in the everyday physics of subatomic particles.

It should be noted that the λ in equations 6, 7 and 8 strictly speaking is not the original wavelength of the photon, but rather the wavelength at the time of the interaction. This wavelength varies from λ at the start to $\lambda + \Delta\lambda$ at the end of the travel, so that the integrated average wavelength should be $\lambda + \Delta\lambda/2$. This is a small correction for the observed cosmological (non-quasar) galactic shifts where z is less than 1, the correction being less than the uncertainty in H and D.

Thus, when $\lambda + \Delta\lambda/2$ is substituted for λ, the result is:

$$z = \frac{HD}{\left(1 - HD/2\right)}. \tag{10}$$

This leads to correspondingly shorter distances for a given z than in the case that $z = HD$. These distance differences can be significant for larger z, resulting in a new form for Hubble's law. As better measurements are made of the redshift-distance relationship, it should be theoretically possible to determine which relationship is the observed one.

It should be noted that the magnitude of the shift in equation 3 is inversely proportional to the mass of the particle. The mass of the electron is about 3500 times smaller than the mass of a hydrogen molecule, so the effectiveness of a density of free electrons in producing a redshift is correspondingly greater than the effectiveness of clouds of hydrogen gas. However, there are now known to be clouds of hydrogen gas between galaxies (Richter *et al.*, 1999) and they may well contribute significantly to the Compton effect redshift in a manner suggested by Marmet [Ref. 9] if their number density is much greater than the number density of free electrons and positrons.

3. The Blurring Problem

It has been suggested that the multiple scatterings of the Compton effect should cause stars to be blurred because the effect requires the photon to change direction to produce a redshift. The answer lies in the dual particle and wave nature of light. The Compton effect is entirely explained in terms of the conservation of energy and momentum. It is not dependent on the charge of the target. Compton (1923) attributed the presence of an unshifted line in his data (in addition to the shifted line from the electron), to the scattering of the photon from the neutral atom in the target, which had too large a mass to produce a significant shift. The electric and magnetic vectors of the photons are undisturbed by these scatterings, so the $\mathbf{E} \times \mathbf{H}$ vector continues to travel in its original direction, but at a reduced velocity in this direction. This is the familiar effect that light has an $\mathbf{E} \times \mathbf{H}$ group velocity that is less than c in a transparent medium. The index of refraction of the medium is the ratio of the speed of the $\mathbf{E} \times \mathbf{H}$ wavefront in the medium to the speed of the photon in a vacuum. The wavefront of the group velocity is reconstructed from the scattering centers in the Huygens secondary wavelets and its wavefront velocity is the vectorial sum of the velocities of the group of photons in the direction of the $\mathbf{E} \times \mathbf{H}$ vector. Reber (1968) performed a computerized random walk analysis that showed the photon stayed within a small circle along the direction to the source from multiple scatterings, so the difference between the group velocity and the speed in vacuum is very small for the rare intergalactic medium. The idea that the photon's momentum-carrying, particle-like velocity can be different from the velocity of its wave-like $\mathbf{E} \times \mathbf{H}$ vector explains how a single photon's $\mathbf{E} \times \mathbf{H}$ vector can produce interference patterns when passing through a diffraction slit. We see the $\mathbf{E} \times \mathbf{H}$ vector of the wave in images and spectra, which contains the information about the source, while energy detectors can detect the energy and momentum of the individual photon. Because the $\mathbf{E} \times \mathbf{H}$ wavefront is reconstructed by the Huygens secondary wavelets in the transparent medium, there is no blurring even though there is multiple Compton scattering along the path. The scattering centers act as the centers of the Huygens secondary wavelets.

4. Static Universe Long Wavelength Background Radiation

A static universe model, in which the redshift is caused by the Compton effect, is what Reber calls an "Endless, Boundless Stable Universe" (Reber, 1977). In this universe there is a need to show that Olbers' paradox is not a problem and that the universe is indeed stable.

If the universe is infinite in extent with a constant density of light sources, then the night sky should appear to be totally bright. This is because the number of galaxies increases with the cube of the distance from an observer on Earth, while the energy only falls off as the inverse square of the distance. This would seem to mean that an infinite amount of energy is being received from such an endless universe model. The fact that this is not observed is often called Olbers' paradox, after the 18th century astronomer Heinrich Olbers. (Olbers' paradox can be a bigger problem for an expanding universe, since the density of sources is greater with distance as we look further back in time when galaxies were supposedly closer together.) However, when one includes the redshift in this calculation, the solution results in a finite answer. This is because the photons from sources at distances approaching infinity have been redshifted to wavelengths approaching infinite length, and therefore approach zero energy. A mechanism for this redshift that allows the energy lost between galaxies in the Compton effect to be converted to mass (and not re-radiated) is given in Ref. 12. This mechanism views the Compton effect from the point of view of the electron (or positron). The electron between galaxies sees radiation of all wavelengths coming from all directions simultaneously. Much of the resulting velocity increase of the electron from the Compton effect vectorially cancels. Thus the electron gains energy without a corresponding increase in velocity and must increase in mass according to $m = E/c^2$.

The result of this solution to Olbers' paradox is that the universe is filled with a long wavelength radiation background. This radiation comes from all directions and is as isotropic as the universe. (Any anisotropy is probably due to motion of our galaxy relative to this general background.) Reber (1968) has measured the background at wavelengths of 144 and 500 meters and found it to be very bright and extragalactic. At 144 meters wavelength it is equivalent to a black body temperature of 3.5×10^6 degrees Kelvin. His maps show that the general brightness has less bright areas where the mass attenuates this radiation in identifiable locations such as the galactic center, and other spots along the galactic plane. This solution to Olbers' paradox predicts that Reber's low frequency measurements, if extended to indefinitely longer wavelengths, show a strong and smooth background. The Compton effect cosmological redshift shifts the radiated spectrum of stars to these longer wavelengths.

5.   Interaction of Long Wavelength Isotropic Radiation with Massive Bodies

Short wavelength radiation, like gamma rays and X-rays, can penetrate matter because the wavelengths are so short they can travel between molecules and atoms. When they interact with matter they cause violent collisions that can ionize the molecules and atoms. For this reason, radiation of these wavelengths is often called 'ionizing' radiation. Medium wavelength radiation, such as ultraviolet, visible and infrared radiation does not penetrate very far into matter. When it interacts it causes surface heating as it gives kinetic energy to individual molecules and atoms. Longer wavelength radiation, such as microwave, is more penetrating and heats matter from the inside as in a microwave oven. Longer wavelengths, such as radio waves, penetrate matter even further, as witnessed by the ability to receive radio signals in a basement of a building. This is because it interacts with all the molecules in the matter as it travels through the body and is slightly attenuated in the process. The attenuation is due to the Compton effect causing each long wavelength photon to be redshifted slightly and thus transfer energy to the body. Even longer wavelength radiation is still more penetrating. When it interacts with the body, it is of such long wavelength that it interacts with multiple numbers of molecules at the same time, thus moving them in bulk to produce a pressure force rather than heating or ionization.

6.   The Mechanism of Gravity

A push of long wavelength radiation as the cause of gravity was first suggested by Brush in 1910 and published in Nature in 1911 [Ref. 13]. (Brush later changed his idea of the pushing radiation to the idea that it may be shorter wavelength radiation after being impressed by the penetrating capabilities of X-rays, although he made no such explicit claims in his 1928 Franklin Medal Award paper (Brush, 1929)).

The mechanism for gravity we introduce in this paper is that the "ultra-mundane" particles of Le Sage are the background long wavelength photons from the static universe. This radiation is highly penetrating and produces forces as it interacts with massive bodies. The cross section of this radiation is very large with respect to the masses of the bodies. When a massive body absorbs this energy from all directions, a significant amount of the energy is vectorially cancelled. That is, energy coming from one direction causes a velocity increase that is cancelled by a nearly equal amount coming from the opposite direction. This means that the massive body is receiving energy without a corresponding increase in kinetic velocity. According to Special Relativity, this means that the mass of the massive body must be increasing according to $E = mc^2$. As each photon passes through the body a small amount of its energy is thus converted to new mass in that body. The presence of a second body near a massive body attenuates the radiation coming from its direction toward the first body and Newton's law of universal gravitation follows. Note that the heating problem associated with Le Sage's theory can be solved since the energy is converted to mass rather than all to heat, although there can be some heating involved, too, at the center of a massive body like the Earth.

The increase in mass of planetary bodies due to this absorption effect also provides a mechanism for expanding Earth theories (Kierein, 1992, Carey, 1988). These theories explain the plate tectonics whereby the continents fit together almost perfectly on a smaller diameter Earth in the geologic past. While the evidence for such expansion of the Earth has been compelling, these theories have not met general acceptance because there was previously no known mechanism for such expansion to occur.

7.   The Solution to the Static Universe Stability Problem

As Tolman (1934) points out, models of a finite, unbounded, static universe with a radius R may not be stable to processes of conversion of mass to energy or energy to mass. This is because R depends on the total gravitational potential and total radiation pressure in such a universe. If there are processes introduced which change these, then R would change, producing an expanding or contracting universe. If mass is converted to radiation, as is observed in stars, then the model contracts. However, the radiation created is balanced by the conversion of energy to mass as in Ref. 12 and results in an increase in the background radiation, which increases the gravitational potential. The increase in radiation pressure is balanced by the increase in gravity. The model is stabilized, since this is a self-correcting mechanism.

8.   The Graviton

One can quantize the gravitational force from this Le Sage mechanism. A quantization of this force identifies the graviton as a quantization of the 'shadow' cast in the long wavelength background radiation field by a mass. It is like the absence of a photon. Thus, the graviton is similar to an electron hole in a semiconductor. This graviton travels at c. (But consider the special case of a beam of long wavelength radiation penetrating a massive body and a second body entering its shadow. The second body instantaneously feels the shadow of the first body as soon as it enters the shadow, so in this sense the second body feels the presence of the first body as though its gravity travelled faster than c.)

9. Mach's Principle

The background radiation field defines a preferred reference inertial coordinate system. This is in agreement with Mach's principle for defining an inertial coordinate system as one being at rest or moving with a constant velocity with respect to the fixed stars. The long wavelength background replaces Mach's fixed stars, (and indeed is a result of redshifted radiation from the fixed stars). The microwave background is the short wavelength end of the spectrum of this background.

10. Bodies in Motion with Respect to the Background

Feynman's objection to Le Sage's theory is that an object in motion should be slowed by the increase in flux of ultramundane particles in the forward direction. He suggests that the Earth should be slowed in its orbit and should therefore fall into the sun if the Le Sage theory holds. However, when one replaces Le Sage's ultramundane particles with long wavelength photons, it is obvious that the increase in flux does not become significant until the velocity of the object approaches the speed of light. When this occurs the increased flux is indistinguishable from an apparent increase in mass due to its velocity. This is just what happens according to the special theory of relativity and indeed produces a physical reason for the validity of this theory.

11. Other Consequences

There are some consequences of this theory that are worth pointing out. The Russian scientists Radzievskii and Kagal'nikova in 1960 suggested that a Brush theory of gravity could explain the Foucault pendulum solar eclipse anomalies observed by Nobel laureate Allais (Ref. 17).

The short wavelength version of this gravity theory applied to small particles has been called "mock gravity" and suggested as being important for both solar system planetary formation by Spitzer (1941) and Whipple (1946) and for galaxy formation by Hogan and White (1986).

References

1. Aronson, S., 1964. "The gravitational theory of Georges-Louis Le Sage," *The Natural Philosopher*, **3**, 51.
2. G.-L. LeSage, *Nouv. Mem. de l'Acad. de Berlin*, 1782.
3. R. Feynman *et al.*, *The Feynman Lectures on Physics*, Addison-Wesley Pub. Co., Reading, Mass., 1963-65.
4. J. Kierein, "Implications of the Compton Effect Interpretation of the Red Shift," *IEEE Trans. Plasma Sci.* **18**, 61, 1990.
5. J. Kierein, "A Criticism of Big Bang Cosmological Models Based on Interpretation of the Red Shift," *IEEE Special Issue of Lasers and Particle Beams* **6**, 453, 1988.
6. A.H. Compton, *Phil. Mag.* **46**, 897, 1923.
7. J. Kierein and B. Sharp, "The Compton Effect Interpretation of the Solar Red Shift," *Solar Physics* **3**, 450, 1968.
8. P. Richter *et al.*, "Discovery of Molecular Hydrogen in a High-Velocity Cloud of the Galactic Halo," *Nature* **402**, 386, 1999.

9. P. Marmet, "The Cosmological Constant and the Red Shift of Quasars," *IEEE Trans. on Plasma Sci.* **20**, 6, 962, Dec. 1992; P. Marmet and G. Reber "Cosmic Matter and the Nonexpanding Universe," *IEEE Trans. on Plasma Sci.* **17**, 2, 267, Apr. 1989.

10. G. Reber, "Cosmic Static at 144 Meters Wavelength," *J. Franklin Inst.* **285**, 1, 1968.

11. G. Reber, "Endless, Boundless, Stable Universe," *U. Tasmania Occasional Paper* No. **9**, 1977.

12. J. Kierein, "A Mechanism for Particle Acceleration in Space Plasmas and for Planetary Mass Accretion," *Apeiron* **14**, 3, 1992.

13. C.F. Brush, "A Kinetic Theory of Gravitation," *Nature* **86**, 130, 1911; *Science* **33**, 381, 1911.

14. C.F. Brush, *Proc. Amer. Phys. Soc.* **68**, 1, 55, 1929; and "Some Experimental Evidence Supporting the Kinetic Theory of Gravitation" *J. Franklin Inst.* **206**, 143, 1928.

15. R. Tolman, *Relativity, Thermodynamics and Cosmology*, pp. 361-407, Oxford U. Press, Oxford, U.K., 1934.

16. V.V. Radzievskii and I.I. Kagal'nikova, "The Nature of Gravitation," Bull. Vsesoyuz. Astronomo-Geod. Obschestva (Moscow), No. 26 (33), pp. 3-14, 1960. (English translation in U.S. Govt. tech. report FTD-TT-64-323/1+2+4 (AD-601762)).

17. M. Allais, *Comptes Rend. Acad. Sci.* **245**, 1875; **245**, 2001; 244, 2469; **245**, 2467; **245**, 2170, 1959. And, in English, in *Aero/Space Engineering*, September and October, 1959.

18. L. Spitzer, *Astrophys. J.* **94**, 232-244, 1941.

19. F.L. Whipple, "Concentrations of the Interstellar Medium," *Astrophys. J.* **104**, 1, 1946.

20. C.J. Hogan and S.D.M. White, "Galaxy Formation by Mock Gravity," *Nature* **321**, 575-578, 1986.

21. S.W. Carey, *Theories of the Earth and Universe: A History of Dogma in the Earth Sciences,* Stanford University Press, Stanford, Cal., 1988.

Induction of Gravitation in Moving Bodies

Matthew R. Edwards[*]

It is assumed that space is filled with a primary form of electromagnetic radiation, the individual quanta of which are termed gravitons, and that these gravitons collectively define a preferred reference frame for physical forces. In such a
frame the relativistic Doppler effect has different forms depending on the specific motions of the source and receiver. While a receiver at rest in this frame
finds the gravitons emitted from moving bodies to be uniformly redshifted, a receiver in motion in the frame conversely finds the background gravitons to be
blueshifted. The redshift in the former case is now interpreted as an energy absorption effect. Bodies in motion in the preferred frame experience a net absorption of gravitons and a resulting increase in mass. This in turn leads to a
Le Sage-type gravitational force. In the model, terrestrial gravity is due principally to the rotation of the Galaxy in the preferred frame.

1. Introduction

The idea that gravity is caused by energetic corpuscles or waves bombarding
bodies from all sides has a long history now stretching into its fourth century at
least. The scientific roots of this idea are mainly traceable to the writings of
Georges-Louis Le Sage in the eighteenth century (*e.g.*, Le Sage, 1784).[†] Subsequently, the theory has undergone a complex history, many details of which
appear elsewhere in this book. A partial listing of some of the more recent
variations of the theory would include the works of Radzievskii and Kagalnikova (1960), Shneiderov (1961), Buonomano and Engel (1976), Adamut (1976,
1982), Veselov (1981), Jaakkola (1996), Slabinski (1998) and Van Flandern
(1999).[‡]

Le Sage-type theories have faced a number of problems historically.
These include accounting for the energy absorbed by matter as a result of collisions with Le Sage corpuscles or waves; the possibility of gravitational aberration; and the resistance that a body should experience in moving through the
Le Sage medium. Of these perhaps the most significant criticism, the one given
by Maxwell (1875), is the conservation of energy problem. In Le Sage-type
theories, there must be absorption of incident particles or waves for gravity to
appear. Reflection alone will not suffice, as it had long ago been shown that

---

[*] Gerstein Science Information Centre, University of Toronto, Toronto, Ontario, Canada M5S 3K3.
E-mail: matt.edwards@utoronto.ca.
[†] Le Sage's contributions are discussed by Evans in this volume. Other early workers on this idea
included Fatio and Prevost. For details on Fatio's theory, which Newton supported for a time, see Van
Lunteren's article in this book. Discussions on the later history of Le Sage's theory can be found in
Aronson (1964) and the author's other paper in this volume.
[‡] The articles by Veselov, Jaakkola and Radzievskii and Kagalnikova are reprinted in this volume,
as well as an adaptation of Slabinski's paper.

secondary interactions of the reflected particles or waves will precisely cancel the gravitational effect. Le Sage's theory in fact seems to require so much energy to be absorbed by bodies that they would be incinerated within seconds. A partial resolution to this problem was recently found by Slabinski (1998). Slabinski showed that the scattering of Le Sage-type particles may augment the gravitational force provided that some absorption is also taking place. Even in this case, however, significant heating of bodies would be expected unless the absorption coefficient is tiny in comparison to the scattering coefficient.

In attempting to address this problem we must first ask: in what form does the energy of the absorbed Le Sage corpuscles or waves finally appear? Clearly the energy cannot appear mainly in the form of heat or the above criticisms would apply. An alternative possibility is that the absorbed energy appears as new mass, but here different possibilities can be envisaged. The energy might appear, for example, in the form of rest mass of newly created particles (*e.g.*, nucleons). While such a notion remains a possibility, it must be acknowledged that we have no evidence as yet for such direct formation of whole particles.

A second possibility, the one to be explored in this paper, is that the absorbed energy increases the mass and rest energy of existing bodies. In the Le Sage mechanism now proposed, such absorption is associated only with bodies that are in motion in a primary reference frame. Gravitation is thus an induced effect in moving bodies. For reasons of momentum conservation, however, moving bodies simultaneously lose speed in the primary frame.

In the model, we will make the following assumptions:

(1) The universe is infinite in time and space and the cosmological processes within it are maintained in a state of continuous equilibrium. The cosmological model which we adopt is broadly similar to Jaakkola's Equilibrium Cosmology (EC) (Jaakkola, 1991, 1993, 1996).

(2) Space is filled with a background of electromagnetic energy, the individual quanta of which are termed gravitons. This medium is analogous to the cosmic microwave background (CBR) and, together with the CBR, defines a preferred reference frame (*PF*) for physical forces.

(3) Gravitons interact only very weakly with bodies and are scattered in the forward direction, with little or no change in their pre-interaction trajectories.

Due to the relativistic Doppler effect, which has a different expression in a preferred reference frame, gravitons emitted by bodies in motion in this frame are seen by a stationary detector to be redshifted, while those of stationary sources are blueshifted for detectors in motion. As shown below, this leads to a net absorption of gravitons in moving bodies and an increase in their masses. Two moving bodies will then be driven together in a Le Sage-type mechanism.

In the model, it is the rapid motion of the Solar System in the *PF* which is seen to dominate the terrestrial gravitational force. The magnitude of the gravitational 'constant' G in a specific stellar system is seen to be proportional to the factor $(\frac{1}{2}v^2/c^2)/4\pi$, where v is principally the rotational speed of the parent galaxy. In the following sections the model is outlined. Subsequently some consequences of the model for cosmology, geophysics and quantum physics are discussed.

2. Nature of the Le Sage Medium

A frequent theme in modern-day versions of Le Sage's theory, which dates back as far as Lorentz (1900), is the replacement of his "ultramundane corpuscles" by waves of electromagnetic radiation. Various models have invoked waves of either very high or very low frequency radiation as the Le Sage radiation.

A conceptual basis for the high-frequency models can be found in quantum electrodynamics (QED). In QED every region of space contains an infinite number of radiation field modes, each of which should contribute a finite amount of energy of $\frac{1}{2}\hbar\omega$ even at a temperature of absolute zero. While these zeropoint fields (ZPF) are seen in QED as virtual fields only, they have been seen as useful in some cases to explain certain phenomena such as the Casimir effect (Milonni et al., 1988). In a related approach, known as stochastic electrodynamics (SED), the electromagnetic ZPF are viewed as fields of real, classical electromagnetic radiation. SED has also had some success in accounting for such phenomena as the Lamb shift, the Casimir effect and the van der Waal's forces (see Boyer, 1980, for a review). In addition, attempts have been made to link SED to gravitation (Puthoff, 1989) and inertia (Haisch et al., 1994; Rueda and Haisch, 1998).

An alternative possibility, that the Le Sage medium may be in the form of very long wavelength radiation, was proposed long ago by Brush (1911). A modified version of Brush's theory was proposed more recently by Kierein (1992; see also this volume).

In the present model, we do not specify a frequency range for the Le Sage waves. We only postulate that in regions of space well away from matter this radiation is homogeneous and isotropic and that it is the absorption of this radiation which gives rise to gravity. In contrast to both QED and SED, however, we suppose that this radiation defines a primary or preferred reference frame, presumably equivalent to that of the cosmic microwave background (CBR), in which proper motions of bodies are detectable. The notion that the CBR frame is coincident with a preferred reference frame (PF) is gaining currency (e.g., Scarani et al., 2000). The radiation will be referred to simply as gravitons, recognizing that in their properties they bear scant resemblance to the gravitons of contemporary physics.

3. Relativistic Doppler Effect in Matter-Graviton Interactions

As a starting point, we suppose that all bodies are continuously exchanging gravitons with the background medium. These exchanges form the basis for all physical forces, including gravity. If all the matter of the universe were uniformly at rest in the *PF*, the radiation spectrum in every direction would be uniform in its properties. In this case there would be no possibility of gravitational forces under the present hypothesis. Due to the motions of bodies in the *PF*, however, the matter-radiation interaction is subject to relativistic effects which give rise to gravity.

We first consider the relativistic Doppler effect as it is normally given in Special Relativity (SR) and the corresponding expression in a preferred frame. In SR, it is not possible in principle to distinguish on the basis of light signals whether the source or the receiver is actually in motion. The relationship between the frequencies of the observed signal v_o and the emitted signal v_s in SR, in the case of a radial recession v_r of a source and receiver, is

$$v_o = v_s \frac{1 - v_r/c}{\sqrt{1 - v_r^2/c^2}} = v_s \frac{\sqrt{1 - v_r/c}}{\sqrt{1 + v_r/c}} \qquad (1)$$

On the other hand, in the *PF* (or CBR frame), it is possible to unambiguously determine the motions of objects relative to this frame. For example, a variety of methods have provided estimates of the Solar System's motion through the preferred frame of 300-400 km sec^{-1} (see Wesley, 1998). The speed of light is assumed to be c in this frame. Expressions for the relativistic Doppler effect in a preferred reference frame have previously been given (Lee and Ma, 1962; Rodrigues and Buonomano, 1976; Buonomano and Engel, 1976; Marinov, 1977; Wesley, 1986). The expression for the same case of radial recession is

$$v_o = v_s \frac{1 - v_o/c}{1 + v_s/c} \frac{\sqrt{1 - v_s^2/c^2}}{\sqrt{1 - v_o^2/c^2}}, \qquad (2)$$

where v_s and v_o are now the velocities of the source and the receiver in the *PF* respectively. Except for the square root terms on the right the expression is just what would be expected under classical physics. Examining the square root terms we see that a motion of the source relative to the preferred frame imparts a redshift to the detected signal but that a motion by the receiver relative to this frame imparts a blueshift. Experimental attempts to verify Eqn. 2 are very difficult, however, as it is hard to eliminate the first order effects (Marinov, 1977).

In the present model, we are interested in the relativistic Doppler effect as applied to gravitons, assumed to be randomly oriented waves in the *PF*. As can be seen in Eqn. 2, the Doppler shift seen in gravitons contains first order terms in v/c. A moving receiver might thus be expected to experience a significant drag force due to receiving heavier gravitons from the forward direction (Darwin, 1905). In this case the planets, for example, would gradually spiral into the Sun. Increasing this drag force further would be the increased flux of gravitons from the forward direction, a point made by Feynman with regard to Le Sage-type theories generally (Feynman *et al.*, 1963). Consequently, the absence of such predicted slowing effects in planetary bodies has been considered a major deficiency of Le Sage theories (Feynman *et al.*, 1963).

The above points might be valid if the incident gravitons were simply reflected from the exteriors of bodies or their components in the manner of the reflection of photons from atoms. In the present model, however, it is assumed that the interaction between gravitons and matter is extremely weak. Gravitons in this case retain almost all of their energy during their interactions with bodies, passing right through them without significant deviation from their initial trajectories.[*] For this reason, it is also necessary to take into consideration the *time interval* during which a graviton is able to interact with a body.

Let us consider first the Doppler effect objection. When a body is at rest in the *PF* the time for a graviton to pass through it is $t_0 = L_0/c$. When the same body is moving in the *PF* at velocity v, its rear edge travels a small distance during the time in which the ray is inside the body. For gravitons meeting the body from the forward direction, the interaction time is therefore reduced to $t = L_0/(c + v) = t_0/(1 + v/c)$. Due to the Doppler shift the force of these gravitons on the moving body is increased by a factor $(1 + v/c)$. The change of momentum of the body due to the gravitons received is given by $d(mv) = F \times dt$. We thus find that the increased force is precisely cancelled by the reduced time interval of the interaction, such that the change of momentum for the graviton interaction is the same. A similar argument can be made for gravitons hitting the body from the rear.

With respect to Feynman's objection, the moving body indeed intercepts gravitons at a greater rate than would the same body at rest in the *PF*. But the exit rate of the gravitons from the body is also enhanced by the same factor. The total number of gravitons interacting with a body at any time is thus unchanged from the situation at rest. In considering the dynamical effects of the incident gravitons, we therefore conclude that the first order terms in v/c may be neglected.[†]

In contrast to the first order terms, the second order, relativistic terms in Eqn. 2 are not direction dependent and so cannot be compensated for in this manner. With regard to their dynamical effects on bodies, the modified expression for the *effective* frequency shift seen in the incident gravitons is given by

---

[*] An analogous forward scattering of light has been postulated in the cosmological redshift mechanisms of Marmet (1988) and Kierein (1988, 1990, 1992; see also this volume).

[†] Similar considerations may also explain the absence of observed gravitational aberration. Since Le Sage's time it had been noted that such aberration in the Solar System should be observed unless the speed of the particles were very much greater than c (see Evans, this volume). In the present case, graviton velocities at or near c might be envisaged, without aberration, since each body effectively establishes its own equilibrium state with the medium.

$$v_o = v_s \frac{\sqrt{1 - v_s^2/c^2}}{\sqrt{1 - v_o^2/c^2}} \cong v_s \left(1 + \frac{1}{2}\frac{v_o^2}{c^2} - \frac{1}{2}\frac{v_s^2}{c^2}\right). \tag{3}$$

The only residual effects are the redshifts seen by stationary receivers in gravitons from moving sources and the blueshifts seen by moving receivers in gravitons emitted by stationary sources.[*]

It would be anticipated that similar asymmetries would also apply to the other familiar situations in which SR predicts symmetrical observations for two bodies in relative motion, such as 'time dilation' and length contraction. In the present case we are interested specifically in the relativistic expression for mass in the *PF*, which ought also to possess such asymmetry. But would asymmetry in this case suggest that the masses of moving bodies in the *PF* are greater than those of resting bodies or lesser? In SR, of course, there is a symmetrical mass increase seen by all bodies in relative motion.[†] In Eqn. 3, however, we find that the gravitons incident on bodies moving in the *PF* are blueshifted relative to those striking bodies at rest in the *PF*. It follows that, for an observer at rest in the *PF* viewing the interactions of gravitons and moving bodies, the masses of the latter would appear *diminished* relative to those of bodies at rest in the *PF*. The mass of a moving body for such a stationary observer would appear to have the form

$$m = m_0 \sqrt{1 - v^2/c^2}, \tag{4}$$

where v is the body's velocity in the *PF* and m_0 is the body's mass when it is actually at rest in the *PF*. As discussed in Sect. 9 and also previously (Edwards, 1999), this equation is consistent with the notion that the kinetic energy of a moving body is 'borrowed' from its rest energy.

The above expressions provide the conceptual basis for gravity in the model. Detectors that are stationary in the *PF* find the gravitons emitted by moving bodies to be redshifted. As discussed in the next section, the latter redshift can be interpreted as an energy absorption effect. Specifically, bodies in motion in the *PF* experience a net increase in graviton absorption and an increase in mass. Two moving bodies shield each other from a portion of the background gravitons, leading to a Le Sage-type attraction.

4. Physical Mechanism of Energy Absorption

As already noted, Le Sage models require a large, continuous absorption of energy by gravitating matter. This energy absorption can be conceptualized using

---

[*] The increased external force acting on a body from each direction might be related to the 'Poincaré pressure', a non-electrical force of external origin which Poincaré thought could be responsible for maintenance of the electron's structure when the electron is in motion (see Granek, 2000). It might also be associated with a Lorentz contraction of the particle (see also Shneiderov, 1961).

[†] Historically, the development of the relativistic expression for mass in SR was a convoluted matter, with acceptance of the present form occurring several years after Einstein's 1905 paper (see Granek, 2000). Experimental verification of the SR relativistic expression in any case has never been perfect, partly because experiments in which *only* the effects of mass variance are seen are difficult to design.

the *PF* relativistic Doppler effect as applied to gravitons. The Compton effect provides a convenient analogy here.[*] In the ordinary Compton expression, the expression for the change in wavelength $\Delta\lambda$ of a photon after interacting with a particle of rest mass m_0 is given by

$$\Delta\lambda = \frac{h(1-\cos\theta)}{m_0 c},$$
(5)

where h is Planck's constant and θ is the angle of deflection. Now consider a particle moving at velocity v in the *PF* and thus possessing a reduced mass $m_0(1 - v^2/c^2)^{1/2}$ (Eqn. 4). In this case the change in wavelength for the interaction is given by

$$\Delta\lambda' = \frac{h(1-\cos\theta)}{cm_0\sqrt{1-v^2/c^2}}.$$
(6)

The wavelength of the emitted photon is thus redshifted relative to the case for the particle at rest in the *PF*. This implies an absorption of energy by the particle and may be interpreted as the extra kinetic energy the particle acquires from the photon recoil by virtue of its smaller size.

Applying this result to the graviton case, we would see that the gravitons emitted by a moving body have their energies diminished by the factor $(1 - v^2/c^2)^{1/2}$. Since gravitons from every direction impart excess momentum to the moving body uniformly, these gains will collectively cancel out. In fact, as discussed below, the body is steadily *losing* velocity in the *PF*. An explanation for this puzzling situation can be found in the interpretation of the cosmological redshift given by Kierein (1988, 1990, 1992; see also this volume). Since no kinetic energy is gained by the moving body, the absorbed energy must appear in the form of an increase in its mass.

5. Derivation of the Le Sage Force

As can be seen in the works of Radzievskii and Kagalnikova (1960) and Shneiderov (1961), a proper treatment of the Le Sage gravitational attraction requires rather complex mathematical expressions involving the attenuation of the gravitational flux as it passes through bodies. Here we will employ a simple method for estimating the Le Sage force valid for small bodies, in which internal shielding of gravitons may be neglected. The approach is based in part on Slabinski's treatment (Slabinski, 1998; also this volume). In contrast to Slabinski, however, we have assumed that scattering of gravitons occurs exclusively in the forward direction.

Consider two small bodies A and B separated by a distance R. Let us suppose that the two bodies are moving together at the same velocity v in the *PF*, i.e., they are stationary relative to each other. Let us view the situation entirely

---

[*] The ordinary Compton effect expression is of course derived from the assumptions of Special Relativity. Nonetheless, it may serve as a close approximation in the present case if non-relativistic velocities are assumed (see Carezani, 1993, 1999; see also Sect. 9).

from the *PF*. In this frame the momentum flux of the gravitons in empty space is Φ_0. A small fraction of this flux on passing through A and B interacts with the matter components therein and is either absorbed or scattered in the forward direction. In the model the degree of absorption will depend on the velocities of A and B in the *PF*. Let the scattering cross-section of matter to the graviton flux for bodies at rest in the *PF* be k_s, in units of cm^2gm^{-1}. Now if A and B were at rest in the *PF*, then the quantity of radiation they intercept from the medium would equal the quantity they emit back into space. In this case there would be no absorption of gravitons and thus no screening effect or Le Sage attraction. Since A and B are moving in the *PF* at velocity v, however, the radiation which they emit back to space, as seen in the *PF*, is redshifted by the factor $(1-v^2/c^2)^{1/2}$ (Eqn. 3).

Let us now determine the force pushing A towards B. In the direction 180 degrees away from B, A intercepts radiation momentum at the rate $\Phi_0 k_s m_A$. In the opposite direction, towards B, A receives a certain quantity of radiation that had been scattered by B. This radiation, however, is redshifted by the factor $(1 - v^2/c^2)^{1/2}$. The 'missing' energy is interpreted as energy that B absorbed by virtue of its motion in the *PF*. If R is large relative to the linear dimensions of A and B, we can regard the flux emitted from B as acting parallel to their mutual axis. B subtends an effective solid angle of $k_s m_B/R^2$ at A with regard to the flux. Due to absorption at B, the flux that is missing at A is then

$$\Delta\Phi = \frac{\Phi_0 k_s m_B \left(1 - \sqrt{1 - v^2/c^2}\right)}{4\pi R^2} . \tag{7}$$

The radiation momentum flux that A intercepts from the direction of B is therefore reduced to $k_s m_A(\Phi_0 - \Delta\Phi)$. Subtracting the flux intercepted from the direction of B from the flux intercepted from 180 degrees opposite, the net force pushing A towards B is $k_s m_A\Phi_0 - k_s m_A(\Phi_0 - \Delta\Phi) = k_s m_A\Delta\Phi$. The force is thus

$$\overline{F}_{AB} = \frac{\Phi_0 k_s^2 m_A m_B \left(1 - \sqrt{1 - v^2/c^2}\right)}{4\pi R^2} . \tag{8}$$

For small v we may write this as

$$\overline{F}_{AB} \cong \frac{\Phi_0 k_s^2 m_A m_B \left(v^2/2c^2\right)}{4\pi R^2} . \tag{9}$$

We should note that other factors in these expressions may also be subject to relativistic corrections arising from the bodies' velocities in the *PF*. The dimensions of the bodies in the direction of motion may be reduced by a factor of $(1 - v^2/c^2)^{1/2}$ due to relativistic length contraction. This factor would be offset, however, by a corresponding increase in their density. Note that a second factor of $(1 - v^2/c^2)^{-1/2}$ for relativistic mass increase is not included. The model supposes a diminishment of mass of bodies in motion in the *PF* (Eqn. 4), this being the cause of net absorption.

The proposed modifications place a significant restriction on the Le Sage force. The kinetic energy term implies that motion through the *PF* is required in order to observe a gravitational force, since the force falls to zero when v is zero. As discussed below, the ordinary force of gravity is primarily an effect of galactic rotational velocities of several hundred kilometres per second. On the other hand, when v begins to approach c, the force becomes

$$\overrightarrow{F}_{AB} \cong \frac{\Phi_0 k_s^2 m_A m_B}{4\pi R^2}. \tag{10}$$

At these high speeds the gravitational force would thus be greater by many orders of magnitude than the force observed in the Solar System. Such large gravitational forces could be significant in astrophysical processes such as the jetting of material from galaxy cores at relativistic speeds. The augmented forces arising in these jets could promote condensation of discrete structures such as quasars, or, in analogous solar jets, planets (see Arp, 1998; see also below). Note that at velocities greater than about .7c, however, the masses of bodies begin to decline abruptly due to the relation $m = m_0(1 - v^2/c^2)^{1/2}$ (Eqn. 4). The gravitational force accordingly begins likewise to decline and, at the speed of light, becomes zero.

6. Quantification of k_s and Φ_0

In attempting to quantify the gravitational force, it would appear necessary, on first inspection, that we know the individual values of k_s and Φ_0. In general, however, attempts to pin down either of these values have not been successful. One of the few positive reports of a gravitational shielding effect was made by Majorana (1920).[*] In relating Majorana's work to the present model, it should be noted that the quantities being absorbed in each case are not the same. In the former, it is a flux emanating from material bodies that is attenuated by the screen. In our Le Sage-type model, it is a flux of background gravitons already redshifted in interacting with a first body which is attenuated. The gravitational flux in Majorana's scheme thus corresponds to the redshifted waves in our model. The degree of screening of these redshifted waves in other bodies would be dictated by the scattering coefficient k_s. We may conclude that Majorana's absorption coefficient h corresponds to the scattering coefficient k_s in our model. The absorption coefficient pertaining to the background graviton flux in our model, k_a, is actually given by $k_a = k_s \times (\frac{1}{2}v^2/c^2)$. Using an average value for the Majorana coefficient h from his two sets of experiments of 5×10^{-12} cm^2 gm^{-1} and using a Galactic rotation velocity of 360 km sec^{-1}, we find $k_a = 3.5 \times 10^{-18}$ cm^2 gm^{-1}.

---

[*] Majorana hypothesized that gravity is caused by a gravitational flux which is emitted by material bodies and absorbed by other bodies. He reasoned that the fluxes between two bodies may potentially be diminished by a third body acting as screen. In two sets of experiments he determined values for his absorption coefficient h of 2.8×10^{-12} and 7.65×10^{-12} cm^{2}gm^{-1}. For discussions of Majorana's work see the papers by Martins (2), Radzievskii and Kagalnikova, Unnikrishnan and Gillies, Borzeszkowski and Treder and the author's other paper in this volume.

For Φ_0 only theoretical estimates have been made and these have ranged widely. In this regard, however, it should be noted that in the model k_s and Φ_0 always appear together as $\Phi_0 k_s^2$. While the latter term is often associated in Le Sage-type models with the gravitational constant G, in the present model we find that it is the *relative* absorption of momentum flux at different velocities in the *PF* which actually determines G. The quantity $\Phi_0 k_s^2$ might thus take the form of a reference value, possibly equal to unity. In the next section, we find that the model gives satisfactory results if we make the identification

$$\Phi_0 k_s^2 \equiv 1, \tag{11}$$

with units the same as for G. Such a value would be consistent with the notion that the inertia of a body is due to the gravitational influences of the whole universe (Sciama, 1953; Assis, 1999; Ghosh, 2000), as it would then arise within the very definition of force.

7. Gravitation in the Solar System

In the model, the gravitational constant G as measured in the laboratory is primarily determined by the motion of the Solar System with respect to the *PF*. Its strength is determined primarily by the main rotation of the Galaxy.[*] For two bodies in the Solar System we have from Eqn. 9 the modified formula $F_{AB} = [\Phi_0 k_s^2 m_A m_B (\tfrac{1}{2} v_S^2 / c^2)]/4\pi R^2$, where v_S is now the motion of the Solar System in the *PF*. For these bodies, or for the Sun itself, we may therefore represent the Newtonian constant approximately as

$$G_S = \frac{\Phi_0 k_s^2}{4\pi} \left(\frac{1}{2} \frac{v_S^2}{c^2} \right). \tag{12}$$

The absolute motion of the Solar System with respect to the background frame has been estimated in many different ways (Lineweaver *et al.*, 1996; Wesley, 1998). These estimates fall in the range of 300-400 km sec^{-1}, with several values centred around 360 km sec^{-1}. When this velocity and the terrestrially measured value of G are inserted for G_S in Eqn. 12, we find that $\Phi_0 k_s^2 \cong 1$, as suggested above.

In the case of the Earth, additional contributions to the Earth's constant, G_E, would be expected from the Earth's orbit around the Sun, the Earth's rotation about its axis and other minor sources. The measured value of G_E in this case would have the form

$$G_E = \frac{\Phi_0 k_s^2}{4\pi} \left(\frac{1}{2} \frac{v_S^2}{c^2} + \frac{1}{2} \frac{v_E^2}{c^2} + \frac{1}{2} \frac{v_r^2}{c^2} \right), \tag{13}$$

where v_r is the Earth's rotational velocity. Other local velocities could be added to this equation as necessary (for instance, a satellite velocity). From Eqns. 12

---

[*] Translational motion of galaxies in the *PF* may or may not be significant in the determination of G. While the traditional view is that galaxies have translational motions of several hundred km/sec, this has recently been challenged by Arp (1998). Arp has provided evidence that mature galaxies are approximately at rest in the *PF*.

and 13 it is seen that the measured strength of G in the Earth's frame and the Sun's frame are different. For the Sun itself the gravitons it receives that were emitted by the Earth have additional redshifts owing to the Earth's orbital and rotational motions. These velocity terms must be multiplied together to acquire the appropriate redshift factor for the Earth's radiation. Neglecting the small rotational motion of the Earth, the term in brackets in Eqn. 8 would be replaced by $[1 - (1 - v_S^2/c^2)^{1/2}(1 - v_E^2/c^2)^{1/2}]$. The gravitational force pushing the Sun towards the Earth is therefore augmented relative to the situation in which the Earth did not possess these extra velocities. The force pushing the Sun towards the Earth would be given approximately as

$$\overrightarrow{F}_{SE} = \frac{\Phi_0 k_s^2 M_S M_E}{4\pi R^2}\left(\frac{1}{2}\frac{v_S^2}{c^2} + \frac{1}{2}\frac{v_E^2}{c^2}\right). \tag{14}$$

Expressed in terms of G_S (Eqn. 12) this force is

$$\overrightarrow{F}_{SE} = \frac{G_S M_S M_E}{R^2}\left(1 + \frac{1}{2}\frac{v_E^2}{c^2}\right). \tag{15}$$

The Earth conversely sees the radiation emitted by the Sun to be blueshifted by a factor $(1 - v_E^2/c^2)^{-1/2}$ due to the Earth's orbit about the Sun. The force on the Earth is therefore reduced relative to the case in which the Sun also possessed this velocity. Expressed in terms of G_E, the force pushing the Earth towards the Sun is

$$\overrightarrow{F}_{ES} = \frac{G_E M_S M_E}{R^2}\left(1 - \frac{1}{2}\frac{v_E^2}{c^2}\right). \tag{16}$$

Evidence in favour of the force given in Eqn. 16 exists, though it is little reported (Van Flandern, 1999, Chap. 4). For many years a known discrepancy has existed between the Earth's period around the Sun as measured optically and as determined through radar measurements. The anomaly in the optical data is such that it would make the Earth's period 5×10^{-9} greater than is obtained using the radar data. The optical data would be consistent with the possibility that the pull of the Sun on the Earth is less than expected. Since $v_E \cong 30$ km sec^{-1}, we see from Eqn. 16 that the model accurately predicts just such an effect.

The model shares common features with some velocity-dependent models of gravity (for reviews, see Jaakkola, 1996; Ghosh, 2000). Unlike most such theories, however, the force in the present case depends on the motions of bodies in a universal frame. For bodies in relative motion, the force may be reduced or enhanced depending on the site of measurement, as seen in the above examples. In its positive dependence on velocity it is perhaps most similar to the model of Waldron (1984).

8. Galaxy Evolution and Earth Expansion

In the model, the graviton energy that is absorbed by moving bodies results in
an increase in their mass. Conservation of energy and momentum therefore
demand that the velocities of the bodies in the *PF* decrease.[*] These decelerations are distinct from any gravitational accelerations induced in the bodies. As
already mentioned, the momentum gains imparted to moving bodies in graviton absorption are uniformly distributed in all directions and thus collectively
cancel. To a close approximation, the external force acting on a moving body is
thus zero. For the momentum equation, we may then write

$$F = \frac{d(mv)}{dt} = v\frac{dm}{dt} + m\frac{dv}{dt} = 0 , \tag{17}$$

from which we obtain

$$\frac{dm/dt}{m} = -\frac{dv/dt}{v} . \tag{18}$$

Assuming likewise that the kinetic energy remains constant while the mass is
increasing, we find the similar expression

$$\frac{dm/dt}{m} = -\frac{d(v^2)/dt}{v^2} . \tag{19}$$

In the case of galaxies we would thus expect a gradual slowing of galactic motions in the *PF*. Due to the relationship between velocity and gravity in the
model, a reduction in a galaxy's rotational speed would also imply a secular
decrease of *G* for that galaxy. Previously, theoretical considerations and astronomical observations led Dirac (1937) and others to postulate a universal decline in *G* of the nature $(dG/dt)/G \approx -H$ (see Wesson, 1973, 1976 for reviews).
Other observations subsequently reinforced this supposition (see below). Assuming that the *local* diminishment of *G* in a particular galaxy conforms to
Dirac's equation, and comparing Eqns. 12 and 19, the fractional rates of
change of several parameters in a particular galaxy would then be given by

$$\frac{dm/dt}{m} = -\frac{dv/dt}{v} = -\frac{d(v^2)/dt}{v^2} = -\frac{dG/dt}{G} \approx H . \tag{20}$$

Here *m* refers to the mass of a body in the galaxy, such as a star, and *v* its velocity in the *PF*.

The decreasing strength of *G* within a galaxy, in turn, would shape its
subsequent evolution. Without further energy inputs, a spiral galaxy would
gradually evolve to an elliptical galaxy, with a characteristic rotational speed
two orders of magnitude smaller. At these rotational speeds the value for *G*
would drop further and star formation rates would decline. In this respect the

---

[*] The idea of a 'velocity redshift' analogous to the cosmic redshift of light was proposed long ago
by Nernst (1937). Assuming this relation Nernst argued that since the kinetic energy of a body can also
be regarded as a form of electromagnetic energy it too should be subject to a progressive depletion over
time. A translation of Nernst's 1937 paper appears in the special issue of *Apeiron* devoted to his cosmological work (Vol. 2, no. 3, July, 1995).

model correctly predicts the observed low star formation rates in elliptical galaxies. In the final stages of a galaxy the rotational velocity would fall off yet again. At a certain point the value for G would drop so low that the galaxy could no longer retain its stars, which would 'evaporate' into space. Even the dense, rapidly spinning end products of star formation, such as neutron stars and white dwarfs, would ultimately spin down and disperse their atoms to interstellar space. In intergalactic space, this matter would either fall towards existing galaxies, fuelling their growth, or perhaps give rise to new galaxies. A galactic cycle can then be envisaged consisting of the condensation of intergalactic matter into a protogalactic cloud, the transformation of the proto-galaxy to a rapidly spinning spiral galaxy, and the spindown and discharge of the stars and their contents back into intergalactic space (see Jaakkola, 1991, 1993; Edwards, 1998). Note that in this scenario the local effects predicted in Dirac's model are reproduced but without the assumption that the decrease in G is universal. Rather, it is supposed that the local declines in mature galaxies are offset by increases in G in nascent galaxies.

Within the Solar System, the secular decrease in G would result in a general increase in the planetary orbital radii, as well as an expansion of the planets themselves. There is much evidence to suggest that the Earth has expanded from an initial radius of about 55-60 per cent of its present value (Carey, 1988; Wesson, 1973, 1976; Pickford, 1996).[*] Earth expansion was a prediction of Dirac's hypothesis and was actively investigated in this context by Jordan (1971). The decline in G in Dirac's hypothesis has been seen as insufficient to generate the amount of expansion observed. In the present model, however, we note that the Earth has also undergone a significant increase in mass, which may have augmented the expansion rate. More generally, a variety of observations point to a gradual slowing of all bodies in the Solar System that is consistent with Eqn. 20 (*e.g.*, the secular decrease in the Earth's rotation speed, the increasing Earth-Moon separation).[†]

9.   Alternative Models of Relativity

In this section, we briefly discuss the relationship of the model to some other conservative models of relativity which have recently been proposed. In particular, the mechanism of energy absorption outlined here is possibly consistent with the idea that the total energy of a particle, the sum of its rest energy and

---

[*] See papers by Kokus and Veselov in this volume. One of the simplest and most convincing arguments in favour of Earth expansion is that the continents can be fitted together perfectly like pieces of a jigsaw puzzle on a globe of smaller dimensions, but not on a globe of present size. This suggests that the continents once formed a continuous cover upon the ancient Earth and that the ocean basins later appeared between the continents. Recent evidence also suggests that mass extinctions were caused not by unique cataclysmic events, such as asteroid impacts, but by a relentless geophysical process involving intense volcanism (Olsen, 1999). Earth expansion would be an obvious candidate for such a process.

[†] A retarding force related to v^2/c^2 also appears in the velocity-dependent inertial induction model of Ghosh (1993, 2000). The reader is referred to Ghosh's work for a discussion of many astrophysical applications of such a force not included here.

kinetic energy, has a *constant* value m_0c^2. In gravitation, for example, it has been proposed that the falling body as it falls gives up a portion of its rest energy to kinetic energy (Nieland, 1992; Carroll, 1993; Dart, 1996; Marmet, 1997; Ginzburg, 1997; Edwards, 1999). The classical concept of potential energy in these interpretations is thus altered or replaced. Similarly, in atomic decay processes, the decaying particle can likewise be viewed as giving up part of its rest mass energy to the kinetic energy of the decay products, with energy and momentum thus being conserved overall (Walz *et al.*, 1984; Carezani, 1992, 1993, 1999).

In both the gravitational and decay cases the expression for the total energy of a test body is therefore not the usual relativistic one, $m_0c^2(1 - v^2/c^2)^{-\frac{1}{2}}$, but is rather a constant value, m_0c^2. In each case some of the rest mass of the body has been converted to kinetic energy. The mass of the body in these situations is therefore reduced to $m_0(1 - v^2/c^2)^{\frac{1}{2}}$, as in Eqn. 4, and the rest energy is correspondingly reduced to $m_0c^2(1 - v^2/c^2)^{\frac{1}{2}}$. The kinetic energy is then given by $E_k = m_0c^2[1 - (1 - v^2/c^2)^{\frac{1}{2}}]$.[*] At very low v, $E_k \cong \frac{1}{2}m_0v^2$, as in SR. The above relations, together with Eqn. 4, form a subset of the 'Autodynamics' equations developed by Carezani.[†] The appropriate experiments which might distinguish between Autodynamics and SR have yet to be done, in part because of their difficulty (see Carezani, 1999).

The rest energy of a particle in this picture could then be viewed simply as that component of the internal electromagnetic energy which is directionally isotropic within the particle. Kinetic energy, on the other hand, would be the component of the internal energy that has an orientation associated with the particle's velocity. Within the particle there is conservation of total energy, since the appearance of kinetic energy is always paired with the loss of an equal quantity of rest energy.[‡]

10. Graviton Emissions and Quantum Physics

If the graviton energy removed from the background through absorption by moving bodies were not replenished somehow, then the energy density of the background would diminish over time, along with gravitational forces. This possibility would be consistent with Dirac's hypothesis discussed above. In the present case, however, a static cosmological model is postulated, in which the

---

[*] This expression for kinetic energy has a quite different appearance than the usual relativistic expression, $E_k = m_0c^2[(1-v^2/c^2)^{-\frac{1}{2}} - 1]$. It can be easily shown, however, that the two expressions are closely related. If we replace m_0c^2 in this expression by $(m_0c^2 + E_k)$ and then solve for E_k the relativistic expression is recovered (Carezani, 1999, p. 49). This point serves to demonstrate that it is only at relativistic velocities that the predictions of the two theories substantially differ.

[†] Carezani and colleagues have advanced a number of Le Sage-type proposals of their own (Carezani, 1999), which they have also included within their 'Autodynamics' program.

[‡] Such revisions would remove a conceptual difficulty in SR whereby a particle moving at light speed supposedly acquires an infinite amount of energy. The high energies recorded in such particles would be due to the conversion of all of their rest energy to kinetic energy. In this context, it should be noted that in the experiments considered as proofs of SR, the tacit assumption is always made that the rest energies of intact particles remain constant.

processes of energy consumption are everywhere in equilibrium with those of regeneration. The simplest manner in which we may visualize the regeneration of graviton energies is that moving bodies simultaneously emit energy at the same rate as they absorb it, this energy corresponding in some sense to their kinetic energy. This possibility would be in keeping with the suggestions in the previous section.

Would the repulsive effects of these emissions cancel out the gravitational effects? As they originate in moving bodies, it would be tempting to identify the kinetic energy emissions with matter waves (de Broglie waves). In this case, the quantum structure of the atom, for example, would be linked to the kinetic energy emissions of its orbiting electrons. These emissions may give rise to a classical interference pattern shaping the orbital trajectories. The electrons might then move along these trajectories without experiencing repulsive effects from their own emissions or from the emissions of other parts of the atom. The kinetic energy emissions within larger masses and systems of masses may also be similarly organized, such that gravitation still holds sway. On larger scales, the Solar System, the Galaxy and systems of galaxies all appear to have properties of quantum systems.[*] In each of these situations the moving components of the system would have trajectories shaped by the de Broglie wave emissions of the components.

Such emissions could allow for simple interpretations of some of the puzzling phenomena of quantum physics. In certain well-known experiments, for example, an interference pattern is created by particles (*e.g.*, electrons) passing through the slits of a double-slit apparatus even when passing through one at a time. Let us suppose that the de Broglie wave of a particle corresponds to a true energy emission. As the particle approaches the apparatus, it radiates gravitons through both slits simultaneously. The radiation as it passes through the slits is diffracted to give a classical interference pattern on the far side of the apparatus. The particle in passing through a slit immediately encounters this pattern and is directed along one of the lines of interference. The collective paths formed by many electrons may then recreate the classical pattern.

On the cosmic scale, the graviton emissions from moving bodies would replenish the gravitons absorbed in gravitation. While such emissions would have specific orientations and phases within a source galaxy, the collective emissions of many galaxies would assume random orientations and phases.

11. The Cosmological Redshift

In a static model, the fractional rate of energy loss by photons in the cosmological redshift is given by

---

[*] In attempting to account for certain apparent quantized phenomena in nature, such as the observed 35 km sec^{-1} quantization of galactic redshifts, Arp (1998) proposed that bodies acquire mass through the exchange of 'machions', wavelike particles analogous to gravitons. The wavelengths of these machions scale with the size of the body in question. In the case of galaxies, the machions would have extremely long wavelengths of about 10^{24} cm or 1 Mpc. For planetary systems Arp and others have proposed that analogous processes may account for the numerous apparent quantum effects found in the Solar System.

$$(dE/dt)/E = -H, \qquad\qquad (21)$$

where E is the photon energy and H is the Hubble constant (Zwicky, 1929). Though cosmological tests support static models over the Big Bang model (Jaakkola, 1991, 1993, 1996; Assis, 1993), a satisfactory mechanism for the 'tired light' effect has yet to be found.

Here we briefly note that the mechanisms for depletion of light in the cosmological redshift and other redshift effects that have been observed (*e.g.*, the solar limb effect, quasar redshifts) could all be entirely analogous to the energy absorption mechanism in gravity postulated herein. These mechanisms would all involve the forward scattering of radiation in the absorption process, as suggested by Marmet (1988) and Kierein (1988, 1990, 1992; see also this volume). Such a possibility would be consistent with the considerable evidence suggesting that redshift effects are enhanced in denser media (Marmet, 1988; Assis, 1992; Jaakkola, 1996) and hotter media (Finlay-Freundlich, 1954; Assis, 1993) and with suggestions of coupling between the redshifts of light and gravity (Jaakkola, 1991, 1993; Van Flandern, 1999).

12. Conclusion

In this paper a new version of Le Sage's theory of gravity has been proposed. The fundamental assumption that we have made is that a gravitational medium of electromagnetic radiation exists which defines a primary reference frame. While confirming evidence for a medium of sufficient energy density is still lacking, its existence poses no special theoretical difficulties. Indeed, the need for a gravitational ether had been expressed even by Einstein.

In this light, a systematic search for an energy-dense electromagnetic background coincident with the CBR frame would appear to be a worthwhile undertaking. For evidence that confirms its existence could lead us, through the steps above, to a new yet old mechanism of gravity, the one originally proposed by Georges-Louis Le Sage.

References

Adamut, I.A., 1976. "Analyse de l'action gravitationelle du rayonnement électromagnétique sur un système de corps. Une théorie électrothermodynamique de la gravitation," *Nuovo Cimento B* **32**, 477-511.

Adamut, I.A., 1982. "The screen effect of the earth in the TETG. Theory of a screening experiment of a sample body at the equator using the earth as a screen," *Nuovo Cimento C* **5**, 189-208.

Aronson, S., 1964. "The gravitational theory of Georges-Louis Le Sage," *The Natural Philosopher*, **3**, 51.

Arp, H.C., 1998. Seeing Red:Redshifts,Cosmology and Academic Science, Apeiron, Montreal.

Assis, A.K.T., 1992. "On the absorption of gravity," *Apeiron* 13:3-11.

Assis, A.K.T., 1993. "A steady-state cosmology," in *Progress in New Cosmologies: Beyond the Big Bang*, Plenum Press, New York, pp. 153-167.

Assis, A.K.T., 1999. *Relational Mechanics*, Apeiron, Montreal.

Boyer, T.H., 1980. "A brief survey of stochastic electrodynamics," in *Foundations of Radiation Theory and Quantum Electrodynamics*, (A.O. Barut, ed.), Plenum, New York, pp. 49-63.

Brush, C.F., 1911. "A kinetic theory of gravitation," *Nature* **86**, 130-132. The same article also appeared in *Science*, **33**, 381-386.

Buonomano, V. and Engel, E., 1976. "Some speculations on a causal unification of relativity, gravitation, and quantum mechanics," *Int. J. Theor. Phys.* **15**, 231-246.

Carezani, R.L., 1992. "The muon decay $\mu^+ \rightarrow e^+ e^+ e^-$ and autodynamics," *Phys. Essays* **5**, 19-26.

Carezani, R.L., 1993. "The Compton effect and autodynamics," *Phys. Essays* **6**, 384-388.

Carezani, R.L., 1999. *Autodynamics: Fundamental Basis for a New Relativistic Mechanics*, Society for the Advancement of Autodynamics, Long Beach, California.

Carey, S.W., 1988. *Theories of the Earth and Universe*, Stanford University Press, Stanford, California.

Carroll, R.L., 1993. "The black hole," *Apeiron* no. 17, 18-20.

Dart, H.P., 1996. "Repulsive gravity," *Toth-Maatian Review* **13**, 6049-6069.

Darwin, G.H., 1905. "The analogy between Lesage's theory of gravitation and the repulsion of light," *Proc. Roy. Soc.* **76**, 387-410.

Dirac, P.A.M., 1937. *Nature* **139**, 323.

Edwards, M.R., 1998. "Evidence of a cosmological matter and energy cycle," *Apeiron* **5**, 157-163.

Edwards, M.R., 1999. "Quasar redshifts- is aging of matter necessary?," *Apeiron* **6**, 124-127.

Feynman, R.P., *et al.*, 1963. *The Feynman Lectures on Physics, Vol. 1*, Addison-Wesley Publishing Co., Menlo Park, Ca., Sections 7-7 and 34-6.

Finlay-Freundlich, E., 1954. "Red shifts in the spectrum of celestial bodies," *Phil. Mag.* **45**, 303-319.

Ghosh, A., 1993. "Astrophysical and cosmological consequences of velocity-dependent inertial induction," in *Progress in New Cosmologies: Beyond the Big Bang*, Plenum Press, New York, pp.305-326.

Ghosh, A., 2000. *Origin of Inertia*, Apeiron, Montreal.

Ginzburg, V.B., 1997. *Spiral Grain of the Universe*, University Editions, Huntingdon, West Virginia.

Granek, G., 2000. "Poincaré's contributions to relativistic dynamics," *Stud. Hist. Phil. Mod. Phys.* **31**, 15-48.

Haisch, B., Rueda, A. and Puthoff, H.E., 1994. "Inertia as a zero-point-field Lorentz force," *Phys. Rev. A* **49**, 678-694.

Jaakkola, T., 1991. "Electro-gravitational coupling: empirical and theoretical arguments," *Apeiron*, **No. 9-10** (winter-spring 1991).

Jaakkola, T., 1993. "Equilibrium cosmology," in *Progress in New Cosmologies: Beyond the Big Bang*, Plenum Press, New York, pp. 111-151.

Jaakkola, T., 1996. "Action-at-a-distance and local action in gravitation: discussion and possible solution of the dilemma," *Apeiron* **3**, 61-75

Jordan, P., 1971. *The Expanding Earth*, Pergamon Press, Oxford.

Kierein, J., 1988. "A Criticism of Big Bang Cosmological Models Based on Interpretation of the Red Shift" *IEEE Special Issue of Lasers and Particle Beams*.

Kierein, J., 1990. "Implications of the Compton Effect Interpretation of the Red Shift," *IEEE Trans. Plasma Science* **18**, 61.

Kierein, J., 1992. "A mechanism for particle acceleration in space plasmas and for planetary mass accretion," *Apeiron*, No. 14, 3-4.

Le Sage, G.-L., 1784 (for the year 1782), "Lucrèce Newtonien," Memoires de l'Academie Royale des Sciences et Belles Lettres de Berlin, 1-28.

Lee, E.T.P and Ma, S.T., 1962. *Proc. Phys. Soc.* **79**, 446.

Lineweaver, C. *et al.*, 1996. *Astrophys. J.* **470**, 38.

Lorentz, H.A., 1900. *Proc. Acad. Amsterdam,* **ii,** 559.

Majorana, Q., (1920). "On gravitation. Theoretical and experimental researches," *Phil. Mag.* [ser. 6] **39**, 488-504.

Marinov, S., 1977. "Concerning Santos' experiment to test special relativity," *Found. Phys.* **7**, 947-951.

Marmet, P., 1988. "A New Non-Doppler Redshift," *Physics Essays* **1**, 24-32.

Marmet, P., 1997. *Einstein's Theory of Relativity versus Classical Mechanics*, Chapter 1, Newton Physics Books, 2401 Ogilvie Rd., Gloucester, Ont., Canada.

Maxwell, J.C., 1875. "Atom," *Encyclopedia Britannica, Ninth Ed.,* pp. 38-47.

Milonni, P.W., Cook, R.J. and Goggin, M.E., 1988. "Radiation pressure from the vacuum: physical interpretation of the Casimir force," *Phys. Rev. A* **38**, 1621-1623.

Nernst, W., 1937. "Weitere Prüfung der Annahme eines stationären Zustandes im Weltall," *Zeit. Phys.* **106**, 633-661. An English translation of this article with comments appears in *Apeiron* **2**, no. 3, 58-71 (1995).

Nieland, J.F., 1992. "Vacuum refraction theory of gravity," *Apeiron* **no. 13**, 13-17.

Olsen, P.E., 1999. "Giant lava flows, mass extinctions, and mantle plumes," *Science* **284**, 604-605.

Pickford, M., 1996. "Earth expansion and plate tectonics: historical review, comparison and discussion," *South African J. Sci.* **92**, 365-370

Puthoff, H.E., 1989. "Gravity as a zero-point-fluctuation force," *Phys. Rev. A* **39**, 2333-2342.

Radzievskii, V.V. and Kagalnikova, I.I., 1960. "The nature of gravitation," *Vsesoyuz. Astronom.-Geodezich. Obsch. Byull.,* **26** (33), 3-14. A rough English translation appeared in a U.S. government technical report: FTD TT64 323; TT 64 11801 (1964), Foreign Tech. Div., Air Force Systems Command, Wright-Patterson AFB, Ohio [reprinted in this volume]

Rodrigues, Jr., W.A. and Buonomano, V., 1976. "A comment on a proposed "crucial experiment" to test Einstein's special theory of relativity," *Nuovo Cimento B* **34**, 240-244.

Rueda, A. and Haisch, B., 1998. "Inertia as reaction of the vacuum to accelerated motion," *Phys. Lett. A* **240**, 115-126.

Scarani, V. *et al.*, 2000. "The speed of quantum information and the preferred frame: analysis of the experimental data," *Phys. Lett. A* **276**, 1-7.

Sciama, D.W., 1953. "On the origins of inertia," *Monthly Not. Roy. Astron. Soc.* **113**, 34.

Shneiderov, A.J., 1961. "On the internal temperature of the earth," *Bollettino di Geofisica Teorica ed Applicata* **3 n. 10**, 137-159.

Slabinski, V.J., 1998. "Notes on gravitation in the Meta Model," *Meta Res. Bull.* **7**, 33-42.

Van Flandern, T., 1999. *Dark Matter, Missing Planets and New Comets, 2nd ed.*, North Atlantic Books, Berkeley, Chapters 2-4.

Veselov, K.E., 1981. "Chance coincidences or natural phenomena," *Geophys. J.* **3**, 410-425.

Waldron, R.A., 1984. "Gravitational forces," *Spec. Sci. Technol.* **7**, 177-189.

Walz, D.R., Noyes, H.P. and Carezani, R.L., 1984. "Calorimetric test of special relativity," *Phys. Rev. A* **29**, 2110-2113.

Wesley, J.P., 1986. "Michelson-Morley result, a Voigt-Doppler effect in absolute space-time," *Found. Phys.* **16**, 817-824.

Wesley, J.P., 1998. "Evidence for Newtonian absolute space and time," in *Open Questions in Relativistic Physics* (F. Selleri, ed.), Apeiron, Montreal, pp. 255-261.

Wesson, P.S., 1973. "The implications for geophysics of modern cosmologies in which *G* is variable," *Quart. J. Roy. Astron. Soc.* **14**, 9-64.

Wesson, P.S., 1978. *Cosmology and Geophysics*, Oxford University Press, New York.

Zwicky, F., 1929. "On the red shift of spectral lines through interstellar space," *Proc. Natl. Acad. Sci. U.S.A.* **15**, 773-779.

Action-at-a-Distance and Local Action in Gravitation[*]

Toivo Jaakkola[†]

A new theoretical framework for gravitation is presented using the theory of equilibrium cosmology (EC) recently developed by the author. In EC, gravitation is an equilibrium process providing energy balance in systems of baryonic matter, while electromagnetic radiation is the contrary effect. Gravitation on a body is a pressure effect of gravitational quanta (gravitons) conducted from the background field by the gravitation field of the body. The formation of the field is outlined. Gravitons and photons interact *via* electro-gravitational coupling (EGC), which causes the redshift effect and an analogous weakening of gravity, as well as the cosmic background radiation which is a re-emission equilibrium effect. From pressure-induced gravitation and EGC, a dynamical theory (EGD) can be constructed which unifies the gravitation effects in systems on different scales; until now, numerous *ad hoc* hypotheses had been necessary to explain the effects.

When EGD is applied to the two-body problem, Newton's law is obtained directly. In it the force is a sum of two equal terms which are due to the two fields of graviton flow into the bodies, which are mutually screened by the second body. While gravitation is basically not an attractive but rather a repulsive pressure force, the two-body attraction results from the screening effect. The dilemma of a distant action versus a local action character of gravitation receives a simple but unexpected solution: both are true. While the momentum due to the pressure of gravitons flowing towards the second body has a distinctly local character, the momentum obtained due to the screening of the body's own field by the second body is an action at the distance of that body. Both are expressions of a single interaction between the mass systems and the background field.

1. Introduction

The mechanism of gravitation is one of the unsolved fundamental questions of physics. Newton, who gave a mathematical law according to which gravitation works in his *Principia*, was fully aware of the need for a physical explanation of the effect. He was not in favour of the mode of action-at-a-distance and searched for a material transmitter of gravitation. In this he was followed by many of the great physicists in the next two centuries. The currently prevailing theory, Einstein's general relativity (GR), belongs to the same tradition of the local action approach, but here the metrical properties of space, instead of some material medium, are the agent. Criticisms of GR have been made throughout

---

[*] This is an adapted version of "Action-at-a-distance and local action in gravitation: discussion and possible solution of the dilemma", which was published posthumously in the memorial issue of *Apeiron* dedicated to Toivo Jaakkola, Vol. 3, no. 3-4, pp. 61-75, 1996. Section 2, which dealt with aspects of AAAD, and Section 3, which discussed Einstein's work, have been omitted, as well as parts of the abstract, Introduction and Discussion. Breaks from the original text are indicated by [...].

[†] Tuorla Observatory, University of Turku, FIN-21500 Piikkiö, Finland

Pushing Gravity: new perspectives on Le Sage's theory of gravitation
edited by Matthew R. Edwards (Montreal: Apeiron 2002)

155

this century, and in the last few years international symposia have been
devoted to the topic. In quantum mechanics, a non-local mode is nowadays
favoured due to apparent faster-than-light velocities implied in the experiments
testing the Bell inequality (see *e.g.* Bertlmann, 1990). For gravitation, the
action-at-a-distance mode still finds supporters (*e.g,*. Hoyle and Narlikar, 1974;
Phipps, 1990).

Therefore, the problem of the nature of physical interactions remains quite
open, obscure and even poorly identified. A solution is a prerequisite for a consistent conceptual basis of physics and the removal of the disturbing dichotomy
in theories of the world at the macroscopic and quantum levels. Moreover, a
solution to the riddle would open the way for advances in concrete problems of
gravitation, which appears to be, in both observations and theory, a more multi-
faceted phenomenon than usually conceived.

I shall discuss three alternative concepts of gravitation in a historical perspective and in the light of recent empirical and theoretical results. These are:
action-at-a-distance (AAAD; Section 2), relativistic local action (RLA, Section
3) and material field local action (MFLA, Sections 4 and 5). […] In MFLA, action is transmitted by a material medium. The composition of the medium and
propagation of the action vary from one theory to another. A stationary, all-
pervading and space-filling æther is the classical form presented for the medium, which is thought also to be required for the propagation of light waves as
well as the conception represented in Sections 4 and 5, *i.e.*, that the medium is
composed of gravitational and electromagnetic quanta (gravitons and photons).
The "field"-term is adopted, with the meaning of structuring of the medium
due to position-dependent variation of density, velocity and energy of the
transmitters.

[…]

4.   Material Field Local Action

The third mode of action of gravitation, MFLA, is based on a material bombardment from space. The theory to be outlined below has its origin in cosmological considerations. It would seem that the idea has a long history: such
names as Huygens, Newton, Le Sage, Maxwell, Compton, Seeliger, Lorentz
and Nernst, among many others, belong to this tradition. Among its present
proponents, I mention Broberg (1982, 1991) and Shlenov (1991a,b). Weber-
type velocity-dependent theories may also be seen in this context (see 2.*iii*). A
more detailed historical account cannot be included here.

i. A Cosmological Frame to Approach the Problem of Gravitation

There are four broad groups of tests of the cosmological expansion hypothesis,
each containing tens of separate tests. The results of the tests indicate convincingly that the Universe does not expand. First, analysis of the redshift effect in
systems of different scales (Jaakkola 1978) proves that it is not a Doppler but

an interaction effect. Second, the cosmological test results are mutually incon-sistent in the expanding theoretical frame, but they are consistent in the static model (Jaakkola *et al.* 1979). Third, the powerful Hubble-Tolman test indicates non-expansion in all four samples analyzed, the critical remarks presented in Jaakkola (1986) apply also to the later contrary conclusion by Sandage and Perelmuter (1989). Fourth, cosmic evolution, necessary for an expanding model, does not exist. The two most strongly argued effects, number evolution of QSOs and colour evolution of galaxies, are artifacts of selection and of the K-effect (Jaakkola 1982; Laurikainen and Jaakkola 1984a,b).

The Universe is not only non-expanding, but it is even in a state of equi-librium. This is indicated by the fourth argument, by proper inferences from the isotropy of the Universe, in a very straightforward manner by the blackbody spectrum of the cosmic background radiation (CBR)—precisely an equilibrium spectrum—and by equality of the CBR energy density with various local en-ergy densities.

The theory of the Universe in equilibrium, equilibrium cosmology (EC), is based theoretically on the (already empirically suggested) strong cosmologi-cal principle (CP), which also contains the temporal aspect, and second (actu-ally as a consequence of CP) on electro-gravitational coupling (EGC; see be-low). EC can be divided into three sections. In radiation cosmology, the exis-tence and properties of the redshift and the CBR are derived and Olbers para-dox is solved, all directly from fundamental principles. In gravitation cosmol-ogy, an explicit expression for the Machian interaction of distant masses, a so-lution of the gravity paradox, isotropy and stability on the large scale, and smaller-scale structure (galaxies, groups, clusters and supergalaxies) are de-rived. The third part of EC concerns the equilibrium processes postulated by CP. This branch of EC is at its beginnings; it may become the central part of science in the coming century.

Within the EC framework, gravitation is an equilibrium process, an ab-sorption effect which provides energy in systems of baryonic matter unchanged on the cosmological scale, while electromagnetic radiation is the contrary ef-fect. Redshift and CBR are equilibrium effects between gravitation and radia-tion. In such contexts, one can speak of a unique effect of electrogravity.

A mode of gravitational action must be sought, which is suitable for con-sideration of various equilibrium processes where gravitation is a counterpart. The following mode was obtained during the search for a gravitational mecha-nism of the redshift effect; gravitation as a general reason for the redshift is implied by several empirical arguments. The same mode may be valid for gravitation in general, as it should be if valid for the redshift effect.

ii. A Modern Æther Concept

Gravitation works *via* gravitational quanta, gravitons (g). This is the only pos-sibility after finding that for classical AAAD its attributes as given by Leibniz are still valid, and a continuous structure of the gravitating agent, *i.e.* GR and relativistic local action, was found empirically and conceptually invalid. Quantized gravitation is also required by the redshift and other equilibrium effects (Jaakkola, 1993a). Gravitons are gravitational equivalent to electromagnetic quanta, photons (γ), both those of the cosmic background radiation CBR (γ_b) and incident photons from galaxies (γ_g). Gravitons, γ and baryonic matter (b) interact and are in equilibrium on the cosmological scale. The γ–g interaction is the redshift effect, and the CBR is re-emission of energy gained by the cosmological gs (g_b) in the redshift effect. Gravitation, as usually understood, is a g-b interaction; this is the equilibrium process which maintains energy balance in systems of baryonic matter, while radiation γ_g is the contrary effect.

A few words about the gravitational æther, and the æther concept in general may be in place here. The æther hypothesis was thought to be buried by the Michelson-Morley experiment, but today it is more alive than ever, in the form of the CBR: experiments capable of finding the æther were not possible in the 1880s, but were possible in the 1960s. In a sense, the electromagnetic æther has always been observed—as the heat of the Sun (since as pointed out, CBR is reprocessed γ_g).

The gravitational æther must be structured much like its electromagnetic counterpart. Local fields would cause the ordinary gravitational processes. Corresponding to CBR, there must be a cosmic background gravitation, CBG, probably with its specific gravitational spectrum. How to observe CBG? It has been already observed, as the cosmological redshift effect, z_c. This z_c should be conceived as a gravitation effect in the same sense as is terrestrial surface gravity. The observation of the CBG is real, provided that the universal redshift effect (including z_c) is ultimately certified to be due to gravitation; the amount of evidence is already remarkable; see references in 3.v. The dark night sky, $i.e.$, the de Cheseaux-Olbers paradox, is the second observation, with the same reserve as above. The equality of surface gravity within a broad range of scales from galaxies to supergalaxies (Jaakkola 1983, 1987, 1993) may be regarded as the third. Further kinds of empirical and theoretical arguments for—or against—the reality of the CBG should be researched.

Returning to Michelson and Morley, the names momentous in the history of the æther, they indeed killed the classical æther hypothesis that can be traced to Descartes and beyond (a closer historical account is not here possible). The Cartesian æther was homogenous and stationary, and through that the Earth was thought to be making its circles. So much was already known about the actual structures in the heavens, that what the 1881 and 1887 results killed was already an anachronism. These experiments say nothing about the æther causing gravity on the Earth, as will be described below, since that æther belongs to the Earth. Just as the brightness of the Sun moves with the Sun in the Galaxy, the gravitational field of the Earth revolves with it in the solar system. That æther could not be observed by the arrangements of Michelson and Morley, it can be observed by sitting on a stool or climbing a mountainside, or by some more sophisticated experiment.

To summarize the author's view of the æther, it contains electromagnetic and gravitational counterparts, composed by γs and gs, respectively. Both have homogenous cosmological components (CBR and CBG, γ_b and g_b), and localized components (γ_g and g_g) connected to the hierarchically organized structure of baryonic mass systems. All are in mutual interaction, and in equilibrium on the cosmological scale. All the main cosmological, astrophysical and physical facts: the gravity and Olbers paradoxes, redshift effects and CBR, gravitation and radiation, and the existence of particles can be conceived in the framework of this æther concept.

Though the author recognizes the "æther" term, the term "gravitational field" will be mainly used below, partly for its neutrality, but mainly because it contains in itself a sense of structurality needed in these contexts.

iii. Gravitation as a Pressure Effect of Gravitational Quanta

Gravitation on a body is a pressure effect of gravitons (g) flowing from the background space. As a rule, due to the equilibrium principle, the flow is proportional to the mass of the body. As for all concentric flows (*e.g.*, radiation) the surface density of the graviton inflow follows the familiar inverse square distance law. The γ–g interaction, which we call electro-gravitational coupling (EGC, Jaakkola, 1991, 1993), can be omitted in the first approximation for small-scale bodies like those in the solar system. The energy of the gravitons is proportional to the parameter which we call "strength of gravitation," G. Therefore, we obtain for the surface gravity on a spherical body with mass M and radius R the familiar Newtonian $a = GM/R^2$.

The g-inflow is conducted by the gravitation field of the body. The field is formed and maintained by interactions of the gravitons of the background field with those of the local field and with the radiation field and the particles of the body and its atmosphere. Hypothetically, there may be cases, rare but interesting, where, *e.g.*, due to rapid explosive displacement of mass the field is not fully developed and M-dependence is not strictly valid.

The background field, which is the source of the graviton inflow, is associated with the higher-order system—for the Earth, the solar system and the Galaxy, which form their own local gravitation fields and hierarchically thereafter, up to the homogenous cosmological background field CBG. The strength of gravitation is a variable, $G(r)$, the locally measured value of which is Newton's constant G_0. The cosmological value corresponding to the g_b's and the CBG is denoted by G_c. I have called the proposed mode of the gravitational action "pressure-induced gravitation" (PIG).

iv. Electro-gravitational Dynamics and Unification of Gravitation Effects in Systems of Different Scales

A substantiation of a new hypothesis may be a fair request. The effect of gravitation appears in nature more ramified than usually conceived: without *ad hoc* appendages, each macroscopic scale requires a particular force law in order to explain the phenomena: $1/r^2$ (solar system), $1/r$ (flat rotation curves of galaxies), $e^{-\alpha r}/r^2$ (Seeliger-Neumann cosmological gravity paradox). The dynamics based on the PIG and EGC hypothesis, which shall be called "electro-gravitational dynamics," EGD, appears capable of unifying all these different gravitational effects.

The γ–g coupling, EGC, means absorption of gravitation, bringing into the force law the familiar exponential absorption factor $e^{-\alpha r}$, and with varying density of light *e.g.* in a galaxy, the absorption coefficient α is a variable, $\alpha(r)$. Due to conservation of energy and momentum in EGC, $\alpha(r)$ is identical to absorption of photon energy, *i.e.*, to redshift. The unit of $\alpha(r)$ is cm^{-1}, and its cosmological value is $\alpha_c = H/c$, where H is Hubble's constant. Due to EGC, the strength of gravitation is variable, $G(r)$, which, due to the conservation principle, is related to $\alpha(r)$ as

$$G(r)\alpha(r) = A \tag{2}$$

where the constant $A \approx 4.22 \times 10^{-35}$ cm^2 g^{-1} s^{-2} (Jaakkola, 1991, 1993). Eq. 2 may be regarded as the electro-gravitational field equation.

Together with arguments given in the preceding subsection, a "generalized Newtonian force law" follows

$$a(r) = \frac{G(r)M(r)e^{-\alpha(r)r}}{r^2} \tag{3}$$

On the cosmological scale $\alpha(r) = \alpha_c = H/c$, $G(r) = G_c \approx 10\, G_0$ (from Eq. 2 and observations of the redshift effects, see above refs.), and $M(r) = \rho_c\, r^2\, dr$ per steradian (ρ_c the mean density). One then obtains the "Machian" gravitational interaction of the masses within r or z:

$$a(r,Z) = \int_0^r G_c\rho_c e^{-\alpha_c r}\, dr = \frac{G_c\rho_c}{\alpha_c}\left(1 - e^{-\alpha_c r}\right) = \frac{G_c\rho_c}{\alpha_c}\frac{Z}{1+Z} \tag{4}$$

When r and Z go to infinity, we have the cosmic force

$$a_c = \frac{G_c\rho_c}{\alpha_c} \tag{5}$$

which, for $\rho_c = 10^{-30}$ g cm^3, is $a_c = 1.1 \times 10^{-8}$ cm s^{-2}. Equations (4) and (5) are an explicit formulation of Mach's principle. The finite value of a_c resolves the Seeliger-Neumann gravity paradox.

Evidence that a_c is at work in the Universe is given by its similarity with the local acceleration $a_1 = G(R)\, M(R)/R^2$ at the edges of supergalaxies, clusters and groups of galaxies and single galaxies. Therefore, the Machian force is the factor which designs and controls macroscopic structure in the Universe. It sets the scale at which the transition from local hierarchic structure to the homogenous isotropic cosmological distribution occurs. Its finite value allows global stability.

EGD resolves the mass paradox in galaxies and systems of galaxies without resorting to dark matter, which has showed unobservable in all wavebands and by all indirect methods. In systems of galaxies, the problem is solved (Jaakkola 1994) by EGD and the observational fact that the high redshift dispersion is due to both intragalactic and intergalactic non-Dopplerian redshifts (Jaakkola, 1971, 1978, 1980, Moles and Jaakkola 1976).

$F \propto 1/r$ corresponding to flat rotation in optically invisible outer parts of galaxies (Sanders, 1990) results from $G(r) \propto \alpha(r)^{-1} \propto r$ (Eq. 2 and redshift data within the Galaxy and other galaxies, Jaakkola *et al.* 1975, 1978, 1984; Jaakkola 1991, 1993a, 1994). The factor $e^{-\alpha r} \approx 1$ on that scale. Rigid inner rotation demanding, in Newtonian dynamics, an unnatural constant mass density within galactic bulges—a second galactic paradox—corresponds to $\rho \propto 1/r$ in EGD. The dependencies $D(r) \propto r$ and $D(R) \propto R$ of the mass discrepancy D, Tully-Fisher relation, and transition rotation in the visible outer parts are derived (Jaakkola 1993b, 1995).

In the solar system $M(r) \approx M(\text{Sun})$, $e^{-\alpha(r)r} \approx 1$ and, since the scale is very much smaller than that of the background field (the Galaxy), $G(r) = \text{constant} = G_0$. Therefore, Newton's law is obtained. (In a closer analysis, gravity anomalies found in the solar system, such as those found in orbits of the Moon, Phobos and inner planets, eclipse effects, "fifth force," and Fischbach *et al.* (1986) composition-dependent gravitation (Ghosh, 1991; Jaakkola, 1991) can be accounted for in the present theoretical framework. The former effects are just the drag expected for an æther gravitation by Newton, and have been a theoretical obstacle since then. Therefore, up to the present state of analysis, EGD contains a unified theory of gravitational phenomena in systems of different scales.

5.   The 2-Body Problem, Newton's Law, and Solution of the Dilemma

i. Derivation of Newton's Law

For the needs of the general topic of the present paper, let us derive Newton's law in yet another way. Consider two spherical bodies B_1 and B_2 with masses m_1 and m_2, radii R_1 and R_2, separated by a distance r. The inflow of cosmic gravitons onto B_1, which is proportional to m_1, is partially blocked by B_2, which covers a fraction $A_2/2\pi$ of the sky on B_1; $A_2 = \pi R_2^2/r^2$ is the solid angle of B_2 seen from B_1. This brings about in B_1 a change of momentum towards B_2, *i.e.* a net force, $S_1 = \eta_2 m_1 A_2/2\pi = \eta_2 m_1 R_2^2/2r^2$. Moreover, B_1 shields the inflow of the gravitons onto B_2, causing a further change of momentum toward B_2, $S_2 = \eta_1 m_2 A_1/2\pi = \eta_1 m_2 R_1^2/2r^2$. Coefficients η_1 and η_2 measure the power with which the bodies B_1 and B_2 absorb gravitons; evidently these are identical with the surface gravity: $\eta_1 = Gm_1/R_1^2$ and $\eta_2 = Gm_2/R_2^2$. Altogether, the change of momentum of B_1 towards B_2 is

$$F = S_1 + S_2 = \frac{Gm_1m_2}{2r^2} + \frac{Gm_2m_1}{2r^2} = \frac{Gm_1m_2}{r^2} \tag{6}$$

This is identical to Newton's law.

The simplicity, almost triviality of the above deduction may hide some points of principle. First, contrary to the common viewpoint, the effect between two bodies is not due to a direct mutual attraction by the bodies, but the link runs *via* the Universe external to the system.

Second, the simple Newtonian formula contains two terms, S_1 and S_2, identified in magnitude, but quite different in character. While the "pushing term" S_2 means the effect of the field of the second body (*e.g.*, of the field of the Sun on the Earth), the "shadow term" S_1 is due to the field of the body (the Earth) itself, when affected by the shadow of S_2 (the Sun). Separation of the two terms may prove to be of significance for some mechanical problems in the solar system, as well as for the tides and some other problems. Newton's third law works such that in S_2, vectorially, $S_1(B_2) = -S_2(B_1)$, $S_2(B_2) = -S_1(B_1)$, $F(B_2) = -F(B_1)$.

Third, the inverse square distance factor in the formula, which in the Newtonian picture of an attractive gravitation force has no rationale except experience, here results from the geometrical contraction of the solid angle subtended by the screening body, and the $1/r^2$ dependence of the surface density of the graviton inflow toward that body. The underlying assumption, discussed further in Sections 4 and 5, is that EGC has no significant effect over the scale under consideration.

Therefore, the above derivation of Newton's law is, though simple, a nontrivial and physically conceivable treatment, valid for spherical bodies. Further physical aspects of the theory are discussed below.

ii. Solution of the Dilemma

When gravitation is treated as a general effect, the mode discussed above implies a distinctly "local" action. As Newton anticipated, gravitation is "impulses" from space. This is evident for gravitation directed to single bodies. In two-body systems, the Earth, *e.g.*, moves in the field of the Sun, with its back face permanently bombarded by gravitons belonging to the stream towards the Sun. This is S_2 in Eq. 6. Though undoubtedly local in character, the meaning of the word may have changed from an exchange of particles in local interactions.

What to say about the term S_1, which deals with the Earth's own field? The Sun acts at its distance as a screen for gravitons streaming from the background space in its direction. S_1 is action-at-a-distance in the same sense that S_2 was of a local character. This is analogous to when a mountain hides the scene behind it.

As to the particular gravitons which are screened by the Sun, the effect on the Earth is instantaneous. For objects in circular orbits, the question of instantaneous or retarded action is not significant, because the configuration between the body, the screen and the background field does not change. For eccentric orbits, graviton velocity v_g may also be significant in the S_1-term.

Nor is the question of the velocity of the action relevant for the Machian interaction of distant masses. More essential there is the progression of the effect through the hierarchically arranged subsequent local fields. Different υ_g-values are probably attached to each level of hierarchy and to the position in each large-scale field.

Hence, if the mode of gravitation outlined in Section 4 and appearing as an attractive effect as explained in 5.1. proves to be correct, the centuries old dilemma of a "local" versus "distant" character of the action of gravitation obtains a surprising solution: both are true. Fundamentally, however, gravitation is an interaction between mass systems and the background field, one of the equilibrium effects maintaining the energy balance between the various substances of the Universe.

iii. **Empirical Tests of MFLA and of the Dual Solution**

The existence of an æther medium connected to the Earth, identifiable with the MFLA theory as described in preceding sections, is indicated by many experiments reviewed by Hayden (1990a,b); these measure the velocity of light in different directions with respect to terrestrial rotation. In 1913 Sagnac (Sagnac and Boyty, 1913) performed an experiment with light circulating around a table which rotated in the opposite directions. A fringe shift was obtained corresponding to a non-isotropy of velocity attachable to the rotation of the Earth. An enlarged version of the Sagnac experiment was made by Michelson and Gale (1925), where the path of light was a rectangle of 340 by 610 meters. Light traveling counterclockwise around the loop lags behind the clockwise motion, again corresponding to $\upsilon_\gamma = c \pm V_r$, where V_r is terrestrial spin velocity (350 meters/s at 40° latitude). There is a curious absence of this notable result in literature concerning the topic of light velocity, in spite of the fact that it is quite essential to relativity theory. The result has since been confirmed several times with larger, more modern devices. A Sagnac-type experiment on a planetary scale using geosynchronous satellites and several ground stations was performed by Allan *et al.* (1985); again east-traveling signals lagged behind westbound signals. Ironically (exposing the scientific practice and "epistemology" behind various "verifications" of the relativity theory), these results have only attained the status of a "Sagnac correction" necessary to synchronize clocks in satellites at various positions around the Earth.

The Michelson-Morley experiment in 1887, designed to check the orbital velocity of 30 km/s through the æther, observed no anisotropy of light velocity. A modern round-trip experiment of a similar type by Brillet and Hall (1979) claim anisotropy down to 30 m/s, also against an effect of the Earth rotation, in contradiction to the results of the Sagnac-type area-enclosing experiments. However Hayden (1990a,b) has shown that this results from the way data has been dealt with, and points out that anisotropy exists in the original data, not in the sidereal coordinates, but clearly in the diurnally rotating laboratory coordinates.

The famous Hafele-Keating (1972) experiment carried atomic clocks in aircraft, and is claimed to support the special relativity prediction that moving clocks are slowed. However, the west-bound clock actually moved faster than the clock in the laboratory. In SR, the change of the time-rate cannot be dependent on direction.

I consider the Sagnac effect and the other data referred to here as evidence supporting the PIG and EGC hypotheses: these indicate that the material gravitational field bound to the Earth exists (PIG), and its effect on the light velocity indicates EGC. The crucial results brought to light by Hayden disprove relativity theory, which is already an anachronism like the Cartesian variant of the æther hypothesis was in the epoch of the Michelson-Morley experiment. They also point to a physics based on a new concept of the æther.

Direct gravitational effects relating to the Earth in rotation other than those on the velocity of light should be investigated, *e.g.*, gravity on preceding and trailing hillsides *etc.*, but the much lower accuracy of gravitational (compared to electromagnetic) measurements and atmospheric effects may hide such effects. Other parameters worth testing, which may be connected to the PIG and EGC hypotheses, but yet lack quantitative predictions, are: distance ($1/r^2$ law), mass, density, material, temperature, time, velocity, acceleration, rotation, shape, orientation with respect to the Earth, Moon, Sun, plane, center and rotation of the Milky Way, and with respect to the CBR dipole, electric field, magnetic field, occultations of the Moon and Sun, and other intervening matter. Existing "anomalous" observations which may be conceived in the EGC-framework have been discussed (Jaakkola, 1991, 1993). The aspects of the new theory may require new experimental setups. Many of the factors listed have not yet been studied, and surprises may await us in future experimental gravity research.

Also the dual nature of two-body gravitation implied by the "shadow" and "pushing" terms S_1 and S_1 involved in Newton's law (Eq. 4) should be tested properly. The eclipses—both solar and lunar—offer possibilities of testing the S_1-term. There are reports of anomalous effects during both kinds of eclipses. Saxl and Allen (1971), in a torsion pendulum experiment during a solar eclipse of March 7, 1970 a 10^5 times larger effect than expected from Newtonian theory. According to them, comparable results had been obtained at Harvard experiments over a period of 17 years. Anomalies have also been reported after later eclipses; an up-to-date review seems to be lacking and would be highly desirable.

The lunar eclipses naturally do not affect the S_1-term on the Earth but do affect it on the Moon. A century ago Newcomb (1895) found anomalous periodic fluctuations in the moon's longitude, and Bottlinger (1912) suggested absorption of gravitation by the Earth during the eclipses (however, see de Sitter (1913b). The present status of the problem is not clear, but in the analysis of Assis (1992) valuable arguments for the reality of the absorption (screening) effect of the S_1-term are given. What would be a better way to celebrate the centenary of Newcomb's important observation, and at the same time Seeliger's (1895) and Newmann's (1896) important cosmological work, all in mutual connection, than arranging in 1995 a joint international effort to settle the status and make new observations in both eclipse problems. Also, the next flight to the Moon should contain, perhaps as its most important load, instrumentation to measure gravity anomalies during the lunar (there solar) eclipses.

Purely terrestrial laboratory experiments of gravitational absorption, the first and evidently the last performed by Majorana (1920, 1930), with positive results, are also relevant to the duality problem and S_1. Naturally, repeating such experiments is most urgent.

The pushing term S_2 can be tested by measuring the diurnal, monthly and annual variations of terrestrial surface gravity, and by analysis of the new and rich existing data in a relevant manner, with no preconceived opinions or too many *ad hoc* models "to save the appearances." As S_2 has the character of the general pressure-gravitation, the numerous test parameters listed above are of interest in this context as well.

6.   Discussion

A historical viewpoint—acquired either before or after the actual work—is one of the author's principles of scientific enquiry. The PIG theory of gravitation presented in Sections 4 and 5 is based on recent results of empirical cosmology and was originally somewhat unhistorical; its counterpart, EGC had some historical substantiation from the start. The PIG theory also involves the AAAD aspect, though basically it is an MFLA effect. Eventually, a historical introduction to all the main hypotheses on the nature of gravitation, the presently prevailing general relativity included, was established as the topic of the present paper. The original aim of presenting the antecedents of the PIG theory in the MFLA tradition is not well fulfilled; rather the phases of its alternatives, relativistic local action and AAAD, are to some extent delineated. This contradictory outcome is due to the fact that the history of MFLA theories is such a vast subject—it involves almost the whole history of physics—that it cannot be packed into the present paper; a separate survey is under way. Some historical glimpses of the MFLA mode were necessarily involved in the accounts of the alternative theories given here. In the history of the views of gravity (since Newton) there has prevailed a tension due to the dichotomy of two opposite views, AAAD and MFLA. During the last century the relativistic mode, relativistic local action, has added to the tension by opposing both of its predecessors. With the crosswise solutions presented, the history of the problem has become an exciting and sometimes dramatic story.

When I embarked on the problem, I also felt like a spectator at a wrestling match where two ghosts are fighting about which of them is real. The ghosts were the AAAD and relativistic local action. In the course of the investigation, both have gained more flesh and blood. In the solution of the dilemma in Section 5, AAAD is real, appearing as the term S_1 of Eq. 4. AAAD may have many appearances in different physical conditions. [...] The other "ghost," relativistic local action (GR), has in the author's mind acquired a lot of reality in the writing of this paper. Historically, it is a completely justified and respectable theory. It is also the best formulated theory yet presented. It has had some empirical successes, but ultimately it fails in this respect. Conceptually it cannot be accepted, except if its notions of space and time are taken only as figurative expressions of the spatial and temporal features of the effects treated and GR is only used as mathematical machinery. Then relativistic local action could be one of the many MFLA theories (which the supporters of GR certainly do not accept).

In spite of the ramifications due to the AAAD S_1 term, gravitation as a general effect works according the MFLA mode. It is an interaction between a mass system and the background gravitation field, acting *via* the local field, which itself is a product of interactions. Furthermore the scope of gravitation contains the effects on the other physical interactions, of which we have only been concerned with the electromagnetic interaction (in EGC contexts). In addition to gravity in mass systems, the redshift, CBR and a part of QSO radiation also fall into the category of gravitational effects. There, the two long-range forces are both so directly present and intermingled that the cause and the effect, electromagnetism and gravity, cannot be separated; rather, a unique interaction is manifest. It might be called "electrogravity." The various gravitational effects found in various physical systems and at various scales can be unified by this concept and the dynamics based on it (Section 4.υ. and Jaakkola 1994a, 1995b). In the cosmological dimension, gravitation has general validity as one of the processes that maintains the energy balance between the various material substances of the Universe.

[...]

References

Allan, D.W., Weiss, M.A. and Ashby, N., 1985, *Science* 228, 69.

Arp, H., 1987, *Quasars, Redshifts and Controversies*, Interstellar Media, Berkeley.

Arp, H., Bi, H.G., Chu, Y. and Zhu, X., 1990, *Astron. Astrophys.* 239, 33.

Assis, A., 1989, *Found. Phys. Lett.* 2, 301.

Assis, A., 1992a, *Apeiron* 12, 10.

Assis, A., 1992b, *Apeiron* 13, 3.

Bertlmann, R.A., 1990, *Found. Phys.* 20, 1191.

Bottlinger, C.F., 1912, *Astron.Nachr.* 191, 147.

Brillet, A., and Hall, J.L., 1979, *Phys. Rev. Lett.* 42, 549.

Broberg, H., 1982, *ESA Journal* 6, 207.

Broberg, H., 1991, *Apeiron* 9-10, 62.

Cohen, L.B., 1980, *The Newtonian Revolution*, Cambridge Univ. Press.

Cook, A.H., 1987, in S.W. Hawking and W. Israel (*eds.*), *Three Hundred Years of Gravitation*, Cambridge Univ. Press, p. 51.

de Sitter, W., 1913, *Phys. Z.* 14, 429.

Einstein, A., 1949, in P. Schilpp (ed.), *Albert Einstein: Philosopher-Scientist*, Tudor, New York, p. 211.

Einstein, A., 1951, *The Meaning of Relativity*, Methuen & Co. Ltd., London (5th ed.), p. 27.

Fischbach, E.B., Sudarsky, D., Szafer, A., Talmadge, C., and Aaronson, S.H., 1986, *Phys. Rev. Lett.* 56, 3.

Freundlich, E., 1913,*Phys. Z.* 14, 835.

Ghosh, A., 1984, *Pramana* 23, L671.

Ghosh, A., 1991, *Apeiron* 9-10, 35.

Goldstein, R.M., 1969, *Science* 166, 598.

Hafele, J.C., and Keating, R.E., 1972, *Science* 177, 166.

Hawking, S.W. and Israel, W. (*eds.*), 1987, *Three Hundred Years of Gravitation*, Cambridge Univ. Press.

Hayden, H.C., 1990a, *Galilean Electrodynamics* 1, 10.

Hayden, H.C., 1990b, *Galilean Electrodynamics* 1, 71.

Hoyle, F., and Narlikar, J.V., 1974, *Action at a Distance in Physics and Cosmology*, W.H. Freeman and Co., San Francisco.

Jaakkola, T., 1971, *Nature* 234, 534.

Jaakkola, T., 1978, *Acta Cosmologica* 7, 17.

Jaakkola, T., 1982, *Astrophys. Space Sci.* 88, 283.

Jaakkola, T., 1983a, in A. van der Merve (ed.), *Old and New Questions in Physics, Cosmology, Philosophy and Theoretical Biology, Essays in Honor of Wolfgang Yourgrau*, Plenum Press, New York and London, p. 223.

Jaakkola, T., 1983b, *Astron. Nachr.* 304, 103.

Jaakkola, T., 1986, in Hïnni and I. Tuominen (*eds.*), *Proc. 6th Soviet-Finnish Astron.* Meeting, p. 190.

Jaakkola, T., 1987, *Apeiron* 1, 5.

Jaakkola, T., 1988, in F. Bertola, J.W. Sulentic and B.F. Madore (*eds.*), *New Ideas in Astronomy*, Cambridge Univ. Press, p. 333.

Jaakkola, T., 1991, *Apeiron* 9-10, 76.

Jaakkola, T., 1993a, in H. Arp, C.R. Keys and K. Rudnicki (*eds.*), *Progress in New Cosmologies: Beyond the Big Bang*, Plenum Publ. Co., p. 111.

Jaakkola, T., 1993b, *Tuorla Obs. Informo* No. 171.

Jaakkola, T., 1994, *Apeiron* 18, 1.

Jaakkola, T., 1995, to be published.

Jaakkola, T., Donner, K.J. and Teerikorpi, P. 1975a, *Astrophys. Space Sci*, 37, 301.

Jaakkola, T., Holsti, N., Laurikainen, E. and Teerikorpi, P. 1984, *Astrophys. Space Sci.* 107, 85.

Jaakkola, T., Moles, M. and Vigier, J.P., 1978, *Astrophys. Space Sci.* 58, 99.

Jaakkola, T., Moles, M. and Vigier, J.P., 1979, *Astron. Nachr.* 300, 229.

Jaakkola, T., Teerikorpi, P. and Donner, K.J., 1975, *Astron. Astrophys.* 58, 99.

Laurikainen, E. and Jaakkola, T., 1985a, in J.L. Nieto (ed.) *New Aspects in Galaxy Photometry*, Springer Verlag, Berlin, p. 309.

Laurikainen, E. and Jaakkola, T., 1985b, *Astrophys. Space Sci.* 109, 111.

Le Sage, G.L., 1784, *Nouveaux Memoires de l'Academie Royale*, Berlin, p. 404.

Mach, E., 1872, engl. transl. 1911, *History and Root of the Principle of the Conservation of Energy*, Open Court, Chicago, p. 56.

Mach, E., 1883, engl. transl. 1960, *The Science of Mechanics*, La Salle: Open Court.

Majorana, Q., 1920, *Phil. Mag.* 39, 488.

Majorana, Q., 1930, *J. de Phys.* 1, 314.

Marmet, P., 1991, *Apeiron* 9-10, 45.

Merat, P., Pecker, J.C., Vigier, J.P., 1974a, *Astron. Astrophys.* 30, 167.

Merat, P., Pecker, J.C., Vigier, J.P. and Yourgrau, W., 1974b, *Astron. Astrophys.* 32, 471.

Michelson, A.A., 1925, *Astrophys. J.* 61, 137.

Michelson, A.A. and Gale, H.G., 1925, *Astrophys. J.* 61, 140.

Michelson, A.A. and Morley, E.W., 1887, *Am. J. Sci.* 34, 333.

Moles, M. and Jaakkola, T., 1976, *Astron. Astrophys.* 53, 389.

Mossotti, O.F., 1936, engl. transl. 1839, *Sci. Memoirs* 1, 448.

Newton, J., 1687, engl. transl. 1952, *Mathematical Principles of Natural Philosophy*, Cajori edition, Chicago.

Newton, J., 1728, *A treatise of the system of the world*, London Nilsson.

K., Valtonen, M.J., Kotilainen, J. and Jaakkola, T., 1993, *Astrophys. J.* 413, 453.

North, J.D., 1965, *The Measure of the Universe, A History of Modern Cosmology*, Clarendon Press, Oxford.

Pais, A., 1982, "Subtle is the Lord...," *The Science and the Life of Albert Einstein*, Oxford Univ. Press.

Phipps, Jr., T.E., 1987, *Heretical Verities: Mathematical Themes in Physical Description*, Urbana, Classic Non-fiction Library.

Phipps, Jr., T.E. 1990, *Apeiron* 8, 8.

Ritz, W., 1911, *Gesammelte Werke*, Gauthier- Villars, Paris.

Roseveare, N.T., 1982, *Mercury's Perihelion from Le Verrier to Einstein*, Clarendon Press, Oxford.

Sadeh, D., Knowles, S.H. and Yaplee, B.S., 1968, *Science* 159, 307.

Sagnac, M.G. and Boyty, M.E., 1913, *Comptes Rendus* 157, 708 and 1410.

Sandage, A. and Perelmuter, J.M., 1991, *Astrophys. J.* 370, 455.

Sanders, R.H., 1990, *Astron. Astrophys.* Rev. 2, 1.

Saxl, E.J. and Allen, M., 1971, *Phys. Rev.* D3, 283.

Seeliger, H., 1895, *Astron. Nachr.* 137, 129.

Shlenov, A., 1991a, *Apeiron* 11, 9.

Shlenov, A., 1991b, preprint.

Surdin, M., 1962, *Proc. Camb. Phil. Soc.* 58, 550.

Tifft, W., 1988, in F. Bertola, J.W. Sulentic and B.F. Madore (*eds.*) *New Ideas in Astronomy*, Cambridge Univ. Press, p. 173.

Torr, D.G. and Kolen, P., 1984, *Precision Measurements and Fundamental Constants 11*, B.N. Taylor and W.D. Phillips (*eds.*), Natl. Bur. Stand. (U.S.), Spec. Publ. 617.

Weber, W., 1846; 1893, *Werke*, Vol. 3, Springer, Berlin, pp. 25-214.

Wesley, J.P., 1988, *Physics Essays* 1, 85.

Will, C.M., 1987, in S.W. Hawking and W. Israel (*eds.*) *Three Hundred Years of Gravitation*, Cambridge Univ. Press, p. 80.

Woodward, J.F., 1983, in A. van der Merwe (ed.), *Old and New Questions in Physics, Cosmology, Philosophy and Theoretical Biology*, Plenum Press, p. 873.

Chance Coincidences
or Natural Phenomena[*]

K.E. Veselov[†]

The author challenges the accepted explanations of such phenomena as the retardation of the rotational speed of the Earth, the changing duration of the terrestrial year, and continental drift. His interpretation of the mechanism responsible for these and other phenomena of a diverse nature is based on the assumption that not only mass-to-energy conversion processes are widespread in nature (nuclear energy, radioactive decay, solar energy, *etc*.), but also processes involving the formation of new mass. As an explanation of these latter processes, he offers a corpuscular model of gravitation and inertia. The effective components of this model are material bodies and the medium encompassing them, which he treats as a gravitational vacuum enabling bodies to form gravitational fields and, hence, to interact gravitationally and inertially. A satellite experiment is proposed as a possible means of verifying the three principal postulates formulated in the paper.

Introduction

It is an established fact that over the past 25 years the rotational speed of the Earth has been slowing down and changing with a one-year period (Figure 1). The duration of the diurnal period has during these years been increasing at an average rate of 12.5×10^{-3} s per year, and the amplitude of diurnal period variation has been 6.1×10^{-4} s. The tropical year has been growing shorter by 6.1×10^{-3} s per year. Besides this, the longitudes of the perihelia of the planets anomalously shift in 100 terrestrial years over appreciable distances: the perihelion of Mercury over 43.1; that of Venus, over 8.1; that of the Earth, over 5.1; and that of Mars, over 1.3 seconds of arc. A beam of light passing near the Sun is curved and its frequency changes; a radio signal sent from the Earth past the Sun and bounced off another planet arrives with a delay that can be adequately measured by contemporary techniques.

There is now highly reliable evidence to support continental drift and related phenomena: sea-floor spreading, the relative youth of sea-floor rocks, the difference between the structure of the oceanic crust and the continental crust, the block structure of the Earth's crust, the global system of rifts, *etc*. All these phenomena are attributed to different causes. The retardation of the Earth's rotation about its axis is attributed to viscous friction in the process of tidal deformations; the periodic change in its rotation rate, to the seasonal shifting of

[*] This article originally appeared in *Geophysical Journal* 3(3), 1981, pp. 410-425. Reprinted with permission of Gordon and Breach, Science Publishers, Inc.

[†] "Soyuzgeofizika" Research and Production Amalgamation, USSR Ministry of Geological Exploration, Moscow. Present address: VNIIGeofiziki, Pokrovrka 22, Moscow, 101000, Russia.

K.E. Veselov

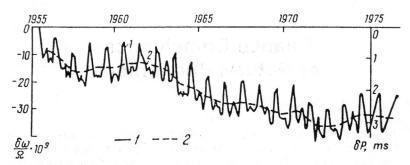

Figure 1. Change in the rotational speed of the Earth: 1-mean monthly values, 2-mean yearly values.

air masses. The change in the duration of the tropical year is traced to the gravitational effect of other planets and to still insufficiently studied phenomena. The shifting of the perihelion longitudes of the planets, the curving of beams of light and the change in its frequency, like the delayed arrival of radio signals reflected from other planets, are accurately predicted by the General Theory of Relativity (GTR). Continental drift on our planet is accounted for by the non-uniform distribution of heat sources inside the Earth and consequent convective movements. Without going into a detailed discussion of these phenomena, let us note that all of them, except those flowing from the GTR, have by no means been explained entirely satisfactorily, either in qualitative or in quantitative terms.

Tidal friction inside the Earth can account for only about one-sixth of the retardation of its rotation. Accordingly, the value of that retardation for the past 25 years obtained experimentally by employing atomic timing devices is simply dismissed as anomalous. The value assumed to be normal is one calculated from astronomical observations over the past few centuries, the timing being done according to the rotational periods and motion of celestial bodies [14]. From these data (Figure 2) it is difficult to infer any definite retardation, and it is evident that this approach is wrong. How well a clock keeps time cannot be checked by that same clock. Moreover, an anomaly also has to be explained.

The seasonal changes in the Earth's rotation rate can, qualitatively, be linked to the pulsation of the atmosphere owing to the annual cycle experienced by the Earth-Sun distance. But simple calculations reveal that only 5-10% of the amplitude can be accounted for in this way. There have also been attempts to trace the seasonal changes in the Earth's rotation rate to the movement of air masses, as recorded by meteorological observations. But this leaves unidentified the reasons for the movement of the atmosphere, and it would even seem more logical to treat the changes in the Earth's rotation rate as causing the seasonal movements of air masses. Indirect evidence supporting the latter explanation is provided by the fact that only a small part of the variation amplitude of the Earth's rotation rate corresponds to the variation amplitude of the wind velocity [15].

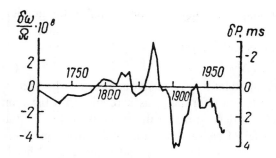

Figure 2. Changes in the rotational speed of the Earth over the past 300 years.

The duration of the terrestrial year may well change according to Newton's law applied to the motions of three or more bodies. In this case it is quite permissible to assume a transfer of kinetic energy from one body to another. Consequently, the orbits of the planets and the periods of their revolution around the Sun may change. Nevertheless, there are as yet no calculations that would provide a satisfactory quantitative explanation of the shortening of the terrestrial year.

As for the movements of the continents, attributing it to a convective mechanism arouses many doubts. But even if we cast these doubts aside, we encounter a still greater difficulty in trying to explain how there arise areas of the Earth's surface unoccupied by lithospheric plates, areas into which they could move. The supporters of the movement of lithospheric masses assume that lithospheric plates can slide up and over one another, but there is no hard evidence to support this contention. Whereas spreading is an indisputable fact, subduction is therefore highly questionable. For this reason the geological theory of the movement of lithospheric plates may be said to be in a state of crisis.

It will be shown below that these diverse phenomenal may be accounted for by assuming that not only processes involving the conversion of mass to kinetic energy (nuclear energy, radioactive decay, the energy of the Sun, stars, *etc.*), but also converse processes of the formation of new mass, of its change and its exchange between bodies are widespread in nature. Such processes may be explained by invoking a corpuscular model of gravitation and inertia (CMGI). The effective components of this model are material bodies, which have an intrinsic momentum, and the material medium encompassing them, which will hereinafter be termed a gravitational vacuum and which enables bodies to form gravitational fields and, hence, to interact gravitationally and inertially.

Basic Postulates

A gravitational vacuum is a space filled with chaotically moving particles–gravitons–which freely pass through all bodies, losing only an insignificant part of their momentum in the process. In line with the notions of Le Sage [4,11], bodies in such a space will be attracted according to Newton's law, and the work performed by gravitational forces will be proportional to the gravitational potential increment.

The relationship between mass and energy

$$E = \Delta mc^2,$$ (1)

provided by the Special Theory of Relativity (STR) is assumed to be strictly observed. However, it is interpreted not formally, as a relationship between mass and velocity, the latter in turn depending on the velocity of the inertial frame of reference, but as a transfer of energy and momentum from one body to another, from the gravitational vacuum to a body and vice versa. What is therefore assumed is accelerated motion, the work of forces, strict observance of energy and momentum conservation, and the extension of these laws to the gravitational vacuum.

Apart from observance of the STR mass-energy relationship, the interaction between the gravitational vacuum and bodies in the CMGI is subject to the following three constraints.

1. The particles of the gravitational vacuum—gravitons—are distributed evenly in density and the direction of movement throughout the space where there are no bodies, and they travel at the speed of light, the limiting velocity for physical interactions and the propagation of information.

2. Bodies at rest or moving by inertia in the gravitational vacuum absorb and emit gravitons, with due observance of a dynamic equilibrium condition in the exchange of momentum. The condition $\Sigma P = 0$, where P is the momentum of the gravitons, has to be observed for each body over sufficiently big intervals of time and space. A body thus acquires as many gravitons of the same momentum as it gives up. Accordingly, bodies at rest should experience no change of mass; bodies moving by inertia, no change of friction forces. Gravitons are emitted and absorbed in portions not smaller than a certain threshold value, and a body is therefore surrounded by waves of excess absorption and emission momentum. The density amplitude of the excess momentum is inversely proportional to the square of the distance from the body and directly proportional to the mass of the body. The wave frequency depends on that mass; the frequency and density of the excess momentum are quantities characterizing the body's static gravitational field, which should evidently be of a very high frequency.

3. In accelerated movement under the influence of an external force the dynamic equilibrium of the exchange between a body and the gravitational vacuum is upset because the compensating momentum is emitted after a certain finite time interval rather than instantly. Depending upon the sign of the acceleration, the body either loses or acquires a certain number of gravitons, its mass changing by a quantity determined by formula (1).

Low-frequency waves connected with the movement of masses or with a change in their quantity will be superimposed on the high-frequency waves of the static field of a body in accelerated motion.

If, inside a gravitational vacuum, there are several bodies possessing momenta, at least three types of interactions may be foreseen: an inertial interaction, in which one body gives up its momentum to another; a gravitational interaction, in which bodies acquire momentum from gravitons, i.e., from the gravitational field, and the interaction of inertial movement with the gravitational field, in which momentum due to the wave character of the gravitational field is added to the momentum of an inertially moving body. Let us consider these three types of interactions in greater detail, formally assuming them to take place independently.

Let one body be capable of transmitting part of its momentum to another, i.e., be capable of transmitting energy and performing work. In the process of momentum transfer, both bodies are in accelerated motion, the acceleration upsetting the dynamic equilibrium of the exchange of gravitons between the bodies and the gravitational vacuum. The accelerated body will capture gravitons with a momentum directed against the accelerating force. As its velocity changes, there will therefore arise a force resisting any change of the initial state of the body's motion, a force called inertia, and the mass of the body will increase in relation to the amount of work performed. The accelerating body will, on the contrary, lose in mass and velocity. In accordance with formula (1), we may write:

$$\Delta m = \frac{\Delta A}{c^2} q = \frac{\Delta E}{c^2} q , \qquad (2)$$

where ΔA and ΔE are the work and energy increments, respectively; c is the velocity of light, and q is a coefficient restricting the velocity of inertial movement to the velocity of light. At a velocity $V << c$ it is close to 1, whereas at $V = c$ it is close to 0. A suitable value will be $q = \sqrt{1 - V^2/c^2}$. The first postulate may thus be formulated as follows: in an inertial interaction the mass of a body changes in proportion to the amount and sign of the work performed, i.e., according to formula (2).

For each body in an inertial interaction the work performed in absorbing momentum from the vacuum will not be equal to the work performed in emitting it, since the masses and velocities of the bodies change. Let us now assume that two bodies are held in place inside the gravitational vacuum. In that case each of them will be pierced by gravitons of the waves of emission and absorption from the other, and the condition of the dynamic equilibrium of the exchange will be observed. But if we now release the bodies, the dynamic equilibrium will be upset, since reciprocal screening will reduce the flux of gravitons from the side of the other body. There will therefore arise an excess momentum of attraction from one body to the other, and they will begin moving toward each other with an acceleration. Work will be performed at the expense of the momentum the bodies acquire from the gravitational vacuum. The mass of the bodies will grow, since the work of the gravitational forces is in this case always positive.

With due consideration for (1), we now have:

$$\frac{\Delta m_1}{m} = \frac{|\Delta\varphi|}{c^2} q ,\tag{3}$$

where $|\Delta\varphi|$ is the absolute value of the gravitational potential increment, and q is the same coefficient as in Eq. (2). The gravitational field can retard or accelerate inertial motion. This acceleration or retardation takes place at the expense of momentum acquired from the gravitational vacuum, and the mass of the body can therefore only increase. The increase of mass occurs at the expense of gravitons with a momentum directed toward the attracting body. Owing to this there arises the additional momentum

$$\Delta P_1 - \Delta m_1 c_g \tag{4}$$

where c_g is a vector in magnitude equal to the velocity of light and in direction coinciding with the force of attraction. At the same time there arises the additional force

$$f_1 = \frac{\Delta p}{\Delta t} .$$

The Newtonian force may be regarded as the force that would arise if the body were placed in the gravitational field of another body before the emission of compensation waves had begun. The work of the forces arising from the acquisition of momentum in the gravitational field of another body will be greater than work performed in yielding momentum to the vacuum; accordingly, the momentum and mass of the body increase, and there arises a force additional to the Newtonian. A second postulate my thus be formulated: *the work of the forces of a gravitational field, irrespective of the direction of motion, is accompanied by an increase in the mass of bodies by a quantity proportional to the amount of work or the growth of the potential, and by the appearance of an additional attraction momentum equal in quantity to the product of the mass increment by the velocity of light, i.e.,* formulae (3) and (4) must be satisfied in a gravitational interaction.

Let us now disregard the forces of gravitational interaction and imagine a body moving inertially in the gravitational field of another body. Depending upon the direction of its movement, it will be situated for a longer interval of time either in an emission or in an absorption wave and will therefore acquire additional energy. In either case the mass of the moving body will, in accordance with (1), be greater than the mass of the body at rest by a quantity m_m proportional to the gravitational potential and the absolute value of the ratio of the velocity V of its motion to the velocity of light c

$$\frac{m_m}{m} = -\frac{\varphi}{c^2}\left|\frac{v}{c}\right|.\tag{5}$$

However, in movement away from the attracting body, this mass will diminish, since the density of the excess momentum in the emission and absorption waves will diminish; conversely, the mass will increase in movement toward the attracting body because of the growth of the density of the excess momentum in the same waves.

We may therefore set down:

$$\frac{\Delta m_2}{m} = -\frac{\Delta\varphi}{c^2}\left|\frac{v}{c}\right|. \tag{6}$$

Simultaneously with the growth of mass, the momentum grows by the quantity Δp_2,

$$\Delta p_2 = \Delta m_2 c_g \tag{7}$$

and there arises a force $f_2 = (\Delta p_2/\Delta t)$. Because formulae (5), (6), and (7) contain the factor $|v/c|$, the relative increase of mass and momentum for small velocities will be negligible. For light these quantities may be large enough to be detected experimentally. Irrespective of the direction of a body's movement in a gravitational field, there arises an additional force of attraction, since in movement toward the attracting body the momentum of the same direction increases, while in movement away from that body there is a decrease of the momentum opposite in direction to the force of attraction.

A third postulate may thus be formulated: *inertial motion in a gravitational field is accompanied by the appearance of additional mass, whose amount is proportional to the gravitational potential and to the absolute value of the ratio of the velocity of the motion to the velocity of light. This additional mass increases in motion toward the attracting body and decreases in motion in the opposite direction. Additional momentum and force arise in the process, so that the direction of the force always coincides with the direction of the force of Newtonian attraction.*

These three postulates governing the relations of bodies with the gravitational vacuum stand in need of rigorous experimental verification. Although they have been derived from the CMGI, this has not been done on the basis of strictly logical reasoning. These rules furnish a broader interpretation of the STR relationships linking mass, energy, and velocity. What this interpretation essentially amounts to is that the change in mass depends quantitatively upon the amount of work performed, *i.e.*, upon the amount of energy expended to alter the velocity.

The postulates formulated thus recognize an actual growth of mass and its change in the movement of a body in a gravitational field, and an exchange of masses in an inertial interaction of bodies. Consequently, the process of the conversion of energy into mass is recognized as an indisputable fact, on a par with the process of the conversion of mass into kinetic energy, which is an indisputable fact without which we could not account for the tremendous energy of the Sun and the stars, or for nuclear energy, which man has learned to utilize. As for the widespread character of the process whereby new inertial mass is born, this is evidenced by the diverse phenomena listed at the beginning of this paper, for which the postulates formulated in the CMGI provide an excellent quantitative explanation.

Experimental Verification

Formulae (2), (3), (4), (5), (6), and (7) may be used for certain calculations. We shall perform these calculations on the assumption that the increases of mass are small compared with the initial mass and that for this reason their effect, during a limited time interval, on trajectory elements determined on the basis of Newton's law will be negligible.

In keeping with formula (2), the relative change in a planet's mass may be written as:

$$\frac{\Delta m}{m} = \frac{V_c V_p}{c^2} \cos \frac{2\pi}{T} t , \qquad (8)$$

where V_c is the projection of the velocity of the solar system's motion onto the plane of the planet's orbit, V_p is the mean linear velocity of the planet's orbital motion, T is the period of the planet's revolution around the Sun, and t is the time. This formula was derived on the assumption that the planet's orbit is circular and that its mass is much smaller than the Sun's. Since the Sun exchanges mass with the planet, the changes in mass should produce regular changes in the rotational periods of the planet and the Sun about their axes.

In Ref. (8) there are calculations of the relative change in the mass of the Sun and the planets in their inertial interaction, and the corresponding values of the amplitude of the rotational period changes. The Table at the end of the present paper gives the amplitudes for the Earth obtained according to formula (8) and from astronomical observations. In these calculations the velocity was determined in relation to stationary stars, and for this reason the satisfactory agreement of the calculations with the experimental data indicates that these stars are stationary or move at a small velocity with respect to the gravitational vacuum.

When a planet moves in an elliptic orbit, its mass will increase according to formula (3). For a single orbit of the planet this increase will equal:

$$\frac{\Delta m}{m} = \frac{4K\varepsilon}{c^2 a(1 - \varepsilon^2)} , \qquad (9)$$

where K is the solar constant, and ε and a are the orbital eccentricity and the semi-major axis of the planet's orbit (5), (6), and (8). In motion along a circular orbit the increase of mass will be equal to zero.

As a planet rotates about its axis in the Sun's gravitational field, its mass increases according to the same formula (3). The relative increase of mass for a single rotation will (5), (6), and (8) equal:

$$\frac{\Delta m}{m} = \frac{K_1 GR}{c^2} \cos \alpha , \qquad (10)$$

Table I

Effect	Calculated value	Experimental value	Source of Experimental Data
Secular increase in period of Earth's rotation about its axis per year in s	$7.7 \times 10^{-5}-$ 12.8×10^{-5}	12.5×10^{-5}	(13)
Secular increase in Earth's radius per year in cm	less than 0.2	0.6-1.0	(3)
Secular decrease in period of Earth's revolution around Sun per year in s	4.6×10^{-2}	$5.3 \times 10^{-3}-$ 6.7×10^{-3}	(12)
Secular rotation of planet perihelia in 100 terrestrial years in seconds of arc			
for Mercury	43.7	42.6	(9),(10)
for Earth	4.5	3.8	
for Venus	7.7	8.4	
for Mars	1.3	1.3	
Amplitude of seasonal change of the Earth's rotational period in s	6.5×10^{-4}	6.1×10^{-4}	(13)
Deflection of beam of light by the Sun in s of arc	1.81	1.75	(9),(10)
Delay in arrival of radio signal reflected from Venus and passing the Sun at a distance from the center (c) equal to its radius in the superior conjunction	197.0×10^{-6}	193×10^{-6}	(14)

where R is the planet's radius, G is the acceleration due to the Sun's pull at the planet's orbit, α is the angle between the orbital plane and the axis of the planet's rotation, and $K_1 = (9\pi/16)$.

The increase in the mass of the planets owing to gravitational interaction with the Sun (formulae (9) and (10)) should cause a growth of their size, a rise in gravity on their surfaces, a retardation of their rotation about their axes, an anomalous flattening at their poles, a shortening of the periods of their revolution around the Sun, a rotation of the perihelion longitudes of their orbits, and other phenomena.

Table I gives the results of calculations for the increase of the Earth's diurnal period, the shortening of the terrestrial year, the rotation of the perihelia of the planets, and their values obtained from observations. The agreement is quite satisfactory. An attempt has also been made to extrapolate the change of the mass of the Earth into the past, in accordance with formula (9). Such a change should also have been accompanied by changes in the Earth's size, gravity, and other parameters. The results of these calculations are given in Figure 3. It should be noted that these results are purely qualitative. By assuming such a possibility, we can reproduce the Earth's planetary geological evolution.

At an early stage in its evolution the Earth was a body covered with a thin crust. Owing to this and to the low growth rate of the Earth's mass, the crust was either distended or else formed narrow fissures, which were then filled in by subcrustal material rising from below (Figure 3a). With the growth of the Earth's mass and size, the crust became thicker and the fissures wider. The crust then began breaking up into big blocks with big inter-block spaces filled with light material (Figure 3b). This continued until the Earth, by virtue of its enhanced gravitational pull, became able to retain an atmosphere and a hydrosphere. At this stage the blocks became bigger, and the depressions between them were filled with sedimentary rocks as well as subcrustal matter. Primordial seas were formed in depressions between the blocks.

Later, as the Earth's mass increased, the crust began to break up into large blocks or groups of blocks behaving as rigid plates floating on the more fluid subcrustal material. The crust now divided into the continental and the oceanic crust, and for this reason, in the case of the young oceans (the Atlantic and the Indian Ocean), the geological structure and the shape of the coastlines of opposite continents exhibit a certain congruity. Afterwards the continental blocks changed little in shape or size, but the interblock spaces (oceans) rapidly expanded, forming a new crust, like that of the early stages of the Earth's evolution. With the passage of time this crust grew thicker and became similar, in composition and structure, in some places to the continental crust, while in others (rift valleys, abyssal faults) there appeared a thin young crust. In the process of evolution there should arise a discrepancy between the curvature radii of the surface of individual crustal blocks and the surface of the subcrustal material. The blocks may be visualized as floating convex crowns. Critical mechanical stresses cause these crowns to break up into a system of faults, including rift zones. The latter may heal or become the nuclei of new oceans either on continents (such as the Red Sea) or else on oceans with a sufficiently thick crust. The process of the breaking up of large crustal blocks should be accompanied by vertical movements and a turning of the blocks, by emanations and intrusions of plutonic rock, the formation of folds, *etc.* (*e.g.,* the Pacific shores).

Consequently, the evolution of the Earth's crust proceeds from the oceanic to the continental. On the Earth there should simultaneously be crusts of all ages, from newly-formed to the most ancient (see Figure 4).

With the growth of the mass and size of the Earth as a whole, the size of the continents thus increases little, but the oceans expand very rapidly, producing the impression of continental drift, which in reality does not take place. The growth of the Earth's mass and size can account for many of the geological phenomena [7] that have given rise to the new theory of plate tectonics, and this dispenses with the need to invoke such explanations as subduction, the descent of one plate under another.

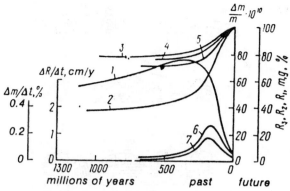

Figure 3. Changes in the mass of the Earth in the past. 1–change in relation to the growth of the Earth's mass in modern year ($\Delta m/m$), 2–change in the Earth's mass (m) and gravity (g) in per cent of their present values due only to density increase, 3–change in Earth's radius (R_1) and gravity (g) in per cent of their present values due to increase of volume, 4 and 5–changes in Earth's radius according to S.V.Keiry (R_2) and O.S. Hilgenberg (R_3) in per cent of its present value, 6–changes in growth of the Earth's mass over 1 million years ($\Delta m/\Delta t$) in per cent of its present value, and 7–curve showing change in the growth rate of Earth's radius ($\Delta R/\Delta t$) cm/y.

The fact that there are large-scale extended faults like the Earth's rifts and other fissures on the Moon, on planets of the solar system and on their satellites suggests that similar processes take place there as well.

The third postulate–concerning the interaction of inertial motion with the gravitational field–is described by formulae (5), (6), and (7). According to this postulate, movement in relation to an attracting body produces additional mass, and a change of mass and momentum. At low velocities these effects are negligible. But at velocities close to the velocity of light they are quite substantial and, moreover, are distinct from the effects of gravitational or inertial interactions.

If a radio signal, which has a definite momentum, is sent, it will, in a gravitational field, in accordance with formula (5), acquire an additional mass $m_m = -m(\varphi/c^2)$. Owing to the momentum conservation requirement, the velocity of the signal's propagation has to diminish by $\Delta V = c(m_m/m)$, which is the reason for the delay in the signal's arrival. If the signal passed at a distance R from the centre of the Sun and was reflected from some planet and received on the Earth, the delay of its arrival can be calculated according to the formula

$$\Delta t = \frac{4K}{c^3} \ln \frac{a_1 a_2}{R^2} \qquad (11)$$

where K is the solar constant (132.7×10^{24}) and a_1 and a_2 are the distances from the Sun to the Earth and to the other planet, respectively. Given in the Table is the result of a calculation of the time delay of a radio signal that was reflected from Venus and passed the Sun at a distance from its centre equal to its diameter. The discrepancy with experimental results does not exceed 3%.

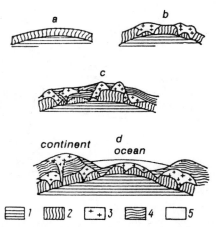

Figure 4. Main stages in the Earth's planetary geological evolution. a–early stage of the development of the Earth's crust, b–second stage of the development of the Earth's crust, but without sedimentary rocks, c–stage of development at which primordial seas and sedimentary rocks appeared, d–stage of the formation of the continental and oceanic crusts; 1–subcrustal material, 2–primary crust, 3–igneous rocks, 4–sedimentary rocks, and 5–ocean water.

In keeping with formula (6), the mass of a body must increase when it travels toward an attracting body and decrease when it travels in the opposite direction. The mass increment is biggest for light and must alter its frequency:

$$\frac{\Delta\gamma}{\gamma} = \frac{\Delta\varphi}{c^2} \qquad (12)$$

where γ is the light frequency. This change of light frequency in a gravitational field has been reliably confirmed in experiments utilizing the Mossbauer effect.

When light travels in a gravitational field, its momentum too increases by a quantity determined by formula (7). This results in the addition of the momenta mC and ΔmC_g, where C and C_g are equal to the velocity of light, but may have different directions; $m = (h\gamma/c^2)$, where h is Planck's constant. If the directions of the vectors C and C_g coincide, only the light frequency changes by the quantity $\Delta\gamma$ in accordance with formula (12). But if there is an angle α between the direction of the light and the direction of the force of gravity, the beam will be deflected by

$$\delta\alpha = \alpha\frac{\Delta m_2}{m} = \alpha\frac{\Delta\varphi}{c^2}. \qquad (13)$$

We can use formula (13) to find the curvature of a beam of light travelling from a star and grazing the solar disk

$$\varphi = \frac{K(\pi - 1)}{c^2 R}, \qquad (14)$$

where R is the radius of the solar disk. The results of the calculation given in the Table are in satisfactory agreement with the experimental data.

In addition to quantitative, there are several qualitative confirmations. These include the 11-year cycle of solar activity, which coincides with the period of Jupiter's revolution around the Sun (*i.e.*, with the period of mass exchange between the Sun and Jupiter) and more accurate measurements of which it may be hoped, will reveal a periodicity connected with the movement of other planets; the secular shortening of the periods of the revolution of the Moon around the Earth and of Phobos around Mars; the anomalous flattening of the Earth at the poles; the peaking of seismic activity at a certain time of the year; the decline in seismic activity from the Earth's Equator to the poles; the changes in the emission frequency of astronomical radio sources and the periodicity of such changes, *etc*.

There is good reason to suspect that irregular changes in the velocity of the Earth's rotation are associated with the interaction of inertial motion with the gravitational field (which moves in relation to the Earth and the Sun). This being so, there is a case for expecting a correlation between changes in solar activity, solar flares, and irregular changes of the velocity of the Earth's rotation. But in that case the velocity of the Earth's rotation, like solar activity, should be a good indicator of incoming gravitational energy.

It is also possible to estimate other effects, whose experimental detection will become possible in the very near future. The change in the periods of the revolution of the sixth and seventh satellites of Jupiter is of the order of 0.002 s per terrestrial year, and the rotation of the pericenter longitude of Amalthea amounts to approximately 2000 s per 100 terrestrial years, *i.e.*, is 50 times bigger than Mercury's. The satellites of Saturn likewise have big rotations of their pericenters: 300 s for Mimas and 170 s for Enceladus.

In 100 terrestrial years the Moon should turn in relation to the Earth by 372 seconds of arc, and in 1000 years, by 37220 s, *i.e.*, by almost one-fifth of its radius. Apart from the secular shortening of the period of the Moon's revolution around the Earth by 0.0009 s a year, there should be periodic changes of that shortening with an amplitude of 0.0052 s, periodic changes of the duration of the rotational period by 0.052 s, and a swaying of the pericenter by 0.21 s. By means of an artificial Earth satellite it should be possible to directly detect the mass increment. For a satellite having an eccentricity of 0.32 and a perigee at 321 km, the relative increase of the mass of a test body should be 2.1×10^{-6} per year. Contemporary weighing techniques make it possible to measure such a quantity with a relative error of the order of 0.5%.

In such an experiment, in addition to the change in weight, it is expedient to try to determine the changes in the physical and chemical composition of test bodies, *i.e.*, to subject them to a highly accurate analysis of chemical and isotope composition and other investigations, before and after orbital flight.

The change in the mass of the satellite will alter the linear velocity of its orbital movement, and the acceleration may attain 4×10^{-8} cm/s^2. At altitudes of over 1000 km such an acceleration can be detected. It may take the form of an apparently anomalously slow decrease in the density of the Earth's atmosphere. It should also be evident in what is termed a "nondrifting satellite." A satellite orbit may be chosen in such a way that the pericenter will rotate hundreds and even thousands of seconds of arc a year, while the period of revolution around the Earth will change about 0.0035 s a year, and the length of the semi-major axis, about 10 m a year. By employing accumulation techniques, such effects can evidently be detected.

The periodic change in the mass of a satellite with the mass of the Earth as they travel around the Sun should be reflected in a periodic change of the period of its rotation about its axis and revolution around the Earth.

This list of effects and of experiments for detecting them can be continued, but the decisive experiment will be that designed to directly measure the relative increase in the mass of a body as it moves in the Earth's gravitational field either aboard a satellite or else on the rim of a rotating disk.

It is thus expedient to first stage an experiment aboard a satellite, since it almost entirely corresponds to the experimental and calculated data obtained for planets and is, besides, much simpler to carry out.

References

1. P.I. Bakulin, L V. Kanapovich and V.I. Moroz, *Kurs obshchei astronomiyi* (A course in general astronomy) (Moscow: Nauka, 1974) (in Russian).
2. Yu. D. Belotserkovskii, in: *Vrashcheniye i prilivniye deformatsiyi Zemli* (The Earth's rotation and tidal deformations) (Kiev: Nauk. dumka) (in Russian).
3. M. Bott, *The Interior of the Earth* (London, 1971).
4. K.E. Veselov, *Prikladnaya geofizika* (Applied geophysics) (Moscow, issue 73, 1974)(in Russian).
5. K.E. Veselov, *Prikladnaya geofizika* (Applied geophysics) (Moscow, issue 80, 1975)(in Russian)
6. K.E. Veselov, *Prikladnaya geofizika* (Applied geophysics)(Moscow, issue 84, 1976)(in Russian).
7. K.E. Veselov, *Sovetskaya geologiya* (Soviet geology) (No. 5, 1976)(in Russian).
8. K.E. Veselov, *Prikladnaya geofizika* (Applied geophysics)(Moscow, issue 87, 1977)(in Russian).
9. D. I. Ivanenko, *Noveishiye problemy gravitatsiyi* (The latest problems in gravitation) (Moscow: Fizmatgiz, 1961)(in Russian).
10 L. D. Landau and E. M. Lifshits, *Field Theory* (London: Pergamon Press, 1960).
11. V.V. Radzievskii and I.I. Kagal'nikov, *Byulleten' vses. Astronomo-geodezicheskogo Obschestva* No. 26 (23), 1960 (in Russian).
12. Yu. A. Ryabov, *Dvizheniye nebesnykh tel* (The movement of celestial bodies) (Moscow: Fizmatgiz, 1962)(in Russian).
13. *Spravochnoye rukovodstvo po nebesnoi mekhanike i astrodinamike* (A manual in celestial mechanics and astrodynamics) (Moscow: Nauka, 1971)(in Russian).
14. N.S. Sidorenkov, *Astronom. Zhurnal*, issue 5, No. 52 (1975) (in Russian).
15. N.S. Sidorenkov, *Tr. Gidromettsentra SSSR*, issue 205, No. 4866 (1978) (in Russian).
16. *Fizika kosmosa* (The physics of the cosmos) (Moscow: Sov. entsiklopediya, 1976)(in Russian).

Deriving Newton's Gravitational Law from a Le Sage Mechanism

Barry Mingst* and Paul Stowe†

In this paper we derive Newton's law of gravity from a general Le Sage model. By performing a general derivation without a specific interaction process model, we can identify generic requirements of, and boundaries for, possible Le Sagian gravitational process models. We compare the form of the interaction found to the "excess" energy of the gas giants and find good agreement.

Introduction

In the eighteenth century, Georges-Louis Le Sage proposed that a universal field of ultra-mundane corpuscles interacting with matter gives rise to a shadowing effect. This shadowing in turn causes matter bodies to be pushed together, resulting in our observation of a gravitational force. Since Le Sage's time similar derivations have been performed by many others (*e.g.*, Shneiderov, 1943, 1961; Radzievskii and Kagalnikova, 1960). For the most part, however, the Le Sage approach has fallen from favor and general knowledge, largely due to the popular belief that phenomenological arguments make the entire idea untenable.

The authors' present purpose is twofold. First, we wish to determine general requirements for any such theory to replicate the Newtonian gravitational formula, in some limit. Secondly, we wish to determine phenomena that result from such a theory, and examine these against experimental limitations. This first paper focuses on the static properties of Le Sagian models. Static properties are those that do not depend on the speed of propagation of gravitational effects. The latter effects are addressed in the companion paper in this volume by Stowe [1].

Derivation of Newtonian Gravitation

If one begins with the postulate that there exists a fluidic medium (aether) composed of some particulate or corpuscular nature, one may be able to make use of many of the known fluid dynamic equations in later derivations. The postulate is therefore made that a fluidic medium is, as Le Sage proposed, comprised of "energetic corpuscles" pervading all of known space. We also take as a basic postulate that these corpuscles are in free motion with respect to each other and make no claims as to the substance or composition of these corpuscles. Let us further postulate that the collisions between corpuscles are fully

* 10370 Boulder Street, Nevada City, CA 95959. E-mail: mingstb@sim-ss.com
† 298 Nottingham Lane, American Canyon, CA 94589. E-mail: pstowe@ix.netcom.com

elastic. These corpuscles are not necessarily required to be matter (particles) or mass in the standard sense. What is of interest at this point is not the corpuscles themselves, but the effect of the corpuscles on matter.

We do not, at this point, claim any knowledge about the corpuscles. Likewise we do not claim knowledge of the innate structure of matter or the microscopic interactions that would take place between aether "corpuscles" and matter "particles." Instead, our approach is the reverse.

The purpose of any theory of gravitation is to produce, at a minimum, the Newtonian gravitational equation in its entirety. Most Le Sagian models manage the inverse square portion of Newton's equation without trouble. Many then go wide of the mark on the strict mass dependence of the resulting equations. Others appear to get into trouble as a result of discrepancies with calculated absorptive heat fluxes [17].

We begin our development therefore with a single premise of the *form* of the interaction with some physical flux, and then see if Newton's law can be derived at all. From Newton's law, we can then determine the specific type of flux that the interaction is *required* to affect. In this paper, we will not attempt to justify *how* that interaction might arise. The result will be a generic requirement that a Le Sagian model may meet, in order to produce Newton's law.

Our primary assumption is based upon standard exponential removal equations. We first define a flux per unit area to be represented by Φ. We presume that, on average, each interaction of the flux with a differential unit volume removes the same fraction of the incident flux, Φ_0. The change in flux due to interaction with matter is generally given in a differential distance by:

$$d\Phi = -\mu_l \Phi dx,$$

where μ_l is the linear flux attenuation (loss) coefficient (in units of inverse length) and x is the thickness of the shield.

One-Body Problem:

We next determine the effect of a stationary, spherical matter body of uniform density on the corpuscular field. Figure 1 identifies the geometric relationships.

The flux at point P along the line T will be affected by the interaction of the corpuscles with the sphere. This interaction may be a removal of corpuscles, a scattering of corpuscles, a removal of corpuscle energy/momentum (without scattering), or some combination of the three. It is not yet necessary to know what the mechanism of interaction will be. The flux will change regardless of the type of interaction taking place. Later, we will determine the type of flux needed to give Newton's law.

The interactions change the flux, Φ, in a given unit volume. This general interaction is then similar to standard ionizing-radiation interactions. It gives rise to a standard thin-shield reduction equation of:

$$\Phi_i = \Phi_0 e^{-\mu_l x}, \tag{1}$$

where Φ_i is the flux after interaction and Φ_0 is the initial flux.

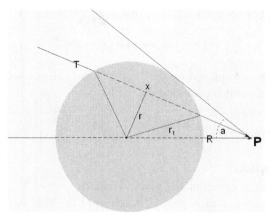

Figure 1

Because we still have the possibility of multiple scattering (multiple interactions in shields of sufficient size and thickness), the thin-shield equation is expanded using a general "buildup" term, $B(\mu_l x)$. This buildup term will correct the equation for multiple scattering events (if any) by corpuscles that are not initially traveling along the line T. The buildup term will depend on the relative importance of each of the three possible interaction modes (removal, scattering, and slowing) in the body, the shape of the body, the size of the body, and the distance of the body from point P. The corrected general removal equation is:

$$\Phi_i = \Phi_0 B e^{-\mu_l x} . \tag{2}$$

In an otherwise isotropic fluid medium, the flux from all directions is identical except where the fluxes traverse the matter body. These interacted fluxes are reduced according to the flux attenuation equation. In Figure 1, the net flux at point P is given as the sum (integral) of the all flux from the left and from the right of point P. The net contribution of fluxes outside angle a is therefore zero. The contribution of fluxes within angle a can be determined by rotating the figure around the line RP. The rotation angle θ coupled with the plane angle a gives the solid angle Ω. The difference between the fluxes from the right (Φ_0) and the fluxes from the left (Φ_i) is:

$$\Delta\Phi = (\Phi_0 - \Phi_i) d\Omega = (\Phi_0 - \Phi_i)\left(\frac{dr}{R}\right)\left(\frac{rd\theta}{R}\right). \tag{3}$$

The sum of all fluxes on possible lines T is then given by the integral:

$$\int \Phi d\Omega = \int \frac{1}{R^2}(\Phi_0 - \Phi_i) r \, dr \, d\theta , \tag{4}$$

which yields:

$$\Phi_{net} = \frac{2\pi\Phi_0}{R^2} \int_0^{r_1} \left[1 - B(\mu_l x)e^{-\mu_l x}\right] r \, dr . \tag{5}$$

The relationship between x, r, and r_1 is given by geometry as:

$$\left(\frac{x}{2}\right)^2 = (r_1+r)(r_1-r) = (r_1^2 - r^2).$$ (6)

Noting that x may be replaced by $2(r_1^2 - r^2)^{1/2}$, the general solution for the current (net flux) at a point is provided by:

$$\Phi_{net} = \frac{2\pi\Phi_0}{R^2} \int_0^{r_1}\left[1 - B\left(2\mu_l\sqrt{r_1^2 - r^2}\right)e^{-2\mu_l\sqrt{r_1^2-r^2}}\right]r\,dr .$$ (7)

The Weak Solution:

The weak solution to equation 7 is given when $2\mu_l (r_1^2 - r^2)^{1/2}$ is much less than 1. This is the case when only a small fraction of the flux is removed to or removed by the body. In this case the buildup term is essentially 1 (there is no significant scattering), and the exponential term may be replaced by the first two terms of the power series approximation. The weak solution simplifies to:

$$\Phi_{net} = \frac{4\pi\mu_l\Phi_0}{R^2} \int_0^{r_1}\sqrt{r_1^2 - r^2}\,r\,dr .$$ (8)

Integrating the above equation gives:

$$\Phi_{net} = \frac{\Phi_0}{R^2}\left(\frac{4\pi r_1^3}{3}\right)\mu_l .$$ (9)

The term in brackets is the volume of the sphere. The linear attenuation coefficient is generally a function of the density of the material. A more general parameter is the mass attenuation coefficient, μ_s. It is defined as $\mu_s = \mu_l/\rho$, where ρ is the material density. Noting that the mass of our uniform sphere is given by $M = \rho V$, the above equation becomes:

$$\Phi_{net} = \frac{\Phi_0}{R^2}\left(\frac{M}{\rho}\right)\mu_l = \Phi_0\frac{\mu_s}{R^2}M .$$ (10)

The weak solution to the one-body problem quantifies the creation of currents (differential flux) in the corpuscular aether fluid that would result from placing a uniform matter sphere in the fluid. The strength of the current is proportional to the mass of the sphere. The direction of the current is *toward* the center of the sphere.

The Strong Solution:

The strong solution to the one-body equation (7) is given when $2\mu_l (r_1^2 - r^2)^{1/2}$ is much greater than 1. This is the case for very strong interactions (of any kind) or when the body is very large. In the strong solution case, essentially all of the flux is removed to or by the body. In this case, the buildup term is inconsequential because essentially all of the flux will be absorbed. The exponential term goes to zero. This strong solution simplifies to:

$$\Phi_{net} = \frac{2\pi\Phi_0}{R^2}\int_0^{r_1} r\,dr .$$ (11)

This equation may be integrated and rearranged to give (where $r_1 < R$):

$$\Phi_{net} = \frac{\Phi_0}{R^2}\left(\pi r_1^2\right).$$ (12)

This is the maximum current that can be created, the strength of which is independent of the mass of the sphere.

Two-Body Problem (weak limit):

The equations determined above provide a description of the effect of a single body on the surrounding field. If a second body is placed in the vicinity of the first, it will be affected by the field's vector potential created by the first body. Suppose a second spherical body (body 2) is placed at the same point P in Fig. 1, where $r_2 \ll r_1 \ll R$. Under these conditions the flux lines that transit both body 1 and body 2 are essentially parallel. Sphere 2 will then see a current (net vector flux) flowing toward the center of the first sphere.

Up to this point, we have been working in very general terms of flux. In order to convert to the observed Newtonian gravitational force equation, we must identify the appropriate type of flux. Newton's second law requires a specific form of flux change:

$$\overline{F} = \frac{d\left(\overline{mv}\right)}{dt} = \delta\Phi A ,$$ (13)

where A is the effective cross-sectional area of the body and where the bars indicate vector quantities. The flux must therefore be a vector *momentum* flux having units of kg/m-sec^2.

Because the average path distance through sphere 2 is $4/3 r_2$, and the cross-sectional area of sphere 2 is πr_2^2, we can combine equations 9 and 13. The weak solution then becomes:

$$F = \Phi_{net}\left(\mu_{l2}\frac{4r_2}{3}\right)\pi r_2^2 = \Phi_{net}\left(\frac{4\pi r_2^3}{3}\right)\mu_{l2} ,$$ (14)

where μ_{l1} and μ_{l2} are the linear absorption coefficients for spheres 1 and 2 respectively. Substituting for Φ_{net} (equation 9) then gives the net interaction as:

$$F = \frac{\Phi_0}{R^2}\left(\frac{4\pi r_1^3 \mu_{l1}}{3}\right)\left(\frac{4\pi r_2^3 \mu_{l2}}{3}\right)$$ (15)

and, using equation 10:

$$F = \frac{\Phi_0}{R^2}\left(M_1\mu_{s1}\right)\left(M_2\mu_{s2}\right).$$ (16)

For ordinary matter we may write $\mu_{s1} = \mu_{s2} = \mu_s$. We therefore obtain:

$$F = \frac{\left(\Phi_0 \mu_s^2\right) M_1 M_2}{R^2}. \tag{17}$$

Since the term in brackets is a constant, this is the same form as the standard Newtonian gravitational force equation. The experimentally derived constant G would be:

$$G = \Phi_0 \mu_s^2. \tag{18}$$

This is both unsurprising and yet unusual. It is unsurprising because Newton's second law is based on momentum as $F = d(mv)/dt$. Since the basic gravitational formulations are based on relationships of *force* between matter bodies, momentum is the quantity of prime concern in this derivation of apparent forces. It is unusual, because as students we are used to dealing with fluxes of scalar quantities such as mass, particles, or energy. The requirement of exponential interaction of *vector* momentum flux gives rise to some deviations from the "standard" renditions of Le Sage theory—which are based on the absorption of fluxes of scalars (particles, mass, or energy).

The weak solution to the basic interaction with matter has *derived* the standard Newtonian gravitational formula for stationary bodies (under conditions where the Newtonian applies). The formulation also provides a *limit* for the effectiveness of the Newtonian formula for stationary bodies. This limit is the limit of the weak solution: $2\mu_l (r_1^2 - r^2)^{1/2} \ll 1$ or $2\mu_s (r_1^2 - r^2)^{1/2} \ll \rho$. This also gives an upper limit to the force, based on the strong solution:

$$F = \Phi_0 \left(\mu_s^2 M_2\right)\left(\frac{\pi r_1^2}{R^2}\right). \tag{19}$$

One can see from the above equations that the weak, stationary (nonrelativistic) solution reproduces the Newtonian gravitational force equation. G is seen as proportional to the product of the momentum flux and the square of the total mass interaction coefficient, μ_s. If this formula is correct, we know that the interaction is very weak. There are no obvious deviations from proportionality (departure from the weak solution) for masses from sizes from dust particles to stellar bodies. In validating these derivations against observation, one must keep in mind that all current mass estimates of planetary and stellar bodies are all based on strict use of the Newtonian (and Einsteinian) formulations, and might have to be adjusted according to the Le Sagian formulae.

If we examine equation 16, our momentum flux postulate gives a more physical explanation of the Newtonian empirical formulation:

$$F = \frac{\Phi_0}{R^2} \left(M_1 \mu_s\right)\left(M_2 \mu_s\right). \tag{20}$$

Here we explicitly see the momentum current set up at any point around a single body as the first two terms. A second matter body (represented by the third term) feels a force from this momentum current as a product of its interaction coefficient and its mass—*not* as a result of its mass alone. The empirical constant, G, has historically "hidden" portions of the matter interaction. We can therefore distinguish between the standard Newtonian gravitational field of body M_1 ($I = F/M_2$) and the Le Sagian "field":

$$I = \frac{F}{M_2 \mu_s} = \frac{\Phi_0}{R^2} \left(M_1 \mu_s \right).$$ (21)

The Newtonian "field" is purely an empirical mathematical concept. The Le Sagian field is a physical measure of the local momentum current imposed by body 1. It is not mass alone, but the mass interaction coefficient of matter that gives rise to the force of gravity. This derivation also includes an implicit derivation of the material-independence of the gravitational force, otherwise known as the relativistic equivalence principle (as confirmed by Eötvös-class experiments).

Energy Deposition

As mentioned in the introduction and illustrated in the derivation above, the Le Sage process involves the interaction of a proposed external field within material bodies. This situation should result in energy deposition. This is a unique prediction of Le Sagian models and has been pointed out by many in the past, including Lorentz and Poincaré. Indeed, it has been argued that if all of the flux is absorbed, a large gravitating body could vaporize [17]. In general, attenuation processes can include pure absorption, pure specular scattering, pure dissipative scattering, or any combination thereof. In the generic approach derived above, we cannot know *a priori* what the ratio of any or all of these are since the actual distribution of the underlying mechanistic processes are not identified or defined. However, we do know that any energy deposition must be proportional to the incident flux Φ_0 and the actual mass attenuation coefficient μ_s. In this model, at the weak static limit, the gravitational interaction is governed by equation 17, and as shown, is proportional to $\Phi_0 \mu_s^2$. The gravitational constant (G) becomes $\Phi_0 \mu_s^2$ in this evaluation. Since we cannot determine the individual values of Φ_0 or μ_s from G alone, we cannot directly derive what the heat deposition is from this Newtonian force equation. However, we do know that any power dissipation must result from the mass exponential-removal postulate we made at the very beginning.

We can now look at known astrophysical phenomena to quantify any excess energy emissions that are observed coming from planetary bodies. The earlier derivation of the Newtonian force equation required a weak solution. That is, $2\mu_l (r_1^2 - r^2)^{1/2} \ll 1$. Under these conditions, we can treat an entire planetary body as a single lump for energy deposition.

Incident sunlight heats a planetary body through combinations of reflection and absorption of the incident sunlight and the reemission of thermal energy. If there is an energy deposition from the interaction of Le Sage-type field, then there should exist an "excess" heat that cannot be readily accounted for by present theory. Regardless of what theory of formation is used, planets should eventually come into equilibrium with the input of solar energy. If we therefore select planetary bodies with relatively small metallic cores and either small size or good thermal mixing, we can quantify this "excess" heat output. The Jovian planets and the Earth's moon all fit these requirements. As it turns out, these bodies all exhibit an emission of "excess" heat. Figure 7 on page 121 of [10] clearly shows an effect consistent with an internal heat source for both Jupiter and Saturn.

If we integrate the absorbed solar heat flux on Jupiter over its surface area, we get a planetary average excess emitted heat flux of 6.6 W/m². Now we need to develop a mathematical relationship to quantify the effect.

Up to this point we have focused solely on the transfer of momentum from the field's flux into material bodies. Now we need to look at the energy flux. For this we must look in more detail at the hypothesized particulate nature of the impinging field. We make the assumption that the constituent corpuscles are of a single mass and irrotational to simplify the analysis. This may not be generally true, but it is sufficient to get an estimate of the magnitude of the heating effect. We further assume that the corpuscles follow Newton's laws of motion under their own interactions—even though they are not necessarily matter in the usual sense. We infer that the average corpuscle speed is the square root of 3 times the wave speed in this corpuscular medium, as is true of standard gases of irrotational particles. Finally, we assume that the wave speed of this medium is equal to the speed of light. This last is a reasonable assumption, as general relativity postulates the speed of gravitational waves to be equal to the speed of light. One can expect the corpuscular fluid wave speeds to be of that order of magnitude.

As we saw in the one-body problem above, any single body imposes a net velocity vector or current potential at every point in the flux field that surrounds it. The current at a particular point arises from the removal of momentum flux by the body. The current increases in strength as the distance from the body diminishes. Mathematically, we may therefore treat the currents as arising from an equivalent average acceleration of free corpuscles towards the body. A second matter body would respond to the corpuscular momentum current produced by the first body. The apparent acceleration of the corpuscles that defines this momentum current should be the same order as the acceleration imparted to matter bodies.

We assume that the rate of energy deposition in a body is equal to the increased energy flux associated with the accelerated corpuscles meeting the body. The increase in kinetic energy of corpuscles that have 'fallen' from an infinite distance to the surface of the body, relative to their initial energy, is then given simply by the change in their gravitational potential energy. We would then have:

$$\frac{\Delta E_k}{E_k} = \frac{\Delta v^2}{c^2} = \frac{2GM}{r_0}, \tag{22}$$

where E_k is the kinetic energy and m is the corpuscle mass. If the energy flux in free space is Ψ_0 (= $\Phi_0 c$), then the equilibrium rate of energy deposition in the body per unit of its spherical surface area, Ψ_{abs}, is:

$$\Psi_{abs} \approx \Psi_0 \frac{2GM}{r_0 c^2} . \tag{23}$$

The last unknown in the resulting equation is the power flux term Ψ_0, and as such must be normalized to a known quantity. Jupiter was selected for this purpose, since its excess heat flux is the best known of the gas giants. The relevant information is taken from reference 10 (p. 121-Fig. 7). The average excess heat flow from Jupiter is 6.6 W/m^2. Setting Ψ_{abs} equal to this value, and with $M = 1.97 \times 10^{27}$ kg and $r_0 = 7 \times 10^7$ m, the predicted total spherical power flux of the Le Sagian field is then:

$$\Psi_0 = \frac{\Psi_{abs} r_0 c^2}{2GM} . \tag{24}$$

$$\Psi_0 = 1.6 \times 10^8 \; W/m^2 . \tag{25}$$

Since this is a calculated value based upon an assumption that Jupiter's excess thermal power is coming from this source, validation can only be confirmed by now using this calculated value to attempt to predict the excess from other planetary candidates. We can combine the constants $2\Psi_0 G/c^2$ into a single term k_f, which has the value of 2.4×10^{-19} m/sec^3. This results in the simple equation for equilibrium power emission of

$$\Psi_{abs} = k_f \frac{M}{r_0} . \tag{26}$$

Utilizing this equation, we obtain the results for the "excess heats" for specified bodies (Table 1). The values for Uranus and Neptune were back calculated from gross temperatures and albedo estimates and so are less reliable than for Jupiter, Saturn and the Moon.

Table 1

	Predicted	Measured
Earth's Moon	10 mW/m^2	10 mW/m^2
Saturn	2.4 W/m^2	2.7 W/m^2
Uranus	0.83 W/m^2	0.4 W/m^2
Neptune	1.0 W/m^2	0.7 W/m^2

These results are of the proper order of magnitude, and within the limits of measurement uncertainties.

We can also do a similar evaluation of the power balance of the Sun. Equation 23 assumed a uniform density throughout the planet. Expected internal variations in the densities of gas giants are under two orders of magnitude. But density variations in the Sun are more than four orders of magnitude (Bahcall, 1989, figure 4.1). If we solve equation 23 for the Sun, then multiply the result by the surface area of the Sun, we get a result of 3.8×10^{23} W, or 0.1% of the total solar photon flux of 3.9×10^{26} W (Bahcall 1987, Table 4.1).

At first glance, this would be a very minor correction to standard solar models. The basic result of this correction would be to *lower* the apparent core temperature of the Sun. This lowering of the core solar temperature comes about from the need to match the boundary condition of measured solar energy flux. If the solar output is unchanged when this new energy term is added to the model, then the amount of energy required from hydrogen fusion to maintain hydrostatic equilibrium in the Sun will be reduced by 0.1%. The core temperature would then be lower than currently expected.

The current solar neutrino "problem" arises from the difference between the measured neutrino flux and the theoretical neutrino flux from the Sun. The neutrino measurements evaluated by the authors included chlorine, water, and gallium detectors. The chlorine and water detectors find between 20 to 50% of "expected" neutrinos. The gallium detectors see a flux that is a "little low" (Bahcall, 1987). Each type of detector looks at slightly different neutrino energy spectrums. The water and chlorine detectors look primarily at the ^{8}B neutrinos, due to their relatively high energy. According to Bahcall, there is a 37% theoretical uncertainty in the results for these neutrinos. The bulk of this uncertainty is the extremely strong temperature dependence of the ^{8}B-neutrino reaction (T^{24}). If the solar core energy is reduced by 0.1%, the core temperature would be reduced by 0.1% to the one-quarter power[*]. The apparent reduction in ^{8}B neutrino reaction rates would then be $1.01^{(24-4)}$, or 22%. The gravitational heat contribution would reduce the theoretical ^{8}B neutrino fluxes approximately to the level measured. However, an analysis of this kind really needs to be run through a standard solar model simulation, due to the extreme density variations and temperature dependencies.

Unfortunately, the combination of our momentum derivation and our energy correlation do not allow us to solve uniquely for Φ_0, Ψ_0 or μ_s because of the radial dependence of our correlation of Φ_0.

Shielding Effects

If models of this nature are used, the effect of gravitational shielding will arise when dealing with three or more matter bodies. This effect arises because a third body will shadow some of the momentum flux passing between two bodies on opposite sides of itself. The available flux is therefore lowered by a fraction that depends on the degree of removal by the third body.

A cursory review of the literature shows it is generally accepted that there is no gravitational shielding effect. Although experiments do exist that show a shielding effect, other experiments apparently show no such effect. Modanese (1995) states flatly that "...experiments, starting from the classical measurements of Q. Majorana, have shown that the gravitational force is not influenced

---

[*] By the Stephan-Boltzmann law, $E = \sigma T^4$

by any medium". Although commonly repeated, this statement is not correct. Majorana (1920) reported very definite positive effects.

The authors note that there is a significant difference in the type of experiment and analysis performed between the interpretations. Direct measurement experiments have found positive effects (*e.g.*, Majorana, 1920; Podkletnov, 1995). Indirect measurement experiments have not found positive effects (*e.g.*, Eckhardt, 1990). There are also theoretical "proofs" that the positive direct measurements "cannot" be valid (*e.g.*, Russell, 1921; Modanese, 1995).

If there are shielding effects, precise measurements of the constant, G, would not be consistent. This would result from unaccounted variations in the positions of the Sun, moon and nearby environmental massive objects during the experiments. A review of the literature shows that unexplained variations in precise measurements of G do exist. Gillies (1987) summarizes the most precise claims (see Table 2) and notes: "… that all these values exclude each other within the limits of the errors quoted. If we weight each of these three results equally, then it is clear that we do not know the value of G with an uncertainty of 10^{-4} as is otherwise suggested by the individual measurements."

Table 2

Authors	Year	Technique	Result ($\times 10^{-11}$ m^3/kg sec^2)
Facy, Pontikia	1972	resonant pendulum	$6.6714 \pm .0006$
Sagitov *et al.*	1979	torsion pendulum	$6.6745 \pm .0008$
Luther, Towler	1982	torsion pendulum	$6.6726 \pm .0005$
CODATA	1986	N/A	$6.67259 \pm .00085$

Precise measurements of the value of G in underground chambers show a greater value for G than those made on the surface of the Earth (Stacey *et al.*, 1987), but the values are not accepted to be consistent with any shielding effect. A good test would be measurements of the value of G during a total solar eclipse. We can use the results we obtained for estimating the planetary energy deposition to get an estimate of the shielding that would be expected from the Moon during a total solar eclipse. Equation 23 gives an estimate of the reduction. $\Psi_{abs}/\Psi_0 = 2GM/c^2r = 6.4 \times 10^{-11}$ per lunar passage. The authors would therefore expect an apparent diminution of the solar gravitational force on the order of 10^{-10} G during a solar eclipse.

As of yet NASA has not released the results of their efforts of August 11, 1999. De Sabbata (1987, p. 202) states that to date "(t)he most carefully done of the dozen or so such experiments appears to be that of Slichter, Caputo and Hager. They used a LaCoste-Romberg gravimeter to search for gravity variations before, during and after the total solar eclipse of February 15, 1961. Power spectrum analyses of their data indicate that λ^* is less than 8.3×10^{-16} cm^2/gm." This is four orders of magnitude below Majorana's ex-

---

[*] λ is given in the weak solution (De Sabbata, 1987, p. 200) as: $q = q_0 \{\lambda \rho x\}$. In this equation, q is the intensity of a gravitational "ray." λ is therefore equivalent to our mass interaction coefficient, μ_s, if the "ray" is momentum flux.

perimental results. De Sabbata does note, however, that "Majorana was known to be a very careful and competent experimentalist". The authors also note that Slichter *et al.* used an indirect measurement and had to build some unstated assumptions into their "power spectrum analyses" of the raw data.

Although the evidence is suggestive, it is not consistent and there is significant disagreement on the interpretation of results. Resolution of the apparent discrepancies in the observational status of gravitational shielding effects is beyond the scope of this paper.

Conclusions

This general approach to the Le Sagian mechanism has resulted in three areas that must be addressed in any physical Le Sage-type model. The Newtonian force law can be derived for a weak solution case. The model will require some internal heating of matter bodies. And gravitational shielding effects must occur. The derivation of the Newtonian force law is a strength of this approach. "Excess" planetary and solar heat is highly suggestive, but not conclusive.

References

1. Stowe, P., "Dynamic Effects in Le Sage Models," in *Pushing Gravity*, Apeiron, Montreal.
2. Majorana, Q., 1920. *Phil. Mag.* [ser. 6] **39**, 488-504.
3. Russell, H.N., 1921. "On Majorana's theory of gravitation," *Astrophys. J.* **54**, 334-346.
4. Shneiderov, A.J., 1943. *Trans. Amer. Geophys. Union*, 61-88.
5. Shneiderov, A.J., 1961. *Bollettino di Geofisica Teorica ed Applicata* **3**, 137-159.
6. Radzievskii, V.V. and Kagalnikova, I.I., 1960. "The nature of gravitation," *Vsesoyuz. Astronom.-Geodezich. Obsch. Byull.*, **26** (33), 3-14.
7. Podkletnov, E. and Nieminen, R., 1992. *Physica C* **203**, 441.
8. Podkletnov, E. and Nieminen, R., 1995. "Gravitational shielding properties of composite bulk $YBa_2Cu_3O_{7-x}$ superconductor below 70 K under electro-magnetic field," Tampere University of Technology Report.
9. Modanese, G., 1995. "Theoretical Analysis of a Reported Weak Gravitational Shielding Effect," MPI-PhT/95-44.
10. *The New Solar System*, 1981 (J.K. Beatty, B. O'Leary, A. Chaikin eds.), Cambridge University Press, p. 121.
11. Eckhardt, D. H., 1990. "Gravitational Shielding," *Phys Rev D* **42**, 2144-2145.
12. Web site: http://science.nasa.gov/newhome/headlines/ast12oct99_1.htm
13. Stacey, F. D. *et al*, 1987. *Rev. Mod. Phys.* **59**, 157.
14. Gillies, G. T., 1987. "Status of the Newtonian Gravitational Constant," in *Gravitational Measurements, Fundamental Metrology and Constants*, p. 195 *et seq.*, (V. De Sabbata and V.N. Melnikov eds.), NATO ASI, Series C, Vol. 230, Kluwer Academic Publishers.
15. Slichter, L. B. *et al*, 1965. *J Geophys Res* **70**, 1541.
16. Bahcall, J. N., 1989. *Neutrino Astrophysics*, Cambridge University Press.
17. Poincaré, H., 1946. *The Foundations of Science*, Science Press, pp. 517-521.

Dynamic Effects in Le Sage Models

Paul Stowe[*]

In this article, we will explore and quantify specific dynamical processes related to the interaction of material bodies with an energetic medium, such as that proposed by Le Sage. Specifically quantified herein are the effects of increased directional attenuation due to inertial motion (Drag), finite propagation speed on the orbital processes (Gravitational Aberration), and field coupling effects due to rotating bodies (Frame Dragging).

Introduction

From its inception, Le Sage's postulate has inherently contained all the elements that are now known to exist as part of the gravitational process. It also has other features that are not currently recognized in modern theories of gravity. One of these is the Le Sage field's power dissipation (induction heating) [1]. In addition, there are various dynamical aspects of the model, such as linear drag and aberrational fling. Historically, it has been argued that these specific elements appear to be in direct conflict with known observations. It is these dynamical elements of Le Sage's theory and their quantification that are the focus of this paper. We will show that, contrary to the historical arguments, these elements need not be in conflict with astronomical observations.

The basic concepts and terms that will be used were discussed in the companion paper in this volume by the author and Barry Mingst. First and foremost is Le Sage's idea of a sea of energetic corpuscles interacting with matter. A key concept associated with this is a term called flux (Φ), which is simply a count of the number of 'events' which, from any direction, will intercept a specified unit surface area in a unit of time. We can define this for many different physical properties, such as mass, momentum, energy, power, *etc.* The term 'current' defines any net or resultant when the vector components of flux are evaluated and summed through a solid 4π angle. The flux is considered isotropic if, at the point of evaluation, the resulting current is zero.

The other key parameter needed to define the Le Sage process is the mass attenuation coefficient μ_s [2]. This term, commonly used in ionizing radiation transport, characterizes field particle interactions with matter on a per unit area basis.

[*] 298 Nottingham Lane, American Canyon, CA 94589. E-mail: pstowe@ix.netcom.com

Pushing Gravity: new perspectives on Le Sage's theory of gravitation
edited by Matthew R. Edwards (Montreal: Apeiron 2002)

195

Drag from Inertial Motion

Consider an arbitrary slab of matter situated in a one-dimensional corpuscular fluid. Half the momentum flux is impinging from the left and half from the right. Therefore, the resulting current is defined by the simple relationship:

$$\Phi_{net} = \frac{\Phi_0}{2} - \frac{\Phi_0}{2} = 0. \tag{1}$$

Here Φ_0 is the momentum flux in free space well away from masses, with units of kg/m-sec^2. Therefore, when the slab is at rest with respect to the field, the impinging flux is isotropic, and $\Phi_{net} = 0$. However, if the slab is set in motion, say towards the right, the result is a non-zero current Φ_{net}. The magnitude of this is defined by the equation:

$$\Phi_{net} = \frac{1}{2}\Phi_0\left[\left(1-\frac{v}{\gamma}\right)-\left(1+\frac{v}{\gamma}\right)\right] = -\Phi_0\frac{v}{\gamma}, \tag{2}$$

and, as indicated by the negative sign, opposes the motion.

At this point, we need to extend our one-dimensional case to three dimensions. In a manner analogous to the one-dimensional case, we obtain the factor of the square root of three in the three dimensional case [12]:

$$\Phi_{net} = -\sqrt{3}\Phi_0\frac{v}{\gamma} \tag{3}$$

For a weakly attenuating body [1], the resulting deceleration is defined as:

$$a_d = -\Phi_{net}\mu_s \tag{4}$$

By inspection of equation 3, we see that as corpuscular speed goes to infinity the current vanishes. Thus, equation 4 will also go to zero, clearly demonstrating that the process of field attenuation resulting from very high corpuscle speed results in drag free inertial motion.

Given that $G = \Phi_0\mu_s^2$ per equation 18 of Ref. [1], we therefore have $\Phi_0 G = (\Phi_0\mu_s)^2$. Combining equations 3 and 4, we then obtain:

$$a_d = \sqrt{3\Phi_0 G}\ \frac{v}{\gamma}. \tag{5}$$

Note that, like normal gravitational acceleration, this term is mass independent, and the resulting deceleration is dependent only upon the speed of the body through the field.

A field power flux Ψ_0 of 1.6×10^8 W/m^2 was derived from equation 24 and given as 25 of Ref. [1]. If we use this value to obtain the related momentum flux, we get $\Phi_0 \propto \Psi_0/c$ or $\Phi_0 = k\Psi_0/c$. The constant k is a geometry factor and could be unity if the geometry of our evaluation were spherical, as was the case for the original derivation of Ψ_0. However, in the current linear situation we find that k needs to be 4π. We then have $\Phi_0 = 4\pi\Psi_0/c$ or 6.7 kg/m-sec^2. Given the assumption $\gamma = \sqrt{3}c$, where the value $\sqrt{3}$ relates the bulk transverse wave speed c to the mean speed of the particles (see Section 5, Chapter 11, Fig. 11-8 Ref. [8]), from equation 5 we obtain:

$$a_d = \sqrt{\Phi_0 G}\ \frac{v}{c} = \Phi_0 \mu_s \frac{v}{c}. \tag{6}$$

As an example we may use the anomalous acceleration of the Pioneer 10 spacecraft [3]. Using $\Phi_0 = 6.7$ kg/m sec^2 (for the case $k = 4\pi$) and given Pioneer 10's velocity of 12,000 m/sec, the computed result from equation 6 is 8.5×10^{-10} m/sec^2. This would be a perfect match with the observed drag on the Pioneer spacecraft.

Gravitational Aberration (Propagation Delay)

The classic Newtonian force equation $F = GMm/R^2$ and its gravitic potential $a = GM/R^2$ are expressions that define the instantaneous force and acceleration generated by the interaction of mass M with any other mass m at the given distance R. As this is explicitly a static solution, no attempt is made to account for any motion of M or m. However, orbiting masses are not a static problem. The above equations are therefore not strictly applicable for any such system if the speed at which the force is transmitted or communicated between the masses is not instantaneous. This is a well-known condition of the interaction of fields with finite propagation velocity. Feynman provides a very good discussion of this for the electric field interaction in Vol. II, Chapter 21 of Ref. [4] and Griffiths provides the full derivation in section 9.2.2 of Ref. [11]. In the case of gravity, the situation is similar: mass M will always see mass m where it was R/γ seconds ago and vice versa. In the literature, this is known by the term retarded potential.

As an illustration, consider two equal masses m and M orbiting each other around a common center. Let the line of sight path from M to m be R' and the actual distance be R. Note that different circular orbits are described by R' for each body. These are offset from each other by Rv/γ. As γ goes to infinity these converge to a single circular orbit (the traditional Newtonian orbit). Because the projected orbits are offset by Rv/γ at every position of the Newtonian projection, it has been argued [10] that there should be an outward radial component of acceleration on each body of the order of $v^3/\gamma R$. This would result in both bodies spiraling outward until they leave the influence of each other.

However, as Feynman points out in his discussion, this effect is canceled by the dynamical effects manifested in the first and second derivatives that result from the field's *potential*. In other words, the classical electrostatics potential equation,

$$E = \frac{e}{4\pi\varepsilon_0 R^2}, \tag{7}$$

also does not account for any motion or finite propagation. The modern Maxwellian formulation is

$$E = -\nabla \cdot V - \frac{\partial \mathbf{A}}{\partial t}. \tag{8}$$

It is this formulation that is key to the lack of observed aberration. Feynman puts it nicely (Vol. I, 28-1 Ref. [4]) when he says:

> The whole thing is much more complicated. There are several more terms. The next term is as though nature were trying to allow for the fact that the effect is retarded, if we might put it very crudely. It suggests that we should calculate the delayed coulomb field and add a correction to it, which is its rate of change times the time delay that we use. Nature seems to be attempting to guess what the field at the present time is going to be, by taking the rate of change and multiplying by the time that is delayed. But we are not yet through. There is a third term—the second derivative, with respect to t, of the unit vector in the direction of the charge. Now the formula *is* finished, and that is all there is to the electric field from an arbitrarily moving charge....

The resulting potential created in the Le Sagian momentum field has an analogous formulation:

$$a = -\nabla \cdot K - \frac{\partial \mathbf{g}}{dt}, \qquad (9)$$

where $K = GM/R$ and $\mathbf{g}$ is the equivalent *vector potential* for the gravitic field. Like electrostatics, the second term vanishes under static conditions resolving equation 10 to $a = GM/R^2$.

Re-writing Feynman's equation I-28.3 [ref 4] in the equivalent gravitational form we get:

$$a_g = GM\left[\frac{\mathbf{u'}}{R'^2} + \frac{R'}{\gamma}\frac{\delta}{\delta t}\left(\frac{\mathbf{u'}}{R'^2}\right) + \frac{1}{\gamma^2}\frac{\delta^2 \mathbf{u'}}{\delta t^2} \right], \qquad (10)$$

where $\mathbf{u'}$ is the vector pointing to R'.

This should not be unexpected. If an instability due to aberration actually existed, it would be as problematic for the General Theory of Relativity (GR), which includes the Newtonian for the weak slow speed limit, as it would be for any Le Sagian model. Carlip recently addressed this specifically for GR [6] and concluded, like Feynman did for EM, that aberration due to finite propagation is almost exactly canceled. The slight residual imbalance remaining for GR results in orbital decay.

Rotational Coupling of Gravitating Bodies

This feature of Le Sage's process is probably one of its most interesting and unique attributes. Since the Le Sage process centers around the interaction of matter with a particulate field, if the matter rotates and the Le Sagian corpuscles have a finite speed, that rotational signature is impressed on, and will be manifested in, the resulting field's potential. As a result, other material objects subject to this will experience torsional field forces.

While standard Newtonian theory has no capacity for such effects (since it is centered solely around the single mathematical formula of the Le Sage weak static solution), the mathematics of the General Theory of Relativity does [5]. This is termed *Inertial, or Reference Frame Dragging*. However, within its conceptual framework, there is no physical basis for it– it is simply a result of the mathematical formulation. As noted by many, the mathematics of GR is inherently based on a hydrodynamic premise [5, 8, 9]; however, any literal interpretation of this as relating to any actual physical media is expressly denied. In the Le Sage concept, it is explicitly a result of inherent hydrodynamic processes.

To understand the basic effect let us consider what happens to a freely floating, centrally located material compass within a rotating hollow sphere or ring. As the outer body rotates, the field interacting with this body is slightly deflected, or twisted. This deflection in turn imparts a rotation or torque on the detached material compass located at the center of the body [7]. The result is that the central compass will slowly acquire the rotational speed of the outer ring. Similarly, a rotating planet or star imparts a torque or drag upon any physical bodies under the influence of its field potential.

The magnitude of this slight effect is related to the potential created by the rotating body (GM) and the maximum rotational velocity (ωr), such that the torsional acceleration a_t is of the order of

$$a_t = \frac{GM}{R^2}\frac{\omega r^2}{R\gamma} = \frac{GM\omega r^2}{R^3\gamma},\qquad(11)$$

where r is the radius of the mass M and R is the distance from the center of mass M to the point of interest. For example, the above equation gives a maximum acceleration on a GPS satellite in earth orbit at 12,500 miles of 3.67×10^{-8} m/sec^2 or 3.44 nano-g's.

Summary

As one can see from these components, orbital dynamics in Le Sagian theories encompasses many subtle elements. There is the potential from aberration to fling masses apart; for orbital decay due to linear drag; as well as for either fling or drag (depending upon the direction of orbital motion) resulting from rotational coupling. One would think that under such conditions a Le Sage model with finite propagation speed would make dynamical stability of orbits rare or impossible. The key to orbital stability, however, lies in fact that in these models aberration is the predominant factor. Thus the controlling equation results from equation 10. As long as the retarded potential from this aberration exceeds the combined effects of all the others (linear drag, rotational coupling), the field will adjust its potential to compensate, maintaining an orbit. In his paper [6], Carlip asked the question "Is Cancellation a Miracle?". The answer of course is no, it is an intrinsic property of the field to seek and establish within itself a stable zero net energy configuration. This is also known as Noether's Theorem. In particular, the effect of drag due to linear motion would only be manifested when a body is not in an orbit, as is the case for the aforementioned Pioneer spacecraft.

Le Sage models have subtle differences from the current standard mathematical representations of gravity, which can have major consequences for large-scale cosmological processes. Looking into these in detail should prove an interesting endeavor.

References

1. B. Mingst, "Deriving Newton's Gravitational Law from a Le Sage Mechanism", *Pushing Gravity*, Apeiron, Montreal, 2002.
2. A. B. Chilton *et al.*, *Principles of Radiation Shielding*, Prentice-Hall, 1984.
3. Pioneer Spacecraft Deceleration, *http://www.aps.org/meet/CENT99/BAPS/abs/S5310002.html*
4. R. Feynman *et al.*, *The Feynman Lectures on Physics*, California Institute of Technology, 1964.
5. J. Islam, *Rotating Fields in General Relativity*, Cambridge University Press, 1985.
6. S. Carlip, "Aberration and the speed of gravity", *Phys Lett A* **267**, pp. 81-87, 2000.
7. E. Harrison, *Cosmology, The Science of the Universe*, Cambridge University Press, 1981.
8. E. Condon and H. Odishaw, *The Handbook of Physics*, McGraw-Hill, Second Edition, 1967. For GR see Section 2, Chapter 6, pp. 2-50.
9. Schutz, *A First Course in General Relativity*, Cambridge University Press, 1990.
10. Lightman *et al.*, *Problem Book in Relativity and Gravitation*, Princeton University Press, 1975.
12. D. Griffiths, *Introduction to Electrodynamics*, Section 9.2.2, Prentice-Hall, 1989.
13. Bueche, *Introduction to Physics for Scientists and Engineers*, McGraw-Hill, 1969, p. 269.

The Electro-Thermodynamic Theory of Gravitation

Nedelia Popescu-Adamut[*]

This paper summarizes the electro-thermodynamic theory of gravitation (TETG) elaborated by Iosif Adamut in the nineteen eighties. In this model, space is filled with a symmetric blackbody electromagnetic radiation field described by a continuous spectrum $0 \leq v < \infty$. Due to attenuation of this radiation in passing through bodies, a Newtonian force is generated between them. Adamut obtained a gravitational formula identical to Newton's law, with the gravitational constant $f \cong k_0 K_{0g} \kappa$. K_{0g} represents the intensity of the radiation field having gravitational effects, κ is the absorption coefficient per unit mass and k_0 is a dimensional constant of homogenization. Gravity is not an active force of attraction between bodies, but results instead as a pushing force. This theory was first applied to two pairs of bodies from our Solar System (Earth-Moon and Sun-Mercury), leading to values for κ ($\kappa = 2.71 \times 10^{-18}$ $m^2 kg^{-1}$), K_{0g}, K_{sg} and u_{0g}. Adamut also applied his model to a proposed laboratory experiment (*i.e.*, a small sample body situated under a large screening body), as well as to a screening experiment (*i.e.*, a sample body at the Equator, using the Earth as a screen), for which the theory is presented.

1. Introduction

Electromagnetic radiation fills all space, including interatomic space; it propagates with a velocity $q \leq c$ (c being the velocity of light); it transports energy, momentum, angular momentum and it leads to continuous motions of bodies in space. Radiation and matter interact by means of emission and absorption processes and transform from one to another by combustion, nuclear reactions, gravitational collapse, absorption, *etc.*

In Newton's law $F_{12} = f\left(M_1 M_2 / r_{12}^2\right)$, F_{12} is the force needed in order to produce the acceleration of a body ($F = ma$). The gravitational constant f was introduced for homogeneity purposes in the force formula. This led to the idea that gravitation means attraction, although Newton himself suggested to search for the gravitational mechanism as a possible impulse or pushing effect (Newton, *Philosophiae Naturalis Principia Mathematica*, B.I. Sect. XI, Introd., p.29, 30). Newton considered that "the cause of gravitation has to be an agent which constantly acts after certain laws" (p.447).

In the same section of the *Principia* Newton also suggested a model of gravitation with two bodies $O_i(a_i, \mu_i)$ of radius a_i and density μ_i and a moving "Any Medium Whatever" (AMW). AMW could be a radiation field (as in TETG, Adamut 1976, 1982, 1983, 1986) or an elastic, continuous material me-

---

[*] Astronomical Institute of the Romanian Academy, Str. Cutitul de Argint, 5, 75212, Bucharest 28, Romania.

Pushing Gravity: new perspectives on Le Sage's theory of gravitation
edited by Matthew R. Edwards (Montreal: Apeiron 2002)

dium, as proposed by Newton (in Queries 21 and 31, paragraph 23 of [26]). Whatever its ultimate nature, the AMW must at least convey impulse and kinetic energy. Neither bodies nor the AMW possess gravity, but only inertia, as "*a vis insita*." Consequently, one must demonstrate that gravity results as an effect of the contiguous interaction. Since Newton considered "the centripetal forces as attractions; though perhaps in a physical strictness they may more truly be called impulses," the model has been called "Newton's Impulse Model of Gravitation," NIM (Adamut 1987, 1989, 1990).

NIM is essentially a mathematical model, because a model of a continuous medium permits the avoidance of any hypothesis regarding the intimate constitution of matter and thus allows a mathematical analysis. It is also a phenomenological model, explaining, at least macroscopically, the mechanism of gravity as resulting from the partial absorption of the AMW while passing through bodies, an idea expressed much earlier by Le Sage (1784). In [5]-[9] Adamut presented the mathematical results of NIM, which he also termed the "AMW-Newton-Le Sage" model.

Within the framework of the Newtonian Attraction Model of Gravitation (a model with one component only, the bodies O_i that generate a gravitational attraction field $\overline{\gamma}_N$), the idea of attenuation was revisited by Laplace (1825) and Majorana (1957). Laplace deduced a formula for the gravitational force between Moon and Earth, F_{0g}, with a "complementary term"—as named later by Poincaré (1911). The theoretical and experimental research of Majorana, discussed in 18 "Notes," leads to a value of the attenuation coefficient, a new physical constant, of $\kappa = 2 \times 10^{-12} \text{ cm}^2 \text{ g}^{-1}$ (see Table 1).

Between 1965 and 1975, Iosif Adamut elaborated the electromagnetic and thermodynamic theory of gravitation (TETG), a theory analogous to the corpuscular theory of Le Sage. This theory was the first step in Adamut's research in the field of gravitation.

Adamut (1976, 1982) developed his theory in the spirit of Faraday's, Maxwell's and Lorentz's ideas on the unity of all physical forces. In TETG the Newtonian force manifests between two bodies as an effect of the attenuation of a symmetric, homogeneous, isotropic electromagnetic radiation band of a specific intensity K_{0g}. The gravitational field is produced in part by the radiation of the celestial bodies and is attenuated when passing through other bodies. Utilizing Newton's second and third laws of dynamics and Coulomb's law, the author has obtained a more developed Laplace-Majorana "complementary term." Other aspects concerning this theory have been treated in other papers (Adamut 1983, 1986).

The present paper attempts to summarize the electro-thermodynamical theory of gravitation. In general, one can say that TETG is a particular case of NIM, in which the medium is the symmetric, homogeneous, isotropic electromagnetic radiation field.

The fundamental ideas of TETG are:

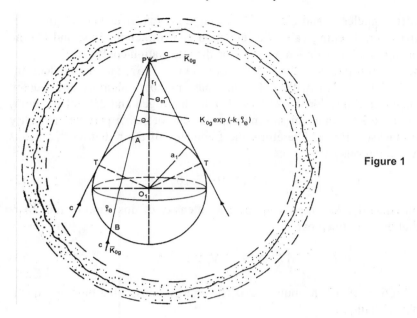

Figure 1

1) Gravitation results from a pushing force exerted by a symmetric, homo-geneous, isotropic electromagnetic radiation band, of a specific inten-sity K_{0g}. This radiation is produced by all bodies in the Universe, most importantly the stars.

2) The "gravitational" radiation, being electromagnetic, is attenuated in passing through bodies. It is this attenuation which gives rise to the New-tonian gravitational force. This idea has existed since 1897 and has been pursued by many researchers.

2. The Matter-Radiation Interaction

Let us consider a spherically symmetric field of electromagnetic radiation in an absolute blackbody spherical enclosure of radius r and an elementary volume V that contains a spherical screen body $O_1(a_1, \mu_1)$, with radius a_1 and density μ_1 (Figure 1). Every monochromatic radiation with specific intensity K_v (with fre-quency $0 \le v \le \infty$, *i.e.*, the radiation has a continuous spectrum) will interact with the substance of the screen body, being partially reflected, absorbed and propagated through the body.

The total specific intensity of the radiation, K_0, is denoted by the relation:

$$K_0 = 2 \int_0^\infty K_v \, dv . \tag{1}$$

We consider the case in which the radiation is partially absorbed and par-tially propagated through the screen body. We suppose that the continuous spectrum of the radiation, emitted by the considered enclosure, contains at least a narrow band of radiation for which the diameters of the screen body's stable

particles (the nucleons and electrons) are large enough that: (1) one may neglect diffraction, keeping valid the reflection and refraction laws; and (2) the
condition $a_1 k_1 \ll 1$ is satisfied, where k_1 is the attenuation coefficient.

The electron radius is 2.82×10^{-15} m (Jackson 1967) and the nucleon radius is $1.2 \times 10^{-15} \sqrt[3]{A}$ m, with $\sqrt[3]{A}$ = the mass number (Shortley and Dudley
1971, Chap.45). Since $1 < A < 239$ (with 1 for hydrogen and 239 for uranium)
and $1 < \sqrt[3]{A} < 6.206$, one can assume that the size of stable particles is nearly
constant (Jackson 1967). Therefore, the frequency of the radiation that meets
the above conditions is:

$$v > \frac{c}{2 \cdot 1.2 \cdot 10^{-15}} = 1.25 \cdot 10^{23} \cong 10^{23} \, \text{Hz} . \tag{2}$$

Consequently, K_{0g}, the mean specific intensity of this band of nonpolar-
ized radiation, is defined by:

$$K_{0g} = 2 \int_{v_x}^{v_y} K_v \, dv \; ; v_y \geq v_x > 10^{23}. \tag{3}$$

(Planck 1966, Sect. 17, formula (12)). The energy transported by every quantum of this radiation is

$$E = h v > h \cdot 10^{23} = 6.6256 \cdot 10^{-34} \cdot 10^{23} = 6.6256 \cdot 10^{-11} \, \text{J} ,$$

where h is Planck's constant. An electromagnetic radiation band that has a
large capacity to penetrate matter will be denoted "gravitational" radiation, due
to its gravitational effects.

From the thermodynamic viewpoint, it would be sufficient to know the
monochromatic intensity of the radiation K_v, for all frequencies. However,
from the electromagnetic point of view it would also be necessary to know the
six electric and magnetic components of the electromagnetic field as a function
of time, at every point in space. Therefore, it would be necessary to know the
amplitude C_n and phase difference θ_n, for all the partial waves constituting the
radiation (Planck 1966, Sect. 113). Since one may assume that only K_{0g} can be
known, this theory can be named the "*electro-thermodynamical theory of
gravitation*" (TETG).

In Figure 1 consider the spherical surface of the body O_1. On the interior
side of this surface, the radiant energy passing through an infinitesimal surface
element $d\sigma = a_1^2 \sin\gamma \, d\gamma \, d\varphi$ in a solid angle $d\Omega = \sin\theta \, d\theta \, d\varphi$ along the direction $\Delta(\theta, \varphi)$ is:

$$dE_t = K_0 d\Omega \, \cos\theta \, d\sigma \, dt = K_0 \sin\theta \, \cos\theta \, d\theta \, d\varphi \, d\sigma \, dt . \tag{4}$$

The spherical angular coordinates are $0 \leq \varphi \leq 2\pi$, while the azimuthal angle is
$0 \leq \theta \leq \pi$. This radiant energy stays within the body for a time interval dt,
which varies between $0 \leq dt = 2a_1 \cos\theta / q \leq 2a_1 / q$. Here $q < c$ (the velocity of
light), when the body O_1 is present, and $q = c$, if O_1 is absent (*i.e.*, the spherical
surface is a mathematical one).

The total energy contained inside the spherical surface of volume V, at a
moment of time t, is:

$$E_t = \frac{4\pi a_1^3 K_{0g}}{3q} \int\limits_0^{2\pi} d\varphi \int\limits_0^{\pi} \sin\gamma \, d\gamma = \frac{4\pi a_1^3}{3} \frac{4\pi K_{0g}}{q} = V \frac{4\pi K_{0g}}{q}. \tag{5}$$

The specific energy u_{0g} has the form:

$$u_{0g} = \frac{4\pi K_{0g}}{q}. \tag{6}$$

In the following, we consider two situations for the considered screen body.

a) *An inactive screen body*. From the point of view of TETG, the gravitational field is produced primarily by the radiation of celestial bodies. In the case of an inactive screen body, in a stationary state, the temperature of the enclosure relative to the screen body is not significant.

As a result, the electromagnetic radiation with a specific intensity K_{0g} passing through the substance of the screen body is attenuated according to the law of Bouguer and Lambert:

$$K_{0g,\rho_\theta} = K_{0g} \exp(-k_1 \rho_\theta), \tag{7}$$

where k_1 is the absorption coefficient and ρ_θ is the distance crossed by the radiation through the screen body substance (Figure 1).

If a_1 is the screen body radius; $\overline{r_1} = \overline{O_1 P}$ is the distance between the center O_1 of the screen body and a point P, a point where the resultant radiation field is calculated; θ is the angle between $\overline{r_1}$ and ρ_θ, pointing to P; θ_m is the angle between $\overline{r_1}$ and the tangent in the point T (Figure 1), we have:

$$\rho_\theta = 2r_1 \sqrt{\zeta_1^2 - \sin^2\theta}, \tag{8}$$

with

$$\zeta_1 = \frac{a_1}{r_1} = \sin\theta_m. \tag{9}$$

The absolute intensity of radiation at point P, at a moment of time t, along a direction $\Delta(\varphi, \theta)$ passing through the screen body has the expression:

$$K\left[P_{\Delta(\rho,\theta)}, t\right] = K_{0g}(t) + \left|-\overline{K}_{0g,\rho_\theta}(t)\right| = K_{0g}\left[1 + \exp(-k_1\rho_\theta)\right]. \tag{10}$$

Using relations (7) and (8) for $r_1 \to \infty$ one obtains for a direction $\Delta(\varphi, \theta)$:

$$K\left[P_{\Delta(\rho,\theta)}, t\right] = K_{0g}(t) + \left|-K_{0g}(t)\right|, \tag{11}$$

with the elementary solid angle $d\Omega = \sin\theta \, d\theta \, d\varphi$, from which the screen body O_1 is viewed, becoming equal to zero.

For a point situated on the screen body, relation (10) becomes:

$$K\left[P_{\Delta(\rho,\theta)}, t\right] = K_{0g}\left[1 + \exp(-2k_1 a_1 \cos\theta)\right], \tag{12}$$

and for the center of the screen body (i.e., $r_1 = 0$):

$$K[O_1, t] = K_{0g}\left[\exp(-k_1 a_1) + \left|-\exp(-k_1 a_1)\right|\right] = 2K_{0g} \exp(-k_1 a_1). \tag{13}$$

The following relation gives the resultant of the radiation field at a point $P(\bar{r_1})$ due to the asymmetry of the radiation field intensity, K_{0g}, in the presence of the screen body O_1 :

$$\delta(P,K_{0g}) = \int\limits_{0}^{2\pi} d\varphi \left[\begin{array}{l} \int\limits_{0}^{\theta_m} K_{0g} \exp\left(-2k_1 r_1 \sqrt{\zeta_1^2 - \sin^2\theta}\right) \sin\theta \, \cos\theta \, d\theta + \\[2mm] + \int\limits_{\theta_m}^{\pi} K_{0g} \sin\theta \, \cos\theta \, d\theta \end{array} \right] =$$

$$= -\frac{\pi K_{0g}}{r_1^2}\left[\exp\left(-2k_1 a_1\right)\left(\frac{a_1}{k_1}+\frac{1}{2k_1^2}\right)-\frac{1}{2k_1^2}+a_1^2\right]. \tag{14}$$

Using the theory of interaction between radiation and matter (Chandrasekhar 1950) one has the relation:

$$k_1 = \mu_1 \kappa , \tag{15}$$

with μ_1 representing the density of the homogeneous and isotropic body and κ representing the absorption coefficient per unit mass.

From (14)–(15) and developing the exponential in a power series one obtains:

$$\bar{\delta}(P,K_{0g}) = -K_{0g} k_{f1}\kappa \frac{M_1 \, \bar{r_1}}{r_1^2 \, r_1}, \tag{16}$$

with the dimensionless form factor:

$$k_{f1} = 1 - \frac{3}{4}a_1\mu_1\kappa + \frac{2}{5}(a_1\mu_1\kappa)^2 - \frac{1}{6}(a_1\mu_1\kappa)^3 + \frac{2}{35}(a_1\mu_1\kappa)^4 - \frac{7}{420}(a_1\mu_1\kappa)^5. \tag{17}$$

A small test body of mass M_2, situated at the point P, is subjected to a force:

$$\bar{F}(P,K_{0g},M_2) = k_0\bar{\delta}(P,K_{0g})M_2 = -k_0 K_{0g} k_{f1}\kappa \frac{M_1 M_2 \, \bar{r_1}}{r_1^2 \, r_1}, \tag{18}$$

with k_0 representing a dimensional constant of homogenization. In the SI system, the specific intensity of the electromagnetic radiation $[K_{0g}]$ is a derived measure having the dimension $[\mathrm{J\,m^{-2}s^{-1}}] = [\mathrm{kg\,s^{-3}}]$.

It is obvious that formula (18) represents a Newtonian force as soon as the following conditions are satisfied:

$$k_0 K_{0g}\kappa \cong f \tag{19}$$

$$k_{f1} \cong 1. \tag{20}$$

If the body situated at the point P has the radius a_2, the dimensionless form factor will be:

$$k_{f12} = k_{f21} = 1 - \frac{3}{4}(a_1\mu_1 + a_2\mu_2)\kappa + \frac{2}{5}(a_1\mu_1 + a_2\mu_2)^2\kappa^2 -$$
$$-\frac{1}{6}(a_1\mu_1 + a_2\mu_2)^3\kappa^3 + \frac{2}{35}(a_1\mu_1 + a_2\mu_2)^4\kappa^4 - \frac{7}{420}(a_1\mu_1 + a_2\mu_2)^5\kappa^5. \tag{21}$$

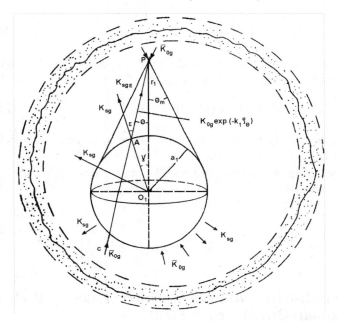

Figure 2

As shown in equation (16), the resultant of the specific intensity vectors along all the directions passing through point P is always negative. This suggests that the body situated at point P will move toward the screen body. At infinity ($r_1 \to \infty$) and in the center of the screen body ($r_1 = 0$) the value of this resultant radiation field becomes zero, while on the surface of the screen body ($r_1 = a_1$) the value is maximal. The force we describe is a passive force, resulting in a pushing effect, and not an active, attractive force, as usually described in the classical theory of gravity.

b) *An active screen body*. If the screen body itself produces electromagnetic radiation of specific intensity K_{sg}, along directions that are normal to the screen body's surface (Figure 2), the test body situated at point P is subjected to an action of repulsion in a direction opposite to the one generated by the universal field K_{0g}. The field $\bar{\delta}(P, K_{sg})$ is denoted by:

$$\delta\left(P, K_{sg}\right) = 2\pi \int_{0}^{\theta_m} K_{sg} \cos\left(\theta + \gamma\right) \sin\theta \, \cos\theta \, d\theta, \tag{22}$$

where

$$K_{sg,\varepsilon} = K_{sg} \cos\varepsilon = K_{sg} \cos\left(\theta + \gamma\right)$$

represents Lamb's formula (Figure 2).

Using $\sin\left(\theta + \gamma\right) = \left(r_1 / a_1\right)\sin\theta$, relation (22) becomes:

$$\delta(P, K_{sg}) = 2\pi \int_{0}^{\theta_m} K_{sg} \sqrt{1 - \frac{r_1^2}{a_1^2}\sin^2\theta} \, \sin\theta \, \cos\theta \quad d\theta, \tag{23}$$

and

$$\bar{\delta}\left(P,K_{sg}\right)=\frac{2\pi a_1^2}{3}K_{sg}\frac{\bar{r_1}}{r_1^3}.$$ (24)

The pressure exerted by the thermal and light radiation of specific intensity K_{sl} on the body situated at point P has the form:

$$\bar{F}\left(P,O_2,O_1,K_{sl}\right)=p\left(O_1,P\right)\pi a_2^2\frac{\bar{r_1}}{r_1}.$$ (25)

This pressure is applied along the same direction as the force due to the field
$\bar{\delta}(P,K_{sg})$. The pressure $p(O_1,P)$ is measured in [N m^{-2}].

The total force acting on the body of mass M_2 and radius a_2, situated at
the point P has the expression:

$$\bar{F}\left(P,K_{0g},K_{sg},K_{sl},M_2\right)=$$

$$=\left[-k_0K_{0g}k_{f12}\kappa\frac{M_1M_2}{r_1^2}+k_0\frac{2\pi a_1^2}{3}K_{sg}\frac{M_2}{r_1^2}+p\left(O_1,P\right)\pi a_2^2\right]\frac{\bar{r_1}}{r_1}$$ (26)

3. The Force between Two Bodies which Generate their own Newtonian Gravitational Field

When the substance of two bodies generates its own Newtonian gravitational
field of attraction, $\bar{\gamma}_N$, the force between the two bodies, F_{12}, is denoted by:

$$\bar{F}\left(O_1,O_2,K_0,\bar{\gamma}_N\right)=\left[-f\frac{M_1M_2}{r_1^2}-k_0K_{0g}k_{f12}\kappa\frac{M_1M_2}{r_1^2}\right]\frac{\bar{r_1}}{r_1}$$

$$=-\left(f+k_0K_{0g}k_{f12}\kappa\right)\frac{M_1M_2}{r_1^2}\frac{\bar{r_1}}{r_1}$$ (27)

with f being the gravitational constant of the considered system of masses (i.e.,
the envelope of the enclosure plus the two bodies), not the usual constant of
gravitation. If the conditions (19)–(20) are satisfied, the total force acting on
the body of mass M_2 is twice the value of the force exerted in fact.

This force is composed of a pushing force, due to the electromagnetic
universal radiation of intensity K_{0g} that interacts with the substance of the
screen body due to absorption effects (absorption coefficient per unit mass κ),
as well as the classical Newtonian attraction force. Laboratory experiments
should make it possible to demonstrate whether the value of the gravitational
force that appears between the two bodies has exactly the value resulting from
its calculation using the formulae of TETG, but without the minor deviation
observed from the Newtonian law. In this case, the force would be undoubtedly
identified as a pushing force.

4. Applications of TETG to the Solar System

Like earlier workers (Faraday 1855; Maxwell 1864, 1885; Lorentz 1916) we
have supposed that the gravitational forces in the Universe have an electro-

magnetic nature. Specifically, we have supposed that gravity results from the interaction between a radiation band of a specific intensity K_{0g}, given by formula (3), and matter. We shall use the condition that the "repulsive" forces (expressed by the formula obtained in TETG) equal the "attraction" forces (expressed by the formula given by the Newtonian theory of gravitation). For the latter, one can consider the equation given by Asaph Hall (Chazy 1928)—used for the two body systems Sun-Mercury and Earth-Moon. In this formula long term astronomical observations have allowed us to know with precision the corrected exponents $2 + \lambda_g$. One must consider also the force due to light pressure (after Lebedev).

In the following we use the symbols E for Earth, M for Moon, Mr for Mercury and S for Sun. The formulae of the TETG are obtained for a stationary system; meanwhile the corrected Newtonian formulae are valid for a dynamic system. Since the linear velocity $v_M = 1.02$ km s^{-1} and the angular velocity $\omega_M = 2.65 \times 10^{-6}$ rad s^{-1} (for the movement of the Moon around the Earth), while respectively $v_{Mr} = 47.9$ km s^{-1} and $\omega_{Mr} = 0.75 \times 10^{-6}$ rad s^{-1} (for the movement of Mercury around the Sun), their influences on the corresponding motions can be neglected. The elliptical form of the orbit and the presence of the other bodies of the Solar System are not taken into account in the following calculations.

Under these conditions we have:

$$-k_0 K_{0g} k_{f,EM} \kappa \frac{M_E M_M}{r_{EM}^2} = -f \frac{M_E M_M}{r_{EM}^{2+\lambda_{g,EM}}} \tag{28}$$

$$-k_0 K_{0g} k_{f,SMr} \kappa \frac{M_S M_{Mr}}{r_{SMr}^2} + k_0 \frac{2\pi a_S^2}{3} K_{sg} \frac{M_{Mr}}{r_{SMr}^2} + p_{Mr} \pi a_{Mr}^2 = -f \frac{M_S M_{Mr}}{r_{SMr}^{2+\lambda_{g,SMr}}} \tag{29}$$

$$p_{Mr} = p_E \frac{r_{ES}^2}{r_{SMr}^2}. \tag{30}$$

Using relations (6), (19), (20), (21) and retaining only the first order terms, the following solutions for the unknown quantities are obtained:

$$\kappa = \frac{4}{3(a_E \mu_E + a_M \mu_M)} \left(1 - \frac{1}{r_{EM}^{\lambda_{g,EM}}} \right), \tag{31}$$

$$k_0 K_{og} = \frac{f}{\kappa r_{EM}^{\lambda_{g,EM}}}, \tag{32}$$

$$k_0 u_{0g} = \frac{4\pi f}{c \kappa r_{EM}^{\lambda_{g,EM}}}, \tag{33}$$

$$k_0 K_{sg} = 2 f a_S \mu_S \left(k_{f,SMr} - \frac{1}{r_{SMr}^{\lambda_{g,SMr}}} \right) - \frac{9}{2} \frac{r_{ES}^2}{4\pi a_S^2} \frac{p_E}{a_{Mr} \mu_{Mr}}. \tag{34}$$

We use the numerical values:
$$a_E^{mean} = 6.36348 \times 10^6 \text{ m}, \quad \mu_E = 5.517 \times 10^3 \text{ kg m}^{-3},$$

$a_M = 1.7379 \times 10^6$ m, $\mu_M = 3.34 \times 10^3$ kg m^{-3}, $r_{EM} = 3.844 \times 10^8$ m,
$\lambda_{g,EM} = 42.1 \times 10^{-10}$, $a_S = 6.9598 \times 10^8$ m, $\mu_S = 1.409 \times 10^3$ kg m^{-3},
$a_{Mr} = 2.385 \times 10^6$ m, $\mu_{Mr} = 5.7 \times 10^3$ kg m^{-3}, $r_{SMr} = 5.791 \times 10^{10}$ m,
$\lambda_{g,SMr} = 15.35 \times 10^{-8}$, $r_{SE} = 1.496 \times 10^{11}$ m (Reabov 1967),
$f = 6.672 \times 10^{-11}$ m^3 kg^{-1} s^{-2}, $p_E = 4.5 \times 10^{-6}$ N m^{-2} (Shortley & Dudley
1971), $\lambda_{g,SMr} = 16 \times 10^{-8}$ (Chazy, 1928).

We then obtain:

$$\kappa = 2.710706814 \times 10^{-18} \ \text{m}^2 \ \text{kg}^{-1}$$

$$k_0 K_{0g} = 2.459874822 \times 10^7 \ \text{m s}^{-2}$$

$$k_0 K_{sg} = 2.329018098 \times 10^{-4} \ \text{m s}^{-2}$$

$$k_0 u_{0g} = 1.03038995 \ \text{s}^{-1}.$$

Either using equation (28) and considering the κ term in (21), or from equation
(29) without the term in $p_{Mr} \pi a_{Mr}^2$ and considering the terms in κ and κ^2 in
(21), we obtain:

$$2.009627391 \times 10^{-18} \leq \kappa \leq 3.221501213 \times 10^{-18}. \tag{35}$$

The above numerical range of the absorption coefficient per unit mass κ
represents an experimental proof of the veracity of TETG. Table 1 presents results obtained by other researchers for the absorption coefficient per unit mass.

With the value obtained for $\kappa = 2.710706814 \times 10^{-18}$ m^2 kg^{-1} one can
determine the form factors, $k_{f,12}$, for the celestial bodies we are studying.
Using formula (26) for the case of the celestial bodies in our Solar System, one
can determine the force exerted by the Sun on each planet. This force is smaller
than the force resulting from Newton's law because (1) the form factor
$k_{f,S-Planet}$ is less than unity (see Table 2); and (2) the Sun's electromagnetic radiation with gravitational effects (with specific intensity K_{sg}) and the Sun's
classical electro-thermodynamical radiation (with specific intensity K_{sl}) are acting in the direction Sun-Planet, the planet being subjected to a repulsive action
(pushing). The force between two planets or satellites is smaller than the force
resulting from Newton's law only due to the fact that the form factor $k_{f,P-P}$ is
less than unity.

The formulae showing the relative diminution of the TETG force, with respect to the classical Newtonian force, are:

$$\Delta_1 = (F_N - F_{TETG}) : F_N = 1 - k_{f,12} \tag{36}$$

$$\Delta_2 = \left(k_0 K_{sg} \frac{4\pi a_S^2}{6} \frac{M_{Mr}}{r_{SMr}^2} \right) : f \frac{M_S M_{Mr}}{r_{SMr}^2} = \frac{K_{sg}}{2 K_{0g} \kappa a_S \mu_S}, \tag{37}$$

$$\Delta_3 = p_{Mr} \pi a_{Mr}^2 : f \frac{M_S M_{Mr}}{r_{SM}^2} = \frac{3}{4} \frac{r_{SE}^2 p_E}{f M_S a_{Mr} \mu_{Mr}}, \tag{38}$$

where F_N, F_{TETG} represent respectively the forces from Newton's theory and
TETG. The values of these deviations are presented in Table 2.

TABLE 1

	Date	Researcher	κ (m² kg⁻¹)	Method	Ref.
1	Before 1686	Newton	very weak	Experiments with pendulum; theoretical (astronomical data)	(27)
2	1825-1826	Laplace		Theoretical (astronomical data)	(20)
3	1911-1912	Bottlinger	3×10^{-16}	Theoretical (astronomical data)	(1)
4	1919-1922	Majorana	2×10^{-13}	Laboratory experiments and theoretical	(24)
5	1921	Russell	2×10^{-17}	Theoretical (astronomical data)	(32)
6	1948	Armellini	$10^{-18} < \kappa < 10^{-17}$	Theoretical (astronomical data)	(11)
7	1954-1955	Thomashek	$< 10^{-15}$	Experimental (total Sun eclipse from June 1954)	(35)
8	1961-1962	Slichter, Caputo, Hager	$< 2.6 \times 10^{-16}$	Experimental (total Sun eclipse from February 1961)	(34)
9	1962	Braginski	$< 10^{-13}$	Laboratory experiments	(22)
10	1976	Adamut	2.7×10^{-18}	Theoretical (astronomical data) in TETG	(1)
11	1984	Vallaots	3.8×10^{-13}	Measuring weight in the center of the 17-storey house in Estonia	(22)
12	1986	Liakhovets	$10^{-16} - 10^{-12}$	Experimental (Solar eclipses)	(22)
13	1987	Adamut, Popescu	5.322×10^{-18}	Theoretical (astronomical data) in NIM model	(8)

TABLE 2

	Sun-Mercury	Sun-Earth	Earth-Moon
k_f	0.9999979350	0.9999979789	0.9999999168
Δ_1	2.0650×10^{-6}	2.0211×10^{-6}	8.320×10^{-8}
Δ_2	$1.780900107 \times 10^{-6}$		
Δ_3	$4.187822370 \times 10^{-14}$	$1.620618969 \times 10^{-14}$	

5. Remarks on the Electromagnetic Radiation Field K_{0g}

The characteristics of the field K_{0g}. TETG assumes the existence of a narrow electromagnetic radiation band, of a specific intensity K_{0g} (formula (3)), throughout the Solar System. The most probable characteristics of K_{0g} are: (a) the specific intensity as a thermodynamic measure: $k_0 K_{0g} = 2.46 \times 10^7 \, \text{m s}^{-2}$; (b) the wavelengths λ satisfy the relation $2.4 \times 10^{-15} \, \text{m} < \varnothing < 14.8944 \times 10^{-15} \, \text{m}$, where $\varnothing$ is the diameter of the substance nuclei; (c) the mean frequencies of the field; $v_{x,mean} > 10^{23} \, \text{Hz}$; (d) the energy transported by each quantum: $E > 6.6256 \cdot 10^{-11} \, \text{J}$; (e) the frequency band of K_{0g} being very narrow it satisfies the condition $10^n < v_{x,mean} < 10^{n+1}$, with $n > 23$, corresponding to the relation $1 < \sqrt[3]{A} < 6.206$. (f) the absorption coefficient per unit mass κ and the specific intensity of the field K_{0g} are fundamental physical constants, given by relation (19).

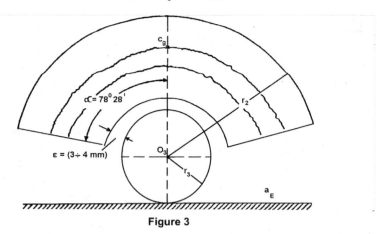

Figure 3

The homogeneity constant k_0. Using the considerations in Section 2, the following relation can be written:

$$-f\frac{M_1 M_2}{r_{12}^2} = -k_0 K_{0g} k_{f,12} \kappa \frac{M_1 M_2}{r_{12}^2}. \tag{39}$$

If the unit of the Newtonian force is Newton [N] and if $\left[K_{0g}\right]=1 \; \mathrm{J\,m^{-2}\,s^{-1}}$ and $\kappa = 2.710706814 \times 10^{-18} \; \mathrm{m^2\,kg^{-1}}$, then considering the relation $k_{f,12} \cong 1$ we obtain:

$$k_0 = \frac{f}{K_{0g}\kappa} = \frac{6.672 \times 10^{-11}}{2.71 \times 10^{-18}} = 2.46 \times 10^7 \, \mathrm{m\,kg^{-1}\,s}. \tag{40}$$

If we suppose that $k_0 = 1 \, \mathrm{kg^{-1}\,m\,s}$, then for the real value of the field K_{0g} in the region of the Solar System, we obtain

$$K_{0g} = 2.46 \times 10^7 \, \mathrm{J\,m^{-2}\,s^{-1}}.$$

6. Development of Experiments to Support TETG

6.1. Laboratory experiments

When a small test body, with mass $M_3 \leq 1$, is placed underneath a screen body having different shapes and a large mass M_2, the way in which the weight of the small body is reduced depends on the screen's shape, in contrast with Newton's law.

For instance, let us weigh a spherical sample body O_3, having radius r_3 and density μ_3, placed under a spherical sector screen body O_2 of radius r_2 and density μ_2. The screen body has an opening 2α in the center and a spherical cutting of radius r_3 at the bottom. The center of gravity is placed in the middle of the sphere from which the spherical sector is cut (Figure 3). The body O_1, with the radius a_E and mass M_E, represents the Earth.

The screen radius r_2, as a function of mass and density, is:

$$r_2 = \sqrt[3]{\frac{3M_2}{4\pi\mu_2 \sin^2(\alpha/2)} + r_3^3} \; . \tag{41}$$

According to TETG, the weight of the small test body of mass M_3, in the absence of the screen, is:

$$G(O_1, K_{og}, M_3) = -k_0\pi K_{0g} \left[\frac{\exp(-2a_E k_E)\left(\frac{1}{a_E k_E} + \frac{1}{2a_E^2 k_E^2}\right) -}{-\frac{1}{2a_E^2 k_E^2} + 1} \right] M_3 \; . \tag{42}$$

In the presence of the screen body we have the formula:

$$G(O_1, O_2, K_{og}, M_3) = -k_0\pi K_{0g} \left[\frac{\exp(-2a_E k_E)\left(\frac{1}{a_E k_E} + \frac{1}{2a_E^2 k_E^2}\right) -}{-\frac{1}{2a_E^2 k_E^2}} \right] M_3 - \tag{43}$$

$$-k_0\pi K_{0g}\left\{1 - \left[1 - \exp(-k_2(r_2 - r_3))\right]\sin^2\alpha\right\} M_3.$$

The weight difference for the small test body is given by:

$$\Delta G = -k_0\pi K_{0g}\left[1 - \exp(-k_2(r_2 - r_3))\right]\sin^2\alpha \; M_3 \; . \tag{44}$$

Expanding the exponential in a power series, neglecting r_3 and introducing relation (41), we obtain:

$$\Delta G = -k_0\pi K_{0g} \sqrt[3]{\frac{3M_2}{4\pi\mu_2 \sin^2(\alpha/2)}}\left(4\sin^2\frac{\alpha}{2}\cos^2\frac{\alpha}{2}\right)k_f M_3 =$$
$$= -2k_0\pi K_{0g} \sqrt[3]{\frac{6M_2}{\pi\mu_2}}\sin^4\frac{\alpha}{2}\cos^2\frac{\alpha}{2}k_f M_3 \tag{45}$$

If we separate the unknown α we obtain the function:

$$y = \sqrt[3]{\sin^4\frac{\alpha}{2}\cos^2\frac{\alpha}{2}} \; .$$

Substituting $\sin(\alpha/2) = x$, one obtains $y_1 = 0$ for $x_{1,2} = \pm 1$, $x_3 = 0$ and $y_2 = 0.32574$ for $x_{4,5} = \pm\sqrt{0.4}$. One then determines $\alpha = 78°28'$.

Consider a copper test body with mass $M_3 = 1\,\text{kg}$ and radius $r_3 = 0.03\,\text{m}$ and a copper screen body with $\mu_2 = 8.9\cdot 10^3\,\text{kg m}^{-3}$, $M_2 = 10^4\,\text{kg}$ and $r_2 = 0.8772\,\text{m}$. From Newton's law, the resulting weight for the test body is:

$$G_N = -f\frac{M_E M_3}{a_E^2} + \pi f(r_2 - r_3)\ \mu_2 M_3 \sin^2\alpha \; .$$

From TETG the weight for the test body is:

$$G_{TETG} = -f\frac{M_E M_3}{a_E^2}k_{fE} + \pi f(r_2 - r_3)\ \mu_2 M_3 k_{f2}\sin^2\alpha \; ,$$

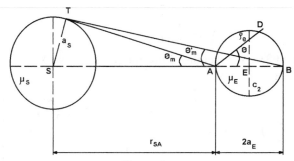

Figure 4

where

$$k_{f2} = 1 - \frac{\kappa\mu_2\left(r_2 - r_3\right)}{2} + \frac{\left[\kappa\mu_2\left(r_2 - r_3\right)\right]^2}{6} \cong 1$$

and $k_{fE} = 0.9999999287$. The difference

$$\left(G_N - G_{TETG}\right)/G_N = \left(1 - k_{fE}\right) = 7.13 \times 10^{-8}$$

is produced by the "screen effect" of the Earth against the artificial laboratory shield. Since the weight difference is less than the precision of the best available balances (Almer, 1975), one could verify the validity of TETG by performing such experiments.

6.2. The screen effect of the Earth in TETG

Another test of TETG is to determine the screening effect of the Earth with respect to the Sun at two times, at noon and at midnight, for an observatory placed at the equator. In TETG the difference between the gravitational accelerations at such a point for the two times will differ from the value obtained in the Newtonian theory. The predicted differences in the two theories have been estimated for the following configuration (Figure 4):

- the Earth and the Sun have their centers collinear through the equator (at equinox);
- the Moon is in the first or in the last quarter so as not to have a vertical component of the gravitational acceleration;
- the effects of the other planets are neglected.

The calculations for the two theories are complex and beyond the scope of this review (for details, see Ref. 2). In Tables 3 and 4 are given the results of the calculations, using the physical and geometrical quantities of the system Sun-Earth (this paper, Sect. 4) and $\kappa = 2.710706814 \times 10^{-18}$ m^2 kg^{-1}, $k_0 = 1$kg^{-1}m s, and $K_{0g} = 2.45987 \times 10^7$ Jm^{-2} s^{-1}.

TABLE 3

Species of accelerations δ	Accelerations at point A		Accelerations at point B	
	Symbols	Values (m s^{-2})	Symbols	Values (m s^{-2})
δ due to Earth	$\delta_N(A,E)$	−9.816616797	$\delta_N(B,E)$	−9.816616797
	$\delta_{TETG}(A,K_{0g},E)$	−9.816616096	$\delta_{TETG}(B,K_{0g},E)$	−9.816616096
δ due to Sun	$\delta_N(A,S)$	0.005926076	$\delta_N(B,S)$	−0.0059250654
	$\delta_{TETG}(A,K_{0g},S)$	0.005926064	$\delta_{TETG}(B,K_{0g},S)$	−0.0059250536
			$\delta_{TETG}(B,K_{Sg},S,E)$	−0.0000195298
	$\delta_{TETG}(A,K_{Sg},S)$	−0.000000011	$\delta_{TETG}(B,K_{Sg},S,E)$	0.000000011
δ due to Earth's rotation and revolution	$\delta(A,\omega_r,E)$	0.033730932	$\delta(B,\omega_r,E)$	0.0337309320
	$\delta(A,\omega_R,S,E)$	−0.005930392	$\delta(B,\omega_R,S,E)$	0.0059308980
Total acceleration	$\delta_{N,A}$	−9.782890181	$\delta_{N,B}$	−9.782880032
	$\delta_{TETG,A}$	−9.782889503	$\delta_{TETG,B}$	−9.782898838
	$\Delta(\delta_{N,A},\delta_{TETG,A})$	−0.000000678	$\Delta(\delta_{N,B},\delta_{TETG,B})$	0.000018806

TABLE 4

Theory	Symbols	Values (m s^{-2})
Newtonian theory	$\Delta\left(\delta_{N,A},\delta_{N,B}\right)$	−0.000010149
TETG	$\Delta\left(\delta_{TETG,A},\delta_{TETG,B}\right)$	0.000009335
	$\Delta\left(\delta_{N,A},\delta_{N,B}\right)-\Delta\left(\delta_{TETG,A},\delta_{TETG,B}\right)$	−0.000019484

Observation: The influence of the Sun's gravitational radiation in TETG is negligible, only 1.1 μgal, meaning that gravitational radiation must be generated by the bodies (the stars) of the whole Universe and is practically stationary radiation.

6.3 Possible verification of the Earth "screen effect" *versus* the Sun

a) We may verify the oscillating period of a pendulum at midday and at midnight comparing them with the calculated values in Newtonian theory and in TETG. Let us consider a pendulum with the length l = 1m:

$$T_{A(B)} = \frac{2\pi}{\sqrt{g_{A(B)}}}.$$

In this case, substituting the experimental, Newtonian and TETG values of gravitational accelerations, we obtain the periods and their differences from Table 5.

b) A more accurate experiment may be realized with the "ballistic gravimeter" (Arnautov *et al.* 1979). With this device the disadvantages of the pendulum,

TABLE 5

	$g(\delta)$ (m s^{-2})		T (s)		$\Delta(T_A - T_B)$
Points	A	B	A	B	
Experimental	9.78034		2.009106191		
Newtonian	9.782890181	9.782880032	2.008844310	2.008845352	-1.042 μs
TETG	9.782889503	9.782898838	2.008844379	2.008843421	0.958 μs
$\Delta(T_{EX} - T_N)$			0.000261881	0.000260839	
$\Delta(T_{EX} - T_{TETG})$			0.000261812	0.000262770	
$\Delta(T_{TETG} - T_N)$			0.000000069	-0.000001931	

such as the deformations of the edge knife and of the pendulum bar, are eliminated. The fall times are calculated with the classical Galilean formula

$$t = \sqrt{\frac{2h}{g_{A(B)}}} .$$

In Table 6 are the calculated times for $h = 5.2$ cm and $h = 0.5$ m.

One sees that these differences are very easily measurable. All these considerations are made for a rigid and homogeneous Earth, neglecting the ocean
tides and the real repartition of the Earth densities. It would also be necessary
to calculate their influence on the value of g.

7. Conclusions

In conclusion, gravity in TETG results as a sort of pushing generated by the
breaking of the symmetry of the universal radiation, K_{0g}, due to the Sun, Earth,
Moon, *etc.* It is a pushing force, not an active force of attraction. The gravitational formula obtained within TETG differs from the Newtonian one only by a
dimensionless form factor, k_{f1}. The gravitational constant is the product of two
fundamental physical constants: K_{0g}, the specific intensity of the universal radiation field in the region of the Solar System, and κ, the absorption coefficient per unit mass. This theory was first applied to two pairs of bodies from
our Solar System (Earth-Moon and Sun-Mercury), leading to values for κ
($\kappa = 2.71 \times 10^{-18}$ m^2 kg^{-1}, in agreement with values obtained by other researchers), K_{0g}, K_{sg} and u_{0g}. The model has also been applied to a proposed laboratory
experiment (*i.e.*, a small sample body situated under a large screen body), as

TABLE 6

	t (s)		t (s)		$\Delta(t_A - t_B)$ μs	
Points	A	B	A	B		
Experimental	0.1031192376		0.3197591816			
Newtonian	0.1031057922	0.1031058497	0.3197175018	0.3197176676	-0.054	-0.166
TETG	0.1031057998	0.1031057505	0.3197175129	0.3197173603	0.049	0.153
$\Delta(t_{EX} - t_N)$	0.0000134414	0.0000133879	0.0000416798	0.0000415140		
$\Delta(t_{EX} - t_{TETG})$	0.0000134378	0.0000134871	0.0000416687	0.0000418213		
$\Delta(t_{TETG} - t_N)$	0.0000000036	-0.0000000992	0.0000000111	-0.0000003073		

well as to a screening experiment (*i.e.*, a sample body at the Equator, using the Earth as a screen).

Finally, TETG may be considered as a particular case of the Newton Impulse Model (NIM), in which the medium is the symmetric, homogeneous, isotropic electromagnetic radiation field.

Acknowledgements

During his researches, I.A. Adamut had fruitful discussions about his theory with Prof. I. Mihăilă, who gave him interesting suggestions. The author of this review also thanks Prof. I. Mihăilă for his support and indications concerning this paper.

References

1. Adamut, I.A. "Analyse de l'action gravitationnelle du rayonnement électromagnétique sur un système de corps. Une théorie électrothermodynamique de la gravitation," *Il Nuovo Cimento*, **32B**, 477-511(1976).
2. Adamut, I.A. "The screen effect of the Earth in the TETG. Theory of a screening experiment of a sample body at the equator using the Earth as a screen," *Il Nuovo Cimento*, **5C**, N.2, pp.189-208 (1982).
3. Adamut, I.A. "Reactualising the theory of classical Newtonian gravitation by hypothesing a stationary gravitational radiation." Contributed papers of *10-th Intern. Conf. on General Relativity and Gravitation*, eds. by B. Bertotti, F de Felice, A. Pascolini, Vol.1, pp.457- 459 (1983).
4. Adamut, I.A. "The consistency of theory of developed Newtonian gravitation (TDMG) partially alias TETG in respect of the attenuation," *Sir Arthur Eddington Centenary Symposium, Vol. 3, Gravitational radiation and relativity*, eds. J. Weber, T.M. Karade, World Scientific Singapore, pp. 401- 417 (1986).
5. Adamut, I. A. "Two useful theorems in the study of the gravitational force, F_{0g}, in the mechanic-model AMW, Newton-Le Sage," Proceed. Colloquy of fluids mechanics and its technical applications, *Rom. Soc. Math. Sci., Suceava*, Oct. 1987, pp.196-206.
6. Adamut, I. A., Popescu, N.A. "Calculation of the terms $F_{0g(1)}$, $F_{0g(2)}$ of the gravitational force F_{0g}, in the mechanic-model, AMW, Newton-Le Sage," Proceed. Colloquy of fluids mechanics and its technical applications, *Rom. Soc. Math. Sci., Suceava*, Oct. 1987, pp.192-196.
7. Adamut, I.A. "Gravitational force F_{0g} in the Newton's models: attraction (NA) and impulse given by Any Medium Whatever (NI-AMW)," Proceed. Scientific Session *Progresses in Astronomy*, ed. ICEFIZ, pp.133-136 (1987).
8. Adamut, I.A., Popescu, N.A. "Contribution of the body O_1 in the second term of the gravitational force F_{0g}, in the model AMW-NIM. Calculation of the quantity κ." Proceed. Scientific Session *Progresses in Astronomy*, ed. ICEFIZ, pp.137-138 (1987).
9. Adamut, I.A. "Gravitation law with Clairaut's and Le Sage-Laplace-Majorana's complementary terms rigorously resulting in Newton Impulse Model (NIM)," *Preprint No.A-16-1990*, Institute of Atomic Physics, CIP Press, Bucharest (1990).
10. Almer, H.E. "Gravitational configuration effect upon precision mass measurements," *Rev. Sci. Instrum.*, Vol. **46**, No. 9, pp.1174-1177 (1975).
11. Armellini, G. "Il moto del perielio di Mercurio nell'ipotesi di un assorbimento del flusso gravitazionale attraverso i mezzi materiali," *Lincei Rend. Sci. Fis., Mat. e Nat.*, **V**, dicembre (1948).
12. Arnautov, G.P., Kalis, E.N., Kokoulin, F.I. *Quantum Electronica*, **6**, 560 (1979).
13. Braginski, P. *Zurn. Eksp. Teor. Fiz.*, **43**, p. 51 (1962).
14. Caputo, M. "*Geofisica: un nouvo limite superiore per il coefficiente di assorbimento della gravitazione,*" nota di M. Caputo, presentata dal corrispondente A. Marussi: *Lincei Rend. Sci. Fis., Mat. e Nat.*, **32**, 509 (1962).
15. Chandrasekhar, S. *Radiative Transfer* (Oxford, 1950).
16. Chazy, J. *La théorie de la relativité et la mécanique céleste* (Paris, 1928).
17. Faraday, M. *Experimental Researches in Electricity*, Vol. 3 (London, 1855).

18. Jackson, J.D. *Classical Electrodynamics*, 6th printing (New York, N.Y., 1967).
19. Lahtin, L. M. *Le mouvement libre dans le champ du sphéroide terrestre* (Moscou, 1963).
20. Laplace, P.S. *Traité de mécanique céleste,* T.V.Bachelier, pp. 448-452 (Paris, 1825).
21. Le Sage, G.-L. "Lucrèce Newtonien," *Nouveaux Mémoires de l'Académie Royale des Sciences et Belles Lettres*, Année 1782, pp. 404-432, A Berlin. Imprimé chez George Jacques Decker, 1784.
22. Liakhovets, V.D. "Evidence for Majorana's Theory of Gravitation," *11-th Internat. Conf. On General Relativity and Gravitation*, p.92, 1986.
23. Lorentz, H.A. *Theory of Electrons and Its Application to the Phenomena of Light and Radiant Heat*, II Edition (Leipzig, 1916).
24. Majorana, S.Q. "Sull'ipotesi dell'assorbimento gravitazionale," nota presentata nella seduta del 13 Aprile 1957, dal Socio Q. Majorana: *Atti Accad. Naz. Lincei*, **22**, 392 (1957).
25. Maxwell, J.C. *Traité d'électricité et de magnétisme* (Chap. XXX, Théorie électromagnétique de la lumiére), II edition (Paris, 1855).
26. Maxwell, J.C. "Dynamical theory of electromagnetical field," *Roy. Soc. Trans. Vol.* **155** (1864).
27. Newton, I.N. *Philosophiae Naturalis Principia Mathematica,* translated in Romanian by Prof. V. Marian, Ed. Academiei R.P. Române, 1956.
28. Newton, I.N. *Optics*, Translated in Romanian by V. Marian, Ed. Acad. R.S.R, Bucuresti (1970).
29. Poincaré, H. *Lecons sur les Hypothèses Cosmogoniques*. Librairie Scientifique A. Hermann et Fils, p.XXI. (Paris, 1911).
30. Planck, M. *Theorie der Wärmestrahlung*, VI Auflage, (Leipzig, 1966).
31. Reabov, Y. Les mouvements des corps célestes (Mouscou, 1967).
32. Russell, H.R. "Majorana's theory of gravitation," *Astrophys. Journal*, **54**, 334, (1921)
33. Shortley, G., Dudley, W. *Elements of Physics*, Fifth Edition (Englewood Cliffs, N.J., 1971).
34. Slichter, L. B., Caputo, M., Hager, L. C. *J. Geophys. Res.*, **70**, 1541 (1965).
35. Thomashek, R. *Nature*, **175**, 937 (1955).

Majorana's Experiments
on Gravitational Absorption

Roberto de Andrade Martins[*]

Around 1920 the Italian physicist Quirino Majorana claimed that he had measured an effect that may be called "gravitational absorption": the reduction of the gravitational attraction between two bodies when one of them is enclosed inside a thick material shell. He published the results of experiments where a test body was surrounded either by mercury or by lead, and in both cases he detected a weight reduction of about one part in 10^9. This paper presents the theory underlying Majorana's work, together with a detailed description of his experiments.

1. Introduction

Many theories attempting to explain gravitation have been proposed since the 17th century (Woodward, 1972). A large proportion of these attempts can be described as *kinetic theories of gravitation* (Taylor, 1876), by their analogy to the kinetic theory of gases. They assume that material bodies do not interact by direct action-at-a-distance, but by acting and being acted upon by particles (or waves) travelling through space. The analysis of these mechanical models led to the conclusion that they would be unable to explain gravitation if only perfectly elastic collisions existed between the particles (or waves) and matter. Hence, all useful kinetic theories of gravitation must assume that matter absorbs or somehow changes these particles or waves.

Although kinetic theories of gravitation were very popular in the 19th century, nobody had endeavoured to detect the absorption of gravitation up to the 1890's. In 1897 Austin and Thwing made the first known experimental test of the existence of a change of gravitational force due to interposed matter using a torsion balance (Austin and Thwing, 1897). No effect was detected. Several other similar experiments were attempted in the early 20th century, but no clear positive result was reported until the publication of Majorana's research (Martins, 1999). In 1919 this Italian physicist announced that he had been able to observe a decrease of the weight of a body when it was enclosed within a thick shield of matter.

This paper will describe Majorana's ideas and experiments on gravitation, with special emphasis on his measurements of gravitational absorption, as they seem the most careful studies on this subject that were ever made.[†]

---

[*] Group of History and Theory of Science, Physics Institute, State University of Campinas (Brazil). P. O. Box 6059, 13081-970 Campinas, SP, Brazil. E-mail: rmartins@ifi.unicamp.br
[†] Information about some recent attempts to detect gravitational absorption may be found in George Gillies' very complete surveys of experimental gravitation (Gillies 1987, 1990, 1997; see also the paper by Unnikrishnan & Gillies in this volume).

Pushing Gravity: new perspectives on Le Sage's theory of gravitation
edited by Matthew R. Edwards (Montreal: Apeiron 2002)

219

Fig. 1 – The Italian physicist Quirino Majorana (1871-1957). Photograph copyright by Maria Majorana & Erasmo Recami. Reproduction kindly authorised by Erasmo Recami.

2. Majorana's Hypothesis

Quirino Majorana (1871-1957)[*] was an Italian experimental physicist who devoted many years of his active life to the search for gravitational absorption. Nowadays Majorana's better known researches are those related to the second principle of the special theory of relativity. He attempted to detect changes in the speed of light emitted (or reflected) by moving bodies, but contrary to his expectations he confirmed that the speed of light is independent of the speed of its source. As this result was the opposite of what he intended to prove, it gives nice evidence that Majorana was a careful experimenter and not one of those scientists who always find what they want to find.

Majorana published the details of his work in several articles that appeared in Italian scientific journals (Majorana, 1918-19, 1919-20a, 1919-20b, 1921-22). He also published shorter accounts of his researches in French (Majorana, 1919a, 1919b, 1921) and in English (Majorana, 1920).

In his first paper on gravitation Majorana presented the speculations that led him to his experimental work (Majorana, 1918-19). His point of departure was a concern with the energy of the stars. At that time, with nuclear physics still in its infancy, it was difficult to reconcile the long duration of the Sun required by geology and evolution theory with the largest possible duration allowed by physical theories. Majorana conjectured that gravitation was due to the flow of gravitational energy from all bodies to their surrounding space. This outward flow of gravitational energy necessarily required some kind of gradual transformation of matter, analogous to radioactivity, but Majorana

---

[*] There are two general accounts of Majorana's scientific contributions, one of them written by Majorana himself (Majorana, 1941 and Perucca, 1958). Quirino Majorana should not be misidentified with his nephew, the nuclear physicist Ettore Majorana. English-speaking readers should be warned that "Quirino" is pronounced as Kweereeno, and that the "j" in "Majorana" should be pronounced as "y" in "yes," with emphasis at the "ri" of "Quirino" and "ra" of "Majorana."

supposed that this transformation was very slow and difficult to detect. He also supposed that matter is not transparent to the gravitational flux. Gravitational energy would be absorbed by matter and transformed into heat. All bodies would therefore be subject to a spontaneous heating effect. This effect would be noticeable only for very large bodies, since the generation of heat from a body would be proportional to its volume, while the emission of heat would be proportional to its surface area. According to Majorana, this absorption and heating effect would account for stellar energy.[*]

Majorana was not altogether clear about the mechanism of gravitation he envisaged. Sometimes he referred to a "gravitational energy flux," sometimes to "particles," and, in his later years, he called these particles "gravitons." He remarked that his "particles" would have strange properties, because when they hit matter they must produce a backward impulse.

Majorana was not a theoretician. His main work, throughout his life, was that of an experimental physicist; so he was not much concerned about the precise mechanism of gravitational absorption. In the absence of any theoretical framework, he attempted to compute some of the consequences of the hypothesis and to test it by delicate experiments.

In order to test his general assumption, Majorana tried to detect a reduction of weight of a lead ball (1 kg) when it was surrounded by 100 kg of liquid mercury. The preliminary experiments, however, produced a result directly opposite to his hypothesis: there seemed to occur an *increase* of 1/30,000,000 of the weight of the test body (Majorana, 1918-19, p. 668).

After the preliminary test he began to study some theoretical features of his hypothesis. First, by taking into account some previous experiments, Majorana gave up the possibility of anything like a gravitational permeability. Analogy with electromagnetic phenomena pointed out that an effect of this kind should be observable even with a low sensitivity and thin slices of matter. Hence, Majorana suggested that only the search for very weak gravitational absorption effects could possibly give any positive result. In order to plan an improved experimental setup, he tried to evaluate the upper order of magnitude of the effect that was to be searched for. This led him to develop a quantitative theory of gravitational absorption (Majorana, 1919-20a, 1919-20b).

Let us compute the gravitational absorption due to a homogeneous material medium. According to the simplest absorption hypothesis, a corpuscle of mass M placed in this medium would produce at the distance r a gravitational field g equal to

$$g = GMr^{-2}e^{-Hr}, \tag{2.1}$$

where H is the characteristic gravitational absorption constant of the medium. Majorana assumed that H does not depend on the chemical composition of the medium, but that it would be proportional to its density: $H = hd$. Assuming that

---

[*] This idea was not developed in Majorana's early works. It was discussed, however, many years later (Majorana, 1954).

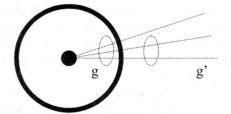

Fig. 2 – When an attracting mass is inside a spherical shell, the gravitational absorption by the shield would produce a smaller gravitational field *g'* outside the shell.

a large sphere of matter would have a non-negligible self-absorption of gravitation, Majorana computed its external field.

3. External Gravitational Field Produced by a Large Body

This very same hypothesis had been dealt with by Laplace one century earlier, and its consequences had been discussed by Henri Poincaré in his lectures on gravitation in the years 1906-1907. Poincaré's work was only published much later (Poincaré, 1953), however, and so Majorana had to compute by himself the consequences of his hypothesis. In what follows, some features of Poincaré's derivation will be used instead of Majorana's, because they are easier to follow and clearer. The final results will agree with Majorana's, however.

Suppose a very small but massive body is enclosed in the centre of a spherical shell (Fig. 2). Let us neglect the self-absorption of gravitation by the mass comprising the shell. Inside the shell, the value of the gravitational field is

$$g = GMr^{-2} \tag{3.1}$$

and outside the shield the field is

$$g' = GMr^{-2}e^{-HL} , \tag{3.2}$$

where L is the thickness of the shield. The force decreases but does not change its direction. Both inside and outside the shield the direction of the gravitational field is radial, and in both cases the force varies as the inverse square of the distance to the attracting body. In both regions the divergence of the gravitational field $\vec{\nabla} \cdot \vec{g}$ is null, because there are no sources or sinks of the gravitational field. The gravitational flux through a closed surface which does not contain the body is also null.

The total gravitational flux Φ traversing a closed surface inside the spherical shell and containing the massive body is

$$\Phi = 4\pi r^2 g = 4\pi\, GM , \tag{3.3}$$

and the total flux Φ' traversing a closed surface outside the spherical shell and containing the massive body is

$$\Phi' = 4\pi\, r^2 g' = 4\pi\, GMe^{-HL} . \tag{3.4}$$

That is, both inside and outside the shield, Gauss' law for gravitation holds, although the total flux has different values inside and outside the shield (Fig. 3).

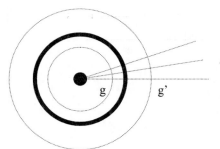

Fig. 3 – If an attracting mass is inside a spherical shell, the total gravitational flux across closed surfaces containing that body will be proportional to its effective gravitational mass. However, the gravitational absorption produced by the shield will decrease the external gravitational field g' produced by the inner body, and hence its external gravitational flux will be smaller than its gravitational flux inside the shell.

Now suppose we have a massive sphere with self-absorption of gravitation (Fig. 4). If the density of this body has spherical symmetry, then the gravitational field outside the sphere must have a radial direction everywhere, according to Curie's law of symmetry, and the intensity of the gravitational field is a function of the distance r to the centre only. Outside the sphere there are no sources or sinks of the gravitational field, and therefore the divergence of the gravitational field is null, *i.e.*, $\vec{\nabla} \cdot \vec{g} = 0$. Therefore Gauss' law applies to the exterior gravitational field, and the total gravitational flux Φ'' across a spherical surface will be the same whatever the radius r of the spherical surface, that is,

$$\Phi'' = 4\pi\, r^2 g''. \tag{3.5}$$

Outside the massive sphere the gravitational field varies as the inverse square of the distance r to the centre of the sphere,

$$g'' = \frac{\Phi''}{4\pi\, r^2}. \tag{3.6}$$

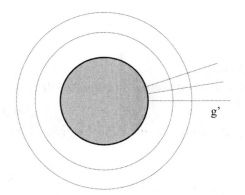

Fig. 4 – When gravitational absorption is taken into account, the external field produced by a large attracting spherical body would be diminished by self-absorption. However, outside the body there is no absorption and the total gravitational flux across any closed surface containing this body will have the same value, whatever its distance from the attracting body. Accordingly, the gravitational field g' will obey the inverse square law.

Therefore, outside the sphere Newton's law of gravitation is valid, but instead of the real mass of the sphere $M = \int \rho\, dV$ it is necessary to take into account a smaller effective (or apparent) gravitational mass $M' < M$.[*]

---

[*] This was a simple and clear result, but in 1948 Giuseppe Armellini published a paper where he arrived at a different result (Armellini, 1948). He claimed that the force produced by a spherical body, taking into account its self-absorption of gravitation, would obey a different law: $g = GM'/(r - \varepsilon)^2$, where ε would represent the distance between the geometrical centre of the body and its effective force

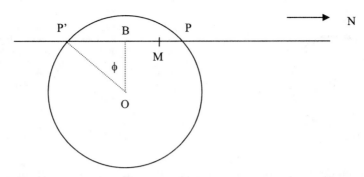

Fig. 5 – In order to compute the effective gravitational mass of a large homogeneous spherical body, following Poincaré's derivation, one computes the mean effective density relative to a distant point N, along different straight lines drawn through the sphere.

In order to use Newton's law of gravitation, now taking into account this effect of self-absorption of gravitation, we need to know the "apparent mass" of a large body. Let us compute its value in the case of a homogeneous sphere.

Consider a homogeneous sphere of radius R and real density ρ, with an absorption coefficient H (Fig. 5). It is easier to compute its gravitational effect relative to a distant point, as the result obtained for its apparent gravitational mass can then be applied to compute its field at any distance from its centre. The apparent mass can be calculated relative to a distant point using a set of parallel lines that cut the sphere, computing the apparent density ρ' of each point inside the sphere and then integrating over the whole sphere. The following symbols will be used (Fig. 5):

$$OP = OP' = R$$
$$BM = y$$
$$MP = q - y$$
$$OB = x = R \cos \phi$$
$$PB = P'B = q = R \sin \phi$$

Relative to a distant point N, the apparent density ρ' at point M will be:

$$\rho' = \rho\, e^{-H(q-y)}. \tag{3.7}$$

Therefore, the mean apparent density ρ'' along the line PP' of length $2q$ will be:

$$\rho'' = \frac{\rho}{2q} \int_{-q}^{+q} e^{-H(q-y)} dy = \frac{\rho}{2qH}\left(1 - e^{-2Hq}\right). \tag{3.8}$$

Now, take a cylindrical sheet of radius $x = OB$ and thickness dx. Its mean density is ρ'' and its volume is equal to $4\pi q\, x\, dx$. Therefore its mass is:

---

centre. He then proved that, once this law is accepted, this would produce a perihelion precession. However, Armellini's law of force is wrong, as it is incompatible with the above proof that the gravitational field outside the sphere must obey the simple law $g = GM'/r^2$. The main error in Armellini's derivation was the use of some equations of classical mechanics that do no apply to this case.

$$dm' = \frac{2\pi\rho}{H}e^{-2Hq}\,xdx\,. \tag{3.9}$$

Replacing x by $R\cos\phi$ and q by $R\sin\phi$, and integrating, we obtain the apparent mass of the whole sphere:

$$M' = \frac{2\pi R^2\rho}{H}\int_0^{\pi/2}\left(1-e^{-2HR\sin\phi}\right)\cos\phi\,\sin\phi\,d\phi\,. \tag{3.10}$$

Integration is straightforward, and the final result is:

$$M' = \frac{2\pi R^2\rho}{H}\left(\frac{1}{2}+\frac{e^{-2HR}}{2HR}+\frac{e^{-2HR}-1}{4H^2R^2}\right). \tag{3.11}$$

Notice that Poincaré computed the apparent mass of the sphere taking into account the gravitational field that would be observed at a distant point. However, as the external field of the sphere obeys the same equation as Newton's law of gravitation (with a reduced mass), the result can be applied to compute the field at any distance from the sphere.

Taking the limit when $H \to 0$, one obtains the real mass $M = (4/3)\pi R^3\rho$. When the absorption is small ($HR \ll 1$) but not negligible, the apparent mass of the sphere will be approximately:

$$M' = \frac{4\pi R^3\rho}{3}\left(1-\frac{3HR}{4}\right). \tag{3.12}$$

Majorana computed the absorption effect using a different mathematical method, but he obtained completely equivalent results. He introduced the concept of apparent active gravitational mass M_a different from the "real" mass $M_v = (4/3)\pi R^3\rho$. He represented the ratio between apparent mass and true mass by ψ (that is, $M_a = \psi M_v$) and computed this factor for a homogeneous sphere[*]. He found

$$\psi = \frac{3}{4}\left\{\frac{1}{RH}-\frac{1}{2(RH)^3}+\left[\frac{1}{(RH)^2}+\frac{1}{2(RH)^3}\right]e^{-2HR}\right\}. \tag{3.13}$$

This result is exactly equivalent to Poincaré's equation (3.11), as may be easily checked.

4. The Upper Limit of the Absorption Constant

As described above, Majorana supposed that the absorption constant H was proportional to the true density of matter: $H = h\rho_v$. The parameter h was supposed to be a universal constant.

Let us now apply these ideas to the Sun. Its effective or apparent active gravitational mass is known from its effect upon the planets. From its effective

---

[*] Majorana experienced some difficulties in deriving this result, and in one of his papers he presented a different result (Majorana, 1919/20b, p. 314). The equation presented here was published in his other articles (Majorana, 1919/20 a, p. 75; Majorana 1919/20 b, p. 420; Majorana 1919a, p. 648; Majorana 1920, p. 494).

gravitational mass, it is easy to compute that the effective mean density of the Sun is about 1.41 g cm^{-3}. If there is gravitational absorption, the real mean density of the Sun must be greater than the above value.

Although the Sun is not homogeneous, Majorana applied the model of the homogeneous sphere to this case. Using values of true density larger than 1.41 g cm^{-3} he computed by successive approximations the corresponding values of h:

ρ_v (g cm^{-3})	ρ_a / ρ_v	h (cm^2 g^{-1})
1.41	1.000	0
2.0	0.705	3.81×10^{-12}
5.0	0.281	7.08×10^{-12}
10	0.141	7.49×10^{-12}
15	0.094	7.63×10^{-12}
20	0.070	7.64×10^{-12}

This computation led to an unexpected result: if the true density of the Sun is supposed to increase and to go to infinity, the absorption constant h approaches a finite value: 7.65×10^{-12} cm^2 g^{-1}. That is, if a simple model (homogeneous density) is applied to the Sun, its known apparent active gravitational mass imposes an upper limit to the value of the constant of gravitational absorption. Of course, the Sun is not a homogeneous sphere. However, even with this simple model, it is remarkable that Majorana could reach an upper limit for the constant of gravitational absorption.

For a variation of the true density from 2 to 20 g cm^{-3} the absorption coefficient h remains always of the order of magnitude of about 10^{-11} cm^2 g^{-1}. Therefore it seems sufficient to suppose that the true density of the Sun is larger than its apparent density [of 1.41], in order to determine the order of magnitude of the "universal constant of absorption" h.[*] Majorana used this upper limit for the constant h to plan a suitable experimental test of the hypothesis, as will be shown below (Majorana, 1919-20b, p. 317).

5. Majorana's First Measurement

Could such a small effect be measured in a laboratory experiment? A simple computation will show that under laboratory conditions the effect would be very small indeed. As a first approximation, the gravitational force acting upon a body inside a spherical shell would undergo a relative reduction of about $hD\rho$, where D is the thickness of the shell. To compute the order of magnitude of the effect, we take $\rho = 10$ g cm^{-3} (lead, mercury), $D = 10$ cm and $h = 10^{-11}$ cm^2 g^{-1}. The relative weight reduction would amount to 10^{-9} (i.e., a reduction of about 1 μ g for a 1 kg body). In order to *measure* such an effect, it

---

[*] This is not correct, of course. If the true density of the Sun is only slightly greater (say, 0.001%) than its apparent density, the constant of absorption would be much smaller than 10^{-12}.

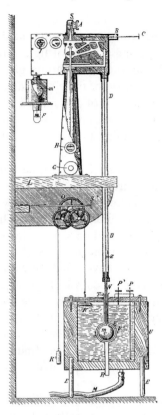

Fig. 6 – Majorana's first measurement of the coefficient of gravitational absorption employed a test body *m* attached to a sensitive balance. The test body could be enclosed by liquid mercury contained in a wood cylinder *U*.

would be necessary to attain a sensitivity at least 10 times better, and therefore it would be necessary to detect changes of 0.1 μ g in 1 kg (that is, 10^{-10}).[*]

No balance of that time could measure such a small change of weight. However, after several trials and improvements, Majorana adapted a system that had the required sensitivity. The experimental work was developed in the Physics Laboratory of the Turin Polytechnic, then directed by Majorana himself. In his papers Majorana provided a detailed description of his highly ingenious solutions for several experimental problems. It is relevant to grasp the main feature of the measurement method he used, since these experiments constitute the most important positive laboratory evidence for gravitational absorption ever obtained. The account provided below is as detailed as the limits imposed upon this paper will allow, but experimental physicists should consult the delightful original account, as it contains a wealth of relevant details and comments.

In these experiments, Majorana used the best available Rueprecht analytic balance, with several additional devices (Fig. 6). The balance and the test bodies were enclosed in a 5 mm thick brass vessel, where a vacuum was produced

---

[*] Of course, it is be possible to increase the thickness of the shield to produce a stronger effect, but other difficulties will arise, in that case.

to avoid any perturbation due to air currents, convection, buoyancy, *etc*. It was possible to manipulate the balance and the rider (of 10 mg) from outside (*C*). The oscillations of the balance were measured using a beam of light reflected by a concave mirror (*S*) at the top of the balance, through a strong glass wall (*A*). The mirror produced a sharp image of the filament of the electrical lamp at a distance of 12 m. In typical experiments, a deflection of 170 mm of the light spot corresponded to 1 mg, and it was possible to measure a displacement of 0.1 mm of the position of the light spot, corresponding to a weight change of 0.59 μ g.

Attached to the left side of the balance there was a 1.274 g sphere of lead (*m'*). Connected to the right side by a long brass wire (about 80 cm long) there was a second lead ball (*m*) of equal mass. It was enclosed in a hollow brass sphere (*V'*) and this was included in another hollow brass sphere (*V*). The two shells did not touch each other. The second sphere could be surrounded by liquid mercury that was introduced in a strong wood cylindrical vessel (*U*). The balance and vessel were covered by a threefold thick cover made of camel hair to avoid changes of temperature. Measurements and control of the apparatus were made from another room, at a distance of 12 m from the balance, to avoid mechanical and thermal influences of the observer upon the apparatus.

No attempt was made to determine the exact weight of the test body. Instead of making two extremely precise measurements and then finding their difference, Majorana tried to observe *changes* of the weight of the test body when it was surrounded by mercury.

First, the system was carefully balanced and brought to equilibrium. The balance was never completely immobile, however, and the reflected light beam kept drifting during all experiments. Measurements were made when the drift of the spot was regular and slow (about 5 mm per hour). During the measurements, mercury was first introduced in the wooden vessel and then taken off, and any change of equilibrium of the balance was observed. The expectation was that the weight of the test body would show a small reduction when mercury was put around it, and then the weight should return to its initial value when mercury was withdrawn from the wood cylinder.

The balance was so sensitive that the best measurements could only be made in the first hours after midnight (from 1:30 to 4:30 a.m.), to avoid vibrations due to street traffic. Smaller vibrations would blur the reflected spot, making precise measurement impossible; larger vibrations due to the passage of trams or trucks would occasionally produce oscillations of the light spot of a few mm. The finest measurement conditions occurred during two general strikes that occurred from 13 to 15 June and from 20 to 21 July 1919. As the strike had been announced several days earlier, Majorana was able to prepare the experimental setup and to make all adjustments to take advantage of this occasion (Majorana, 1919-20b, p. 26).

The room where the experiment was performed was kept at a stable temperature (it would vary less than 2° C during daytime). A typical series of measurements would take a few hours. The enclosure around the test body guaranteed that its temperature could never vary more than a few hundredths of a degree during the experiments. The vacuum inside the apparatus was kept by a Gaede mercury pump that was turned on many hours before any observation was made, and that was kept running during the measurements. It maintained an internal pressure lower than 0.1 mm of mercury. Majorana computed the possible buoyancy effects and noticed that they were smaller than the sensitivity of the balance.

The test body had to be placed exactly at the centre of the hollow sphere, and the level of the mercury inside the wood cylinder had to be adjusted so that the hollow sphere was exactly between its upper and lower levels. The position of all solid parts of the apparatus was established with an accuracy of about 0.1 mm using a cathetometer. The motion of the liquid mercury was controlled at a distance, and its level was detected by electrical contacts. After several improvements of this system, Majorana was able to control this level with an accuracy of 0.1 or 0.2 mm.

The sensitivity of the balance was checked using the 1 mg rider, and it was noticed that the sensitivity was not constant. It was necessary first to prepare the experiment — to produce the vacuum and then to wait for several days until the system would become stable. After three days, the sensibility would remain nearly constant (varying about 1%). Majorana also checked the sensibility of the balance, filling the wood cylinder with mercury up to the level of the test body and observing the resultant Newtonian force of attraction. The computed force was 32.6 μ g, and the observed displacement of the light spot agreed with the predicted value of 5.6 mm.

The balance beam oscillated continuously with a period of about 2 minutes, and therefore the light spot was never at rest: it oscillated with an amplitude of about 1 mm. In addition, there was also a slow drift of the equilibrium position. All position measurements were therefore the result of three observations: the upper position h_1 of the light spot in one oscillation, its lower position h_2 in the same oscillation, and its upper position h_3 in the next oscillation. The mean position of the spot was computed as $p = (h_1 + h_3 + 2h_2)/4$. Each position was measured to 0.1 mm, but Majorana used two decimal places to represent the mean.

Observations were made in the following way. When the apparatus had attained stable conditions and the wood cylinder was full of mercury up to the required level, the position of the light spot on the scale was measured, to within 0.1 mm, by the method described above. This would take 2-3 minutes. Let the first mean position be C_1. Then, mercury was withdrawn from the hollow wood cylinder. This operation took about 2 minutes. Then the position of the light spot was measured again (S_2). Immediately afterwards, mercury was introduced again in the hollow wood cylinder, and its level was adjusted. This operation took about 3 minutes. Immediately after the adjustment of the mercury level the position of the light spot was determined again (C_3). If the posi-

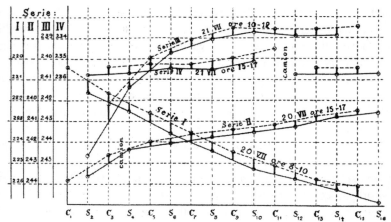

Fig. 7 – In Majorana's experiments the equilibrium position of the balance kept drifting all the time. To detect weight changes he made successive determinations of the equilibrium position when the test body was surrounded by mercury (C marks) and without mercury (S marks). In this graph, the points corresponding to measurements without the gravitational shield are joined by full lines, and the points corresponding to measurements with the gravitational shield are joined by dotted lines. In each series of measurements the two lines are clearly distinct and roughly parallel to each other.

tion of the light spot did not drift, C_1 would be equal to C_3. As a matter of fact they were always slightly different. For that reason, instead of comparing S_2 with C_1 or C_3, Majorana compared it with their mean $(C_1 + C_3)/2$. He was careful to make sure that the time intervals between the three measurements were equal. A graph presented by Majorana (Fig. 7) exhibits four series of measurements. One can perceive the slow drift of the equilibrium position, and it is easy to perceive that "C" measurements (those with mercury surrounding the test body) and "S" measurements (those without mercury) show a distinct difference.

Each series usually took a few hours, and during this time it was possible to obtain 10 to 30 measurements. In the strike days of 20-21 July 1919 Majorana was able to obtain 57 values of the weight change of the test body when mercury was introduced in the wood cylinder. In all cases he observed a weight *decrease*. The mean of these 57 observations was 0.358 ± 0.012 mm corresponding to a weight change of 2.09 ± 0.07 μ g.

It was necessary to correct this result taking into account several known influences, however. In each experiment, about 100 kg of mercury were displaced from 6 containers to the wood cylinder and back to the containers. The test body was placed exactly at the middle of the containers and of the wood cylinder; therefore it experienced no resultant gravitational force. However, it was necessary to take into account the gravitational attraction of the mercury upon the balance beam and upon the counterweight. Majorana computed these effects and noticed that they were not negligible. When mercury was displaced to the wood cylinder, the Newtonian gravitational forces would simulate a

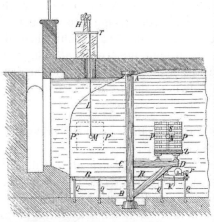

Fig. 8 – Majorana's second experimental setup (a) made use of a large lead cube *PP* as a gravitational shield. The test body *M* in the basement was attached to a balance *H* kept at the ground floor of the building. The two halves of the lead cube were supported by wood structures that could rotate around the pillar *AB* and be brought to the position *P'P'*. Measurements were made both with the test body surrounded by the lead cube and without it. The photographs show the actual arrangement, with the lead cube away from the test body (b) and enclosing it (c).

weight reduction corresponding to 1.12 μ g (that is, about half the observed effect). Therefore, discounting the attraction forces, the net measured effect was a weight decrease of 0.97 μ g.

Could this decrease be due to other classical causes? It was natural to check whether a small error in the position of the test body inside the hollow sphere, or a small error in the position of the mercury level, could explain this weight decrease. However, Majorana was able to show that it would be necessary to introduce a difference of about 5 mm of the upper level of mercury to account for the observed effect, and he was sure that the uncertainty of the mercury level was below 0.2 mm. An asymmetry of the wood cylinder or uncertainties in positioning the hollow sphere and the test body at the centre of the mercury shield could only produce weight changes of about ± 0.09 μ g, according to him.

Electrical forces were easily dismissed, because the whole apparatus was electrically shielded and connected to the earth. Magnetic forces, however, could be in play and Majorana made several tests to check this possibility. He finally dismissed this classical explanation, too. After taking into account all known influences and possible errors, he arrived at the final result: when the test body was surrounded by mercury, its weight underwent a change of $-0.97 \pm 0.16\ \mu$ g. Taking into account the size of the wood vessel and the density of mercury, Majorana computed the following value for the constant h:

$$h = (6.7 \pm 1.1) \times 10^{-12}\, cm^2 g^{-1}.$$

The value obtained in this measurement was compatible with the previously determined upper limit of 7.65×10^{-12} cm^2 g^{-1}.

Applying this result to the Sun, Majorana computed that its real density should be about three times its apparent density. This result was, however, computed from the simple model of a sphere with uniform density.

The above described results were also published, in summary form, in the proceedings of the French Academy of Sciences (Majorana, 1919a, 1919b) and in the *Philosophical Magazine* (Majorana, 1920).

6. Majorana's Second Measurement

Two years after the first series of measurements, Majorana repeated the experiment, but this time he surrounded the test body with 9,603 kg of lead instead of the 104 kg of mercury previously used (Majorana, 1921-22). For practical reasons, the mass of lead had a cubic form, instead of the cylindrical form used in the case of mercury. Instead of a solid block, he used 288 lead bricks to build two equal half-cubes that could be joined around the test body or moved away from it.

According to the previous measurement, and supposing that gravitational absorption depended only on density but not on other properties of the shielding substance, it was possible to anticipate that the reduction of weight, in this case, should be 5.4 times greater. Therefore, it was expected that the new measurement would afford an improved value of the gravitational absorption constant h.

In this second experiment, the absorption of gravity was produced by a lead cube with dimensions of 95 cm and total weight close to 10 tons—that is, about one hundred times the mass of mercury employed in the first experiment. The Newtonian attraction produced by the lead cube would be correspondingly larger, and to avoid strong perturbations upon the counterweight and the apparatus Majorana increased the distance between the test body and the balance (Fig. 8). The lead cube was mounted in the basement of the building. The balance (H) was on the ground floor, and a hole connected the two rooms. The two separate half-cubes could be moved 3 m away from the test body (M), by rotating them around the axis (AB) of their supports.

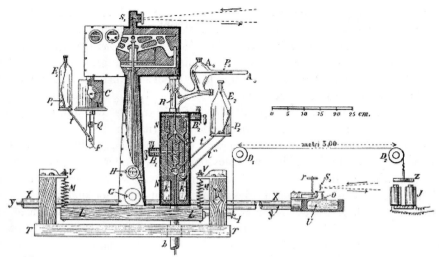

Fig. 9 – In the case of Majorana's second experimental setup, the displacement of the heavy lead blocks produced a noticeable tilting of the balance with a consequent change of the equilibrium position. To avoid this problem the Italian physicist built a special support for the balance that could be adjusted from a remote observation place, to cancel the tilting.

Majorana improved his apparatus to avoid several previous problems. There were, however, huge new experimental problems. The motion of the large mass of lead produced a small but relevant bending of the whole building where the experiment was made. The building deformation produced a tilting of about 10" of the balance. It was necessary to measure and to attempt to compensate for or evaluate all such changes. Majorana chose to compensate for the tilting, through a suitable mounting of the balance upon a platform that could be brought back to a horizontal position after motion of the lead shield (Fig. 9). He devised special ways of detecting a tilting smaller than 1" and he could compensate these changes using a small electromagnet.

It was necessary to take into account the attraction of the lead blocks upon the counterweight, as in the former experiment, but there were new perturbations. The lead blocks were held by massive wood pieces, and this suspension produced relevant forces both upon the counterweight and upon the test body. In addition, the lead blocks were moved by an electric motor and its Newtonian attraction had also to be taken into account. Majorana could not avoid using some iron pieces in the underground arrangement, and there were significant magnetic effects upon the balance.

The Newtonian effects were computed and taken into account in the calculations. The magnetic forces were measured by disconnecting the test body from the balance and using a third equivalent weight at the balance level instead.

In one typical measurement, Majorana observed a gross weight change equal to $+1.04 \,\mu$ g (that is, a weight *increase*) when the test body was surrounded by the lead blocks. However, in this position the magnetic influences produced a downward force equivalent to +1.47 μ g and therefore there was a non-magnetic *upward* force of 0.43 μ g. The displacement of the lead blocks, together with its suspension and other attached bodies (electric motor, *etc.*), produced a downward Newtonian effect equivalent to 3.78 μ g, and the Newtonian attraction of the lead blocks upon the counterweight produced an upward effect equivalent to 2.75 μ g. Taking all these forces into account, there remained a net upward force of 1.79 μ g that was interpreted as a weight decrease produced by the absorption of gravitation.

Notice that the systematic errors were very large—larger, indeed, than the measured effect. In these circumstances one could wonder if Majorana could be measuring anything at all. Majorana himself was worried about this, and made a delicate test. He put a 15 kg lead disk at the floor of the basement room, below the test body. The Newtonian gravitational attraction produced by this lead disk upon the test body amounted to a few μ g. Repeating his experiment, he noticed that he could measure this effect—that is, the errors did not mask a very small influence such as this. Therefore, he concluded that the measured effect was real.

Majorana discussed other possible explanations of the observed reduction of weight. Perhaps the test body was not exactly at the centre of the lead shield, *etc.* However, a downward displacement of 5 mm was necessary to produce the observed weight reduction, and he was confident that positioning errors were smaller than 0.5 mm.

Taking into account all corrections Majorana obtained in 19 series of observations the mean reduction of weight of 2.01 ± 0.10 μ g (Majorana, 1921-22, p. 144). This was about half the expected value. Therefore, in the lead experiments, Majorana obtained a different value for the constant h:

$$h = \left(2.8 \pm 0.1\right) \times 10^{-12} \, cm^2 g^{-1}.$$

This difference could be ascribed either to experimental errors, or to a dependence of gravitational absorption on chemical composition of the absorbing body. Majorana did not, however, choose any of these alternatives. He did urge other scientists to reproduce his experiments in order to check his results.

7. Majorana's Later Work

Majorana's experimental work was never criticised. Indeed, when one reads the detailed account of his measurements, it is very difficult to suggest any source of error that he had not taken into account. Discussion following the publication of these results focused on its consequences and compatibility with other accepted results. Majorana himself always stressed the importance of reproducing his experiments in order to check his results, but no one else ever performed them. Albert Abraham Michelson once wrote to Majorana asking his permission to reproduce these experiments in the Mount Wilson Observatory. Majorana agreed enthusiastically, but the experiment was never reproduced. Perhaps Michelson gave up because he perceived that it was very difficult to reproduce or to improve that delicate experiment with available instruments.

In 1930, Majorana was invited to present a lecture to the French Physical Society. He talked about his gravitational experiments (Majorana, 1930). There, he again remarked:

> I really do not intend to state that my experiments (...) are completely conclusive. However, in my opinion, it would be useful if my experiments could be repeated by other more skilled colleagues that could make use of improved means. It could certainly occur that these eventual researches would conclude that the *effect* that I have found should be reduced in a greater or smaller extent, or that the limit of sensitivity or the observational errors do not really allow the certain determination of this effect. Even in this case, however, the physicist would do a work useful to scientific progress (Majorana, 1930, p. 314).

Majorana's experiments had been performed in the Physics Laboratory of the Turin Polytechnic. At the end of 1921, however, Majorana assumed the chair of Physics at the University of Bologna, as a successor to Augusto Righi. It seems that the new laboratory was better equipped than the former (*cf.* Perucca, 1954, p. 359). Majorana began a new series of experiments on absorption of gravity, but their detailed account was never published.

The main difficulty encountered by Majorana in his experiments had been the deformations of the building resulting from displacement of approximately 10 tons of lead. In order to avoid this problem, in Bologna Majorana reduced the weight of lead to only 380 kg. The arrangement of the balance was also different: a cylindrical lead shield was successively placed around each of *two* test bodies attached to the balance, in order to double the effect. Majorana stated that there were new sources of error and that it was impossible to derive any reliable value for the coefficient of absorption of gravitation from these measurements (Majorana, 1930, p. 321).

At Bologna, Majorana also tried to improve his mercury experiments. In this case, a new arrangement of the mercury vessels was chosen, so that its whole weight was always applied to the same point of the pavement. In 1930, Majorana was still improving the suspension of his balance and could present no quantitative results:

> The few measurements that have already been done seem to give results that confirm the sense of the formerly established effect, that is, an absorption of gravitational force. Although I cannot provide today quantitative results on the searched for effect, I am confident that with the new apparatus that is now under test I will be able, after some time, to say my definitive word *on the subject* (Majorana, 1930, p. 321).

Majorana's new measurements were never published. What happened? It seems that other interests had called his attention. Around 1930, Majorana was deeply involved in the development of communication by ultraviolet and infrared radiation, for military purposes (see Majorana 1941, pp. 81-82). It seems that his gravitational experiments were successively postponed and never finished. Indeed, in 1941 Majorana still referred to his Bologna attempts, remarking:

> The effect is of the same order of magnitude as that already observed in Turin. However it was impossible for me to establish its precise value in a definitive way. There are many causes of perturbation that act in an inconstant way when the experiment is varied. Notwithstanding this, hitherto the existence of the effect has always been confirmed. These are highly delicate researches that require months and years of accurate work for their preparation. If they are improved, they may in the future provide the last word on this interesting subject (Majorana, 1941, p. 80).

This future time never arrived. To the time of his death, in 1957, Majorana published several works that refer to his gravitational experiments[*], but he was not able to repeat them.

8. Did Majorana Measure the Absorption of Gravitation?

In the 1920's everyone agreed that Majorana was a careful researcher, and his experimental method was never criticised. There are, however, three doubtful points.

First: in his measurements the attained sensibility was of the same order of magnitude as the measured effect. Indeed, any single position of the light spot on the scale was read within 0.1 mm, corresponding to a weight change of 0.6 μ g. In the mercury experiments the net measured effect was a weight decrease of 0.97 μ g, and in the lead experiments 2.0 μ g. Many measurements were taken, and the mean exhibited a small standard deviation, but it is always risky to attempt to measure an effect of the same order of magnitude as the sensibility of the measuring apparatus.

Second: known systematic errors were of the same order of magnitude as (and sometimes larger than) the measured effect. Majorana was always attempting to reduce these perturbations, and in some cases it was easy to see how his experiments could be improved. For instance: the magnetic effects upon the balance and the Newtonian effects produced by the lead masses upon the counterweight could be reduced to about 25% if Majorana could transfer the balance to the next floor of the building. It seems that in the Bologna experiments he was trying to reduce several perturbations, but he could not achieve definitive results.

Third: Majorana did not make public all his experimental results, and he certainly *chose* some of his measurements for publication. The mercury results presented by him were computed using only the 57 measurements he obtained on the 20th and 21st July 1919. What about all other measurements he made? And why did he never publish any data of his Bologna experiments? It is likely that he would have published more data if they were consistent with his previous results. Maybe in different series of experiments he obtained widely different effects and saw that no conclusion could be drawn from the complete set of

---

[*] The last ones seem to be Majorana 1957a, 1957b.

data he had obtained. Only a careful study of his unpublished laboratory notes (if they have survived) could elucidate this point.

Perhaps the absorption of gravitation does not exist, and Majorana was measuring some unknown variable influence. Indeed, both in old gravitational experiments and in recent ones, it is usual to find unexplained systematic effects (Cook 1987, 1988). As Cook put it, "it is difficult to attain an adequate understanding of experiments at the limit of available techniques" (Cook 1987, p. 76). Majorana was certainly pushing the sensibility of weight measurements to its limit. Although he was a careful experimenter, some systematic error might be responsible for his results.

However, Majorana's measurements cannot be dismissed just because it is possible to *doubt* they are correct (and because they conflict with the most widely accepted gravitational theory). Until an improved reproduction of his experiments yields a null result, one should accept that *there is* observational evidence of the existence of gravitational absorption by matter.

Acknowledgement

The author is grateful to the State of São Paulo Science Foundation (FAPESP) and to the Brazilian National Council for Scientific and Technological Development (CNPq) for their support of this research.

References

Armellini, Giuseppe (1948). "Il moto del perielio di Mercurio nell'ipotesi di un assorbimento del flusso gravitazionale attraverso i mezzi materiali." *Atti della Accademia Nazionale dei Lincei. Rendiconti* **5**: 288-94.

Austin, Louis Winslow and Thwing, Charles Burton (1897). "An experimental research on gravitational permeability." *Physical Review* **5**: 294-300.

Cook, Alan (1987). "Experiments on gravitation." In *Three hundred years of gravitation*. Stephen Hawking and Werner Israel, eds. Cambridge: Cambridge University Press, pp. 51-79.

Cook, Alan (1988). "Experiments on gravitation." *Reports of Progress in Physics* **51**: 707-757.

Gillies, George T. (1987). "The Newtonian gravitational constant." *Metrologia – International Journal of Scientific Metrology* **24** (Suppl): 1-56.

Gillies, George T. (1990). "Resource letter MNG-1: Measurements of Newtonian gravitation." *American Journal of Physics* **58**: 525-534.

Gillies, George T. (1997). "The Newtonian gravitational constant: recent measurements and related studies." *Reports of Progress in Physics* **60**: 151-225.

Majorana, Quirino (1918-19). "Nuove ipotesi cosmogoniche e nuovo fenomeno gravitazionale." *Atti della Reale Accademia delle Scienze di Torino* **54**: 667-9.

Majorana, Quirino (1919a). "Sur la gravitation." *Comptes Rendus des Séances de l'Académie des Sciences de Paris* **169**: 646-649.

Majorana, Quirino (1919b). "Expériences sur la gravitation." *Comptes Rendus des Séances de l'Académie des Sciences de Paris* **169**: 719-721.

Majorana, Quirino (1919-20a). "Sulla gravitazione." *Atti della Reale Accademia delle Scienze di Torino* **55**: 69-88.

Majorana, Quirino (1919-20b). "Sulla gravitazione." *Atti della Reale Accademia dei Lincei. Rendiconti. Classe di Scienze Fisiche, Matematiche e Naturali* [series 5] **28** (2° Semestre): 165-174, 221-223, 313-317, 416-421, 480-489; **29** (1° Semestre): 23-32, 90-99, 163-169, 235-240.

Majorana, Quirino (1920). "On gravitation. Theoretical and experimental researches." *London, Edinburgh and Dublin Philosophical Magazine* [series 6] **39**: 488-504.

Majorana, Quirino (1921). "Sur l'absorption de la gravitation." *Comptes Rendus des Séances de l'Académie des Sciences de Paris* **173**: 478-479.

Majorana, Quirino (1921-22). "Sull'assorbimento della gravitazione." *Atti della Reale Accademia dei Lincei. Rendiconti. Classe di Scienze Fisiche, Matematiche e Naturali* [series 5] **30** (2° Semestre): 75-9, 289-94, 350-4, 442-6; **31** (1° Semestre): 41-5, 81-6, 141-6, 221-6, 343-6.

Majorana, Quirino (1930). "Quelquer recherches sur l'absorption de la gravitation par la matière." *Journal de Physique et le Radium* [series 7] **1**: 314-323.

Majorana, Quirino (1941). "Le mie ricerche scientifiche." *Nuovo Cimento* **18**: 71-86.

Majorana, Quirino (1954). "Su di un'ipotesi cosmogonica." Atti della Accademia Nazionale dei Lincei. Rendiconti. Classe de scienze fisiche, matematiche e naturali [series 8] **17**: 150-157.

Majorana, Quirino (1957a). "Sull'ipotesi dell'assorbimento gravitazionale." *Atti della Academia Nazionale dei Lincei. Rendiconti. Scienze fisiche, matematiche e naturali* [series 8] **22**: 392-397.

Majorana, Quirino (1957b). "Ipotetiche conseguenze dell'assorbimento gravitazionale." *Atti della Academia Nazionale dei Lincei. Rendiconti. Scienze fisiche, matematiche e naturali* [series 8] **22**: 397-402.

Martins, Roberto de Andrade (1999). "The search for gravitational absorption in the early 20th century." In: Goemmer, H., Renn, J., & Ritter, J. (eds.). *The expanding worlds of general relativity* (Einstein Studies, vol. 7). Boston: Birkhäuser, pp. 3-44.

Perucca, Eligio (1958). "Commemorazione del socio Quirino Majorana." *Rendiconti delle Sedute della Accademia Nazionale dei Lincei* **25**: 354-362.

Poincaré, Jules Henri (1953). "Les limites de la loi de Newton." [1906-07] *Bulletin Astronomique* **17**: 121-269.

Taylor, W. B. (1876). "Kinetic theories of gravitation." Annual Report of the Board of Regents of the Smithsonian Institution, 205-282.

Woodward, James F. (1972). *The search for a mechanism: action-at-a-distance in gravitational theory.* Denver: University of Denver (PhD. thesis, UMI 72-33,077).

Gravitational Absorption According to the Hypotheses of Le Sage and Majorana

Roberto de Andrade Martins[*]

According to kinetic models of gravitation such as Le Sage's and Majorana's, it should be possible to reduce the gravitational attraction between two bodies by the use of material shields. It is usually supposed that Majorana's theory would only predict this effect when the shield is placed between the two bodies, and that Le Sage's theory would predict the existence of this effect in the case of an external shield. This paper presents a quantitative analysis of both theories leading to the conclusion that their predictions are always the same, and that a reduction of gravitational force will always occur whenever straight lines drawn from the test body cut two material bodies.

1. Introduction

Since Newton's time, many authors have proposed mechanical models to explain gravitational forces (Woodward, 1972). Huygens and Leibniz attempted to account for the inverse square law by supposing that "empty" space was full of particles travelling around the gravitating bodies. Newton himself attempted to explain gravitation by several ether models (Aiton, 1969; Hawes, 1968; Rosenfeld, 1969), and at one time he thought that a corpuscular model proposed by Fatio de Duillier (Gagnebin, 1949) would be able to explain all features of these forces. Later he gave up these attempts, and as a result of misinterpretations of his famous "*hypotheses non fingo*," most followers of Newton in the 18th century supposed that one should not attempt to explain gravitational forces. Georges-Louis Le Sage (1784), however, proposed a theory very similar to Fatio's that became famous and gave rise to many other analogous hypotheses in the 19th century. In the early 20th century Hugo von Seeliger (1909), Kurt Bottlinger (1912) and Quirino Majorana (1919, 1920) proposed a new kind of model, assuming that all bodies emit in all directions particles (or waves) of a special type that produce the gravitational forces. These authors emphasised that their theories would imply partial absorption of the gravitational force by matter (Martins, 1999). Theories such as Fatio's or Le Sage's, however, also lead to the same consequence. Both Le Sage's and Majorana's theories belong to the general kind of *kinetic theories of gravitation* (Taylor, 1876). This paper will refer to Le Sage's and Majorana's theories, but the considerations presented here also apply to most similar models.

According to both Le Sage's and Majorana's theories, the gravitational attraction between two bodies is produced by the action of high-speed, invisible

[*] Group of History and Theory of Science, Physics Institute, State University of Campinas (Brazil). P. O. Box 6059, 13081-970 Campinas, SP, Brazil. E-mail: rmartins@ifi.unicamp.br

Pushing Gravity: new perspectives on Le Sage's theory of gravitation
edited by Matthew R. Edwards (Montreal: Apeiron 2002)
239

particles travelling through space. There is no action-at-a-distance in the proper sense, according to these theories: the gravitational force is reduced to local exchange of momentum between the high-speed particles and matter. The interaction of the particles with matter is very weak, however, such that the particles traverse the whole Earth without suffering much absorption.

There are several variant forms of these theories. Some of them replace the particles by waves and introduce different auxiliary hypotheses. For the sake of generality, let us call "gravitational rays" the particles, or waves, or whatever one fancies, that produce the gravitational effects. The distinguishing feature of theories following Le Sage's hypothesis is that material bodies *do not produce* gravitational rays: the whole of space is full of gravitational rays coming from all directions, and material bodies can only change and/or produce absorption of this cosmic background of rays. On the other hand, theories that follow Majorana's hypothesis assume that all material bodies *produce* gravitational rays, besides being able to change and/or produce absorption of the gravitational rays reaching them.

Is it possible to devise experiments that could distinguish between these two kinetic theories of gravitation? Their basic hypotheses are so different that one would expect that they would lead to many conflicting predictions. Majorana himself thought that it was possible to distinguish between the two theories in experiments concerning gravitational absorption; and Radzievskii and Kagalnikova (1960) attempted to prove that Russell's objection against Majorana's theory does not hold when this theory is replaced by a modern version of Le Sage's theory. This paper will show, however, that the forces computed according to both hypotheses are the same, and therefore force measurements (or any other consequence depending only on dynamic effects) cannot be used to choose one of them and to reject the other.

2. Majorana's Analysis and Experiment

In his second series of experiments concerning the absorption of gravitation, Majorana tried to decide whether gravity was due to something emitted from the Earth (his own hypothesis), or something coming to the Earth from space (such as Le Sage's corpuscles). He supposed that in the first case the weight of the test body would be decreased by a screen placed *between* the Earth and the test body, but not if the screen were placed *above* the test body. In the second case, the converse would be true.

> Let us suppose two bodies A and B attracting each other. According to the first model [Majorana's hypothesis], when one puts a third body C between them, the original attractive force would be diminished, because some of the particles travelling between A and B would be absorbed by C. In the case of the second model [Le Sage's hypothesis], the attraction of A towards B is explained as the reciprocal protection or shielding action of these masses against the collisions of the energetic particles that come from distant places of the universe, from all directions. If the third body C were a shield *external* to both masses A and B, it would produce a reduction of the attractive

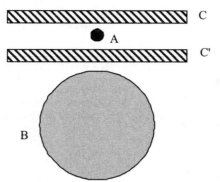

Fig. 1 – When the Earth *B* attracts a test body *A* placed between two thick plates *C* and *C'* the weight of this body should decrease, due to gravitational absorption. Majorana claimed that, according to Le Sage's hypothesis (gravitational rays coming from space) only the plate above the test body should produce gravitational absorption, and that, according to his own hypothesis (gravitational rays emitted by the Earth) only the plate below the test body should produce gravitational absorption.

force between them, because some of the particles would be captured by C. One may also see that even when the shield is not closed this reduction would occur, although in a lesser measure. Therefore, according to Le Sage's hypothesis, even putting the three bodies in the order A B C, this would engender a diminution of the attractive force between A and B; however, this diminution would only occur, according to the first model, if the three bodies are placed in the order A C B (Majorana, 1921-1922, p. 78).

Majorana attempted to choose between the two hypotheses by comparing the weights of a test body when placed above and below a massive lead shield.

Suppose that *B* is the Earth and *A* is a test body (Fig. 1). According to Le Sage's theory, the gravitational force acting upon *A* is produced by gravitational rays coming from all directions of space. The Earth reduces the flux of upward gravitational rays reaching *A*, and the excess of downward gravitational rays produces the resultant force acting upon *A*—its weight.

According to this hypothesis, we would expect that a thick material plate *C* put above *A*, besides attracting *A*, will also reduce its weight because it will act as a gravitational shield, reducing the flux of gravitational rays coming from space and pushing *A* toward *B*. On the other hand, according to Le Sage's hypothesis, we would expect that a similar plate put in position *C'*, between *A* and the Earth, will attract *A* and increase its weight, but will not decrease the force produced by the Earth, because it will not reduce the flux of gravitational rays coming from space and reaching *A*.

Conversely, according to Majorana's hypothesis, we would expect that when the plate is put between *A* and *B* (position *C'*) its gravitational absorption will decrease the force produced by the Earth upon *A*, but no effect should exist when the plate is in position *C*.

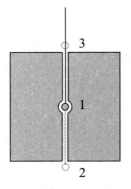

Fig. 2 – In his attempt to choose between Le Sage's and his own hypotheses, Majorana compared the weight of a test body in three positions: at the centre of a lead cube (1), below the cube (2) and above it (3).

    To check the hypotheses, Majorana measured the weight of a small test body when it was (1) at the centre of a lead cube; (2) 5 cm below the cube; and (3) 5 cm above the cube (Fig. 2).

    The test body was a lead sphere weighing 1.274 kg. The sides of the lead cube, built of lead bricks, measured 95 cm, and its weight was 9,616 kg. In a series of ten measurements, Majorana observed that when the test body was at the centre of the lead cube its weight suffered a reduction amounting to 0.00201 mg, with a standard deviation of 0.00010 mg (Majorana 1921-1922, p. 144). Notice that the standard deviation is about 10^{-10} of the mass of the test body. Majorana was unable to measure the mass of the sphere with this precision. He could only measure very small mass *changes*.

    The gravitational attraction of the lead cube, computed according to the Newtonian theory of gravitation, was about 0.217 mg—that is, about 100 times the weight change observed when the test body was at the centre of the cube (Majorana, 1921-1922, p. 222). Therefore, if there were no gravitational absorption, the test body would suffer equal weight changes when it was placed above and below the cube: its weight would *increase* by about 0.2 mg above, and would *decrease* about 0.2 mg below the lead cube.

    When Majorana put the test body above the lead cube he observed a weight increase of about 0.2 mg, and when the test body was below the lead cube there was a weight reduction of about 0.2 mg. The two changes were not exactly equal, however. Comparing eight series of measurements, Majorana arrived at the result that when the test body was below the lead cube its weight change was about 0.004 mg larger than when it was above the cube (Majorana, 1921-1922, pp. 223-5, p. 343). That difference was twice the weight reduction of the test body when it was at the centre of the lead cube (0.002 mg).

    Majorana's conclusion was that the first hypothesis is the correct one, that is, gravitation is produced by gravitational rays emitted by the attracting bodies, and not by rays coming from space (Majorana 1921/22, p. 79). This experiment is inconclusive, however. Indeed, according to both hypotheses, the change of weight of the body below the cube should be greater than its change of weight above the cube. This can be shown by the following argument.

According to Majorana's own hypothesis (gravitational rays emitted from the Earth), when the test body is above the lead cube (position 3), its weight W would increase by F (the attraction of the cube) and would decrease by f (the absorption of gravitational attraction of the Earth). When the test body is below the lead cube (position 2), its weight W would decrease by F (the attraction of the cube).

According to Le Sage's hypothesis (gravitational rays coming from space), when the test body was above the lead cube, its weight W would increase by F (the attraction of the cube). When the test body was below the lead cube, its weight W would decrease by F (the attraction of the cube) and would decrease by f (the absorption of the gravitational attraction of the Earth).

	Test body above the cube	Test body below the cube
Majorana's hypothesis	$W + F - f$	$W - F$
Le Sage's hypothesis	$W + F$	$W - F - f$

Suppose that $F = 200$ μ g and $f = 4$ μ g, as in Majorana's experiment. In this case, the changes of weight would be:

	Test body above the cube	Test body below the cube
Majorana's hypothesis	196	−200
Le Sage's hypothesis	200	−204

In both cases, therefore, the change of weight with the test body below the cube should be greater than with the test body above the cube. Majorana's test could not distinguish between the two hypotheses.

3. Comparison between the Two Theories

In the analysis described above, Majorana assumed that a plate between the test body and the Earth would decrease the weight of the body only according to Majorana's own hypothesis, and that a plate above the test body would decrease the weight of the body only according to Le Sage's hypothesis. Majorana's conclusion was shown above to be wrong. Now let us discuss these very assumptions which seem so "natural", but which are, nevertheless, wrong.

Let us consider the following situation (Fig. 3): Two bodies A and B are inside a thick spherical shell S. The resultant force of the shell upon body A is null, according to the Newtonian theory of gravitation. The shell will act, however, as a partial gravitational shield, according to Le Sage's hypothesis, because according to that hypothesis the gravitational force acting upon A is produced by the gravitational rays coming from space, and inside the shell there

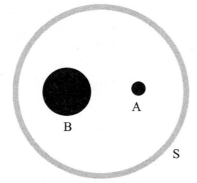

Fig. 3 – According to Le Sage's hypothesis, when two bodies *A* and *B* are inside a thick spherical shell *S*, the force produced by the shell upon them will be null. However, the gravitational force between *A* and *B* will decrease, because the shell will reduce the flux of gravitational rays coming from the outer space, which produce the force between the two bodies.

will be a smaller density of gravitational rays than outside it. Consequently, *B* will produce a smaller force upon *A*.

According to Majorana's hypothesis, on the other hand, it seems that the force produced by *B* upon *A* cannot be influenced by the spherical shell *S*, because the force acting on *A* is produced by gravitational rays emitted by *B* and the shell does not have any influence on that emission. A more careful analysis of the situation, however, shows that according to Majorana's hypothesis the force acting upon *A* should be smaller when the shield *S* is introduced.

Indeed, when *A* alone is inside the spherical shell and body *B* does not exist, the resultant force acting upon it is null. However, when *B* is introduced inside the shell, it will produce a twofold effect (Fig. 4). First, its gravitational rays will produce a force upon *A*. Second, *B* will act as a partial gravitational shield as regards *S*, because some of the gravitational rays emitted by *S* will pass through *B* before reaching *A*. Therefore, the force produced by the shell upon *A* in the direction of *B* will be smaller than the force it produces upon *A* in the opposite direction. Adding this effect to the attraction produced by *B*, we see that the resultant force acting upon *A* is smaller than the force produced by *B* alone. The shell *S* is not acting as a screen, but nevertheless it does reduce the force between *A* and *B*.

So, both according to Le Sage's hypothesis and according to Majorana's hypothesis, the external shield will reduce the force between *A* and *B*.

The above analysis is sufficient to show that a comparison between the two hypotheses is not as straightforward as it might seem at a first sight. Of course, this qualitative analysis cannot establish whether the effect of the spherical shell has the same value according to both hypotheses. It is necessary to *compute* the forces to compare them.

4. Le Sage's Theory in One Dimension

Let us compute the effects of gravitational absorption in the cases of Majorana's hypothesis (that is, gravitational rays emitted by material particles) and Le Sage's hypothesis (that is, gravitational rays coming from space). First

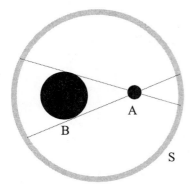

Fig. 4 – According to Majorana's hypothesis, when two bodies A and B are inside a thick spherical shell S, the gravitational force between them should be the same, because the shell cannot affect the emission of gravitational rays by the two bodies. However, B will act as a partial shield of the rays coming from the shell towards A, and therefore there will be a non-null resultant force produced by the shell upon A.

let us consider this issue in the one-dimensional case, and then in the three-dimensional situation.

As we are interested here only in the computation of *forces* between bodies, let us adopt a simple model where gravitational rays are not reflected: they can only traverse matter or undergo absorption. Let as also assume that there is a single kind of gravitational ray, carrying a momentum p. More complicated models, with a spectrum of rays and considering reflection, diffusion and transformation of gravitational rays would follow similar lines.

First, according to Le Sage's hypothesis, space is full of gravitational rays travelling in all directions. Let us call Φ_0 the momentum flux $p(dN/Sdt)$ of these rays in empty space. Consider a single slab of matter with surface S, thickness L and density ρ (Fig. 5).

When the rays that are travelling from the left to the right pass through the slab of matter they suffer partial absorption, and the flux changes from Φ_0 to $\Phi_1 = \Phi_0\, e^{-h\rho L}$. Of course, the rays travelling in the opposite direction suffer an equal change.

The absorption of gravitational rays produces a force equal to $p\, dN'/dt$, where p is the momentum of each ray and dN'/dt is the rate of absorption of rays. If there were only rays travelling from the left to the right, they would produce a force F on the matter slab equal to

$$F = p\frac{dN'}{dt} = S(\Phi_0 - \Phi_1) = S\Phi_0\left(1 - e^{-h\rho L}\right) \qquad (4.1)$$

Let us introduce in (1) the absorption factor $\mu = 1 - e^{-h\rho L}$ (approximately equal to $h\rho L$) and the equation becomes:

$$F = S\Phi_0\left(1 - e^{-h\rho L}\right) = S\Phi_0\mu \qquad (4.2)$$

Of course, there is an opposite force produced by the absorption of rays travelling in the opposite direction, and the net force upon the matter slab is null.

Let us now consider two matter slabs A and B (Fig. 6).

Suppose the bodies have different densities and thickness. Each one will therefore have a different absorption factor $\mu = 1 - e^{-h\rho L}$. Let μ_A be the absorption factor of body A, and μ_B the absorption factor of body B.

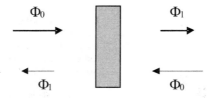

Fig. 5 – According to Le Sage's hypothesis, each material body is traversed by gravitational rays coming from all directions. The flux of gravitational rays must decrease in traversing the material body, because of gravitational absorption.

The following relations will hold:

$$\Phi_1 = \Phi_0 \left(1 - \mu_A\right) \tag{4.3}$$

$$\Phi_2 = \Phi_1 \left(1 - \mu_B\right) = \Phi_0 \left(1 - \mu_A\right)\left(1 - \mu_B\right) \tag{4.4}$$

$$\Phi_3 = \Phi_0 \left(1 - \mu_B\right) \tag{4.5}$$

$$\Phi_4 = \Phi_1 \left(1 - \mu_A\right) = \Phi_0 \left(1 - \mu_A\right)\left(1 - \mu_B\right) \tag{4.6}$$

The force produced upon A by the gravitational rays that are travelling from the left to the right is:

$$F_A^+ = p \frac{dN'}{dt} = S\left(\Phi_0 - \Phi_1\right) = S\Phi_0 \mu_A \tag{4.7}$$

The force produced upon A by the gravitational rays that are travelling from the right to the left is:

$$F_A^- = p \frac{dN''}{dt} = S\left(\Phi_3 - \Phi_4\right) = S\Phi_0 \left(1 - \mu_B\right)\mu_A \tag{4.8}$$

Therefore the net force acting upon A will be:

$$F = F_A^+ - F_A^- = S\Phi_0 \mu_A - S\Phi_0 \left(1 - \mu_B\right)\mu_A = S\Phi_0 \mu_A \mu_B \tag{4.9}$$

The net force F_B acting upon B has an equal value and opposite direction, as may be easily seen—therefore, the law of action and reaction holds in this case. Notice that μ_A and μ_B have roles similar to the masses of the attracting bodies in Newton's gravitational law. As $\mu = 1 - e^{-h\rho L} \cong h\rho L$, and since the mass M of each plate is $M = \rho LS$, we have $\mu \cong hM/S$.

According to this model, the gravitational force between two bodies is due to two circumstances: first, to the existence of a cosmic background of gravitational rays; second, to the partial absorption of gravitational rays by matter. Each body attracts the other one because it acts as a partial screen for the cosmic background of gravitational rays.

Let us now consider the case of three matter slabs A, B and C (Fig. 7). In this case, the force produced upon A by the gravitational rays that are travelling from the left to the right is the same as in the former case:

$$F_A^+ = p \frac{dN'}{dt} = S\left(\Phi_0 - \Phi_1\right) = S\Phi_0 \mu_A \tag{4.10}$$

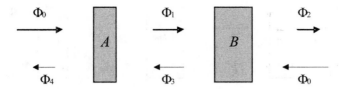

Fig. 6 – A simple one-dimensional model helps to understand the gravitational interaction between two bodies A and B, according to Le Sage's hypothesis. The gravitational flux Φ_0 coming from the outer space will undergo successive reductions as it traverses the two bodies. There will be a resultant force acting upon the body if it absorbs a non-null momentum from the gravitational rays.

The force produced upon A by the gravitational rays that are travelling from the right to the left is:

$$F_A^- = p\frac{dN''}{dt} = S(\Phi_6 - \Phi_5) = S\Phi_0(1-\mu_C)(1-\mu_B)\mu_A \tag{4.11}$$

Therefore the net force acting upon A will be:

$$F_A = F_A^+ - F_A^- = S\Phi_0\mu_A - S\Phi_0(1-\mu_C)(1-\mu_B)\mu_A \therefore$$
$$\therefore F_A = S\Phi_0\mu_A(\mu_B + \mu_C - \mu_B\mu_C) \tag{4.12}$$

If only A and B existed, the net force would be:

$$F_{AB} = S\Phi_0\mu_A\mu_B \tag{4.13}$$

On the other hand, if only A and C existed, the net force would be:

$$F_{AC} = S\Phi_0\mu_A\mu_C \tag{4.14}$$

Therefore,

$$F_A \neq F_{AB} + F_{AC} \tag{4.15}$$

Notice that the net force may be represented in two ways:

$$F_A = S\Phi_0\mu_A(\mu_B + \mu_C - \mu_B\mu_C) = F_{AB} + F_{BC} - \mu_B F_{AC} \tag{4.16}$$

$$F_A = S\Phi_0\mu_A(\mu_B + \mu_C - \mu_B\mu_C) = F_{AB} + F_{BC} - \mu_C F_{AB} \tag{4.17}$$

We might say that when B is introduced between A and C it produces an attraction upon A, and at the same time decreases the attraction between A and C (that is, B acts as a partial gravitational shield because it is between A and C). That is the interpretation of (4.16).

However, as the equation of the net force acting upon A is completely symmetrical as regards B and C, it might also be interpreted the other way around: when C is introduced close to the interacting bodies A and B, it produces an attraction upon A, and at the same time decreases the attraction between A and B, because it acts as a partial screen relative to the cosmic background of gravitational rays. That is the interpretation of (4.17).

The net force upon B can be easily computed in a similar way:

$$F_B^+ = S(\Phi_1 - \Phi_2) = S\Phi_0(1-\mu_A)\mu_B \tag{4.18}$$

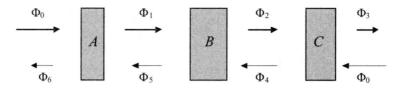

Fig. 7 – According to the simple one-dimensional model of Le Sage's hypothesis it is possible to calculate the resultant force acting upon A when two nearby bodies B and C act as partial shields of the flux of gravitational rays. The computation shows that the effect is not additive, that is, the force acting upon A when both B and C are present is smaller than the sum of the forces produced separately by B and C.

$$F_B^- = S(\Phi_4 - \Phi_5) = S\Phi_0(1 - \mu_C)\mu_B \tag{4.19}$$

$$F_B = F_B^+ - F_B^- = S\Phi_0\mu_B[(1 - \mu_A) - (1 - \mu_C)] = S\Phi_0(\mu_C - \mu_A)\mu_B \tag{4.20}$$

The net force acting upon C will be:

$$F_C^+ = S(\Phi_2 - \Phi_3) = S\Phi_0(1 - \mu_A)(1 - \mu_B)\mu_C \tag{4.21}$$

$$F_C^- = S(\Phi_0 - \Phi_4) = S\Phi_0\mu_C \tag{4.22}$$

$$F_C = F_C^+ - F_C^- = S\Phi_0\mu_C[(1 - \mu_A)(1 - \mu_B) - 1] \therefore$$
$$\therefore F_C = S\Phi_0\mu_C(-\mu_A - \mu_B + \mu_A\mu_B) \tag{4.23}$$

The sum of the three forces $F_A + F_B + F_C$ is equal to zero. It is easy to see that $\Phi_3 = \Phi_6$, that is, the net decrease of the flux of gravitational rays is the same in both directions.

What exactly is the force between A and B in this case? If one assumes Le Sage's theory, there is no definite answer to such a question. As a matter of fact, A and B are not acting upon one another: they are acting on and being acted upon by the gravitational rays.

However, if one prefers to describe the interaction as occurring between the material bodies, one might say that there is a force between A and B and that it is not changed by the presence of C:

$$F_{AB} = S\Phi_0\mu_A\mu_B = -F_{BA} \tag{4.24}$$

In that case, it would be necessary to interpret the remaining part of the force acting upon A as due to C:

Fig. 8 – According to Majorana's hypothesis each material body is incessantly emitting gravitational rays in all directions.

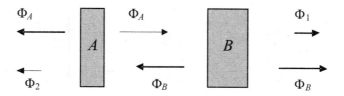

Fig. 9 – A simple one-dimensional model helps to understand the gravitational interaction between two bodies A and B, according to Majorana's hypothesis. The gravitational fluxes Φ_A and Φ_B emitted by these bodies will undergo a reduction as they traverse the other body. The absorbed momentum will produce a resultant force upon each body. It is necessary to suppose that the momentum carried by each gravitational ray is opposite to its velocity.

$$F_{AC} = S\Phi_0 \mu_A \mu_C \left(1 - \mu_B\right) = -F_{CA} \qquad (4.25)$$

This division of the total force acting upon A corresponds to the interpretation of B as a partial shield of the force between A and C.

According to the alternative interpretation, one might say that the force between A and B is changed by the presence of C:

$$F_{AB} = S\Phi_0 \mu_A \mu_B \left(1 - \mu_C\right) = -F_{BA} \qquad (4.26)$$

In that case, the force between A and C would be:

$$F_{AC} = S\Phi_0 \mu_A \mu_C = -F_{CA} \qquad (4.27)$$

According to this interpretation, the force between B and C would be partially screened by the presence of A, too:

$$F_{BC} = S\Phi_0 \mu_B \mu_C \left(1 - \mu_A\right) = -F_{CB} \qquad (4.28)$$

Remember, however, that (4.16) and (4.17) are completely equivalent equations and that, from the mathematical point of view, both interpretations lead to the same result.

5. Majorana's Theory in One Dimension

Let us now develop a similar analysis following Majorana's hypothesis. According to that hypothesis, each body is continually emitting gravitational rays in all directions. Let us disregard the cosmic background of gravitational rays that would be produced by that emission.

Consider a single slab of matter with surface S, thickness L and density ρ (Fig. 8). As a first step let us consider the one-dimensional case, and let us suppose that this body emits gravitational rays with a momentum flux $\Phi = p(dN/Sdt)$ in each direction. This flux will depend on the properties of the body, and it will be approximately proportional to its thickness and its density, when self-absorption is small. Let us suppose that the emitted flux is proportional to a magnitude M that we shall call the "active gravitational mass" of the body: $\Phi = kM$.

There is no net force acting upon the slab, because the rate of emission of gravitational rays in both directions is the same.

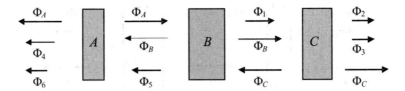

Fig. 10 – According to the simple one-dimensional model of Majorana's hypothesis it is possible to calculate the resultant force acting upon A when there are two nearby bodies B and C. The computation shows that the effect is not additive, that is, the force acting upon A when both B and C are present is smaller than the sum of the forces produced separately by B and C, because the gravitational rays coming from C to A will be partially absorbed by B.

Let us now consider two matter slabs, A and B (Fig. 9). The gravitational flux emitted by each body is proportional to its active gravitational mass: $\Phi_A = kM_A$ and $\Phi_B = kM_B$.

Suppose again that the bodies have different densities and thickness, and thus that each will have a different absorption factor $\mu = 1 - e^{-h\rho L}$. Let μ_A be the absorption factor of body A, and μ_B the absorption factor of body B.

When the rays emitted by A to the right pass through B they suffer partial absorption, and the flux changes from Φ_A to $\Phi_1 = \Phi_A (1 - \mu_B)$. Of course, the rays emitted by B that pass through A suffer a similar change: $\Phi_2 = \Phi_B(1 - \mu_A)$.

The absorption of gravitational rays produces a force equal to pdN'/dt, where p is the momentum of each ray and dN'/dt is the rate of absorption of rays. According to Majorana's hypothesis, the momentum imparted by the gravitational rays is in a direction opposite to their velocities. Therefore, rays travelling to the right produce a force to the left, and *vice versa*. In what follows, only the absolute value of these forces will be computed.

• The force produced upon A by the partial absorption of the gravitational rays emitted by B is:

$$F_A = p\frac{dN'}{dt} = S\left(\Phi_B - \Phi_2\right) = S\Phi_B\mu_A \qquad (5.1)$$

The force produced upon B by the partial absorption of gravitational rays emitted by A is equal to:

$$F_B = p\frac{dN''}{dt} = S\left(\Phi_A - \Phi_1\right) = S\Phi_A\mu_B \qquad (5.2)$$

But $\Phi_A = kM_A$ and $\Phi_B = kM_B$, therefore:

$$F_A = SkM_B\mu_A \qquad (5.3)$$

$$F_B = SkM_A\mu_B \qquad (5.4)$$

If these forces obey the law of action and reaction, we must have $F_A = F_B$, and therefore $M_B\mu_A = M_A\mu_B$. Hence $M_B/\mu_B = M_A/\mu_A$, that is, the active gravitational mass M of each body must be proportional to its absorption factor μ. Let us assume that the law of action and reaction is valid, and that $M = k'\mu$. Hence,

$$F_A = F_B = Skk'\mu_B\mu_A \tag{5.5}$$

Now let us consider the case of three bodies A, B and C (Fig. 10). The gravitational flux Φ_A emitted by body A becomes $\Phi_1 = \Phi_A(1 - \mu_B)$ after traversing the body B, and $\Phi_2 = \Phi_A(1 - \mu_B)(1 - \mu_C)$ after passing through body C. The gravitational flux Φ_B emitted by body B becomes $\Phi_3 = \Phi_B(1 - \mu_C)$ after traversing the body C, and $\Phi_4 = \Phi_B(1 - \mu_A)$ after passing through body A. The gravitational flux Φ_C emitted by body C becomes $\Phi_5 = \Phi_C(1 - \mu_B)$ after traversing the body B, and $\Phi_6 = \Phi_C(1 - \mu_B)(1 - \mu_A)$ after passing through body A.

The total force produced upon A will be due to its partial absorption of the gravitational rays emitted by both B and C:

$$F_A = S(\Phi_B - \Phi_4) + (\Phi_5 - \Phi_6) = S[\Phi_B + \Phi_C(1 - \mu_B)]\mu_A \tag{5.6}$$

Replacing Φ_B by $kk'\mu_B$ and Φ_C by $kk'\mu_C$ we obtain:

$$F_A = Skk'(\mu_B + \mu_C - \mu_B\mu_C)\mu_A \tag{5.7}$$

If only A and B existed, the net force would be:

$$F_{AB} = Skk'\mu_A\mu_B \tag{5.8}$$

On the other hand, if only A and C existed, the net force would be:

$$F_{AC} = Skk'\mu_A\mu_C \tag{5.9}$$

Therefore,

$$F_A \neq F_{AB} + F_{AC} \tag{5.10}$$

Notice that the net force acting upon A may be represented in two ways:

$$F_A = Skk'(\mu_B + \mu_C - \mu_B\mu_C)\mu_A = F_{AB} + F_{AC} - \mu_B F_{AC} \tag{5.11}$$

$$F_A = Skk'(\mu_B + \mu_C - \mu_B\mu_C)\mu_A = F_{AB} + F_{AC} - \mu_C F_{AB} \tag{5.12}$$

This result is mathematically equivalent to that obtained under Le Sage's hypothesis, equations (4.16) and (4.17). The interpretation, however, is slightly different. In the case of Majorana's hypothesis, it is more natural to regard B as reducing the force between A and C, because it produces a partial absorption of the gravitational rays emitted by A and by C towards each other. It would be odd to say that C reduces the force between A and B. However, this is just a matter of interpretation. The equation of the net force acting upon A is completely symmetrical as regards B and C, exactly as in the case of Le Sage's model.

6. Le Sage's Theory in Three Dimensions

So, the predictions of the two models are the same, in the one-dimensional case. Does this result hold in real, three-dimensional situations?

Let us suppose that A is a very small test body. According to Le Sage's hypothesis, the gravitational force acting upon this body is the result of differences between the fluxes of gravitational rays coming from different directions (Fig. 11). Consider a cone with its vertex at A, comprising a very small solid

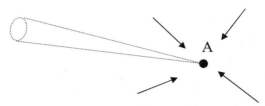

Fig. 11 – In the three-dimensional case, according to Le Sage's hypothesis, each body is acted upon gravitational rays coming from all directions and the resultant force is derived by computing the gravitational flux reaching A from an elementary cone, and integrating over all directions.

angle $d\Omega$. The axis of the cone has the direction $\hat{r}$. Suppose that the flow $d\phi$ of gravitational rays reaching the body A from direction $\hat{r}$, coming through the cone comprising the solid angle $d\Omega$ is

$$d\phi = f(\hat{r})d\Omega \qquad (6.1)$$

The resultant gravitational force acting upon A will be proportional to the resultant flow of gravitational rays reaching A.

$$\vec{F} = k \iint f(\hat{r})\hat{r}d\Omega \qquad (6.2)$$

Let us suppose that B is a large body close to A (Fig. 12). Let us assume that B has a homogeneous composition, that is, a constant density. The form of B is arbitrary. The dimensions of A are negligible when compared to its distance to B and to the dimensions of B. Let us compute the force produced by B upon A, according to Le Sage's hypothesis.

Consider a cone with its vertex at A, comprising a very small solid angle $d\Omega$. The axis of the cone has the direction $\hat{r}$. The axis of the cone intersects B between the distances r_1 and r_2. These distances are a function of the direction of $\hat{r}$.

Suppose that $d\phi_0 = f_0 \, d\Omega$ is the isotropic flow corresponding to the cosmic background of gravitational rays. This is the flow reaching A from every direction $\hat{r}$ except those directions that intercept the body B. The flow $d\phi$ reaching A from directions $\hat{r}$ that intercept the body B will be:

$$d\phi = f_0 e^{-h\rho L}d\Omega, \qquad (6.3)$$

where L is the thickness of body B traversed by the gravitational rays before they reach body A. This thickness is a function of the direction:

$$L = r_1 - r_2 = L(\hat{r}) \qquad (6.4)$$

The resultant gravitational force acting upon A will be proportional to the resultant flow of gravitational rays reaching A from all directions

$$\vec{F} = -k \iint \hat{r}d\phi = -\iint f_0 e^{-h\rho L}\hat{r}d\Omega \qquad (6.5)$$

Replacing $e^{-h\rho L}$ by $1 - \lambda(\hat{r})$ and taking into account that $\iint f_0 \hat{r} \, d\Omega = 0$ we obtain:

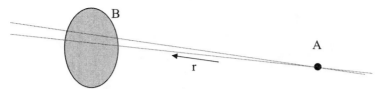

Fig. 12 – According to Le Sage's hypothesis, a test body *A* is drawn towards *B* because the gravitational absorption reduces the flux of gravitational rays coming from *B*. To find the force acting upon *A* it is necessary to compute the reduction of the gravitational flux reaching *A* from each elementary cone passing through *B*.

$$\vec{F} = -\iint f_0 \left[1 - \lambda(\hat{r})\right]\hat{r}d\Omega = kf_0 \iint \lambda(\hat{r})\hat{r}d\Omega \tag{6.6}$$

This is a general result that is valid both when *A* is inside *B*, and when it is outside *B*.

Let us now analyse the case of two large bodies *B* and *C* acting upon *A* (Fig. 13). Consider again a cone with its vertex at *A*, comprising a very small solid angle $d\Omega$. The axis of the cone has the direction $\hat{r}$. Depending on the direction, the cone will intersect both *B* and *C*, or only *B*, or only *C*, or none of them. Let $L_B(\hat{r})$ be the length inside body *B* traversed by the axis of the cone, and let $L_C(\hat{r})$ be the length inside body *C* traversed by the axis of the cone. Both quantities depend on the direction $\hat{r}$, and one of them or both may be null in some directions.

Since $d\phi_0 = f_0 \, d\Omega$ is the flow corresponding to the cosmic background of gravitational rays, the flow $d\phi$ reaching *A* from directions $\hat{r}$ that intercepts the bodies *B* and *C* will be:

$$d\phi = f_0 e^{-h\rho_B L_B} e^{-h\rho_C L_C} d\Omega \tag{6.7}$$

Replacing exp($-h\rho L$) by $1 - \lambda(\hat{r})$ we obtain:

$$d\phi = f_0 \left[1 - \lambda_B(\hat{r})\right]\left[1 - \lambda_C(\hat{r})\right]d\Omega \tag{6.8}$$

The resultant gravitational force acting upon *A* will be proportional to the resultant flow of gravitational rays reaching *A* from all directions

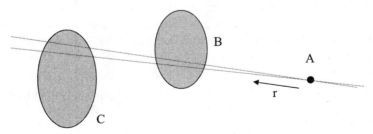

Fig. 13 – According to Le Sage's hypothesis, when there are two bodies *B* and *C* in the same direction, close to *A*, they will both absorb the gravitational rays reaching *A* from that direction. To find the force acting upon *A* it is necessary to compute the reduction of the gravitational flux reaching *A* from each elementary cone. In the case of the rays passing through both *B* and *C* the effect is not additive, and hence the resultant force acting upon A is smaller than the sum of the forces produced by *B* and *C* separately.

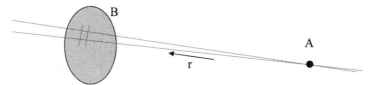

Fig. 14 – In the three-dimensional case, according to Majorana's hypothesis, a body B acts upon another body A by emission of gravitational rays. However, it is also necessary to take into account that a fraction of these rays are absorbed within the emitting body itself. To find the force acting upon A it is necessary to compute the attraction produced by each mass element of B, taking into account the reduction of this attraction due to the absorption of gravitational rays inside B.

$$\vec{F} = -k \iint \hat{r} d\phi = -k \iint f_0 \left[1 - \lambda_B (\hat{r}) \right] \left[1 - \lambda_C (\hat{r}) \right] \hat{r} \, d\Omega \qquad (6.9)$$

Taking into account that $\iint f_0 \, \hat{r} \, d\Omega = 0$ we obtain:

$$\vec{F} = k f_0 \left[\iint \lambda_B (\hat{r}) \hat{r} d\Omega + \iint \lambda_C (\hat{r}) \hat{r} \, d\Omega - \iint \lambda_B (\hat{r}) \lambda_C (\hat{r}) \hat{r} \, d\Omega \right] \qquad (6.10)$$

The first term is the force that acts upon A when only B exists. The second integral is the force upon A when only C exists. The third integral is the effect associated to the shielding of the gravitational rays. The integrand is different from zero only in the directions that intersect both B and C. As $\lambda_B(\hat{r})$ and $\lambda_C(\hat{r})$ play symmetrical roles in the equation, it is possible to interpret this term as a shielding effect produced by B (which is between C and A) reducing the force between C and A, or as an "external" shielding effect produced by C, reducing the force between B and A.

If no radius vector drawn from the test body A crosses both bodies, the third integral will be null, and the force acting upon A will be just the sum of the forces produced by B and C.

7. Majorana's Theory in Three Dimensions

Let us now consider Majorana's hypothesis. We assume that there is no background flux of gravitational rays. Suppose that the small test body A is close to a large body B, as in the former hypothesis. Now, each part of body B should be regarded as an active source of gravitational rays that are emitted in all directions. It is also necessary to take into account the self-absorption of the gravitational rays inside B (Fig. 14).

Let us suppose that the body B is homogeneous, with a constant density ρ_B. However, taking into account the whole space around A, we may regard the density ρ at any point around A to be a function of its radius vector $\vec{r} = r \hat{r}$.

Consider again the cone with its vertex at A, comprising a very small solid angle $d\Omega$. The axis of the cone has the direction $\hat{r}$. The mass dm encompassed within this cone between the distances r and $r + dr$ is:

$$dm = \rho(\vec{r}) \, r^2 d\Omega \, dr \qquad (7.1)$$

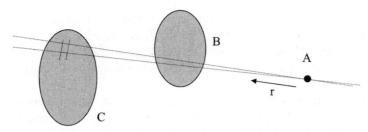

Fig. 15 – According to Majorana's theory, when there are two bodies B and C in the same direction, close to A, they will both emit and absorb gravitational rays towards A. To find the force acting upon A it is necessary to compute the attraction produced by each mass element of each body upon A, taking into account the absorption of gravitation in both B and C. In the case of the rays passing through both B and C the effect is not additive, and hence the resultant force acting upon A is smaller than the sum of the forces produced by B and C separately.

The axis of the cone intersects B between the distances r_1 and r_2. These distances are a function of the direction of $\hat{r}$. The density is null, for each direction, when $r > r_1$ or $r < r_2$.

If the mass of the body A is M, the gravitational attraction between A and the mass dm encompassed within this cone between the distances r and $r + dr$ is:

$$d\vec{F} = -GMe^{-h\rho(r-r_2)}r^{-2}\hat{r}dm \; \therefore$$

$$\therefore d\vec{F} = -GMe^{-h\rho(r-r_2)}\rho(\vec{r})\,\hat{r}\,d\Omega\,dr \tag{7.2}$$

This expression is valid whatever the value of r, because when $r > r_1$ or $r < r_2$ the density ρ is null, and therefore the force is also null. The total force acting upon A because of the presence of B is the integral of (7.2) over all space:

$$\vec{F}_B = -GM \iiint e^{-h\rho(r-r_2)}\rho(\vec{r})\,\hat{r}\,d\Omega\,dr \tag{7.3}$$

Keeping the direction $\hat{r}$ constant and varying r, the density is null outside B and it is equal to ρ_B between r_1 and r_2. Therefore, integrating (7.3) over r, we obtain:

$$\vec{F}_B = -(GM/h) \iint \left[e^{-h\rho_B(r_1-r_2)} - 1\right]\hat{r}\,d\Omega \tag{7.4}$$

Replacing $\exp[-h\rho_B(r_1 - r_2)]$ by $1 - \lambda_B(\hat{r})$ we obtain:

$$\vec{F}_B = -(GM/h) \iint \lambda_B(\hat{r})\,\hat{r}\,d\Omega \tag{7.5}$$

Notice that the result has the same form as equation (6.6) obtained according to Le Sage's hypothesis.

Let us now consider the case of two large bodies B and C acting upon A (Fig. 15). According to Majorana's hypothesis, the force produced by B upon A will not be influenced by the body C which is placed outside the region encompassing A and B. The force produced by C upon A, however, is influenced by B, because this body is between them, and there will be a partial absorption of the gravitational rays emitted by C towards A.

Consider once more a cone with its vertex at A, comprising a very small solid angle $d\Omega$. The axis of the cone has the direction $\hat{r}$. Depending on the direction, the cone will intersect both C and B. Let us suppose that the axis of the cone enters body C at a distance r_3 and leaves the body at a distance r_4, with $r_4 > r_3$.

Let us suppose that the body C is homogeneous, with a constant density ρ_C. The gravitational force upon A produced by each small element of C comprised inside the cone and between the distances r and $r + dr$ is:

$$d\vec{F}_C = -GMe^{-h\rho_C(r-r_3)}\left[1-\lambda_B(\hat{r})\right]r^{-2}\,\hat{r}\,dm\therefore$$
$$\therefore d\vec{F}_C = -GMe^{-h\rho_C(r-r_3)}\left[1-\lambda_B(\hat{r})\right]\rho_C\,\hat{r}\,d\Omega\,dr \tag{7.6}$$

In some directions the cone does not intercept the body B, and in these cases $\lambda_B(\hat{r}) = 0$.

The total force produced by C upon A is the integral of (7.6) over the volume of C:

$$\vec{F}_C = -GM\iiint e^{-h\rho_C(r-r_3)}\left[1-\lambda_B(\hat{r})\right]\rho_C(\vec{r})\,\hat{r}\,d\Omega\,dr \tag{7.7}$$

Keeping the direction $\hat{r}$ constant and varying r between r_3 and r_4 we obtain, by integration over r:

$$\vec{F}_C = -(GM/h)\iint\left[e^{-h\rho_C(r_4-r_3)}-1\right]\left[1-\lambda_B(\hat{r})\right]\hat{r}\,d\Omega \tag{7.8}$$

Replacing $\exp[-h\rho_C(r_4 - r_3)]$ by $1 - \lambda_C(\hat{r})$ we obtain:

$$\vec{F}_C = (GM/h)\iint\lambda_C(\hat{r})\left[1-\lambda_B(\hat{r})\right]\hat{r}\,d\Omega\therefore$$
$$\therefore \vec{F}_C = (GM/h)\iint\lambda_C(\hat{r})\,\hat{r}\,d\Omega - (GM/h)\iint\lambda_B(\hat{r})\lambda_C(\hat{r})\,\hat{r}\,d\Omega \tag{7.9}$$

The first integral corresponds to the force that would be produced by C upon A if B did not exist. The second integral corresponds to the reduction of the force produced by C upon A because of the partial absorption by B of the gravitational rays coming from C.

Therefore, the total force acting upon A is:

$$\vec{F}_A = \vec{F}_B + \vec{F}_C =$$
$$= (GM/h)\left[\iint\lambda_B(\hat{r})\,\hat{r}\,d\Omega + \iint\lambda_C(\hat{r})\,\hat{r}\,d\Omega - \iint\lambda_B(\hat{r})\lambda_C(\hat{r})\,\hat{r}\,d\Omega\right] \tag{7.10}$$

Notice that the final result is completely symmetrical as regards B and C. If we compare this result with that obtained according to Le Sage's hypothesis in equation (6.10),

$$\vec{F} = kf_0\left[\iint\lambda_B(\hat{r})\hat{r}d\Omega + \iint\lambda_C(\hat{r})\hat{r}\,d\Omega - \iint\lambda_B(\hat{r})\lambda_C(\hat{r})\hat{r}\,d\Omega\right]$$

we see that they are completely equivalent, since they contain exactly the same integrals. Therefore, if the constants in both equations are adjusted so that the forces produced by each body (B and C) upon A are the same in both models, the absorption force will also be equal according to both theories.

8. Final Comments

Let us now return to the situation described at the beginning of this paper. Majorana assumed that his own theory and Le Sage's theory would lead to different absorption effects and that experiments would be able to distinguish between them. That guess was grounded upon loose qualitative analysis, but it went unchallenged up to the present.

Now, according to the quantitative analysis developed above, it becomes clear that when a plate C is put above a test body A, it will produce no gravitational absorption effect, because no radius vector drawn from A will pass through both B and C. This result is valid according to both Majorana's theory and Le Sage's. In this situation the force acting upon A is simply the vector sum of the forces produced separately by B and C. On the other hand, when the plate is put between the test body and the Earth (C'), it will produce a gravitational absorption effect, according to both theories, and the value of this effect is exactly the same, independently of the chosen theory. As both theories lead to the same force effects, no experimental measurement of forces will be able to provide a criterion for choosing between them.

Acknowledgement

The author is grateful to the State of São Paulo Science Foundation (FAPESP) and to the Brazilian National Council for Scientific and Technological Development (CNPq) for their support of this research.

References

Aiton, E. J. (1969). "Newton's aether-stream hypothesis and the inverse square law of gravitation." *Annals of Science* **25**: 255-60.

Bottlinger, Kurt Felix Ernst (1912). *Die Gravitationstheorie und die Bewegung des Mondes*. Freiburg: C. Trömer.

Gagnebin, Bernard (1949). "De la cause de la gravitation. Mémoire de Nicolas Fatio de Duillier, présenté à la Royal Society le 26 février 1690, reconstitué et publié avec une introduction." *Notes and Records of the Royal Society of London* **6**: 105-60.

Hawes, Joan L. (1968). "Newton's revival of the aether hypothesis and the explanation of gravitational attraction." *Notes and Records of the Royal Society of London* **23**: 200-12.

Le Sage, Georges-Louis (1784). "Lucrèce Newtonien." *Mémoires de l'Académie Royale des Sciences et Belles-Lettres de Berlin*. Translated by Samuel Langley: *Smithsonian Institution Annual Report* 1898, pp. 139-60.

Majorana, Quirino (1919). "Sur la gravitation." *Comptes Rendus des Séances de l'Académie des Sciences de Paris* **169**: 646-649.

Majorana, Quirino (1920). "On gravitation. Theoretical and experimental researches." *London, Edinburgh and Dublin Philosophical Magazine* [6] **39**: 488-504.

Majorana, Quirino (1921-1922). "Sull'assorbimento della gravitazione." *Atti della Reale Accademia dei Lincei. Rendiconti. Classe di Scienze Fisiche, Matematiche e Naturali* [5] **30** (2° Semestre): 75-9, 289-94, 350-4, 442-6; **31** (1° Semestre): 41-5, 81-6, 141-6, 221-6, 343-6.

Martins, Roberto de Andrade (1999). "The search for gravitational absorption in the early 20th century." In: Goemmer, H., Renn, J., & Ritter, J. (eds.). *The expanding worlds of general relativity (Einstein Studies, vol. 7)*. Boston: Birkhäuser, pp. 3-44.

Radzievskii, V.V. & Kagalnikova, I.I. (1960). "The nature of gravitation." *Byulleten Vsesoyuznoe Astronomo-Geodezicheskoe Obshchestva* (USSR), No. 26 (33), pp. 3-14.

Rosenfeld, Léon (1969). "Newton's view on aether and gravitation." *Archive for History of Exact Sciences* **6**: 29-37.

Seeliger, Hugo von (1909). "Über die Anwendung der Naturgesetze auf das Universum." *Sitzungs-berichte der Königlich Bayerische Akademie der Wissenschaften zu München Mathematisch-physikalische Klasse* (4. Abhandlung) **39**: 1-25.

Taylor, W. B. (1876). "Kinetic theories of gravitation." *Annual Report of the Board of Regents of the Smithsonian Institution*, 205-282.

Woodward, James F. (1972). *The search for a mechanism: action-at-a-distance in gravitational theory.* Denver: University of Denver (Ph.D. thesis, UMI 72-33,077).

Constraints on Gravitational Shielding

C. S. Unnikrishnan[*†] and G. T. Gillies[‡]

A brief review of the constraints on the shielding of the gravitational interaction from laboratory experiments is presented.

Introduction

The empirical physical basis of general relativity—the equivalence principle—is possibly an exact physical principle, and if that is the case it is hardly possible to expect any physical effect that is not described or contained within the general theory of relativity in the classical regime. However, there have been empirical questions that were pursued regarding the nature of the gravitational interaction, which continue to have interest even after we have a near perfect classical theory of gravitation. Some of these questions, like the question of violation of the equivalence principle, have found a new theoretical basis, as in string theory, whereas some others have continued to be purely empirical. The shielding (screening) of gravitational interaction is an issue in the latter category. Any experimental observation of shielding of gravity would indicate gravitational physics beyond the general theory of relativity. (There are small nonlinear corrections predicted by the theory, but in this paper we are discussing genuine shielding effects that are conceptually very different from these corrections).

The similarities between the electromagnetic interaction and the gravitational interaction naturally lead to the question of whether or not it is possible to screen the gravitational interaction. But the dissimilarities between them are crucial in ruling out the most obvious kind of gravitational shielding. Many attempts have been done to examine this problem experimentally (see Ref. [1] for a review). The most significant of these were the experiments of Q. Majorana [2,3], started around the same time as the confirmation of the bending of light in a gravitational field that was predicted by the General Theory of Relativity.

Our interest in this article is in the experimental configurations in which insertion of some kind of matter between the source of gravitation and a test body was done for the purpose of searching for a reduction of the gravitational interaction. The exact form of the hypothetical modification is dependent on the physical model. If one invokes analogy with shielding in electromagnetism,

---

* Gravitation group, Tata Institute of Fundamental Research, Mumbai – 400 005, India. E-mail: unni@tifr.res.in
† NAPP Group, Indian Institute of Astrophysics, Bangalore – 560 034, India.
‡ School of Engineering and Applied Science, University of Virginia, Charlottesville, Virginia 22904-4746, U S A. E-mail: gtg@virginia.edu

Pushing Gravity: new perspectives on Le Sage's theory of gravitation
edited by Matthew R. Edwards (Montreal: Apeiron 2002)

259

then a reduction of the external field is usually achieved by a rearrangement of the charges or currents, and therefore the fields, inside the intervening matter. In the case of gravitation this is probably not a good model, since there is only one sign for the gravitational charge.

Another empirical possibility for shielding could be described as an absorption of the field in the intervening matter. This physical picture demands a description of the gravitational interaction in terms of a flux of particles that could be absorbed by intervening matter. Majorana's formulation of the problem [2] introduced such an absorption coefficient h defined in the modified gravitational interaction between two bodies of mass M and m as

$$F = \frac{GMm}{r^2} e^{-\int h\rho \, dr} \tag{1}$$

Majorana's estimate for h, from phenomenological considerations, was between 10^{-11} and 10^{-12} cm^2/gm. Clearly, experimental determination of such a small shielding factor would be very difficult, requiring very sophisticated measurements capable of resolving fractional changes in force of the order of 10^{-10}.

In the modern context, the analysis of shielding of gravitation requires a more elaborate framework than offered by Majorana's analysis since gravity is a multi-component field. In the least, the analysis should encompass the two important components, namely the gravito-electric and the gravito-magnetic fields. In the weak-field limit, the equivalent "electric" part of the gravitational field, g, is essentially the same as the Newtonian gravitational field, and the gravitomagnetic field, B_g, is generated by moving or spinning masses, similar to the magnetic field in electromagnetism.

In this article we further specialize to the question of the shielding of the electric part of gravity—the same as the Newtonian gravitational field probed by Majorana. (In fact, we think that it may not be easy to formulate a consistent model of shielding of gravitation if the full complexity of the gravitational field is taken into account together with the fact that the gravitational charge is of one sign). We will discuss some of the robust experimental constraints on the Majorana shielding parameter, deduced independently of an underlying theory. The constraints are expected to be valid for a wide class of physical models of gravitational shielding because the experiments are done with weak gravitational fields and the first order shielding is expected to be linear in physical parameters like the density and the size of the intervening matter for a wide class of physical possibilities.

Majorana's results and some early constraints

In a carefully conducted experiment with elaborate remote operation schemes, Majorana compared the weights of two lead balls, one used as a tare mass and the other as the test mass. The test mass could be "shielded" by a large quantity of matter (in this case, about 100 kg of mercury) from the Earth's gravitational field [2]. The theoretical analysis needed to postulate and quantify such an absorption was also outlined by Majorana and he observed an effect amounting to a weight correction of about 8×10^{-10}. The resolution of the modified weighing balance he used was about 6×10^{-10} in a single measurement and close to 10^{-10} for repeated observations. These experiments were repeated several years later with the same kind of balance and different arrangements with much larger masses (the shielding matter was about 10,000 kg of lead) and a slightly smaller shielding factor was measured [3]. The absorption coefficient h deduced from these experiments was 6.7×10^{-12} and 2.8×10^{-12} cm^2/g respectively, consistent with Majorana's phenomenological estimates. Clearly these results indicated effects which were beyond the General Theory of Relativity and received many criticisms, mostly on principle and in comparison with planetary physics, which seemed to be in conflict with Majorana's results.

One of the early criticisms of Majorana's results was by H.N. Russell [4]. Russell examined the consequences of Majorana shielding to planetary motion with the assumption *that gravitational absorption does not affect the inertial mass*. Such a violation of the equivalence principle will then alter Kepler's third law in gross violation of observed planetary orbits. Russell also considered the motion of the moon and the Earth in the Sun's gravitational field to rule out Majorana's shielding. According to Russell's analysis the value of h was limited to about 1/5000 of the value observed by Majorana. Following the same idea, Eckhardt has obtained a much more stringent limit of $h = 1.0 \times 10^{-21}$ cm^2/g from an analysis of the laser ranging data on the moon's orbit [5]. In the following sections we will discuss model-independent constraints, mainly from direct laboratory experiments.

Constraints from laboratory experiments

The laboratory experiments are mainly of two types. In one type of experiments, a medium of uniform density ρ and spatial extent l is interposed between the attracting mass (like the Earth) and the test mass. Then the exponential factor is well approximated as $1-h\rho l$, where l is the effective screening length provided by the medium. The combination $h\rho l$ represents the integrated gravitational opacity of the medium. The typical value for the quantity $h\rho l$ accessible for such experiments is in the range of 10^{-9} to 10^{-10} and the corresponding values for h are in the range of $10^{-12} - 10^{-13}$ cm^2/g.

Another type of experiment that has been more sensitive relies on direct measurements of local gravity on Earth using a sensitive gravimeter. If the mass element of the gravimeter is shielded due to some intervening matter different from its support point—the Earth itself—then a differential signal is expected. One possibility is to observe the gravimeter during a solar eclipse in which a small portion of the Earth is geometrically shielded for a short time from the Sun by the moon [6,7]. Another idea, first proposed and used by Harrison [8], and recently applied to modern gravimeter data by us [9], is to rely on the partial shielding of the gravimeter mass element from the Sun by the Earth itself during night. In the former case, the expected gravimeter signal corresponds to an increase in the local gravity, whereas in the latter case one expects a reduction in local gravity if there is shielding. The difference is due to the difference (flip) in the relative positions of the center of mass of the Earth and of the gravimeter with respect to that of the Sun.

At this point it is worth mentioning that some of the torsion balance experiments done during solar eclipses to probe the question of gravitational shielding are conceptually erroneous. One of the most quoted anomalous results is that of Saxl and Allen [10], who observed a large variation of the period of a torsion balance during a total solar eclipse. The torsion balance is a torque sensor and one would not expect any torque on a torsion balance during an event like a solar eclipse even if there is some amount of gravitational shielding since there is no possibility of large enough differential forces acting on the pendulum mass element.

A gravimeter based experiment in 1954 by Tomaschek [6] which could use the 'unique opportunity' offered by the total solar eclipse observed at Unst, Shetlands, had null results which constrained the Majorana shielding factor considerably. The standard deviation of the measurements was about 1/3700 mgal, and the estimated sensitivity for observing any shielding effect was about $\Delta g/g \sim 3 \times 10^{-9}$. No anomaly during the eclipse that lasted 86 seconds was seen, and the shielding factor of the sun's gravity was estimated to be less than 10^{-5}. From this, Tomascheck estimated an upper limit on the Majorana factor h as less than 10^{-14}, more than a factor of 100 lower than what was measured by Majorana.

A decade later a similar experiment was conducted by Slichter et al. during the total solar eclipse observed in Florence, Italy [7]. Slichter et al. had modeled in detail the expected behaviour of the gravimeter during the eclipse and arrived at a constraint that was about 5 times better than that from the earlier experiment by Tomaschek.

Braginsky investigated gravitational shielding in two modern experiments operated in resonance mode [11,12]. Two identical brass cubes were fixed to a duraluminum frame, with a gap between the cubes. The whole frame was mounted on a knife edge with a counter mass for balancing and this system executed low frequency oscillations on the knife edge. The shielding matter consisted of two steel rotor blades, 10 cm thick, which periodically rotated into the space between the brass cubes, enabling shielding of the Earth's attraction on one of the cubes. The other cube served the purpose of canceling out the attraction of the rotor blade itself. The sensitivity of the experiment was similar to that of Majorana. Elaborate statistical analysis was required to conclude that the probability of having seen an effect of magnitude comparable to that seen by Majorana was smaller than about 4%.

The sensitivity of this experiment was not enough to conclusively rule out Majorana's hypothesis with large statistical significance. A later experiment

[12], the most sensitive direct experiment until recently, employing a torsion balance was an order of magnitude more sensitive. It gave a limit of about 2×10^{-13} cm^2/g for h. This improved sensitivity was due to a clever experimental scheme in which the torsion balance mass element was geometrically shielded from part of the Earth's mass in such a way that a substantial torque would be generated. Since the size of the Earth is vastly larger than the size of the shielding masses, it is possible to arrange the shielding masses to expose a mass element of the torsion balance to part of the volume vertically below, but keep it geometrically shielded from a substantial volume in one hemisphere. This leads to a differential force and hence a torque if there is gravitational shielding.

A year ago we observed that a new beam balance experiment at the Physik-Institut, Universität Zürich [13], aimed at measuring the gravitational constant at the 10 ppm level, could also give very useful information on the Majorana gravitational shielding [9]. We analyzed their results, which provided the value of G at the 200 ppm level, in terms of the gravitational shielding hypothesis. This gave the constraint that gravitational shielding in the experiment is smaller than a value corresponding to $h = 4.3 \times 10^{-14}$ cm^2/g. This is the best limit available from any controlled laboratory experiment to date [9].

The heart of the experiment is an ultra-high precision beam balance which has a precision of 100 ng in a single weighing, for weighing a 1 kg mass. Statistically averaged measurements can reach a precision of 10 ng, more than two orders of magnitude better than in Majorana's experiment. In the experiment, two test masses are compared by alternatively connecting them to the balance. The weight difference is modulated by two cylindrical source masses that are tanks which can be filled with a liquid like water or mercury. In various arrangements used in the experiment, the source masses geometrically shield the test masses from the Earth's gravitational field. The two determinations of G with water-filled and mercury-filled tanks agree with each other within about 50 ppm. Since the densities of water and mercury differ by an order of magnitude, the gravitational opacities are also different by the same factor. This allowed us to derive the constraint on gravitational shielding [9]. The Zürich experiment can also directly search for gravitational shielding since it has many features in its design similar to the original Majorana experiment. As the precision improves in the G measurement, the same experiment will be able to probe gravitational shielding at the level $h = 1 \times 10^{-14}$ cm^2/g.

Very recently we noticed another situation that provided an excellent opportunity for deriving tight constraints on gravitational shielding [14]. We were examining a recent claim [15] that some anomalous gravimetric signal observed during the 1997 total solar eclipse in China was possibly due to gravitational shielding or due to some new property of gravitation. It became obvious to us from various considerations that the observed anomaly was neither due to gravitational shielding nor to some unknown strange property of gravitation. While presenting our argument against the claim of gravitational shielding we noticed that the very same gravimetric data was of very low noise during several days before and after the eclipse and that this could be used for constraining the shielding parameter to unprecedented levels [14].

The idea is originally due to Harrison [8], who obtained a constraint on the Majorana parameter by observing that gravitational shielding of the Sun's field at the gravimeter by the Earth itself would give rise to a differential force to which the gravimeter responds. This can be considered as shielding due to the pseudo-eclipse of the gravimeter by the Earth. The effect begins when the Sun goes below the horizon, peaks when the Sun is at the 'midnight' position and drops to zero when the Sun comes up at the other horizon. So, this signal is diurnal, but it is a periodic wave that is truncated to zero for about half the period. Since the extent of matter through the Earth on a line connecting the gravimeter and the Sun is $l > 2R_E\cos(\theta_z)$, where θ_z is the zenith angle, the change in the Sun's gravity at the location of the gravimeter is $\Delta g_S > 2g_S h\rho R_E \cos(\theta_z)$: g_S is the Sun's gravity at the Earth. The vertical component of this diurnal 'tide' is

$$a_\varpi > 2g_S h\rho R_E \cos^2\left(\theta_z\right) \tag{2}$$

The Chinese gravimeter data extended for about 11000 minutes bracketing the eclipse [15]. We did a Fourier analysis of the data for a diurnal signal. There was no detectable feature above noise near the diurnal period. A diurnal signal of $a_\varpi \geq 0.06 \mu$gal would have been detected at the 2σ level. This corresponds to a limit on h of

$$h \leq 2 \times 10^{-17} \text{ cm}^2\text{g}^{-1} \tag{3}$$

This represents the best limit on the Majorana parameter from any terrestrial experiment [14].

A comparable limit can be obtained using laser ranging data during the total lunar eclipse. The moon is more or less totally shielded for several hours and this extended shielding can give rise to an anomalous differential acceleration between the Earth and the Moon. Since the relative distance is measured to an accuracy of several centimeters for integration times of a few hours, we can get a reliable and significant limit on gravitational shielding from LLR data during the eclipse [16].

The interest in gravitational shielding was recently revived due to the claims by Podkletnov on the observed shielding of the gravitational attraction of the Earth on a test body when weighed above a rotating levitated disc of a high-temperature superconductor like YBCO [17]. The claimed effect was very large, on the order of 0.1%. An analysis of the data by Unnikrishnan [18] led to the observation that the data was inconsistent with the hypothesis of gravitational shielding. The fraction of the Earth's mass seen by the test mass above the disc would vary appreciably as a function of the test mass height above the disc, but Podkletnov's data had no signature for this essential variation. A static shielding experiment with a sensitivity of about 10^{-4} was done by Unnikrishnan [18] in which glass samples were weighed above a superconductor. No evidence for shielding was found. A group in NASA has done high sensitivity experiments on gravitational shielding by a static superconducting disc [19] and they do not find any evidence for shielding at the level of $\Delta g/g \sim 10^{-8}$.

We summarize the best model-independent constraints on gravitational shielding from laboratory and terrestrial experiments in the following table. The first row contains the positive results by Majorana. (Liakhovets [20] claimed a result consistent with that of Majorana, but so little is known of that experiment that we do not examine it here.)

Experiment	Reference	2σ Constraint on h (cm^2/g)
Majorana – Beam balance	[2] 1920	$h > 6.7 \times 10^{-12}$
Majorana – Beam balance	[3] 1930	$h > 2.8 \times 10^{-12}$
Tomaschek – Gravimeter/Eclipse	[6] 1954	$h \leq 10^{-14}$
Slichter – Gravimeter/Eclipse	[7] 1964	$h \leq 5 \times 10^{-15}$
Harrison – Gravimeter	[8] 1963	$h \leq 5 \times 10^{-15}$
Unnikrishnan & Gillies Zürich G experiment – Beam balance	[9] 2000	$h \leq 4.3 \times 10^{-14}$
Unnikrishnan, Mohapatra & Gillies. Gravimeter (Wang *et al*)	[14] 2001	$h \leq 2 \times 10^{-17}$

Do the constraints described here—up to five orders of magnitude more stringent than the positive results obtained by Majorana—mean that gravitational shielding is not a physical possibility? Though one might argue, based on the tensorial structure of gravity as we know it, that gravitational shielding as imagined by Majorana and many others might not be possible, there could be more complicated and theoretically viable possibilities. This is plausible due to the possible existence of 'strange sources of gravity' like the cosmological constant, and its 'polarization' around normal gravitating matter. While the resulting effect may not be strictly of the nature of shielding, the empirical data might be interpreted as due to an effective shielding, just as the effect of the dark matter condensed around galaxies might empirically look like anti-shielding (or 'running coupling constant') of gravity at large distances.

References

[1] G. T. Gillies, *Rep. Prog. Phys.* **60**, 151 (1997).

[2] Q. Majorana, *Phil. Mag.*, **39**, 488 (1920).

[3] Q. Majorana, *J. Phys. Radium*, **1**, 314 (1930).

[4] H. N. Russell, *Ap. J*, **54**, 334 (1921).

[5] D. H. Eckhardt, *Phys. Rev. D* **42**, 2144 (1990).

[6] R. Tomaschek, *Nature*, **175**, 937 (1955).

[7] L. B. Slichter, M. Caputo, and C. L. Hager, *J. Geophys. Res.* **70**, 1541 (1965).

[8] J. C. Harrison, *J. Geophys. Res.* **68**, 1517 (1963).

[9] C. S. Unnikrishnan and G. T. Gillies, *Phys. Rev. D* **61**, 101101(R) (2000).

[10] E. J. Saxl and M. Allen, *Phys. Rev. D* **3**, 823 (1971).

[11] V. B. Braginsky, V. N. Rudenko and G. I. Rukman, *Sov. Phys. JETP*, **16**, 36 (1963).

[12] V. B. Braginsky and V. K. Martynov, *Moscow Univ. Phys. Bull.* **21**, 35 (1968)

[13] F. Nolting, J. Schurr, St. Schlamminger, and W. Kundig, *Meas.Sci. Technol.* **10**, 487 (1999).

[14] C. S. Unnikrishnan, A. K. Mohapatra, and G. T. Gillies, *Phys. Rev. D* **63**, 062002, (2001).

[15] Q.-S. Wang *et al.*, *Phys. Rev. D* **62**, 041101(R) (2000).

[16] C. S. Unnikrishnan and G. T. Gillies, (unpublished).

[17] E. Podkletnov and R. Nieminen, *Physica C* **203**, 441, (1992); E. Podkletnov and A. D. Levit, pre-print, Report MSU-95 chem (1995).

[18] C.S. Unnikrishnan, *Physica C* **266**, 133 (1996).

[19] N. Li, D. Noever, T. Robertson, R. Koczor, and W. Brantley, *Physica C* **281**, 260 (1997).

[20] V. D. Liakhovets, *Abstracts of the 11th International Conference on General Relativity and Gravitation*, Vol. 1, p. 92 (1986).

Non-Relativistic Effects in Gravitation

H.-H. v. Borzeszkowski[*] and H.-J. Treder[†]

We review the following non-relativistic effects in gravitation and their associated theories: (1) gravity as the shielding of a discontinuous ether by matter (according to Le Sage, Thomson, and Isenkrahe); (2) gravity as absorption of a continuous ether by matter (according to Riemann)[‡]; (3) absorption of the gravitational flow by matter (according to Euler, Laplace, Bottlinger and Majorana); (4) absorption of the gravitational flow by space (according to von Seeliger and C. Neumann); (5) suppression of gravity (self-absorption) by the dependence of gravitational mass on the gravitational potential; (6) suppression of gravity by the dependence of inertial mass on the gravitational potential (Machian effects).

I. Introduction

All deviations from the gravitational theories of Newton and Einstein touch fundamental problems of present-day physics and should be examined experimentally. In particular, such examination provides further tests of Einstein's general theory of relativity (GRT), which contains Newton's theory as an approximate case. Therefore, it makes sense to systematically analyze all effects that differ from the well-known Newtonian and post-Newtonian ones occurring in GRT (let us call them non-relativistic effects). If these effects can be excluded experimentally, then this would provide further support for GRT; otherwise one would have to change basic postulates of present-day physics.

Of all possible non-relativistic effects, we shall focus in this paper on the aforementioned effects of shielding, absorption and suppression of gravity. We shall begin in Sect. II with remarks on the early search for a mechanism explaining the Newtonian action-at-a-distance gravitational law and then discuss non-relativistic effects occurring in certain local theories of gravity. In Sect. III, those non-relativistic effects will then be briefly discussed which are typical features of non-local (telescopic) theories of gravity.

II. From Le Sage-type theories to local theories with absorption or suppression of gravity

To analyze non-relativistic effects of gravity it is useful to remember pre-relativistic *Ansätze* of the nineteenth century, sometimes even going back to pre-gravitational conceptions. One motivation for these *Ansätze* was to find a mechanical model that could explain Newton's gravitational inverse-square-

[*] Institut für Theoretische Physik, Technische Universität Berlin, Hardenbergstr. 36, D-10623 Berlin, Germany
[†] Rosa-Luxemburg-Str. 17a, D-14482 Potsdam, Germany
[‡] For this, see the paper by H.-J. Treder in this volume.

Pushing Gravity: new perspectives on Le Sage's theory of gravitation
edited by Matthew R. Edwards (Montreal: Apeiron 2002)

267

law by something (possibly atomic) that might exist between the attracting bodies. In our context, such attempts are interesting to discuss, for they mostly imply deviations from Newton's law. Another reason for considering such rivals of Newton's law was that there were several anomalous geodesic, geophysical, and astronomical effects which could not be explained by Newtonian gravitational theory. Furthermore, after the foundation of GRT, some authors of the early twentieth century believed that there remained anomalies which also could not be explained by GRT. As a result, pre-relativistic assumptions continued to be considered and relativistic theories competing with GRT were established.

One influential early author of this story was G.-L. Le Sage [25, 26]. In the eighteenth century, he proposed a mechanical theory of gravity that was to come under close examination in the nineteenth century (for details on Le Sage's theory, see also P. Prevost [38] and S. Aronson [2]). According to this theory, space is filled with small atomic moving particles which due to their masses and velocities exert a force on all bodies on which they impinge. A single isolated body is struck on all sides equally by these atoms and does not feel any net force. But two bodies placed next to each other lie in the respective shadows they cast upon each other. Each body screens off some of the atoms and thus feels a net force impelling it toward the other body.

Under the influence of the kinetic theory of gases founded in the 1870's Le Sage's theory was revived by Lord Kelvin [46][*], S. T. Preston [36, 37], C. Isenkrahe [21] and P. Drude [13], bringing Le Sage's hypothesis up to the standard of a closed theory. However, this approach to gravity was rejected by C. Maxwell [32] with arguments grounded in thermodynamics and the kinetic theory of gases. On the basis of these arguments, it was discussed critically by Poincaré and others (for the English and French part of this early history, cf. Aronson [2]).

The search for a mechanistic explanation of gravity and the idea of a shielding of certain fluxes that intermediate gravitational interaction were closely related to the question of the accuracy of Newton's gravitational law. In fact, this law containing only the masses of the attracting bodies and their mutual distances can only be exactly valid when neither the space between them nor the matter itself absorbs the gravitational force or potential. Therefore, it is not surprising that the possibility of an absorption of gravity had already been considered by Newton in his debate with E. Halley and N. Fatio de Duillier[†], as is documented in some of the Queries to Newton's "Opticks." The first research program looking for an experimental answer to this question was formulated by M.W. Lomonosov [27] in a letter to L. Euler in 1748. The program was however only realized 150 years later by R. von Eötvös and Q. Majorana, without explicit reference to Lomonosov. At about the same time, Euler discussed with Clairaut, a prominent specialist in celestial mechanics, the possibil-

---

[*] Later he reconsidered it from the view of radioactivity (Thomson [47]).
[†] Le Sage himself stated that his speculations go also back to the work of Fatio.

ity of detecting deviations from Newton's gravitational law by analyzing the lunar motion. Clairaut believed for a time that he had found a fluctuation of the lunar motion testifying to an absorption of gravity by matter, in this case, by the earth.

For a long time, the lunar motion has been the strongest criterion for the validity of the Newtonian and, later, the Einsteinian theory of gravity (today one would study the motions of artificial satellites). This is due to the fact that the gravitational influence of the sun on the moon exceeds the influence of the earth by the factor 9/4. This solar action varies in dependence on the distance of the system 'earth-moon' from the sun. Regarding this effect and, additionally, the action of the other planets on the lunar motion, a reaming fluctuation of the motion of the moon could possibly be due to an absorption of solar gravity when the earth stands between the sun and the moon. This early idea of Euler was later revived by Seeliger, and just as Clairaut had analyzed the lunar motion in order to corroborate it, later Bottlinger [8, 9] did the same in order to find support for the hypothesis of his teacher von Seeliger [43].

The first *Ansatz* for an exact mathematical description of absorption in the sense of Euler and Lomonosov was made by Laplace [24] in the last volume of his *Mécanique Céleste*. He assumed that the absorption $d\vec{F}$ of the flow $\vec{F}$ of the gravitational force is proportional to the flow $\vec{F}$ itself, the density ρ, and the thickness dr of the material penetrated by the gravitational flow, $d\vec{F} = \rho \vec{F} dr$. Accordingly a mass element dm_1 exerts on another element dm_2 the force

$$\left| d\vec{F} \right| = \frac{G \cdot dm_1}{r^2} \exp(-k\rho_1 r),$$ (1)

where k is a universal constant of dimensions $(\text{mass})^{-1}(\text{length})^2$.

In the early twentieth century, when Newton's gravitational theory was replaced by GRT, the two aforementioned attempts by Bottlinger and Majorana were made to furnish observational and experimental proof of absorption effects in the sense of Euler and von Seeliger. Such effects do not exist in GRT and so evidence for them would have been a blow against the theory.

Using H. von Seeliger's hypothesis of 1909 (von Seeliger [42]), F.E. Bottlinger [8, 9] tried to explain short-period fluctuations of the motion of the moon (later it became clear that this explanation was not correct), while Majorana attempted to detect such absorption effects by laboratory experiments from 1918 till 1930. Being aware of previous experiments performed to detect an absorption of gravity by matter, Majorana turned to this problem in 1918. He speculated that gravity was due to a flow of gravitational energy from all bodies to the surrounding space which is attenuated on passing through matter. The attenuation would depend exponentially on the thickness of the matter and its density. Based on a theoretical estimation of the order of magnitude of this effect he carried out experiments the results of which seemed to confirm the occurrence of gravitational absorption. According to present knowledge, they must have been erroneous (for details of the history of these experiments, see, *e.g.*, Crowley *et al.* [11], Gillies [18], Martins [1]).

Another conception competing with absorption or shielding of gravity by matter also goes back to papers by von Seeliger [42]. In these papers, now for cosmological reasons, he considered a modification of Newton's law by an exponential factor. Similar ideas were proposed by C. Neumann [34]. At first sight, it would appear to be the same modification as in the former cases. This is true, however, only insofar as the form of the gravitational potential or force is concerned. For the differential equations to which the respective potentials are solutions, there is a great difference. In the first case, one is led to equations with a so-called potential-like coupling,

$$\Delta\phi = 4\pi G \rho \phi \,, \tag{2}$$

while in the second case one arrives at an equation with an additional vacuum term,

$$\Delta\phi - k^2\phi = 4\pi G \rho \,. \tag{3}$$

The latter equation requires the introduction of a new fundamental constant k corresponding to Einstein's cosmological constant λ (*cf.* [50], where in particular it is shown that, regarding cosmological consequences, both approaches are equivalent).

Equation (2) shows that the potential-like coupling of matter modeling the conception of an absorption of the gravitational flow by the material penetrated can also be interpreted as a dependence of the gravitational number on the gravitational potential and thus on space and time. Therefore, to some extent it models Dirac's hypothesis within the framework of a pre-relativistic theory, and a relativistic theory realizing Dirac's idea could have equation (2) as a non-relativistic approximation. Another possible interpretation of (2) is that of a suppression of gravity (self-absorption) by the dependence of the active gravitational mass on the gravitational potential. Indeed, the product of the matter density and the gravitational potential can be interpreted as the active gravitational mass.

The atomic hypotheses assuming shielding effects lead in the static case to a modification of Newton's gravitational law that is approximately given by the potential introduced by von Seeliger and Majorana. Instead of the r^2-dependence of the force between the attracting bodies given by the Newtonian fundamental law,

$$\vec{F}_{12} = -G \int \frac{\rho(\vec{r}_1)\rho(\vec{r}_2)}{r_{12}^{\,3}} \vec{r}_{12} d^3 x_1 d^3 x_2 \,, \tag{4}$$

where $G = (2/3)10^{-7} cm^3 g^{-1} s^{-2}$ is the Newtonian gravitational constant, one finds,

$$\vec{F}_{12} = -G \int \frac{\rho(\vec{r}_1)\rho(\vec{r}_2)}{r_{12}^{\,3}} \vec{r}_{12} e^{-k\int \rho d r_{12}} d^3 x_1 d^3 x_2 \,. \tag{5}$$

Here the exponent $k \int \rho dr$ means an absorption of the flow of force $\vec{F}$ by the atomic masses between the two gravitating point masses. Since, for observational reasons, one has to assume that the absorption exponent is much smaller than 1, as a first approximation, (5) may be replaced by Laplace's expression,

$$\vec{F}_{12}* = -G \frac{M_1 M_2}{r_{12}^3} \vec{r}_{12} e^{-k\rho dr} \approx -G \frac{M_1 M_2}{r_{12}^3} \vec{r}_{12} \left(1 - k\rho\Delta r\right). \tag{6}$$

Equation (6) contains a new fundamental constant, namely Majorana's "absorption coefficient of the gravitational flow"

$$k \geq 0, \quad [k] = cm^2 \cdot g^{-1}. \tag{7}$$

This value can be tested by the Eötvös experiment, where one can probe whether the ratio of the gravitational and the inertial mass of a body depends on its physical properties. In the case of absorption of gravity the value of this ratio would depend on the density of the test body. Gravimetric measurements of the gravitational constant carried out by Eötvös by means of a torsion pendulum and gravitational compensators showed that k has to be smaller than

$$k < 4 \cdot 10^{-13} cm^2 g^{-1}. \tag{8a}$$

By comparison Majorana [28-30] obtained in his first experiments the value

$$k \approx 6,7 \cdot 10^{-12} cm^2 g^{-1}, \tag{8b}$$

which was compatible with his theoretical analysis. (Later, after some corrections, he arrived at about half this value [31]).

A more precise estimation of k can be derived from celestial-mechanical observations. As mentioned above, Bottlinger hypothesized that certain (saros-periodic) fluctuations of the motion of the moon are due to an absorption of solar gravity by the earth when it stands between the sun and the moon[*]. If we assume this hypothesis, then, following Crowley et al. [11], the amplitude Λ of these fluctuations is related to the absorption coefficient k via

$$\Lambda \approx 2ka\rho, \tag{9}$$

where ρ denotes the mean density and a the radius of the earth. If one assumes that

$$k \approx 6,3 \cdot 10^{-15} cm^2 g^{-1}, \tag{10}$$

then the value of Λ is in accordance with the so-called great empirical term of the moon theory. This, however, also shows that, if the fluctuations of the motion of moon here under consideration had indeed been explained by von Seeliger's absorption hypothesis, then greater values than the one given by (10) are not admissible as they would not be compatible with the motion theory. That there is this celestial-mechanical estimation of an upper limit for k had already been mentioned by Russell [40] in his critique of Majorana's estimation (8b).

---

[*] A. Einstein commented Bottlinger's theory in [15, 16, 17] (see also [51]).

A better estimate of k has been reached by measurements of the tidal forces. According to Newton's expression, the tidal force acting upon earth by a mass M at a distance R is

$$Z = -2\frac{GM}{R^2}\frac{a}{R}, \tag{11}$$

where a denotes the radius of the earth. Seeliger's and Majorana's *Ansatz* (5) however provided

$$Z^* \approx -2\frac{GM}{R^2}\frac{a}{R} - \frac{\Lambda GM}{2R^2} \approx -2\frac{GMa}{R^3}\left(1 + \frac{\Lambda R}{4a}\right), \tag{12}$$

with the absorption coefficient of the earth body

$$\Lambda \approx 2ka\rho \approx 6.6 \cdot 10^9\, cm^{-2}g \cdot k. \tag{12a}$$

Considering now the ratio of the tidal forces due to the sun and moon, Z_s and Z_m, one finds in the Newtonian case

$$\frac{Z_s}{Z_m} \approx \frac{M_s}{M_m}\left(\frac{R_m}{R_s}\right)^3 = \frac{5}{11}, \tag{13}$$

and in the Seeliger-Majorana case

$$\frac{Z_s{}^*}{Z_m{}^*} \approx \frac{M_s}{M_m}\left(\frac{R_m}{R_s}\right)^3(1 + \Lambda\frac{R_s}{a}) = \frac{5}{11}(1 + 4k \cdot 10^{13}\, cm^{-2}g). \tag{14}$$

Measurements carried out with a horizontal pendulum by Hecker [20] gave the result

$$\frac{Z_s{}^*}{Z_m{}^*} \leq 1, \text{ that is, } k < 2 \cdot 10^{-14}\, g^{-1}cm^2. \tag{15a}$$

This result is still compatible with Bottlinger's absorption coefficient, but not with Majorana's value (6b), which provided a sun flood 1,000 times greater than the moon flood (Russell [40]).

Later, Hecker's estimation was improved by Michelson and Gale [33], who by using a "level" obtained

$$\frac{Z_s{}^*}{Z_m{}^*} = 2,2 \pm 0,1, \text{ i.e., } k < 2 \cdot 10^{-15}\, g^{-1}cm^2. \tag{15b}$$

This implies a value of k also casting doubt on Bottlinger's theory. (The real precision of these measurements, however, was not quite clear.)

Bottlinger [8, 9] had also proposed to search for jolting anomalies in gravimeter measurements occurring during solar eclipses due to a screening of the gravitational flow of the sun by the moon. In an analysis performed by Slichter *et al.* [44], however, this effect could not be found and those authors concluded that k has the upper limit $k \approx 3 \cdot 10^{-15} cm^2 g^{-1}$. However, as argued earlier [5], measurements of this effect provide by necessity null results due to the equivalence of inertial and passive gravitational masses verified by Eötvös.

The latest observational limits on the size of the absorption coefficient is $k < 10^{-21}$ cm^{2}g^{-1}. It was established by a reanalysis of lunar laser ranging data. (Eckardt [14], cf. also Gillies [19]). This would rule out the existence of this phenomenon, at least in the in the way that it was originally envisioned. (For an estimation of that part which, from the viewpoint of measurement, is possibly due to shielding effects, cf. [55].)

About the same estimate follows from astrophysics [45, 51]. Indeed, astrophysical arguments suggest that the value for k has to be much smaller than 10^{-21} cm^2 g^{-1}. This can be seen by considering objects of large mass and density like neutron stars. In their case the total absorption can no longer be described by the Seeliger-Majorana expression. However, one can utilize a method developed by Dubois-Reymond (see Drude [13]) providing the upper limit $k = 3/R\rho$, where R is the radius and ρ the density of the star. Assuming an object with the radius 10^6 cm and a mass equal to 10^{34} g one is led to $k = 10^{-22}$ cm^2 g^{-1}.

As in the aforementioned experiments, these values for k exclude an absorption of gravity in accordance with the Seeliger-Majorana model. But it does not rule out absorption effects as described by relativistic theories of gravity like the tetrad theory, where the matter source is coupled potential-like to gravity [5]. The same is true for other theories of gravity competing with GRT that were systematically investigated as to their experimental consequences in Will [54]. For instance, in the tetrad theory proposed by one of us (H.-J. T., see [5]), the relativistic field theory of gravity is constructed such that, in the static non-relativistic limit, one has

$$\Delta\phi = 4\pi G \rho (1 - \frac{\alpha|\phi|}{c^2 r_{12}}) , \quad \alpha = const . \tag{16}$$

From this equation it follows that there is a suppression of gravity by another mass or by its own mass. In the case of two point masses, the mutual gravitational interaction is given by

$$m_1 \ddot{\vec{r}}_1 = -\frac{Gm_1 m_2}{r_{12}^3} \vec{r}_{12} \left(1 - \frac{2Gm_1}{c^2 r_{12}}\right), \quad m_2 \ddot{\vec{r}}_2 = -\frac{Gm_1 m_2}{r_{12}^3} \vec{r}_{12} \left(1 - \frac{2Gm_2}{c^2 r_{12}}\right). \tag{17}$$

Thus the effective active gravitational mass m is diminished by the suppression factor $(1 - 2Gm/c^2 r_{12})$. Such effects can also be found in gravitational theories with a variable 'gravitational constant' (Dirac [12], Jordan [22, 23], Brans and Dicke [10]). Furthermore, in the case of an extended body one finds a self-absorption effect. The effective active gravitational mass $\bar{M}$ of a body with Newtonian mass M and radius r is diminished by the body's self-field,

$$\bar{M} = GM\left(1 - \frac{4\pi G}{3c^2} \rho r^2\right), \tag{18}$$

where exact calculations show that the upper limit of this mass is approximately given by the quantity $c^2/(G\rho)^{1/2}$.

The modifications of the Newtonian law mentioned above result from modifications of the Laplace equation. In their relativistic generalization, these potential equations lead to theories of gravity competing with GRT. On one hand GRT provides, in the non-relativistic static approximation, the Laplace equation and thus the Newtonian potential and, in higher-order approximations, relativistic corrections. On the other hand, the competing relativistic theories lead, in the first-order approximation, to the above mentioned modifications of the Laplace equation and thus, besides the higher-order relativistic corrections, to additional non-Newtonian variations. All these relativistic theories of gravity (including GRT) represent attempts to extend Faraday's principle of the local nature of all interactions to gravity. Indeed, in GRT the geometrical interpretation of the equivalence principle realizes this principle insofar as it locally reduces gravity to inertia and identifies it with the local world metric; this metric replaces the non-relativistic potential and Einstein's field equations replace the Poisson's potential equation. Other local theories introduce additional space-time functions which together with the metric describe the gravitational field. In some of the relativistic rivals of GRT, these functions are of a non-geometric nature. An example is the Jordan or Brans-Dicke scalar field, which, in accordance with Dirac's hypothesis, can be interpreted as a variable gravitational 'constant' G. (For a review of theories involving absorption and suppression of gravity, see [5].)[*] In other theories of gravity, these additional functions are essentials of the geometric framework, as for instance the metric-affine theories working in Riemann-Cartan space-times that are characterized by non-vanishing curvature and torsion.

III. Machian absorption effects in telescopic theories of gravity

M. Planck [35] pointed out that the local and global (non-local) points of view are not equivalent.[†] According to the field-theoretical locality principle, the forces acting at a point depend only on the infinitesimal vicinity of this point (therefore, Planck called a field theory an "infinitesimal theory"), while any non-local action-at-a-distance theory holds that these forces are determined by all bodies of the universe. Accordingly, Planck concluded that the locality principle, postulating the reducibility of all non-local interactions ("telescopic" interactions he called them), implies a simplification of, and also a restriction upon, the nature and mode of action of all natural forces. For him, the answer to the question, whether the non-local (telescopic) action-at-a-distance theory or local (infinitesimal, or, as called by C. Neumann, "microscopic") field theory is valid, depended on the measure of success achieved by the respective theory in describing interactions. Moreover, according to Planck, the global as-

---

[*] For a listing of all the recent observational data concerning a variation in G, see Gillies [19] and the literature cited therein.

[†] For the following passages, see also Ref. [53]. p. 109 *fortissimo*, and [7].

pect is always the more general one, in the sense "that a finite quantity includes an infinitesimal as a special case."

As for gravity based on the principle of equivalence, this means that one can raise the question of whether the latter principle should be realized microscopically or telescopically. Einstein's GRT and other alternative local theories of gravity realize it microscopically by reducing gravity to inertia, *i.e.*, to free motion in metric and possibly supplementary fields. As this leads to problems in quantum gravity it might be considered one reason to turn to a telescopic realization of the equivalence principle [7, 53]. Further reasons are:[*] (1) Despite continued success of field theories, theoreticians have not succeeded in eliminating all telescopic elements from local, *i.e.*, field, theories. Prominent among these elements are the initial and boundary conditions, which are necessary for the integration of the field equations. (Therefore, local physics must be supplemented by telescopic elements.) (2) The power of the local-theory conception derives possibly from the nature of the interaction. And, since gravity is the most "telescopic" interaction we know, a breakdown of the local description of interactions is most likely to occur in the area of gravitational interaction. (According to our above argument, the latter seems to be corroborated in the quantum regime, where gravity leads even to limitations on relativistic field theory.)

Turning to a telescopic description, one can first ask what telescopic elements one should assume to start with. On this question, it is helpful to be reminded of the following point.[†] Due to the telescopic elements missing in local theories, the relativistic field theory realizes its principles of relativity and covariance by offering an infinite variety of "universes" as mathematically possible and virtually contained in the variety of possible world models. However, the actual cosmos embodies one and only one reference system as its 'proper system'.

Indeed, in the actual cosmos investigated by astronomy there is an empirical equivalence of three reference systems which are introduced by three different methods: the inertial system of celestial mechanics determined dynamically, the astronomical fundamental system given by the galaxies, and the black-body background radiation defining the same class of reference systems.[‡] This coincidence seems to imply a cancellation of the relativity principles.

From the viewpoint of a field theory these reference systems defined macroscopically are equivalent to a purely accidental choice of boundary and initial conditions. The cosmological world models of local field theories like GRT specifying these reference systems are, from the local viewpoint, certain special solutions of field equations with a matter source. However, the cosmos is unique (at any rate, there is no other assumption which is epistemologically satisfying). With respect to this assumption, on the one hand, the microscopic

---

[*] *Cf.* Ref. [53], p. 110.

[†] *Cf.* [53], p. 46 *fortissimo*.

[‡] The isotropy of the background radiation even leads to Newton's absolute reference system.

principles do too much; they provide not only the actual cosmos but an infinite variety of models as well. On the other hand, they are not able to determine macroscopic physics at all. They furnish only necessary but no sufficient conditions. The microscopic character of field physics imposes a special supposition on physical laws, leading to the fact that they have to be formulated as differential equations. Therefore, local physics must be supplemented by telescopic (integral) principles. In general, integral principles uniquely lead to differential equations, while the inverse operation is ambiguous. (This reminds us of Planck's statement mentioned above.)

The concept of an absolute space determined by the cosmic masses (let us call this conception "Mach's principle") implies such telescopic elements. However, this space cannot be Newtonian space since, despite Mach's attempts at reinterpreting Newtonian mechanics, it is not determined by the cosmic masses (and it is the proximity of local theories to Newton's theory that makes it so difficult to realize Mach's principle in the GRT framework (see [53])). The problem is that the telescopic theory (in Planck's sense) cannot be formulated in either three-dimensional space or in the four-dimensional space-time of the strictly local theory of relativity. From the telescopic point of view, every degree of freedom of the N point-like particles of a physical system generally provides one dimension of the Hertzian configuration space V_3.

If the particles are identical, as is assumed in classical physics (especially by Hertz), then the N factor spaces V_3 may also be identified. In the Hertzian configuration space, for the "total universe" it is now possible to formulate the dynamics with respect to the cosmic particles themselves and, accordingly, to use in dynamics only reciprocal functions of the particles, as was required by Huygens, Leibniz, and Poincaré. Following Mach and Einstein, one has then to postulate that the inertia of the N point masses A is completely induced by their mutual gravitation; inertia has to be described by a homogeneous scalar function of the local gravitational potential. Its main part stems from the average gravitational potential of the universe.

In contrast to GRT and other local theories of gravity, the equivalence of inertia and gravity now means a reduction of inertia to the quasi-Newtonian gravitational interaction. The metric of the Hertzian configuration space V_{3N} of the N particles is also a homogeneous function of the gravitational interaction between these particles. This principle combining the equivalence between inertia and gravity with Mach's principle of the relativity of inertia (and thus with the postulate that there are cosmically determined reference systems) we call "Mach-Einstein doctrine."[*] The reference to the totality of cosmic masses implies a basically non-local approach to gravitation.

The first attempts to realize Mach's principle within such a mechanics were made by R. Reissner [39] and E. Schrödinger [41]. Later this approach was elaborated in detail by one of us [48, 49] (for a summary and further references, see also [53]) and by Barbour [3] and Barbour and Bertotti [4].

---

[*] For details, *cf.* [53] and the literature cited therein.

In our approach [53], a Machian 'inertia-free' mechanics is based on the Lagrangian L containing only the Riemannian potential of a system of N particles with masses m

$$L = G \sum_{A>B}^{N} \frac{m_A m_B}{r_{AB}} \left(1 + \frac{\beta}{c^2} \dot{\vec{r}}_{AB}^2 \right),$$ (19)

where β is a numerical constant, the m are the gravitational masses of the particles, and r_{AB} and $\dot{\vec{r}}_{AB}$ denote, respectively, the relative distances and velocities of the particles.

As a consequence, the inertial mass m of a body is induced by the gravitational action of the totality of the cosmic bodies and the effective inertial mass m^* depends on the local gravitational potential in the following manner:

$$m^* = m \left(1 - \frac{3\phi}{c^2} \right) > m.$$ (20)

This dependence leads, from this pre-relativistic level, to 'relativistic' effects like the perihelion motion. New effects result in the case of the three-body problem. There one has to distinguish between the center of inertia and the center of gravity, a fact leading to a modification of the third Kepler Law. As a consequence, via the definition of time given by this law, one finds Machian effects competing with relativistic effects.

References

[1] R. de Andrade Martins, "The Search for Gravitational Absorption in the Early Twentieth Century," in: *The Expanding Worlds of General Relativity*, ed. by H. Goenner, J. Renn, J. Ritter, and T. Sauer (Boston, 1999).

[2] S. Aronson, *Natural Philosopher* **3**, (1964) 51.

[3] J. B. Barbour, *Nature* **249** (1974) 328. (Corrigenda in *Nature* **250**, p.606).

[4] J. B. Barbour and B. Bertotti, *Nuovo Cimento* **38B** (1977) 1.

[5] H.-H. v. Borzeszkowski, U. Kasper, E. Kreisel, D.-E. Liebscher, and H.-J. Treder, *Gravitationstheorie und Äquivalenzprinzip*, ed. by H.-J. Treder (Berlin, 1971).

[6] H.-H. v. Borzeszkowski and H.-J. Treder, *Apeiron* **5** (1998) 143.

[7] H.-H. v. Borzeszkowski and H.-J. Treder, "Bohr's and Mach's Conceptions of Non-Locality in Gravity," in: *Classical and Quantum Nonlocality: Proceeding of 16th Course of the International School of Cosmology and Gravitation*, ed. by P. G: Bergmann and V. de Sabbata (Erice 1999).

[8] K. F. Bottlinger, *Astronomische Nachrichten* **191** (1912) 147.

[9] K. F. Bottlinger, *Die Gravitationstheorie und die Bewegung des Mondes* (Freiburg, 1912).

[10] C. Brans and R. H. Dicke, *Physical Review* **124** (1961) 925.

[11] R. J. Crowley, J. F. Woodward, and W. Yourgrau, *Astronomische Nachrichten* **295** (1974) 203.

[12] P. A. M. Dirac, *Nature* **139** (1937) 323.

[13] P. Drude, Beilage zu *Annalen der Physik* **62** (1897).

[14] D. H. Eckardt, *Physical Review* **D42** (1990) 2144.

[15] A. Einstein, *Über spezielle und allgemeine Relativitätstheorie* (Braunschweig, 1917).

[16] A. Einstein, *Sitzungsberichte der Preussischen Akademie der Wissenschaften zu Berlin* (1919), p.433.

[17] A. Einstein, *Sitzungsberichte der Preussischen Akademie der Wissenschaften zu Berlin* (1919), p.711.

[18] G. T. Gillies, *Metrologia* **24** (Supplement) (1987) 1.

[19] G. T. Gillies, "Modern Perspectives on Newtonian Gravity," in: *Spin in Gravity*, edited by P. G. Bergmann, V. de Sabbata, G: T. Gillies, and P. I. Pronin (Singapore, New Jersey, London, Hong Kong, 1998).

[20] O. Hecker, *Veröffentlichungen des Geodätischen Instituts Potsdam*, No. 32 (1907).

[21] C. Isenkrahe, *Das Rätsel von der Schwerkraft* (Braunschweig, 1879).

[22] P. Jordan, *Die Herkunft der Sterne* (Stuttgart, 1947).

[23] P. Jordan, *Schwerkraft und Weltall* (Stuttgart, 1952).

[24] P. S. de Laplace, *Mécanique Céleste*, Vol. 5 (Paris, 1825); *cf.* also *Oeuvres*, Vol. 5 (Paris, 1882)

[25] G.-L. Le Sage, "Essai sur l'origine des forces mortes," MS, *Univ. of Geneva Library* (1749).

[26] G.-L. Le Sage, *Memoires de l' Académie Royale des Science et Belles-Lettres de Berlin*, pp. 1-28 (1784).

[27] M. W. Lomonosov, Letter no. 195 to Euler written in July 1748 (Correspondence between Euler and Lomonosov led in German and Latin), in: *Wegbereiter der deutsch-slawischen Wechselseitigkeit* , Vol. III, ed by A. P. Juskevic and E. Winter (Berlin, 1976); see also the other letters no. 193-202.

[28] Q. Majorana, *Comptes Rendus des Sèances de l'Académie de Sciences de Paris* **169** (1919a) 646.

[29] Q. Majorana, *Comptes Rendus des Sèances de l'Académie de Sciences de Paris* **169** (1919b) 719.

[30] Q. Majorana, *Philosophical Magazine* **39** (Sixth series) (1920) 488.

[31] Q. Majorana, *Journal de de Physique et le Radium* **1** (Seventh series) (1930) 314.

[32] J. C. Maxwell, "Atom," *Encyclopaedia Britannica*, 9th edn., Vol.3 (Edinburgh, 1890).

[33] A. A. Michelson and H. L. Gale, *Astrophysical Journal* **50** (1919) 342.

[34] C. Neumann, *Allgemeine Untersuchungen über die Newtonsche Theorie der Fernwirkung* (Leipzig, 1896).

[35] M. Planck, *Das Prinzip von der Erhaltung der Energie* (Leipzig , 1913).

[36] S. T. Preston, *Philosophical Magazine* **4** (Fifth series) (1877) 365.

[37] S. T. Preston, *Philosophical Magazine* **11** (Fifth series) (1881) 391.

[38] P. Prevost, *Notice de la Vie et des Ecrits de Georges-Louis Le Sage* (Geneva, 1805).

[39] H. Reissner, *Physikalische Zeitschrift* **15**, 371 (1914); *Physikalische Zeitschrift* **16**, 179 (1915).

[40] H. N. Russell, *Astrophysical Journal* **54** (1921) 334.

[41] E. Schrödinger, *Annalen der Physik* **77**, 181 (1925).

[42] H. von Seeliger, *Astronomische Nachrichten* **137**, (1895) 129.

[43] H. von Seeliger, *Sitzungsberichte der Königlichen Bayrischen Akademie der Wissenschaften zu München, Mathem.-phys. Klasse* **39** (4. Abhandlung) (1909).

[44] L. B. Slichter, M. Caputo, and C. L. Hager, *Journal of Geophysical Research* **70** (1965) 1541.

[45] M. Steenbeck and H.-J. Treder, *Möglichkeiten der experimentellen Schwerkraftforschung* (Berlin, 1984).

[46] W. Thomson (Lord Kelvin), *Philosophical Magazine* **45** (Fourth series) (1873) 328.

[47] W. Thomson (Lord Kelvin), *Report of the Meeting of the British Association for the Advancement of Science* **73** (1903), pp. 535-537.

[48] H.-J. Treder, *Die Relativität der Trägheit* (Berlin, 1972).

[49] H.-J. Treder, *Über Prinzipien der Dynamik bei Einstein, Hertz, Mach und Poincaré* (Berlin, 1974).

[50] H.-J. Treder, *Elementare Kosmologie* (Berlin, 1975).

[51] H.-J. Treder, *Gerlands Beiträge der Geophysik* **85** (1976) 513.

[52] H.-J. Treder, *Astronomische Nachrichten* **289** (1977) 237.

[53] H.-J. Treder, H.-H. von Borzeszkowski, A. van der Merwe, and W. Yourgrau, *Fundamental Principles of General Relativity Theories. Local and Global Aspects of Gravitation and Cosmology* (New York, 1980)

[54] C. M. Will, *Theory and Experiment in Gravitational Physics. Revised Edition* (Cambridge, 1993).

[55] J. F. Woodward, Ph.D. thesis (University of Denver, 1972).

Gravitational Ether and Riemann's Theory of Gravity

H.-J. Treder[*]

Riemann attempted to extend his three-dimensional geometry of curved spaces into a unified theory of an ether of gravity, electricity and magnetism. As part of this effort, he developed a specific *Ansatz* of a gravitational ether, which was later partly realized in Einstein's general relativity. Unlike Einstein, however, Riemann intended to found a theory where, in domains with nonvanishing matter density, there is an absorption of the flux of ether by matter causing a gravitational interaction of masses filling such regions. In our paper, Riemann's *Ansatz* of a gravitational theory is reconstructed, and it is shown that, in a four-dimensional version, it can be formulated as islands of non-Riemannian geometry lying in the sea of Riemann-Einstein geometry.

Riemann considered his formulation of differential geometry (Riemann [8]) as a first step towards a unified geometrical theory of an "ether of gravity, electricity and magnetism" [6]. He identified the ether with the physical properties of the structured three-dimensional spatial manifold. One finds the same idea of a gravitational ether later in Einstein's 1920 talk in Leiden (*cf.* also Einstein [3]), now of course referred to as a four-dimensional curved space-time. This idea was subsequently taken over from Riemann and Einstein by Weyl [11].

As to the gravitational interaction, Riemann formulated an explicit *Ansatz*, however, in which he expresses his belief that this ether would prove to be the unified ether of gravity, electricity, magnetism and light. He started from the observation that, in contrast to electricity and magnetism, the gravitational flow $\propto -\partial_k \Phi$ has sinks but no sources. Indeed, due to the fact that there are only positive gravitational charges, *i.e.*, positive masses, one always has $\Delta \Phi > 0$, such that the flow is negative. Anticipating the modern conception, according to which there exists a connection between space-time mirror symmetry and charge conjugation $Q \to -Q$, he concluded that, due to the missing negative masses and thus the missing charge conjugation, the gravitational law cannot be invariant under time inversion. Therefore, he assumed the gravitational interaction to be a dissipative ether flow. In regions with ponderable matter, the differential equation for the gravitational potential Φ should show a time-dependence of the ether describing this dissipation. From this point of view, it was logical to postulate in matter-dominated regions a differential equation containing a term with the first time derivative $\partial/\partial t$ in order to exclude the invariance of this equation under time inversion. Accordingly, in regions filled with ponderable matter, the ether and thus the three-dimensional metric show a secular variation.

[*] Rosa-Luxemburg-Str. 17a, D-14482 Potsdam, Germany

Pushing Gravity: new perspectives on Le Sage's theory of gravitation
edited by Matthew R. Edwards (Montreal: Apeiron 2002)

279

In more detail, Riemann [7] assumed the ether to be a perfect fluid satisfying the equation of continuity where the ether density is given by the square-root of the determinant g of the metric g_{ik}, and the velocity field u^i corresponds with the potential flow $\propto -\partial_k \Phi$ of the ether,

$$u^i = Kg^{ik}\partial_k\Phi. \tag{1}$$

Here K is a constant which will be determined below (cf. (9a)).

In empty space domains, Riemann's ether is stationary and, as a consequence of the definition of its density, incompressible, i.e.,

$$\frac{\partial}{\partial t}g^{ik} = 0,$$
$$\partial_i\left(\rho u^i\right) = 2\mu K\left(g^{1/2}\partial_k\phi\right) = 0 \tag{2}$$

In matter-dominated regions with $\sigma = \sqrt{g}\sigma_0 > 0$ the stationarity of the ether flow, and thus its incompressibility, is destroyed because the matter represents sinks of the ether flow,

$$\partial_i\left(\rho u^i\right) = k\rho c\sigma_0 = 2c\mu g^{1/2}\sigma_0 = 2kc\mu\sigma, \tag{3}$$

such that

$$\partial_l\left(g^{1/2}g^{lk}u_k\right) = kcg^{1/2}\sigma_0 = kc\sigma. \tag{3a}$$

Here the light velocity c is assumed to be the dissipation velocity, i.e., the velocity of the ether absorption; accordingly the absorption coefficient k has the dimension g^{-1} cm^2. Due to the validity of the continuity equation demanded by Riemann,

$$\frac{\partial}{\partial t}\rho + \partial_i\left(\rho u^i\right) = 2\mu\left[\frac{\partial}{\partial t}g^{1/2} + \partial_i\left(g^{1/2}g^{ik}u_k\right)\right] = 0, \tag{4}$$

one then obtains in matter regions, where $\sigma > 0$, for the density $\rho = 2\mu\sqrt{g}$ the relation

$$\frac{\partial}{\partial t}\rho = 2\mu\frac{\partial}{\partial t}g^{1/2} = -2\mu kcg^{1/2}\sigma_0. \tag{5}$$

The solution of this equation,

$$\rho = 2\mu\exp(-kc\sigma_0 t), \quad g \propto \exp(-kc\sigma_0 t), \tag{6}$$

shows that the ether density continuously decreases.

As a consequence of the identification of the velocity of the ether flow with the gradient of the gravitational potential assumed in (1), one obtains in vacuum regions from (2) the Laplace equation

$$\Delta\phi := \partial_i\left(g^{1/2}g^{ik}\partial_k\phi\right) = 0, \tag{7}$$

and in matter regions the Poisson equation

$$\Delta\phi := \partial_i\left(g^{1/2}g^{ik}\partial_k\phi\right) = 4\pi G_0 g^{1/2}\sigma_0 = 4\pi G\sigma \tag{8}$$

(here G_0 denotes Newton's gravitational constant and G the effective gravitational coupling constant).

The comparison of (8) and (3) shows that

$$K = \frac{kc}{4\pi G_0} \tag{9a}$$

and thus

$$u^i = K g^{ik} \partial_k \phi = \frac{kc}{4\pi G_0} g^{ik} \partial_k \phi , \tag{9b}$$

so that the Poisson equation (8) can be written as

$$\frac{kc}{4\pi G_0} \Delta\phi = k g^{1/2} \sigma_0 = -\frac{\partial}{\partial t} g^{1/2} = -\frac{1}{2} g^{1/2} \frac{\partial}{\partial t} g . \tag{10}$$

Thus, in Riemann's theory, one finds an absorption in matter regions that, as equations (6) and (8) show, can also be interpreted as a variation of the effective gravitational constant. In cosmology, this means that for a universe with a finite average mass density $\sigma_0 > 0$ this provides a secular decrease of the gravitational interaction as postulated by Dirac [5]. (It will be shown below that the absorption coefficient is that of Bottlinger and Majorana (see the paper by v. Borzeszkowski and Treder in this volume)).

In Riemann's theory, the gravitational attraction of N masses is a "hydrodynamic action-at-a-distance force" which was introduced by C. A. Bjerknes [1] and V. Bjerknes [2] (where C. A. Bjerknes [1] proposed however another theoretical *Ansatz* than Riemann's).* According to V. Bjerknes, it is due to a "kinetic buoyancy" what can be seen by discussing Euler's equation which, beside the continuity equation, forms the basis of Riemann's theory.

Euler's equation written in a curved three-dimensional space reads

$$\frac{d}{dt} u^i = \frac{\partial}{\partial t} u^i + u^i_{;k} u^k = 0 , \tag{11}$$

where the semicolon denotes the covariant derivation with respect to the Christoffel symbols of this space. Together with the continuity equation (6), this leads to Bernoulli's equation which provides a condition for the continuity of the energy flow $(1/2) \rho \, u^2 u^k = \mu \sqrt{g} \, u^2 u^k$ of the ether. With Riemann's *Ansatz* (5), one then has

$$\mu \partial_l \left(g^{1/2} u^2 u^l \right) = \mu g^{1/2} \left[kc\sigma_0 - \frac{\partial}{\partial t} u^2 \right] \tag{12}$$

With $u \approx c$ and $\partial u^2 / \partial t \approx \partial c^2 / \partial t$, (12) defines a dissipation of "the kinetic energy of the ether" caused by completely inelastic impacts of the (continuously distributed) infinitesimal ether particles on the ponderable matter ($u \approx c$ is the velocity of the ether particles, $\rho = 2\mu$ the mass density of the ether flow,

---

* C. A. Bjerknes was a disciple of Riemann's predecessor, P. L. Dirichlet, in Goettingen. Dirichlet influenced Riemann's and Bjorknes' investigations on the motion of bodies in ideal fluids (cf. Riemann [9]).

kM the cross section of the mass of the heavy ponderable bodies $M = \int \sigma d^3 x$).

Using V. Bjerknes' method of kinetic buoyancy, for $(G_0/r)\int \sigma d^3 x \ll c^2$ and $\dot{r} = 0$, one can derive from the above relations the following hydrodynamic action-at-a-distance force acting between two masses M_1 and M_2,

$$\vec{K}_{12} = -\frac{\vec{r}_{12}}{r_{12}} \frac{k\mu c^2}{4\pi} \frac{M_1 M_2}{r_{12}^2} G_0 = \frac{k^2 \mu c^2}{4\pi}. \tag{13}$$

Equation (13) is Newton's expression where the gravitational constant is given as

$$\vec{K}_{12} = -\frac{\vec{r}_{12}}{r_{12}} \frac{k\mu c^2}{4\pi} \frac{M_1 M_2}{r_{12}^2} G_0 = \frac{k^2 \mu c^2}{4\pi}. \tag{14}$$

In the case that there is additional mass of density $\sigma^* > 0$ between the two bodies then one finds a 'screened' attractive force of Bottlinger and Majorana (see paper by v. Borzeszkowski and Treder in this volume),

$$\left|\vec{K}*_{12}\right| = G*\frac{M_1 M_2}{r^2} = G_0 \frac{M_1 M_2}{r^2} \exp(-k\int \sigma * dr), \tag{15}$$

where $k\sigma *$ is the absorption coefficient.

It is interesting to consider the four-dimensional and thus general relativistic generalization of Riemann's theory and compare this with Einstein's general theory of relativity (GRT) (Treder [10]). To this end, one has to replace the above-introduced three-dimensional metric g_{ik} by the metric $g_{\mu\nu}$ of a four-dimensional space ($\mu, \nu = 0, 1, 2, 3$) and to complete the velocity u^i of the ether by a fourth component to become a timelike four-vector $u^\mu = \{u^0, u^i\}$ satisfying the relation $g_{\mu\nu} u^\mu u^\nu = -c^2$ (the Lorentzian signature is chosen to be +2).

Then the general-relativistic generalization of (5) is given by (for more details, cf. [10])

$$\left[\left(-g^{(4)}\right)^{1/2}\right]_{\perp\alpha} = \frac{1}{2}\left(-g^{(4)}\right)^{1/2} g^{\mu\nu} g_{\mu\nu,\alpha} = -\left(-g^{(4)}\right)^{1/2} \frac{ku_\alpha}{c^3} T, \tag{16}$$

where $g^{(4)}$ denotes the determinant of $g_{\mu\nu}$, $\perp$ the covariant derivative with respect to $\Gamma^\alpha{}_{\mu\nu}$, and T the trace of the energy-momentum tensor $T_{\mu\nu}$. This is a differential equation for the connection $\Gamma^\alpha{}_{\mu\nu}$. Assuming a symmetric connection $\Gamma^\alpha{}_{\mu\nu} = \Gamma^\alpha{}_{\nu\mu}$, the general solution of (16) reads

$$g_{\mu\nu\perp\alpha} = \partial_\alpha g_{\mu\nu} - g_{\mu\lambda}\Gamma^\lambda{}_{\nu\alpha} - g_{\nu\lambda}\Gamma^\lambda{}_{\mu\alpha} = -\frac{kv_\alpha}{c^3}\left(AT_{\mu\nu} + Bg_{\mu\nu}T\right), \tag{17}$$

where A and B are numerical constants satisfying the condition $A + 4B = 2$. Thus one is led to an interesting generalization of Riemannian geometry resting on the basis of GRT. In matter regions, one obtains non-Riemannian spaces* with vanishing torsion and non-vanishing nonmetricity, where the connection

---

* For this geometry see, e.g., Eisenhart [4].

depends on the matter described by $T_{\mu\nu}$. In vacuum, however, Riemannian geometry is recovered.

In regions with $T_{\mu\nu} \neq 0$, in the case $A = 0$, $B = 1/2$ one obtains from (17) Weyl's semi-metrical geometry [11]:

$$\Gamma^{\alpha}_{\mu\nu} = \left\{ {}^{\alpha}_{\mu\nu} \right\} + \frac{1}{4}\frac{k}{c^3} T g^{\alpha\lambda} \left(-g_{\mu\nu}u_{\lambda} + g_{\nu\lambda}u_{\mu} + g_{\lambda\mu}u_{\nu} \right) \qquad (18)$$

In this case, Einstein's GRT is recovered in all regions where $T = 0$, *i.e.*, rest masses are absent. For $A = 2$, $B = 0$ one finds a geometry with the connection

$$\Gamma^{\alpha}_{\mu\nu} = \left\{ {}^{\alpha}_{\mu\nu} \right\} + \frac{k}{c^3} g^{\alpha\lambda} \left(-T_{\mu\nu}u_{\lambda} + T_{\nu\lambda}u_{\mu} + T_{\lambda\mu}u_{\nu} \right). \qquad (19)$$

Finally, it should be mentioned that, in vacuum, this generalization of Riemann's *Ansatz* not only recovers the Riemannian geometry but, in the static case, also the corresponding Einstein field equation. In this case the time-time component of Einstein's field equations is identical with the four-dimensionally generalized Riemannian condition of incompressibility.

The temporal asymmetry of Riemann's *Ansatz* (10) (and, respectively, the non-integrability of the transport of lengths of the non-Riemannian geometry given by (18)) occurs only in regions where the average density of matter is greater than zero, $\bar{\sigma}_0 > 0$. The major effect of this asymmetry is a cosmological time dependence of the gravitational number G^* given by the expression $G^* \approx G_0^* \exp(-k\bar{\sigma}_0 ct)$ postulated, as mentioned before, by Dirac [5]. Following Riemann's *Ansatz*, however, the *contemporary* variation $\dot{G}^*/G^*$ is much smaller than that assumed by Dirac. Instead of Dirac's value of the order of magnitude of the Hubble constant $H \sim 10^{-18}$ s^{-1}, one finds the immeasurably small value $\dot{G}^*/G^* \approx -kc\bar{\sigma}_0 \geq 10^{-41}$ s^{-1}.

References

[1] C. A. Bjerknes, *Hydrodynamische Fernkräfte* (*Ostwalds Klassiker No. 195*, Leipzig, 1915).

[2] V. Bjerknes, *Die Kraftfelder* (Braunschweig, 1909).

[3] A. Einstein, *Äther und Relativitätstheorie* (Berlin, 1920).

[4] L. P. Eisenhart, *Non-Riemannian Geometry* (New York, 1927).

[5] P. A. M. Dirac, "The Cosmological Constants," *Nature* **139** (1937) 323.

[6] B. Riemann, Schwere, *Elektricität und Magnetismus*, 2nd edition by K. Hattendorf (Hannover, 1880).

[7] B. Riemann, *Mathematische Werke*, 2nd Edition, edited by H. Weber (Leipzig, 1897).

[8] B. Riemann, *Über die Hypothesen, welche der Geometrie zu Grunde liegen*, edited by H.Weyl (Berlin, 1919).

[9] B. Riemann, *Partielle Differentialgleichungen*, ed. by K. Hattendorf (Reprint: Braunschweig, 1938).

[10] H.-J. Treder, "Die Asymmetrie der kosmischen Zeit und Riemann's Gravitationstheorie," *Astronomische Nachrichten* **299** (1978) 165.

[11] H. Weyl, *Raum, Zeit, Materie*, 6th Edition (Berlin, Heidelberg, New York,1979).

Alternate Theories of Gravity and Geology in Earthquake Prediction

Martin Kokus[*]

For decades there have been strong correlations between seismic eruptions and the positions of the earth, moon and sun as well as the level of solar activity. While a few of the weaker correlations can be incorporated into the standard theories, the stronger and more predominate relationships have no explanation within accepted theories of gravity and geology. There are also peculiarities in earth rotation which cannot be explained by Newtonian gravity but are consistent with other observed gravitational anomalies.

This paper reviews the literature on these correlations and discusses nonstandard theories of geology and gravitation which may explain them. The most common correlation could be the result of an expanding or pulsating earth. Another suggests gravitational shielding. Others hint at a more complex gravity, one that reduces to Newtonian gravity when two bodies are involved but has added terms when there are three or more bodies. There is further discussion concerning the relationship between earth expansion models and gravitational shielding models.

I. Introduction

Throughout history, mankind has sought order in the apparent randomness of earthquakes and volcanic eruptions. It was only natural to look for correlations with periods belonging to the sun and moon. Many researchers have independently come up with similar patterns. Some of these patterns have been explained with models where ocean or earth tides provided an additional "nudge" to plates that were moving in accordance with the accepted theory (continental drift) resulting in an earthquake. But even with this, there is quite often a problem. The researchers often find it necessary to add a "phase" to the peak tides in order to obtain a causal relationship. This phase frequently has an unrealistic interpretation, such as the earthquakes preceding the peak tidal stress by over three days.

The predominate pattern suggests a tectonic model where plate motions would not be triggered by the local tidal stress, but by the effects that the tides have on the moments of inertia of the various plates and by their effects on the earth rotation as a whole. The models that fit this category have the earth radius expanding or pulsating. Expanding earth models generally rely on a physical mechanism that is not contained within the standard theories.

There are also very strong claims for correlations that appear to require a stronger rewriting of gravitation. Those that indicate a higher seismic potential

---

[*] c/o Robert Stumpf, 766 Orchard Road, Mercer, PA. 16137, U.S.A.

Pushing Gravity: new perspectives on Le Sage's theory of gravitation
edited by Matthew R. Edwards (Montreal: Apeiron 2002)

285

around eclipses or during the night could suggest gravitational shielding. Others suggest something even more complex.

Theorists working on alternate paradigms in gravity have quite often considered using the earth, sun and moon system as a laboratory. The problem is not that there is too little evidence to support a different gravity, but so much data is interpreted or "calculated" assuming Newtonian gravity or a static radius that it is difficult to identify anomalous phenomena. There are many curiosities with earth rotation and even the magnetic field that can be explained away by increasingly complicated models functioning within the standard theories. But if many complications can be simplified by a small change in the standard theories, then we should start looking for that change.

II. Earthquake Patterns and Related Anomalies

In the standard theories, earthquakes and volcanic eruptions are treated as random occurrences. Most researchers in seismic prediction assume that any non-randomness would be a small variation brought about by tides. They are usually surprised by the depth and self-consistency of the literature on a subject that they have ignored. There are strong relationships between earth, solar and lunar positions; solar activity; and seismic activity, most of which cannot be explained by the local tides. These relationships are referred to as signatures by Bagby (1960-1975) or cosmolocations by Tamrazyan (1957-1993). What follows is an attempt to describe the signature archetypes and then to discuss their origin in either alternate gravitational or geologic theories.

The nature of tides. When the earth rotates about the sun, centrifugal force and gravity are perfectly balanced at the center of the earth. On the side away from the sun, the sun's gravity is weaker and the centrifugal force is stronger; therefore, there is a bulge. On the side toward the sun, the sun's gravity is stronger than the centrifugal force and there is a bulge toward the sun that is just about equal to the first one. The earth has bulges from both the sun and moon. The magnitude of the bulges changes with the distances from the earth to the tide producing body. The position of the bulges varies with the orientation of the earth's axis to the sun and the position of the moon relative to the earth's equator. There is also the complicated interaction between the solar and lunar tides as the moon orbits the earth. It is the tidal variation due to this interaction that is associated with the most difficult to explain earthquake signatures. This is also where we will look for non-Newtonian/non-Einsteinian gravity.

As the earth rotates, different parts of it pass through different parts of the bulges. A locality will pass through two tidal bulges per day (diurnal variation). The magnitude of the bulges will vary with a period half of the lunar cycle (fortnightly variation) and with the distance to the moon and sun. (For a more rigorous treatment of tidal periods see Longman (1959) or Pollack (1973).)

Tides, solar activity and earth rotation. The earth rotates about its axis approximately once every 23 hours and 56 min, but this rate is not constant. The length of a day varies on the order of a millisecond. This change is caused by the positions of the sun and moon. As the solar and lunar positions change, the locations of the tidal bulges are altered. The changing positions of the tidal bulges, in turn, affect the earth's moment of inertia. The rate of rotation changes because angular momentum is conserved.

Table 1. Cycles in Earth rotation

Cycle Length	Change in Length of Day in Milliseconds	Description
13.63 days	0.34	The moon is in the plane of the ecliptic every 13.63 days where on the average it increases the moment of inertia.
13.66 days	0.82	The moon is above the equator every 13.66 days.
14.77 days	0.078	The time between full and new moon.
27.56 days	0.87	The time between perigees.
182.62 days	5.1	The sun is over the equator every half year.
1 year	1.6	Time between perihelia.
4.42 years		The 13.66 and 27.56 day periods are in phase.
9.3 years		The 13.63 and 13.66 day periods are in phase.
9.5 years		The half yearly and 13.66 day periods are in phase at the same lunar-solar angle.
11 years	0.16	Solar activity cycle.

Imagine a spinning figure skater. When her arms are outstretched, her moment of inertia is maximized and she turns slowly. As she brings her arms in toward her axis of spin, her moment of inertia decreases and she spins faster. It doesn't matter whether her arms are above her head, down at her sides, or folded against her chest; as long as the mass is brought close to the axis of spin, the effect is the same.

The earth's tidal bulges have the same effect as the figure skater's arms. When the tidal bulges are brought near the earth's axis, or are diminished in magnitude, the moment of inertia decreases and the earth picks up speed. The tidal bulges are brought nearer to the axis by increasing their distance from the equator. This happens when the declination of the moon and/or sun increases. The tidal bulges are diminished when the sun and moon are at right angles to each other (first and last quarter) or when the moon or sun is further away.

Table 1 shows the principle periods in the earth's rotation and their approximate change in the length of day. (See Munk and McDonald (1960), Yoder *et al.* (1981) and Kokus (1988c) for further discussion of changes in the length of day.) The peaks of these periods will occasionally add together, and the periods between the combined peaks are also listed in Table 1.

Solar activity also produces a measurable effect on the earth's rotation. When there are solar flares, the atmosphere expands, its moment of inertia increases and this produces a drag on the earth, slowing it down. The earth reaches its maximum rotation rate about two or three years after a minimum of solar activity. During periods of high solar activity, the earth rotates slower, but this is also when it experiences its greatest decelerations. These phenomena have been described by Sytinsky (1963-1982), Kalinin (1974), Kalinen and Kiselev (1976), Gribben (1971) and Currie (1980).

Ocean tidal loading and earthquakes. Earthquakes and volcanoes tend to oc- cur more frequently near the boundaries between two plates. One plate may be sliding underneath the other. This motion is not smooth, and the plates are most often in a stuck position. If an ocean plate is sliding under a continental plate, the additional force downward on the ocean plate due to a high tide above it could be the additional nudge that would "unstick" the plates. This would unleash an earthquake. Leypoldt (1941) and Berg (1966) have both shown evi- dence for this mechanism.

Earth tides and seismic events. The solid earth has tides, much the same as the ocean, except that the magnitudes are much smaller. According to the stan- dard model, the earth tidal force is much smaller than the tectonic forces in- volved in earthquakes, but it may be "the straw that broke the camel's back." Davison (1896, 1934a, 1934b, 1938), Oldham (1903), Fuller (1912), Yamaguti (1931), Allen (1936), Stetson (1937), Mount Serat (1940), Hoffman (1961), Robson (1962), Ryall (1968 and 1981), Shlein (1972), Filson (1973), Kayano (1973), Bloxsom (1974), Sauck (1975), Tamrazyan (1974), Heaton (1975), Klein (1976), Dzurisin (1980), Mohler (1980), Souriau (1982) Palumbo (1986), Ulrich (1987), and Berkland (1988) found positive correlations between shal- low focus earthquakes and earth tides. Stetson (1935) found a positive correla- tion for deep focus earthquakes and tides. Mauk and Kienle (1973), Mauk and Johnston (1973), McNutt and Beavan (1981,1984) and Lowenstein (1987) de- tected tidal correlations with volcanic eruptions.

Tidal triggering in shallow focus quakes is contradicted by Knopoff (1964), Willis (1974), Shudde and Barr (1977), Shlein and Toksoz (1970) Simpson (1967a) and Heaton (1982). Spitaler (1937) and McMurray (1941) found no correlation between earth tides and deep focus quakes. Semmola (1898) did not find a lunar period in Mt. Vesuvius eruptions.

Why do different researchers get different results? The positive studies tend to look at very limited types of quakes and allow for a phase difference between the maximum tidal stress and the occurrence of the quake. Allen (1936) put it this way: "The second obstacle (to the acceptance of tidal trigger- ing) has been the idea, now disappearing, that the lunar effect, if it exists, should appear in the same manner over the entire earth, without regard to the strike or hade of the faults involved, or the nature of the earth stresses acting upon these faults. In consequence, statistics from the entire globe were assem- bled by men who doubted the possibility of a lunar effect, to prove their case. This procedure naturally would cancel the differing effects upon different fault structures, and result in the display of a negligibly small correlation." Klein (1976) makes a similar point: "An approach that has failed to demonstrate significant tidal triggering is the use of large catalogues of earthquakes from a large geographic area. Any tidal correlation of earthquakes in a small region, in a certain magnitude range, or of a particular type such as aftershocks may be masked by averaging with a large sample of random earthquakes."

The negative studies also make an error in logic. They assume that the only effect that the sun and moon can have on earthquakes is through the action of earthtides at the fault. The evidence strongly suggests another mechanism. Most studies that look for a diurnal period usually find one. Studies that look for a correlation with the fortnightly tide do not, while most of the studies that find a relationship with lunar phase find one that would not indicate a tidal effect.

Seismic periods related to variations in earth rotation. Solar tides cause annual and semiannual periods in earth rotation. Seismic variations with these periods have been observed by Spalding (1915), Conrad (1933,1934), Davison (1893,1928,1938), Morgan *et al.* (1961), Eggars and Decker (1969), Shneiderov (1973), DeSabbatta and Rizzati (1977), McClellan (1984) and Stothers (1989a).

Every 4.42 years the moon is simultaneously above the equator and at its point of orbit where it is closest to the earth. Jaggars (1945), Bagby (1972, 1975b), Winkless and Browning (1975), Rinehart (1973) and Roosen *et al* (1976) all found 4.42 year seismic periods.

Every 9.3 years, half-nodical and half-sidereal terms are in phase. Jaggar (1945), Ward (1961), Lamakin (1966), Hamilton (1973) and Shirokov (1973,1983) found periods close to 9.3 years in volcanism and earthquakes.

Every 9.5 years the half-yearly, and half sidereal terms are in phase at the same lunar-solar angle. This is perhaps the most curious of seismic periods, but it is the one with the strongest evidence. Hamilton (1973) detected a 9.5 year period in volcanic eruptions. Stothers (1989b) undertook the most detailed study of volcanic cycles to date. With a global sample of 380 events over a 400 year period he found a 9.5 year period at a very high confidence level (he could rule out a 9.3 year period). This is especially noteworthy because, as his study notes, he was looking for an 11 year period. Kokus (1988c), using the archives of the Foundation for the Study of Cycles, has traced the 9.5 year cycle from the volcanic dust veil index, to climate variation, to biological populations, to agricultural yields, and even to business cycles. We will return to this anomaly later.

Not only does the earth's rotation vary with the approximate 11 year sunspot cycle, but quick decelerations due to solar flares are common during the active part of the cycle. It should be no wonder that researchers find seismic peaks at both sunspot minimums and maximums. Kluge (1863), Poey (1874), Swinton (1883), Koppen (1896, 1914), Espin (1902), Jensen (1902, 1904), O'Reilly (1899), Lyons (1899), Davison (1927, 1938), Jaggar (1931, 1945), Stearns and MacDonald (1946), Dewey (1958), MacDonald (1960),

Machado (1960), De Mendoca Dias (1962), Sytinskiy (1966,1973a, 1973b, 1982), Simpson (1967b), Tamrazyan (1968a), Gribben (1971), Abdurakhomanov *et al.* (1974, 1976), Kalinin (1974), Bagby (1975a), Kalinin and Kiselev (1976), Singh (1978), Jakubcova and Pick (1987), Barsukov (1988), Stothers (1989b), and Kokus (1988a,b) found correlations between seismic activity in a variety of samples and the 11 year solar activity cycle. Feyman *et al.* (1984) found a correlation with the 88 year Gleissburg cycle of sunspots. (For a more thorough discussion of seismic periods see Kokus 1989.)

Seismic periods and lunar phase. There is much folklore concerning lunar phase and seismic activity. Much of it turns out to have some truth in it. If we look at volcanoes or earthquakes that tend to repeat themselves, we get three distinct patterns. Seismic events tend to cluster at either full and new moon, or first and last quarter, or when the angle between the sun and moon is near 45, 135, 225 or 315 degrees. The full and new moon signature is compatible with tidal stress which has been covered. Seismic signatures that contain the first and last quarters of the moon were found by Wood (1918), Jaggar (1920-1947), Hawaiian Volcanic Observatory (1927), Davidson (1938), Johnston and Mauk (1972), Mauk and Johnston (1973), Hamilton (1972), Sauers (1986a), Ritter (1987), Kokus and Ritter (1988) and Kokus (1988b). Clustering about 45, 135, 225, and/or 315 degrees has been reported by Henry (1917), Allen (1936), Bagby (1975b), Ritter (1987), Kokus (1988a) and Berkland (1988).

Earthquakes and eclipses. The folklore relating eclipses to seismic events ranges from Aristotle, to the Book of Matthew, to Disney's Fantasia, and anecdotal evidence abounds. But there are very few rigorous studies that have been published. In a sample of major quakes in the western United States, Kokus (1988b) found that their temporal correlation with eclipses had a 0.97 significance.

Shimshoni effect. Davison (1938) stated that quakes occur more frequently at night. Shimshoni (1971), in a very rigorous landmark study, found that low intensity quakes tended to occur at night. This was disputed by Davies (1972), Flinn *et al.* (1972) and Knopoff and Gardner (1972), but their objections seem to have been adequately answered by Shimshoni (1972). In a sample of major quakes in the western U.S., Kokus (1988b) found that quakes occurring during the quarter phases of the moon happened mostly at night, while those occurring near full and new moon happened throughout the day.

Earth-moon alignment in absolute space. Sadeh (1972, 1978), Sadeh and Meidav (1973), and Shirley (1986b, 1986c, 1988) discovered a relationship between increased seismic activity and the position of the moon from the earth as measured from the distant stars. This correlation was disputed by Mast (1972) and Hunter (1978). The lunar position associated with the increase in activity coincided with the vernal equinox. Therefore this particular alignment tended to put the tidal bulge due to the moon over the earth's equator, maximizing the earth's moment of inertia.

Typical seismic signatures. Seismic signatures can be grouped into three basic archetypes. 1). Events that cluster around full and new moon when other factors are combined to enhance the tidal bulges. These could very well be the result of tidal triggering. 2). Events that cluster around the first and last quarters of the moon with the other factors combining to minimize the earth's moment of inertia and maximize its rotation rate. This also tends to exaggerate the difference in the moments of inertia of oceanic and continental plates. It also minimizes tidal magnitudes. This signature is not compatible with the standard theories but the author will argue that it is a direct consequence of earth expansion. 3). Events that cluster around lunar-solar angles of 45, 135, 225, and 315 degrees. This is the pattern of quakes that occur at the most studied fault site in the world—Parkfield on the San Andreas fault. These quakes also tend to occur about 2 years after the sunspot minimum or when the earth's rotation reaches its minimum during the solar cycle. Other anomalous relationships worth discussing are: 1). Events that occur near eclipses. 2). Events that occur at night (which also seem to occur during lunar quarter phases). 3). Events that occur when the earth-moon vector is pointing toward some point in space.

Anomaly in length of day (LOD). Yoder *et al.* (1981) and Munk and McDonald (1960) developed formulas for predicting the change in the length of day due to tidal induced changes in the earth's moment of inertia. These changes are on the order of a millisecond and of course there are many assumptions about the earth's interior made in these calculations. This makes it hard to tell if there are problems with the gravitational theory used. One possiblity is posed by a nine year study by Robertson et al (1994) where they used the very long baseline interferometry (VLBI) observations to determine fluctuations in the length of day. The basic periods and their amplitudes were calculated. While the amplitudes of the various components were in remarkably good agreement with theory, there is one curiosity. The term due to lunar phase is larger in comparison to the other terms than theory predicts. In comparison to the anomalistic term (the anomalistic term is due to the variation of earth-moon distance and is the most accurately determined term) it is about 40% too large.

Undue planetary influence. There is also considerable folklore about planetary positions influencing events far beyond what their meager gravitational fields should cause. One example where there again appears to be some truth is in the planetary triggering of sunspots (Kokus 1990b, 1991a). Another concerns the Chandler wobble. The earth's axis of rotation is not fixed, but oscillates about a fixed point. Most of these oscillations are forced by the sun and moon acting on the earth's elliptical shape and are well understood. The Chandler wobble is more complex. If the earth is excited by an external or internal torque, the disturbed axis would precess about the average axis with a natural frequency of about 14 months. Carey (1976) shows evidence that this oscillation is excited when the earth lies between the Sun and Jupiter. The problem is that any force that Jupiter could exert on the earth is several orders of magnitude too small if we accept the standard theories of gravitation.

III. Alternate Theories of Gravity

Popular science is generally written as if general relativity has been proven beyond all doubt. "Tests," devised by the theory itself, are trumpeted as successes. Phenomena not predicted by general relativity are ignored or treated as statistical flukes that will go away if enough data is taken. Entire courses on gravity are taught without looking at data.

Data against general relativity. Newtonian gravity is a good approximation to reality under certain circumstances. If we are dealing with the gravitational attraction of one large body and we are not close to or within the mass of the body, then Newtonian (and Einsteinian) gravity describes the phenomena within the accuracy of measurement.

If there is appreciable mass around the position where we are testing gravity, then deviations from Newton's law have been measured. These are sometimes interpreted as deviations from the inverse square law and sometimes as gravitational shielding. Majorana (1919) has reported evidence of gravitational attraction being reduced by intervening matter between the major body and the test body.

If there are two large bodies, we also see deviations from Newton and Einstein. There are departures from the calculated values of gravitational attraction when we are near a line running through the center of the two bodies. There are also variations from the predicted inertial plane as we approach this line.

Yarkovskii (1889) claimed observable anomalies in pendulum motion during an eclipse, but his exact observations were unavailable to this author. Allais (1959) observed that the inertial frame implied by a paraconical pendulum rotated slightly toward the moon or sun. This effect appeared to be shielded during an eclipse. Saxl and Allen (1971) found that the period of a torsional pendulum rose during an eclipse. Van Flandern (1996) found an anomalous decrease in the earthward acceleration of artificial satellites when their planes of orbit allowed the earth to eclipse the sun.

Kinetic theories of gravity. Le Sage (1784) developed a theory of gravity where the gravitational attraction is the result of unobservable particles traveling very fast in a random motion throughout space. They collide with anything that has a mass. If a massive body is isolated, then the collisions will cancel out. If two bodies are near each other, then the bodies will screen out some of the particles that would hit the other body from their side. This would cause the remaining collisions to drive the bodies together. Le Sage showed that this type of model would yield an inverse square law in the absence of other masses. The model differs from Newton's theory in what would happen during an eclipse. During a solar eclipse on earth, Newton or Einstein's theories would predict that the gravity fields of the sun and moon would simply add as vectors. Le Sage would have the moon "shielding" the earth from part of the sun's gravity.

Another interesting property of this theory stems from the requirement that the collisions be inelastic. If the collisions were elastic, these particles would bounce back and forth between two bodies canceling the shielding effect. But if these particles are colliding inelastically, they must be transferring energy to all massive bodies. Where this energy comes from and what happens to it once it is transferred to a body is a question for discussion. Would it heat the body as Shneiderov (1943-1961) suggested? Would it increase the mass of the body, as Veselov (1981) suggested? And most importantly, would it cause the earth to expand and provide a mechanism for the quantization of the mass of astronomical bodies and redshifts? These questions will be discussed in later sections.

Rotating ether theories. There are a variety of ether based theories where gravity is not a force at all. When a body is orbiting another we have been taught to treat it as an equilibrium between gravity and centrifugal force. The problem is analyzed assuming that the "distant stars" establish an inertial frame. But this might be an illusion. There might be a rotating hierarchy with satellites orbiting planets, planets orbiting stars, stars orbiting the galaxy, galaxies orbiting groups, groups orbiting super groups and so on. The inertial coordinate system we should be looking at is defined locally. If we define our inertial coordinate system as one with an axis connecting the sun and earth, then both centrifugal force and gravity become fictitious forces. Gravity appears when we are looking at this system from another coordinate system (see Pope 2000 and Kokus 1996, 1997b, 1999). Essentially, the local ether determines the local inertial coordinate system (see also Hatch 2000, Stilmar 2000 and Deen 2000). If we have a three body system like the earth, sun and moon, then the inertial coordinate system would behave something like a weighted average of the two. This would create a motion such as the one described in Allais' pendulum experiment.

IV. Earth Expansion

The case against plate tectonics or continental drift theory is growing, but is not often reported in the popular literature and is much too long to present here. Essentially, all of the arguments raised against plate tectonics in the early 70's are still valid. The more we know about continental roots and the mantle, the more unlikely it is that thermal convection exists there. The "theory" has been accepted as fact for over 30 years and its proponents still cannot agree upon a final map of convection cells. There is a clear absence of evidence for subduction along the African and Antarctic coasts even though it is required to maintain a constant circumference and avoid geometric paradoxes. The satellite measurements that are supposed to be the strongest support for continental drift clearly contradict it and support a rate of earth expansion of about 1 cm per year (Carey, 1988, 1996).

The basic appeal of earth expansion is its simplicity. When the earth was about 50-60% of its present radius, it was covered completely by solid continent with no oceans. As it expanded, the continents broke and then drifted apart with material upwelling from the mantle along the cracks to fill in the gaps and form the oceans and mid-oceanic ridges. Continental drift is just an illusion created by the insistence that the earth's radius is constant. The theory was first proposed by Yarkovskii (1889) and is best described by its chief architect, Warren Carey (1976, 1982, 1988, 1996).[*]

A strong argument for earth expansion is that the goodness of fit between the continental plates improves when the earth's radius is reduced. Owen (1983) used computer simulations to determine the earth radius where the continents would best fit together and got about 55% of the present radius. Vogel (1983, 1994) manually reconstructed the continents on globes of different radius and came to the same conclusion. Maxlow (2000) created a computer animation which shows the positions of the continents as the earth expands.

A strong objection to the theory is that there is no mechanism for the expansion within current interpretations of standard theories of physics. For a while, a decrease in the universal gravitational constant was considered a possible explanation, but it alone would not create the expansion rate required by present models. Scalara (1994) and Davidson (1994, 1997) have concluded that mass is being created within the earth. Hunt (1990), Hunt et al. (1992) and Larin (1993) have asserted that mass in the form of hydrogen is being created in the earth's interior. This of course is compatible with Le Sage's theory. The absorption of the particles which produce the gravitational force would increase the mass of the earth. The connection between earth expansion and Le Sage cosmology has been made by Shneiderov (1943-1961) and Veselov (1981).

Another objection to earth expansion is that if the earth has expanded at the proposed rate, its rotation would have slowed much more than that calculated from the fossil record (Wesson 1978). This problem can be explained somewhat if we assume a rotating ether along with mass creation (Kokus 1999).

Earth expansion complements another current controversy, astronomical quantization. Arp (1999) has shown that redshifts and the masses of astronomi-

---

[*] For further discussion of earth expansion see Hilgenberg (1967), Shields (1983, 1997), Kremp (1996), Hoshino (1998), Maxlow (1999), and Smerchanski (1999).

cal bodies are quantized. Kokus (1999) described how both earth expansion and astronomical quantization can be explained by the same changes in the standard theories. If the electron model of Battey-Pratt and Racey (1980) (see also Wolff 1990) is combined with Barut's (1986) leptonic theory of matter and employed in a universe consisting of rotational hierarchies, we would have mass created where mass already exists. It would be created proportional to the existing mass. Elementary particle masses would vary with quantum steps producing quantized redshifts. Astronomical bodies would grow in distinct steps making their masses quantized. The universe would be a self-organizing, self-replicating system.

V. Earthquakes and Earth Expansion

The principal earthquake signature can be explained with an earth expansion model. In the best developed model of an expanding earth, Carey (1976, 1982, 1988) argues that the primary sources of crustal deformation on an expanding earth are not simple tensions but global torsions. These torsions are the result of the asymmetric distribution of continents on the earth. The continental crust, being less dense and much thicker than the oceanic crust, has a center of mass about 2 kilometers higher on the average. This causes continents to have a greater moment of inertia per mass than oceans. As the earth expands, the westward acceleration of the plates due to conservation of angular momentum will be proportional to their moments of inertia per mass. Since the northern hemisphere is mostly continent and the southern hemisphere is mostly ocean, the northern hemisphere twists westward compared to the southern hemisphere. This is referred to as the Sinistral Tethyan Torsion. There are also other inhomogeneities in the crust which can give rise to lesser torsions.

Let us now look at everything that can modulate the Tethyan torsion. Assume two adjacent latitudinal cross sections of the earth, their angular momentums would be equal to their respective moments of inertia times their angular velocities. The torsion between the two cross sections is proportional to the difference between the time derivatives of the two angular momentums divided by the distance between the cross sections. There are several ways that the tidal bulges and sunspots can affect the torsion. The moments of inertia, the angular velocity and the angular acceleration all vary and are interrelated. The torsion between these two cross sections would be maximized when the difference of the moments of inertia between them would be maximized and the velocity would be maximized. This would happen when the moon is at quarter phases, the moon is at maximum declination, the earth is near summer solstice and the sunspot cycle is about 2 years after minimum. This is identical to the configuration during which volcanic eruptions peak near the equator.

VI. Earthquakes, Earth Rotation and Kinetic Theories of Gravity

Some of the other earthquake signatures and earth rotation anomalies might be explained by the effect that gravitational shielding would have on the earth.

Lunar-solar tidal anomalies. If gravitational shielding occurs, then the force of gravity from the sun or moon would decrease more as it traverses the earth than it would under standard tidal theory. Therefore, kinetic theories of gravity would predict slightly higher tides. Presently, our knowledge of the earth is too inadequate to predict or measure the tides directly with the accuracy to test the theory. But there is another possibility. The earth's rotation varies as the tidal bulges vary, but with gravitational shielding the terms would vary differently than with the standard theory.

The component of the bulges due to shielding would not vary as much with distance as the component due to the standard theory would. Therefore, the variation of earth rotation due to the lunar phase term would be larger in comparison to the anomalistic term than predicted by the standard theory. This effect has been observed by Robertson *et al.* (1994) as described above.

Eclipses. If gravitational shielding occurred, it would produce unaccounted for strains on the earth during eclipses. A correlation with seismic activity should not be surprising.

Shimshoni effect. Presently it is impossible to describe the exact mechanism whereby gravitational shielding could give rise to an increase in seismic activity during the night. One possibility is that with gravitational shielding, the tidal bulges are less symmetrical about the center of earth rotation than they would be under standard theory. The bulge on the nocturnal side would be further out and therefore would have a slightly higher rotational velocity. This would be in agreement with Kokus (1988b). The quakes which tended to occur at night also occurred when the moment of inertia is minimized and rotational velocity was maximized by other tidal and sunspot effects.

Increased seismic activity when the earth and moon are oriented in a peculiar direction in absolute space. An effect, such as that measured by Sadeh (1972, 1978), Sadah and Meidav (1973), and Shirley (1986b&c, 1988) could be much more easily explained by the kinetic theories of gravity than the standard theories. The only modification required would be an anisotropic distribution of Le Sage's corpuscles, perhaps due to some type of undetectable shielding.

VII. Earthquakes and Other Theories of Gravity

Maurice Allais in his 1959 paper argued that there must be a new, unique field resulting from the interaction of the earth, sun and moon. If this is true, then a natural manifestation of this field should be observed in the behavior of the earth's surface. And it is in this field where the explanation for the most peculiar earthquake signature may lie.

When searching for an explanation for earthquakes that occur near 45, 135, 225 and 315 degrees, it is logical to look for something in conventional mechanics that is maximized at that configuration. The acceleration of earth rotation due to lunar phase is maximized then; but this acceleration is small compared to the acceleration due to changes in the moon's distance or angle above the equator, and no increase in seismic activity has been noticed when these terms are maximized.[*]

Then there are the torques exerted by the gravity of the sun and moon acting on the tidal bulges. Some of these are maximized near these angles, but again, these forces are small compared to other terms which seem to have no effect on seismicity.

Essentially, there is good reason to look for a non-Newtonian/non-Einsteinian explanation for this earthquake pattern. While deviations from the standard theory were small in Allais' experiment and Saxl and Allen's experiment, these deviations, when summed over continental plates, could become significant.

VIII. Conclusions

Within this century over 2,000,000 people died in earthquakes. This exceeds all other causes of violent death during peacetime. Unlike other sources of human suffering such as famine or war, its solution lies largely within the scientific realm. Unfortunately, its solution is impeded by religious adherence to geologic and gravitational dogma.

There is sufficient non-randomness in the seismic record to question the prevailing theory of geology. And, I am confident, this questioning will lead others in the direction that it led me—to further questioning of scientific dogma.

References

Abdurakhmanov, A.I., Firstov, P.P., Shirikov, V.A., 1974. A possible link between volcanic eruptions and cycles of solar activity (in Russian). 15th General Assembly of MGGS theses. Symposium on volcanism and earthquakes in the upper mantle, Moscow. pp. 3-4.

Abdurakhmanov, A.I., Firstov, P.P., Shirikov, V.A., 1976 (in Russ.). *Byul. Vulkanol. Stantsiy* 52:3-10.

Allais, Maurice, 1959. *Aerospace Engineering*, September and October.

Allen, A.M., 1936. *Bull. Seism. Soc. Am.* 26:147.

---

[*] John Bagby, in personal communication, has suggested that the third derivative, or "jerk," of the monthly tide component is maximized at these angles. But even so, the third derivative of the diurnal and other tidal terms is greater and there is no compelling evidence of an increase in seismic activity at these times.

Arp, H.C., 1998. *Seeing Red*. Apeiron, Montreal.

Bagby, J.P., 1969. *Icarus* 10:1-10.

Bagby, J.P., 1972. Chandler wobble and earthquake incidence. Proceedings of the Annual Meeting, G-42-1, American Geophysical Union, Washington. Abstracted in *EOS, Trans*. AGU 53:719.

Bagby, J.P., 1973. Further evidence of tidal influence on earthquake incidence. *The Moon* 6:398-404.

Bagby, J.P., 1974. A second order method of earthquake prediction. *EOS, Trans. AGU* 55:222.

Bagby, J.P., 1975a. Sunspot cycle periodicities. *Nature* 253:482.

Bagby, J.P., 1975b. *The Cornell Engineer* 41:6-13,24-26, correction 43:10.

Barsukov, O.M., 1986. *Izvestiya, Earth Physics* 22, no. 6:488-489.

Barut, A.O. 1986. *Annalen der Physik* 43:83-92.

Battey-Pratt, E.P., Racey, T.J. 1980. *Int. J. Theor. Phys.* 19:437-473.

Berg, E., 1966. *Nature* 210:893-896.

Berkland, Jim, 1988. Personal correspondence. Earthquakes in Santa Clara County, California, show a tendency to occur when the full or new moon is in conjunction with perigee.

Bloxsom, Jr., D., 1974. *Bull. Seism. Soc. Am.* 64:2005-2006.

Carey, S.W., 1976. *The Expanding Earth*. Elsevier, New York, 1976.

Carey, S.W., 1982. *The Expanding Earth: A Symposium*. Earth Resources Foundation, University of Sydney.

Carey, S.W., 1988. *Theories of the Earth and Universe*. Stanford University Press.

Carey, S.W., 1996. *Earth, Universe, Cosmos*. U.of Tasmania Earth Science Bookshop, Hobart.

Casetti,G., Frazzetta,G., Romano,R. 1981. *Bull.Volcanol.* 44:283-284.

Conrad, V., 1933. *Gerlands Beitr. z. Geophysik* 53:111-139.

Conrad, V., 1934. Periodicity of earthquakes. *Nature*, October 20, p. 631.

Currie, R.G., 1980. *Geophys. J. Roy. Astron. Soc.* 61:131-140.

Davies, D., 1972. Nocturnal earthquakes. *Geophys. J. Roy. Astron. Soc.* 28:305-306.

Davidson, John K., 1994. Earth expansion requires increase in mass. In: *Frontiers of Fundamental Physics*, F.Selleri and M.Barone, ed. pp.295-300.

Davidson, John K., 1997. *Marine and Petroleum Geology*. 14:53-549.

Davison, C., 1893. On the annual and semiannual seismic periods. *Phil. Mag.* 5:36, 310.

Davison, C., 1896. On the diurnal periodicity of earthquakes. *Phil. Mag.* 5:42, 463.

Davison, C., 1927. *Nature* 120:587. Earthquakes peak before sunspot minima.

Davison, C., 1928. The annual periodicity of earthquakes. *Bull. Seism. Soc. Am.* 18:246.

Davison, C., 1934a. The diurnal periodicity of earthquakes. *J. Geol.* 42:449.

Davison, C., 1934b. *Geological Magazine* 71:493.

Davison, C., 1938. *Studies on the Periodicity of Earthquakes*. Thomas Murphy and Co., London.

Deen, Glen W. 2000. Dayton C.Miller's 1933 Cosmic Ether Model. Presented at the Natural Philosophy Alliance Conference, Storrs, Connecticut, June 10, 2000.

De Mendoca Dias, A.A., 1962. *Bull. Volcanol.* 24:211-221.

De Sabbata, V., Rizzati, P., 1977. *Lettre al Nuovo Cimento* 20(4)117-120.

Dewey, E.R., 1958. *Cycles* 9:86-87 (March).

Dzurisin,D. 1980. *Geophys. Res. Lett.* 7:925-928.

Eggers, A.A., Decker, R.W., 1969. *EOS. Trans.* AGU 50:343 (AGU).

Espin, T.E., 1902. Volcanic eruptions and their relation to sunspots. *English Mechanic* 76:13.

Feynman, J., Fougere, P.F., 1984. *J. Geophys. Res.* 89:3023-3027.

Filson, J., Simkin, T., Leu, L., 1973. *J. Geophys. Res.* 78:8591.

Flinn, E.A., Blandford, R.R., Mack, H., 1972. *Geophys. J. Roy. Astron. Soc.* 28:307-310.

Fuller, Myron L., 1912. The New Madrid earthquake. *U.S. Geolog. Surv. Bull.* 494.

Gribbin, John, 1971. Relation of sunspot and earthquake activity. *Science* 173:558.

Hamilton, W.L., 1973. *J. Geophys. Res.* 78:3356-3375.

Hatch, Ronald R., 2000. A modified Lorentz ether theory. Presented at the Natural Philosophy Alliance Conference, Storrs, Connecticut, June 2000.

Hawaiian Volcano Observatory, 1927. Volcano Letter No.170, March 29. There is an increase in Hawaiian earthquakes near the quarter phases of the moon.

Heaton, T.H., 1975. Tidal triggering of earthquakes. *Geophys. J. Roy. Astron. Soc.* 43:307-326.
Heaton, T.H., 1982. Tidal triggering of earthquakes. *Bull. Seism. Soc. Am.* 72:2181-2200.
Henry, J.R., 1917. Great earthquakes and certain lunar longitudes. *English Mechanic* 104:473.
Hilgenberg, Otto C., 1967. Why earth expansion? Published by author, Berlin.
Hoffmann, R.B., 1961. *U.S. Geolog. Surv. Prof. Paper* 424-C:267-270.
Hoshino, M., 1998. *The Expanding Earth.* Tokai University Press, Tokyo.
Hunt, C.W., 1990. *Environment of Violence.* Polar Publishing, Calgary.
Hunt, C.W., L.Collins and E.A.Skobelin, 1992. *Expanding Geoshperes.* Polar Publishing, Calgary.
Hunter, R.N., 1978. *J. Geophys. Res.* 83:B3, 1253-1256.
Jaggar, T.A., 1920. *Bull. Seismol. Soc. Am.* 10:155-275.
    1931. Volcanic cycles and sunspots. *Volcano Lett.* 326:1-3.
    1938. Structural development of volcanic cones. *Eos Trans.* AGU 19:23-32.
    1945. *Volcanos Declare War: Logistics and Strategy of Pacific Volcano Science.* Paradise of the Pacific Ltd., Honolulu.
    1947. Origin and development of craters. Mem. 21, p. 39, 318, Geolog. Soc. Amer., Boulder, CO.
Jakubcova, I., Pick, I., 1987. *Annales Geophysicae* 5B:135-142.
Jensen, H.I., 1902. *J.R.Soc.N.S.W.* 36:42-60.
Jensen, H.I., 1904. *J.R.Soc.N.S.W.* 38:40-90.
Johnston, M.J.S., Mauk, F.J., 1972. *Nature* 234 (September 29).
Kalinin, Yu.D., 1974. Preprint IFSO-21f. *Krasnoyarsk, In-t fiziki SO AN SSSR.*
Kalinin, Yu.D., Kiselev, V.M., 1976. Preprint IFSO-53F. *Krasnoyarsk, In-t fiziki SO AN SSSR.*
Kayano, I., 1973 (in Japanese*). Bull. Earthquake Res. Inst.* 26:178-203.
Klein, F.W., 1976. *Geophys. J. Roy. Astron. Soc.* 45:245-295.
Klein, F.W., 1976. Tidal triggering of reservoir associated earthquakes. *Eng. Geol.* 10:197-210.
Kluge, E., 1863a. *Ueber synchronismus und antagonismus von vulkanischen eruptionen und die beziehungen derselben zu den sonnenflecken und erdmagnetischen variationen,* Leipzig.
    1863b. *Z. Dtsch. Geol. Ges.* 15:377-402.
Knopoff, L., 1964. *Bull. Seism. Soc. Am.* 54:1865-1870.
Knopoff, L., Gardner, J.K., 1972. *Geophys. J. Roy. Astron. Soc.* 28:311-313.
Kokus, M., Ritter, D., 1988. *Cycles* 39:56-57 (March)
Kokus, M., 1988a. *Cycles* 39:230-233 (September/October).
    1988b. *Cycles* 39:266-270 (November).
    1988c. *Cycles* 39:288-291 (December).
    1989. *Seismic periodicities that can be related to lunar and solar cycles: A comprehensive review and bibliography.* A special report for the Foundation for the Study of Cycles, Wayne, Pa.
    1990a. *Cycles* 41:76-79.
    1990b. The solar cycle and planetary periods. *Cycles* 41:249-251.
    1991a. Solar cycle update. *Cycles* 42:19-21.
    1991b. Volcanic cycles and climate. *Cycles,* 42:189-195.
    1991c. Lunar cycles and the Sierra Madre (California) earthquake of June 28, 1991. *Cycles* 42:236.
    1993. Earth expansion and earthquake prediction. *The Frontiers of Fundamental Physics.* F.Selleri and M.Barone, eds. Plenum Press
    1993. Quantized redshifts and the fractal geometry of the universe. *Advances in Fundamental Physics.* F.Selleri and M.Barone, eds., Plenum Press.
    1994. Cosmological Coincidences: An update. *Apeiron* 20:1.
    1996. Spherical Rotation, particles and cosmology. *Astrophysics and Space Science.* 244:353-356.
    1997a. *New Concepts in Global Tectonics.*4:13-16
    1997b. Fundamental Hypothesis: An outline of a simple approach for unifying natural phenomena. *Conference on the Fundamental Structure and Mechanisms of the Universe,* Ray Tomes, ed. For the Alexandria Foundation.
    1999. Toward a new paradigm. *Frontier Perspectives* 8:44-48.
    unpublished. The fine structure constant and cosmic structure.
Koppen, W. 1896. *Himmel Erde* 8:529-532.

1914. Lufttemperaturen, sonnenflecken und vulkanausbruche. *Meteorol. Z.* 31:305-328.

Kremp, G.O.W., 1996. Convincing evidence of earth expansion. *Paleobotanist* 45:152-180.

Lamakin, V.V., 1966 (in Russian). *Doklady An SSSR* 170(2):410-413.

Larin, V.N.,1993. *Hydridic Earth*, Polar Publishing, Calgary.

Le Sage, Georges-Louis, 1784. *Memoires de l'Academie Royale des Sciences et Belles-Lettres de Berlin*. Translated by Samuel Langley *Smithsonian Institution Annual Report 1898*. pp.139-180.

Leypoldt, H., 1941. Sea level changes as trigger forces. *Bull. Seism. Soc. Am.* 31:233.

Longman, I.M., 1959. *J. Geophys. Res.* 64:2351.

Lowenstein, P.L., 1987. Tidal triggering of volcanic earthquakes at Rabaul, Papua-New Guinea. 1987 *Symposium on how volcanoes work.*

Lyons, C.J., 1899. Sunspots and Hawaiian eruptions. *Monthly Weather Review* 27:144.

MacDonald, G.A., 1960. Prediction of eruption of Hawaiian volcanoes, *Bull. Volcanol.* 23:211.

Machado, F., 1960. *Bull.Volcanol.* 23:101-107.

1967a. Activity of the Atlantic volcanoes, 1947-1965. *Bull.Volcanol.* 30:29-34.

1967b. Geological evidence for a pulsating gravitation. *Nature* 214:1317-1318.

Majorana, Quirino, 1919. *London, Edinburgh and Dublin Philisophical Magazine* 39:488-504.

Mast, T.S. *et al*, 1972. *Nature* 240:140-142.

Mauk, F.J., 1979. *Eos Trans. AGU* 60:833.

Mauk, F.J., Johnston, M.J.S., 1973. *J. Geophys. Res.* 78:3356-3362.

Mauk, F.J., Kienle, J., 1973. *Science* 182:386-389.

Maxlow, James, 1999. Alternatives to plate tectonics. *New concepts in Plate Tectonics* 10:14-16.

Maxlow, James, 2000. <www.geocities.com/capecanaveral/launchpad/6520>

McClellan, P.H., 1984. *Nature* 307 (January 11).

McMurray, H., 1941. Periodicity of deep-focus earthquakes. *Bull. Seism. Soc. Am.* 31:33-57.

McNutt, S.R., Beavan, R.J., 1981. *Nature* 294:615-618.

McNutt, S.R., Beavan, R.J., 1984. *J. Geophys. Res.* 89: no.B5, pp.3075-3086.

Mohler, A.S., 1980. *Bull. Seism. Soc. Am.* 70:1583-1594.

Morgan, W.J., Stoner, J.O., Dicke, R.H., 1961. *J. Geophys. Res.* 66:3831-3843.

Mount Serrat, 1940. Moon, sun help release pent up volcanic energy. *Science News Letter* 37:233.

Munk, W, MacDonald, J.F., 1960. *The Rotation of the Earth*. Cambridge University Press, New York.

Oldham, R.D., 1903. Periodicities of the tidal forces and earthquakes. *Nature* 68:111.

O'Reilly, J.P. 1899. *Proc. R. Irish Acad.* 5:392-432.

Owen, H.G., 1983. *Atlas of Continental displacement: 200 million years to the present*. Cambridge University Press, Cambridge.

Palumbo, A., 1986. Lunar and solar tidal components. *Geophys. J. Roy. Astron. Soc.* 84:93-99.

Pines, David, Shaham, Jacob, 1973. *Nature* 245:77-81.

Poey, A., 1874. *C. R. Hebd. Seances Acad. Sci.* 78:51-55.

Pollack, H.N., 1973. *J. Geophys. Res.* 78:2598.

Pope, Viv 2000. The angular momentum ether. Presented, the Natural Philosophy Alliance Conference, June 2000, Storrs, Conn.

Press, Frank, Briggs, Peter, 1975. *Nature* 256:270-273.

Rinehart, J.S., 1973. *7th International Symposium on Earth Tides*, Sopron, Hungary. A 4.42-year cycle in geyser activity.

Ritter, D.C., unpublished. A possible earthquake frequency exists which can be associated with a tidal cycle. Earthquakes have a very high occurrence in certain areas when the moon is at quarter phase, at maximum declination, and at apogee. An accurate 30-day prediction, time and locality, was made.

Robertson, Douglas S., Ray, Jim R., Carter, William E., 1994. *J. Geophys. Res.* 99:621-636.

Robson, G. *et al*, 1962. Earthquake series in St.Kitto-Nevis, 1961-62. *Nature* 195:972-974.

Roosen, R.G., Harrington, R.S., Giles, J., Browning, I., 1976. *Nature* 261:680-681.

Ryall, A., Van Wormer, J.D., Jones, A.E., 1968. *Bull. Seism. Soc. Am.* 58:215-248.

Ryall, A., Ryall, F., 1981. *Bull. Seism. Soc. Am.* 71:747-760.

Sadeh, D., 1972. Possible sidereal period for the seismic lunar activity. *Nature* 240:139-141.

Sadeh, D., 1978. *J. Geophys. Res.* 83:1251-1252. A sidereal period exists.

Sadeh, D., Meidav, M., 1973. *J. Geophys. Res.* 78:7709-7715.

Sauck, W.A., 1975. *Geophys. Res. Lett.* 2:506-509.

Sapper, K. 1930. Cycles of volcanic activity. *Volcano Lett.* 302:2-4.

Sauers, Jack, 1986a. Speaking of lunar and other cycles. *Cycles* 37:46-47 (March).

Sauers, Jack, 1986b. *Cycles* 37:203-204 (December).

Saxl, E.J., Allen, M., 1971. 1970 solar eclipse as seen by a torsion pendulum. *Phys. Rev. D* 3:823-825.

Scalera, G., 1994. Earth complexity vs. plate tectonic simplicity. *Frontiers of Fundamental Physics*, M.Barone and F.Selleri, ed. Plenum Press, New York.

Semmola, Eugenio, 1898. *Nature* 57:613.

Shaw, J.J., 1917. Earthquakes and lunar longitudes. *English Mechanic* 104:510.

Shields, Oakley, 1983. Trans-Pacific biotic links that suggest earth expansion. pp.198-208 in Carey, S.W. (ed.): *Expanding Earth Symposium*, University of Tasmania.

Shields, Oakley, 1997. Rapid earth expansion, an eclectic view. *Gondwana Research* 1:91-94

Shimshoni, M., 1971. *Geophys. J. Roy. Astron. Soc.* 24:97-101.

Shimshoni, M., 1972. *Geophys. J. Roy. Astron.* Soc. 28:315.

Shirley, J.H., 1986. Temporal patterns in historic major earthquakes in Chile. *Investigating Natural Hazards in Latin American History*, R.H. Claxton, editor, W. Georgia College Stud. Soc. Sci. 25.

Shirley, J.H., 1986c. *Gerl. Beitr. Geophysik* 95:509-515.

Shirley, J.H., 1988. *Geophys. J. Roy. Astron. Soc.* 92:403-420.

Shirokov, V.A., 1973. The cosmos and volcanoes. *Man and the Elements* (in Russian), Leningrad, Gidrometeoizdat, p. 26-28.

Shirokov, V.A., 1983. The influence of the 19-year tidal cycle on the large scale eruptions and earthquakes in Kamchatka, and their long term prediction. *The Great Tolbachik Fissure Eruption*, S.A. Fedotov and Ye. K. Markhinin, editors, Cambridge University Press.

Shlien, S., 1972. Earthquake-tide correlation. *Geophys. J. Roy. Astron. Soc.* 28:27-34.

Shlien, S., Toksoz, M.N., 1970. *Bull. Seism. Soc. Am.* 60:1765-1787.

Shneiderov, A.J., 1943. The exponential law of gravitation and its effects on seismological and tectonic phenomena: A preliminary exposition. *American Geophysical Union, Reports and papers, seismology--1943*, pp.61-88.

Shneiderov, A.J., 1961. *Bollitino Di Geofisica Teorica ed Applicata*, 3:137-159.

Shneiderov, A.J.: 1961. *Bollitino Di Geofisica ed Applicata*, 3:215-239.

Shneiderov, A.J., 1973. Astroseismology project in 1973. *EOS, Trans AGU* 54(11):1138.

Shudde, R.H., Barr, D.R., 1977. *Bull. Seism. Soc. Am.* 67:1379-1386.

Simpson, J.F., 1967a. *Earth Planet. Sci. Lett.* 2:473-478.

Simpson, J.F., 1967b. *Earth Planet. Sci. Lett.* 3:417-430.

Singh, Surendra, 1978. Geomagnetic activity and microearthquakes. *Bull. Seism. Soc. Am.*, 68:1533.

Smerchanski Gerry, 1999. *New Concepts in Global Tectonics* 12:17-18.

Souriau, M., Souriau, A., Gagnepain, J., 1982. *Bull. Seism. Soc. Am.* 72:165-180.

Spalding, W.A., 1915. Seasonal Periodicity of earthquakes. *Bull. Seism. Soc. Am.* 5:30.

Spitaler, R., 1937. *Gerlands Beitr. z. Geophysik* 49:296-297.

Stearns, H.T., MacDonald, G.A. 1946. *Hawaii Div.Hydrogr.Bull.* 9:123-126.

Stetson, H.T., 1935. *Science* 82:523-524.

Stetson, H.T., 1937. *Proc. Am. Phil. Soc.* 78:411-424.

Stilmar,R.L. 2000. The key to the universe-the electromechanical analogies. presented Natural Philosophy Alliance Conference, June 2000, Storrs, Conn.

Stothers,R.D., 1989a. *Geophys.Res.Lett.* 16:453-455.

        1989b. Volcanic eruptions and solar activity. *J. Geophys. Res.* 94:17,371-17,381.

Swinton, A.H., 1883. Sun-spottery. *Journal of Science* 20:77.

Sytinskiy, A.D., 1963. *Geomagnetizm i aeronmiya* 3:148.

Sytinskiy, A.D., 1966 (in Russian*). Geomagnetizm i aeronmiya* 4:726-752.

Sytinskiy, A.D., 1973a. *Dokl. Akad. Nauk SSSR* 208:1078.

Sytinskiy, A.D., 1973b. *Uspekhi fiz. Nauk* 111:367.

Sytinskiy, A.D., 1982. *Dokl. An SSSR* 265(6):1350-1353.

Tamrazyan, G.P., 1957. *Reports Acad. Sci. Georgian SSR* 19(2).

1958. *Izvestia Acad. Sci. USSR, Geophys. Ser.* No.5,664-8.

1959. *Izvestia Acad. Sci. USSR, Geophys. Ser.* No.4:598-603.

1962a. *Izvestia Acad. Sci. USSR, Geophys. Ser.* No.1,76-89. Reprinted in *Cycles* 18:232-241, (September 1967).

1962b. *Doklady Acad. Sci. USSR* 147:1361-1364.

1966. *Journal of Physics of the Earth* (Japan) 14:41-48.

1967. *Indian Geophysical Union Journal* 4:131-141.

1968. *Icarus* 9:574-592.

1968b. *J. Geophys. Res.* 73 (September 15).

1969a. *Intern. Journal of the Solar System* 10:164-168.

1969b. *Boletin Acad. Cienias Fisices, Matematicas y Naturales* (Venezuela) 82:34-71.

1970a. *Geologische Rundschau* (German Federal Republic) 59:623-636.

1970b. *Boletin Academia de Ciencias Fisicas, Matematicas y Naturales* (Venezuela) 30:25-32.

1972. Peculiarities in the manifestation of gaseous-mud volcanoes. *Nature* 240:406-408

1974. *Geophysical Journal of the Royal Astronomical Society* 38:423-429.

1977. *Izvestia Acad. Sci. Armenia SSR, Ser. Terrestrial Sciences,* No.3, 3-10.

1978a. *Doklady Acad. Sci. Armenia SSR* 66:98-107.

1978b. *Izvestia Acad. Sci. Armenian SSR, Ser. Terrestial Sciences,* No.4 17-31.

1979. *Izvestia Acad. Sci. Armenian SSR,* Ser. Terrestial Sciences, No.2, 57-60.

1980. *Doklady Acad. Sci. Armenian SSR* 71:98-103.

1991. Prediction of the Armenian earthquake of December 7, 1988. *Cycles* 42:93-99 and 134-140.

1993. Cosmic conditions during catastrophic earthquakes of the twentieth century. *Cycles* 44:81-85.

Ullrich, J., 1987. Tidal triggering of earthquakes. *J. Geophys.* 61(3):150-157.

Van Flandern, Tom, 1997. Possible new properties of gravity. *Modern Mathematical Models of Time and their Applications to Physics and Cosmology,* W.G.Tifft and W.J.Cocke, ed.

Veselov, K.E., 1981. Chance Coincidences or Natural Phenomena. *Geophysical Journal* 3:410-425.

Vogel, Klaus, 1983. Global models and earth expansion. *Expanding Earth Symposium,* U.of Tasmania Press, S.W.Carey, ed.

Vogel, Klaus: 1994. Global models of the expanding earth. In: *Frontiers of Fundamental Physics.* M.Barone and F.Selleri, ed. Plenum Press, New York.

Ward, L., 1961. *Cycles* 12:317-319 (December).

Wesson, Paul S., 1978. *Cosmology and Geophysics.* Oxford University Press, New York.

Willis, D.E. *et al,* 1974. Explosion-induced ground motion, tidal and tectonic forces and their relationship to natural seismicity. Dept. of Geological Sciences, University of Wisconsin, Milwaukee.

Winkless, N., Browning, I., 1975. *Climate and the Affairs of Men.* Harpers Magazine Press, New York, p. 42-81.

Wolff, Milo, 1990. *Exploring the Physics of the Unknown Universe.* Technotran Press, Manhatten Beach, CA.

Wood, H.O., 1918. On cyclical variations in eruption at Kilauea. *Amer. J. Sci.* 4:45-146.

Yamaguti, S., 1931. Tidal frequency of earthquakes. *Nature* 127:908.

Yarkovskiy, I.O. 1889. *Vseminoye tyagateniye, kaksledstviye obrazovovaniya vesomoy materii.* (Universal Gravitation as a Consequence of Formation of Substance within Celestial Bodies.) Moscow.

Yoder, C.F., Williams, J.G., Parke, M.E., 1981. *J. Geophys. Res.* 86(B2):881-891.

Young, D., Zurn, W., 1979. *Geophysics* 45:171-182.

Co-operative Phenomena as a Physical Paradigm for Relativity, Gravitation and Quantum Mechanics

Vincent Buonomano[*]

We take co-operative phenomena as a common physical conceptual base to speculate on the existence of a medium and the properties that it must have to physically understand some of the problems in Special Relativity, gravitation and quantum mechanics.

Introduction

We would like to speculate on the existence of a preferred physical universal reference frame, that is, a medium, and its structure. The basic purport of this work is that the area of co-operative phenomena (Refs. 1-2) may furnish a common physical conceptual basis to better understand gravitation, Special Relativity and quantum mechanics. The medium, the patterns and the equilibrium states that are formed in it are taken as the fundamental concepts to understanding the physical world. Some of these speculations began in earlier works (Refs. 3 and 4).

Before continuing with this task we think it appropriate to recall the following. The word medium is frequently taken as a synonym for the word ether. The ether was an attempt to justify a medium as a mechanical fluid to support the transverse vibrations of electromagnetic waves in a manner completely analogous to how waves are justified in a fluid. That is, the attempt to justify an ether was in terms of what was then considered to be the more basic theory or paradigm, basically that of Newtonian mechanics. This attempt occupied some of the best scientists of the second part of the last century. It was a dismal failure, of course. This without doubt gave a 'bad name' and an unsophisticated sense to any research involving a medium.

Today it is clear that the concepts from stochastic processes and co-operative phenomena give us much more general structures from which to try to justify and physically understand a medium than does mechanics. There are profound conceptual simplifications in having a medium. Our own opinion is that our discarding the concept of a medium along with the failed classical fluid (the ether) has forced us to give up some essential absolute concepts and reference points. This constrains us to use more complicated conceptual constructs analogous to Ptolemy's geocentric astronomical system compared with the Copernican system.

[*] Instituto de Matemática (Retired), Universidade Estadual de Campinas, Campinas, São Paulo, Brazil, 13081-970, e-mail: vincent@correionet.com.br

Pushing Gravity: new perspectives on Le Sage's theory of gravitation
edited by Matthew R. Edwards (Montreal: Apeiron 2002)

303

In the sections below we describe the rough physical properties that we feel one needs to confront some of the difficulties in modern physics. The properties that we want to impose on this medium, without doubt, relate to our own view of these problems. They are speculations, nothing more than physical ideas that may find justification.

Gravitation

We assume that the medium consists of unknown particles in stochastic motion, and we simply will call them medium particles. All other particles like electrons, neutrons, atoms, *etc.*, will be called normal particles[*]. The number of medium particles is taken to be extremely large and that they permeate all other matter. The medium particles are in constant collision with each other in some sort of stochastic equilibrium, described by their normalized density, $p(x,v) = p(x,v,t)$, in position, x, and velocity, v. Let $p(x) = \int p(x,v)\mathrm{dv}$ and $p(v) = \int p(x,v)dx$. The reference system in which the average stochastic velocity of the medium particles is zero is taken to define a preferred or absolute reference system, S.

In contrast to Le Sage and others we assume that concepts like mass and momentum do not apply to these medium particles. The number and frequency of collisions of normal particles with these medium particles will define the concepts of mass and momentum but only for normal particles. We are necessarily vague about what happens when two medium particles collide, other than that the collisions are impenetrable and that their before-and-after velocities must only be conserved on average.

Gravitational Force

Let m be a small test mass at rest in the medium at some point x. That is, on average, its velocity is zero in any direction in relationship to the preferred reference system. If m is far from any mass distribution, then $p(x)$ is taken as constant independent of x, and $p(v)$ is taken to be some fixed unknown distribution independent of x.

Let us then place a large, spherical mass M at some distance from m, also at rest. Then m is no longer in an isotropic medium because of the blocking or shadowing effect that M has, completely analogous to any Le Sage theory. That is, $p(x,v)$ is altered by the mass M and is symmetric about M. Our test mass, m, is then no longer in an isotropic medium. It falls toward the mass M because it suffers more collisions on one side than on the other because of a gradient in position and velocity density of the medium. Gravitational force is taken be the greater probability of experiencing collisions in certain directions than others. If the masses are not at rest then one must imagine that the same logic may be

---

[*] What is a normal particle? Is it made up of medium particles? Is it, itself, a very stable pattern in the medium, something like in the Game of Life? Although this question is fundamental, it is largely irrelevant in this work.

applied because of the physics behind the Lorentz transformations. Any Le Sage theory must also confront the question of non-linearity at some point or other because of the shielding or shadowing effect of the shielding on itself.

Inertial and Gravitational Mass

It is important here to imagine that if a single normal particle and a single medium particle collide then the laws of mechanics governing collisions do not apply. It makes no sense here to say that the normal particle, being larger, 'pushes' the medium particles more than *vice versa*. Mass and momentum are not intrinsic properties of the medium particles or normal particles. Normal particles acquire these properties because of the large number of collisions with the medium particles and the equilibrium of the medium particles with themselves.

Gravitational and inertial mass are both taken to be basically a property of the size of the object. Gravitational mass is the disturbance that an object produces in the medium in the manner of Le Sage. Inertial mass is its resistance to acceleration because of the greater number of collisions in the direction of the acceleration.

Probabilistic Potential Theory

In the 1950's the fundamental mathematical result that potential theory and stochastic processes are isomorphic was formalized (Ref. 5). That is, every theorem in potential theory had a corresponding theorem in stochastic processes and *vice versa*[*]. In particular, the Newtonian potential corresponds *exactly* to Brownian motion. Letting $V(x)$ be the Newtonian potential of the mass distribution $M(y)$, one expresses this by the formulae

$$V(x) = \frac{1}{2\pi} \int \frac{1}{|x-y|} M(y) dy = \iint P(y, 0 \rightarrow x, t) M(y) dy dt$$

where $P(y, 0 \rightarrow x, t)$ is the probability a particle undergoing Brownian motion at y at time 0 is at x at time t. The integral in t is from 0 to infinity and must be understood as a limit over larger and larger finite time intervals. P is the probability that a particle in Brownian motion goes from y to x in time t,

$$P(y, 0 \rightarrow x, t) = \frac{1}{(\pi 2Dt)^{3/2}} e^{-(x-y)^2/2Dt},$$

where D is the unknown diffusion constant. In words, within the stochastic paradigm, one would say that the potential $V(x)$ at a point x from a single point mass M at $x = 0$ is the sum of the probabilities over a long time period that particles in Brownian motion starting at $x = 0$ arrive at x weighted by M.

Presumably one should relate this D to the diffusion coefficients $D_{xx}(x,v)$ of the stochastic process $p(x,v,t)$ representing our medium in the following manner. Let $P(x,v,t \rightarrow x',v',t')$ be the transition probability density of the sto-

---

[*] There are various mathematical regularity conditions that we are omitting here.

chastic medium. Here x, v, x' and v' are three-dimensional vectors. By definition

$$D_{xx}(x,v) = Lim_{t'\to t} \frac{1}{t'-t} \int (x'-x)^2 P(x,v,t \to x',v',t') dx' dv'.$$

We then take D as equal to $\int D(x,v)dv$ independent of x. Further it is natural to want to try to show that the previous would be consistent with taking $p(x,v,t)$ to satisfy the time independent Fokker-Planck equation and, in particular, detailed balancing. It is also natural here to want to consider energy as directly related to probability, and that conservation of energy expresses the conservation of probability.

Special Relativity

It is well known[*] that all the effects of Special Relativity may be derived from any theory which assumes the following: (1) there is a preferred or absolute reference frame, S, and that the velocity of light has the constant value c relative to it; (2) a rod undergoes a real physical contraction given by $\Delta l_0 (1-v^2/c^2)^{1/2}$ as a function of its velocity v relative to S, where Δl_0 is the initial length in S; and (3) a clock's rhythm undergoes a real physical dilation given by $\Delta t_0 (1-v^2/c^2)^{-1/2}$ as a function of its absolute velocity v. This suffices to derive the Lorentz transformation between two arbitrary inertial reference systems and therefore all the effects of Special Relativity. Of course, any such physical theory must justify the medium and why clocks and rods behave like this.

Here, as in any Lorentzian or preferred reference frame theory, time and space are our classical understanding of these concepts, that is, pre Einstein's theory of Special Relativity. Time and space are independent concepts and not the space-time of Einstein. Of course, it is another thing to give concrete experimental significance to these real contractions. In real experiments space are time are always mixed up. We believe it impossible to distinguish between a preferred reference frame theory and Einstein's within the domain of the effects of the Special Theory of Relativity itself.

Why do rods contract?

A rod is a very large collection of atoms, which in principle may be described by quantum mechanics. To make our point let us consider our rod to consist of only one atom at rest in the medium. We know from quantum mechanics that it is actually undergoing a complex movement with its average velocity being zero. The extent or size of these movements is characterized partially by its standard deviation, which is determined by its state preparation. We associate the length of m with this standard deviation. We assume that it is this standard deviation that is somehow contracting because of its stochastic movement when it has an absolute velocity v. The work of Cane (Refs. 6-7) seems rele-

---

[*] For example, see Reference 4.

vant here. She has derived a Lorentzian factor for the change in the standard deviation of a Brownian particle on a one- dimensional lattice with a velocity v. That is, the probability to go right is greater than the velocity to left by a certain factor, such that the mean position of the particle moves with the velocity v. Her proof is not directly applicable here since the Lorentzian factor does not apply to the initial distribution but to its spreading in time. If we consider a clock to be validly represented by a rod with mirrors at each end in which the number of cycles represents the time, then the time dilation assumption may be justified (if the length contraction may be justified *à la Cane*).

Quantum Mechanics

The stochastic interpretation of quantum mechanics is well known (Ref. 8). It is mathematically equivalent to quantum mechanics and expresses the Schrödinger equation as a Fokker-Planck equation. It imagines that a particle is undergoing constant stochastic motion. The probabilistic density function, entrance and exit velocities of this stochastic motion are calculable from the wave function, $\Psi(x,t)$, and *vice versa*. The diffusion constant $D = \hbar/m$.

State preparation, the double slit experiment and the non-locality controversy will now be discussed. More details are given in Ref. 9.

State Preparation

It is important to say that when you prepare a quantum mechanical state, you are not preparing the state of the particle but the system, that is, the medium *and* the particle. It is invalid to separate the medium here. For example, compare the state preparations of our test particle, m, in two different Gaussian states with, say, the second state having a width ten times the value of the first state. In the first case what you have prepared is a particle along with a local pattern in the medium that accompanies it. This pattern has a certain average size, that of the wave packet of the prepared state. In the second case the particle is in a different equilibrium or order with the system. The pattern, or the local equilibrium, that is traveling with the particle in the medium is 10 times larger then in the previous case. You have prepared the system consisting of the particle and the traveling stable pattern in the medium. The stochastic medium's properties depend in general on the state preparation.

One of the consistent criticisms of the stochastic interpretation of quantum mechanics is that the stochastic process of any test particle, m, will be non-Markovian. This simply means the properties of the imagined stochastic medium depend on the state preparation. This criticism is clearly answered here.

Inertial Reference Systems

A very old and difficult question is why are inertial systems special? Another way of asking this is, why can a particle undergo rectilinear motion without any energy consumption, but to accelerate it one must spend energy? Within our view we would have to say that the medium supports certain stable equilibrium states with the particle and not others. Here the difference between an inertial and non-inertial state would be the difference between an equilibrium and non-equilibrium state. The inertial velocities are modes of the system. In the case of an inertial particle we know its quantum mechanical velocity distribution must be constant from quantum mechanics. This distribution is somehow stable in the medium.

The velocity of light is considered to be a limiting velocity at which the medium can support certain modes or equilibrium states with normal particles.

Global Patterns in the Medium

We want to assume that our medium can form various global periodic patterns or modes, in some currently undefined sense, which are completely stable. The exact pattern in a given region will depend on the physical objects in the region. The relevant objects here, such as slits, beam splitters, mirrors, polarizers, parts of the state preparation, *etc.*, determine the pattern or mode of the medium, *i.e.*, the global state. The possible paths or ways in which the medium can interact with itself must be taken as important when contrasted with classical boundary value problems.

We imagine that the particles of the medium co-operate, that is, they organize themselves into a global pattern depending on the objects (mirrors, slits, *etc.*) in it. The size of the region of a pattern or mode is taken to be at least the size of the coherence volume of all the possible beams in a given first or second order interference experiment. One might want to think of something analogous to the Bernard's rolls* existing in shallow, slowly heated water, but not consuming energy. Normal particles are guided by the medium.

The Double Slit Experiment

If you make two slits in a screen then after a certain relaxation time (it must be taken to be very fast) the medium will enter a new mode, that is, reorganize itself into a new co-operative state. The exact new state or mode will depend on the size of the slit and the distance between the slits, not on the material of the slit (*e.g.*, paper or lead). If you block one slit or the other then the mode would be different than if both were open. It is more important here to imagine that the slits determine the way the medium can interact with itself to enter a new stable state or mode. A photon (or electron or neutron) passes through one slit only. It 'knows' if the other slit is open or closed from the global mode of the medium. The medium would be in a different mode if only one slit was open. It is being guided by the pattern in the medium.

In the rotor experiment (Ref. 10) one must imagine that the medium enters into a one-arm mode and a two-arm mode consecutively for part of each revolution. The medium must be taken to enter into a mode magnitudes faster than the rotation of the rotor.

---

* For example, see Ref. 2, Page 3.

The Correlation Experiments

Bell's work in 1964 did much to clarify the situation in the foundations of quantum mechanics (Ref. 11). He defined a class of theories, called local realistic theories, which must disagree with quantum mechanics in certain experiments. These experiments measure the correlation of measurements (also called second order interference) made on two particle systems at far sides of an apparatus. The quantum mechanical predictions are non-local but cannot be controlled (*i.e.*, used to make a telephone).

Here one imagines that the states of the measuring apparatus on both sides of an experiment to measure the correlations are completely correlated because of the medium. If we change the angle of a polarizer on one side of the apparatus, then the medium is forced into a new global stable state or mode which includes the other polarizer (mirrors, slits...) on the other side of the apparatus. The whole apparatus must be described by one global state or mode. First and second order interference are explained here in the same manner.

Of the more than 20 correlation experiments preformed to date which confirm quantum mechanical versus local realistic theoretical predictions only Aspect's experiment (Ref. 12) has attempted to measure some sort of communication between the two sides of a correlation apparatus. A series of others are in progress (Ref. 13). Aspect, with some restrictions, eliminated communication up to the velocity of light. To agree with this experiment one would have to assume that the objects of the medium are magnitudes faster than the velocity of light in order for our complex system, *i.e.*, the medium, to enter into a new equilibrium or ordered global state. This view is experimentally testable in a variation of Franson's experiment (Ref. 9).

Summary

We have imagined that there exists a stochastic medium whose elementary or medium particles do not carry any momentum in and of themselves (in contrast to Le Sage's particles). The force of gravity caused by a mass, M, is taken to result from a variation in the position and velocity density of these medium particles about M. This makes it more probable for an object to have a net movement in the direction of M. This is why Newton's apple falls here. The exact mathematical relationship between Brownian motion and the Newtonian potential in probabilistic potential theory is taken to give some mathematical credibility to this position. One must assume that the particles have impenetrable collisions with their before-and-after velocities being conserved only on average.

Further it was imagined that what we call the size of an object (a macroparticle) is the standard deviation of its stochastic movement according to laws of stochastic quantum mechanics. Rods contract physically as a function of their velocity relative to the medium because their standard deviation of this movement has this property. The Lorentz transformations may be derived from this and the assumption that the velocity of light is constant relative to S.

In an experimental apparatus to measure first or second order interference effects, we imagine that there exists a stable global pattern that is at least the size of the coherence volume of all the involved beams. If you change the position of a mirror, beam splitter, polarizer, state preparation, *etc.*, or block a beam, then a new and different stable global state is entered very quickly. The medium particles must be taken to have superluminal velocity to be consistent with Aspect's experiment. It is experimentally testable as a local realistic theory in a variation of Franson's experiment. It is necessary to understand that the quantum mechanical state preparation prepares both the medium and particle, that is the equilibrium, or ordered state, between them. You cannot separate the medium from the particle here.

The velocity of light is considered to be a limiting velocity at which the medium can support certain modes or equilibrium states with normal particles. An inertial motion of a particle is taken to be one of these modes or equilibrium states.

References

1. H. Haken, *Synergetics*, Springer-Verlag, (1978).
2. H. Haken, *Advanced Synergetics*, Springer-Velag (1983).
3. V. Buonomano and A. Engel, "Some Speculations on Relativity, Gravitation and Quantum Mechanics," *Int. J. Theor. Phys.* **15**, 231-246 (1976).
4. V. Buonomano, "A New Interpretation of the Special Theory of Relativity," *Int. J. Theor. Phys.* **13**, 213-226 (1975). Observation: There was a mix-up between the proofs of this work and an earlier version. This published version is in error with regard to the conclusion that the horizontal rotor experiment could be used to test Lorentzian type theories. Corrections: The following items should be eliminated: (1). Next to last sentence of the Abstract. (2). Last paragraph of Section II-A. (3) Section *V*-C and (4) Section *V*-E.
5. A.W. Knapp, "Connection between Browninan Motion and Potential Theory," *J. Math. Anal. Appl.* **12**, 328-349 (1965) and references therein.
6. V.R. Cane, "Random Walks and Physical Processes," pp. 621-639, *Statistics in Physical Sciences II* (full reference unavailable).
7. V.R. Cane, "Diffusion Models with Relativity Effects," pp. 263-273, *Perspectives in Probability and Statistics*, (J.Gani, ed.) (1975), Applied Probability Trust.
8. G.C. Girardi, C. Omero, A. Rimini and T. Weber, "The Stochastic Interpretation of Quantum Mechanics: A Critical Review," *Riv. Nuovo Cimento*, **1**, 1-34 (1978) and references therein.
9. V. Buonomano, "Speculations on a Co-operative Phenomena Type Local Realistic Theory," *Physics Essays*, To be published.
10. H. Rauch and J. Summhammer, *Phys. Lett.* **104**, 44 (1984).
11. J.F. Clauser and A. Shimony, *Rep. Prog. Phys.* **41**, 1881-1927 (1978) and references therein.
12. A. Aspect, *P.* Dalibard and G. Roger, *Phys. Rev. Lett.*. **49**, 1804 (1982).
13. G. Weihs, H. Weinfurter and A. Zeilinger, "Towards a Long Distance Bell-Experiment with Independent Observers," in *Quantum Mechanical Studies for Abner Shimony*, Eds: Robert S. Cohen, M.A. Horne and John Stachel, Kluwer (Dordrecht, Netherlands, 1997) 271-280.

A Brief Survey of
Gravity Control Experiments

G.D. Hathaway, P.Eng.[*]

Man has harnessed all the basic forces of nature to a greater or lesser extent. Gravity alone remains unconquered. Many have tried to manipulate it without understanding it completely, hoping that it would yield to technology before physics, in a way similar to the early development of the electrical industry. This article will describe the efforts of some of these researchers.

Introduction

The history of attempts to manipulate gravity can be broadly divided into two eras, pre-1965 and post-1965. Before the mid 1960s, there was considerable optimism in the academic community and even more so in industry that the era of gravity control was imminent. However, a shift occurred in the mid 1960s after which the subject of gravity control became anathema to the physics community. This did not stop individual pioneers from the attempt, however.

Charles Brush

At the end of the 19th century, after selling his profitable electric company, Charles Brush turned his considerable talents at theory and experimental design to the subject of gravity. The prevailing scientific view of gravity was that it was somehow linked to the all-pervasive aether, but the precise mechanism of attraction between two bodies was unknown. Brush theorized that gravity was a manifestation of kinetic energy absorbed by or released from the aether as bodies are separated or let fall together. This is how bodies acquire their kinetic energy upon falling which is then released as heat, sound, *etc.* This idea formed what Brush called his "Kinetic Theory of Gravity." In his earliest theorizing he assumed that the aether energy was in the form of relatively low-frequency vibrations of some kind: aether waves, not electromagnetic waves as we know them today. However, by the time his experiments were in full swing, he considered the possibility of extremely high-frequency transverse waves (1). This required that the aether be endowed with a very great intrinsic energy, as Oliver Lodge had postulated earlier. Comparison can be made to the theory of zero point fluctuations as a modern analog of aether and Wheeler's calculation of the enormity of the energy residing in these fluctuations.

As pointed out by Brush (2), all prior theories about gravitation, with the exception of the Le Sage school, assumed it is an intrinsic quality of matter. Although Brush agreed with Le Sage in placing the seat of the gravitational in-

---

[*] Hathaway Consulting Services, 180 Beverley St., Toronto, Ontario, M5T 1Y8, Canada

Pushing Gravity: new perspectives on Le Sage's theory of gravitation
edited by Matthew R. Edwards (Montreal: Apeiron 2002)

311

teraction outside the material atoms comprising a body, he maintained that it was essentially a wave-like interaction mediated by the aether rather than a particulate (corpuscular) interaction. Brush further stated that material bodies play only a secondary role in gravity, that of disturbing the normally isotropic distribution of the aether's wave-like kinetic energy resulting in a push of bodies together rather than a pull.

He tried to refute the heating objections leveled against Le Sage by claiming that the frequency of aether waves were of such a magnitude as to penetrate most matter without interaction. However, he maintained that some bodies would evidence a resonant interaction with aether waves to a greater extent than others by dint of their chemical and atomic makeup. This led him to the belief that certain materials would continue to give off sensible heat for much longer than others even accounting for differences in thermal capacity:

> My own thought was that the maintenance of the earth's internal heat might perhaps be due, in part at least, to a continual small generation of heat in some of its constituents by gravitation aether waves... (3)

To prove this assertion, he constructed several precise calorimeters. The calorimeters were constructed so that differential cooling rates over long periods could be measured simultaneously from two different samples in the same overall enclosure. Usually one sample was a control. Many rock types were tried as well as various metals and alloys. Unmistakable signs of anomalous heat generation in some rocks, principally volcanic basalts, were measured. Much care was taken to remove artifact and allow stable readings to better than the third decimal degree C. Indeed, the National Bureau of Standards confirmed his calorimetric results in tests of their own (4). Brush went further and hypothesized that the conversion of gravitational energy into heat would reduce the rate at which the anomalous heat generators fell to Earth. Using a very precise spark photography technique he compared the fall rates of various substances and, amazingly, found evidence for just such an effect.

Yet, perhaps because of the advent of special relativity, Brush's results were never taken seriously by the scientific community.

Electro-Gravity

The early apparent successes of Einstein to do away with the aether put an end to the connection between the aether and gravity, replacing it with an even more arcane concept, that of geometrical space-time. Now the quantities of energy or mass concentrations required to alter gravity technologically were so far out of reach of humanity that the pursuit of any experimental techniques was considered a mere pipedream.

However, with the success of the Manhattan Engineering District project at turning essentially theoretical understanding of atomic fission and later fusion into applied technology in a short time, engineers started to consider once again various experimental approaches to overcoming gravity. An additional impetus was the apparent success of Thomas Townsend Brown in the period from 1950 to 1970 at producing lift in bodies subjected to extremely high electrostatic potentials. Brown experimented in many areas including detection of anomalous diurnal and secular variations in the self-generated electrical potential of certain rocks, especially igneous rocks such as granite. However, it was his discovery that a unidirectional thrust could be produced by massive high-K dielectrics subjected to potentials of 50-200 kV that helped rekindle an interest in experimental gravity manipulation techniques (6).[*]

North American research into practical anti-gravity and its alter ego, electro-gravity (the control of gravity by electromagnetic means) has an interesting, albeit brief history (7-14). Concerted efforts by government and industry seemed to materialize out of nowhere beginning in 1957 and 1958 and then just as suddenly disappear eight years later. Perhaps the impetus was Sputnik, or the Soviet announcement of a forthcoming "graviplane" based on cooling matter to absolute zero.

Things got off to an exciting start at the January 1958 meeting of the Institute of Aeronautical Sciences in New York. Delegates were told by W.W. Bender that the Martin Co. was setting out to test Einstein's concepts regarding equivalence of gravitational and inertial mass as well as gravitational curvature versus gravitational radiation. S.M. Gluhareff of Gluhareff Helicopters suggested that reinvestigation of Le Sage-like 'pushing' gravity theories would lead to progress. Charles Tilgner, Jr., chief aeronautical engineer at Grumman Aircraft Engineering Corp. suggested four ways of controlling gravity. Lockheed Aircraft and Sperry Rand were present as well as the U.S. Dept. of Defense. Just prior to that, George S. Trimble, Vice President of the Glenn L. Martin Co., referred to electro-gravitic propulsion by stating:

> I think we could do the job in about the time that is (sic) actually required to build the first atomic bomb if enough trained scientific brain-power simultaneously began thinking about and working towards a solution.

During those heady years prior to 1965/66 it was said that:

> ...the most important fact about the whole problem of gravity and anti-gravity research is that the scientists are now discussing the problem out in the open.

In 1960, Martin Kaplan, senior research engineer at Ryan Aeronautical Co., was actively researching two approaches to "force field propulsion," namely an anti-gravitation force directed only toward or away from a second body, and a reaction force against free space in any desired direction. I.A. van As described his approach to anti-gravity based on intensely diamagnetic alloys (*e.g.*, of bismuth and aluminum) and magnetic fields. Clyde Murtaugh, engineer with Bendix Systems Div., expected new rocket engines to rely on pure gravitation, electrical or magnetic forces. Gravity shields were discussed by W.F.G. Swann of the Bartol Research Foundation and debated by scientists (15,16). Prominent anti-gravity researcher R.L. Forward at Hughes Aircraft Co. theorized about giant toroidal anti-gravity machines based on what

---

[*] Brown's thrust was later found to be most likely due to ion wind effects.

he termed the "protational" force field. He published a very useful paper in 1963 describing this and other relativity-based approaches to the subject (17).

Electro-gravitics research was rather cryptically summarized in 1976 by Perl (18). He based some of some of his work on the Gravity Research Foundation, whose descendants, the Association of Pushing Gravity Research and the Gravity Power Research Association (19), sponsored contests for papers on the subject of understanding and harnessing gravitational forces, emphasizing neo-Le Sage theories.

It is curious that all of this investigation, at least in the unclassified world, suddenly came to a halt in the mid 1960s. Since then, work on novel methods of gravity manipulation has been almost entirely purely theoretical.

Quantum Vacuum Fluctuation Electrodynamics

The fruition of quantum electrodynamics has allowed several researchers to pick up where others left off in the 1960s. Prominent among these are Haisch, Rueda and Puthoff (HRP) (20), publishing treatises on the relationship between quantum zero point fluctuations (ZPF), inertia and gravity. In the case of gravity, Puthoff expanded on Sakharov's original 1968 work in a much more detailed investigation (21).

Quantum vacuum fluctuations are those electromagnetic fluctuations left over in a system after the attainment of exactly zero temperature (the "zero point"). At scales on the order of the Planck length (10^{-33} cm) these fluctuations are manifest as virtual particles emerging from and falling back almost instantaneously into the vacuum. Virtual photons in this view can be likened to Le Sage's ultramundane particles, continually bombarding all matter, and thus being external agents for inertia and gravity rather than something intrinsic to matter itself.

Careful analysis of the energy spectrum of the zero-point fluctuations shows that it obeys a cubic frequency distribution. This turns out to be the only distribution allowing Lorentz invariance, preventing absorption of virtual photons by matter and thus circumventing matter-heating objections to a Le Sage-like treatment of gravity. This distribution also eliminates another objection, namely that of expected drag forces on matter due to isotropic bombardment by ultramundane particles in a gravitating system.

Analysis of the spatial distributions of resultant forces on matter immersed in a sea of zero-point fluctuations shows a classic inverse square relationship with distance. In contrast to the Le Sage explanation, however, the zero-point fluctuation model is not based on shadowing. Rather, geometric cancellation of fields arises due to readjustments of the field correlation when matter is surrounded by virtual particles. This is similar to the explanation of the Casimir force and van der Waals forces. In the words of HRP (22):

> Expressed in the simplest possible way, all matter at the level of quarks and electrons is driven to oscillate ... by the ZPF. But every oscillating charge will generate its own minute electromagnetic fields. Thus any particle will

experience the ZPF as modified ever so slightly by the fields of adjacent particles… and this is gravitation!

Experiments are currently being designed by Puthoff and co-workers to test aspects of the relationship between gravity and zero-point fluctuations (23).

Spinning Superconductors

In 1992, Podkletnov and Nieminen published an account of an experiment involving a levitated high-temperature superconductor spinning in an RF field (24). This assembly caused objects of any composition placed above it to lose up to 2 per cent of their weight in subsequent experiments. Bizarre inertial effects involving high voltages and superconductors are being investigated by Podkletnov's team in Moscow. Work is underway at NASA and another private research laboratory to attempt to duplicate some of the effects (25).

This experiment presents evidence for the strongest interaction with the local gravitational field yet published in the peer-reviewed scientific literature. As with cold fusion, it was greeted by some with complete disdain and cries of "artifact". Those who chose to investigate it further found that it was an extremely difficult experiment to duplicate and even NASA after almost four years of effort has yet to reproduce it in its entirety. However, several laboratories worldwide have conducted stripped-down versions of the Podkletnov experiment and have seen small effects, on the order of one part in 10^4 (e.g., the work of Gonnelli at the Politecnic in Turin (26) and Reiss (27)).

The experiment requires a specially fabricated 2-layer YBCO bulk ceramic superconductor, one layer of which is a normal high-temperature superconductor and the other being a superconductor only at liquid helium temperatures. This is pressed into a ring shape with dimensions at least 150 mm diameter by approximately 10 mm thick. It is supported by the Meissner effect several millimeters above a support coil or coils carrying 10^5 Hz current. It is caused to spin up to several thousand rpm by additional coils placed around its periphery carrying current optimally at between 3 and 4 mHz. The whole assembly is operated at temperatures between 10 and 50 Kelvin, i.e., in the vapours of liquid helium. So far, fabrication of the 2-layer ring has been the major stumbling block of the replication efforts.

The most prominent theoretician to attempt to understand the Podkletnov findings is G. Modanese (28). His approach involves treating the superconductor as a Bose condensate which induces strong localized gravitational fluctuations in a quantum general relativistic context. A class of dipolar vacuum fluctuations with virtual sources is postulated to reach macroscopic proportions and thus effect ponderable matter as gravity. However, a vacuum energy or cosmological term is hypothesized which cuts off part of these fluctuations so that they are not normally discernible. This is not a direct Le Sage approach except for the use of gravitational vacuum fluctuations, which could be seen as a virtual form of Le Sage's corpuscles.

Conclusion

Proper experimental investigation into the phenomenon of gravity is extremely difficult. Technological requirements from general relativity still assume enormous amounts of energy or mass density to effect the local spacetime curvature. New insights based on recent experiments and re-analyses of earlier proposals, such as Le Sage's, may yet enable us to crack the enigma of gravity.

References

1. C. Brush, *Proc. Amer. Phil. Soc.* **65**, 21 (1926).
2. C. Brush, *Nature* **86**, 130 (1911).
3. C. Brush, "Discussion... " *op cit*, p. 217.
4. C. Brush, *Proc. Amer. Phil. Soc.* **68**, 68 (1929).
5. C. Brush, *ibid.*, p. 67.
6. W.M. Cady, "An Investigation Relative to T.T. Brown," *File 24-185 Office of Naval Research* (1952), available as Report #R-503 from W.L. Moore Publications & Research, Burbank, CA. See also: L.A.A. Gerardin, "Electro-Gravitic Propulsion," *Inter Avia* **VXI** #12, 992 (1956).
7. Anon., "Pure Research Group Investigates Gravity," *Aviation Week* p. 121 (March 18, 1957).
8. F. Edwards, *Fate* **10**, 51 (Aug. 1957).
9. Anon., "Electrogravitics: Science or Daydream," *Product Engineering*, p. 12 (Dec 30, 1957).
10. Anon., "How to Fall Into Space," *Business Week*, p. 51 (Feb 8, 1958).
11. Anon., "Force Field Shows Propulsion Promise," *Missiles and Rockets*, p. 27 (July 11, 1960).
12. I.A. VanAs, *Newnes Practical. Mechanics*, p. 30 (Oct. 1961).
13. B.H. Frisch, "How to Fall Up," *Science Digest*, p. 42 (Dec 1965).
14. D.C. Peaslee, "The Nonexistence of Gravity Shields" (letter), *Science* **124**, 1292 (1956).
15. P.G. Bergman, "Gravity Shields," *Science* (letter) (Mar 1957).
16. L.M. Stephenson, "Electromagnetic and Gravitational Shielding," *Proc. IEEE*, p. 676 (Apr 1966).
17. R.L. Forward, "Guidelines to Antigravity," *Amer. J. Phys.* **31**, 166 (1963).
18. M.L. Perl, *The Gravitics Situation*, Gravity Rand Ltd., London, (Dec 1976). Available from the Rex Research, Berkley, California report 94-p.
19. *The Great Cosmic Coverup*, Association for Pushing Gravity Research: Conference Proceedings, (Mar 7, 1981) Huntington Beach, CA and Gravity Power Research Association, c/o 36 Mountain Rd., Burlington, Mass. 01803
20. B. Haisch, A. Rueda and H. Puthoff, "Advances in the Proposed Electromagnetic Zero-Point Field Theory of Inertia," *34th AIAA Joint Propulsion Conference*, paper #98-3143 (July 13, 1998).
21. H. Puthoff, "Gravity as a Zero-Point Fluctuation Force," *Phys. Rev.* A **39**, 2333 (1989).
22. B. Haisch, A. Rueda and H. Puthoff, *op cit*.
23. H. Puthoff, "Can the Vacuum be Engineered for Spaceflight Applications? Overview of Theory and Experiments," *NASA Breakthrough Propulsion Physics Workshop* (1997) NASA LeRC Cleveland.
24. E. Podkletnov and R. Nieminen, *Physica C* **203**, 441(1992).
25. R. Koczor and D. Noever, "Experiments on the Possible Interaction of Rotating Type II Ceramic Superconductors and the Local Gravity Field," *NASA Breakthrough Propulsion Physics Workshop* (1997) NASA LeRC Cleveland.
26. R. Gonnelli, private communication.
27. H. Reiss, "A Possible Interaction between Gravity and High Temperature Superconductivity - by a Materials Property?," submitted to *15th European Conference on Thermophysical Properties*, Wurzburg FRG (Sept 1999).
28. G. Modanese, epublication xxx.lanl.gov gr-qc/0005009 (May 3,2000).